THE ENDURING HEMINGWAY

An Anthology of a Lifetime in Literature

EDITED, WITH AN INTRODUCTION BY

CHARLES SCRIBNER, JR.

New York

CHARLES SCRIBNER'S SONS

Note

Now it is more than twenty years, a whole new generation of readers, since a potpourri of Ernest's work has been published. Meanwhile he wrote some of his most memorable pieces—of himself when young in Paris and the Vorarlberg in Austria, of that thoughtful, complicated submarine-hunter Thomas Hudson, of our wacky safari in East Africa. Among these samplings book readers are apt to find a good companion.

MARY HEMINGWAY

Contents

❀   PART II. *THE GREAT WAR*

❀   PART III. *TOROS Y TOREROS*

Introduction

IN deciding what to include in this book the publishers have taken the interest and pleasure of the reader as their primary goals. Such goals are particularly appropriate for a Hemingway anthology. Throughout his career as a writer, from his first by-lined stories as a reporter to the time of his death, Hemingway never forgot that books were written to be read. He never forgot about the readers on the other side of what he wrote, and like virtually all great writers he wanted above all to be read and appreciated by his contemporaries. Perhaps that explains in part why he was so often impatient with critics or scholars who theorized about his work in ways that seemed to him to be unnecessary. For him the most important thing about a book was what it gave its readers directly, without any need of interpreters.

In this collection all but four of the selections can be read as complete works in themselves. As for the exceptions—the chapters from *The Sun Also Rises, Green Hills of Africa, The African Journal,* and *For Whom the Bell Tolls*—we have tried to choose sections that can be read separately with understanding and enjoyment, keeping in mind Hemingway's own dislike of teasing the reader by snippets.

All the selections have been organized around a few themes: the various experiences and interests that were especially important in Hemingway's career as a writer. Thus the book is divided into six parts, each one of which includes works of fiction and nonfiction related to the theme of that particular part. The sequence of these parts is roughly chronological, but we have not adhered to that order whenever there seemed to be a good reason not to.

❖

THE two chapters from *A Moveable Feast,* "A Good Café on the Place St.–Michel" and "There Is Never Any End to Paris," provide a natural introduction to the anthology as a whole, inasmuch as they present Hemingway (as he recalled years later) at the very dawn of his success as a writer. And of all the many different things that interested Hemingway during his life, there was nothing that absorbed him so completely or so unremittingly as his passion for writing well. All the parts of this book are the products of that lifelong passion.

The first part also contains the entire text of Hemingway's first commercially published book, a collection of short stories entitled *In Our Time.* It is not possible to associate these stories with any single period in the author's life since they range from childhood experiences well into his first marriage. In composition they were not his earliest fiction, almost all of which (except for juvenilia) was lost in a railway station in Paris, but they may very well be the first stories he wrote after having arrived at his own conception of the aims of fiction and after having worked out his own techniques for attaining those aims. In that sense, *In Our Time* is a mature work of art. Few books of stories have had greater influence both on the craft of writing and on literary taste; every one of its stories has been published and republished in anthologies throughout the world.

Part of its impact was the result of its style: the apparent simplicity of the writing and the seeming naturalness of the language. Each story is told so directly that the narration seems like a pane of perfectly clear glass through which one simply "sees" what is happening. But deeper than these now familiar and widely imitated features of his style lies Hemingway's almost inimitable ability to create a subjective dimension in his fiction by engaging the imagination of the reader fully, and by inducing in him specific emotional reactions.

This dimension of Hemingway's fiction could not be produced by stylistic devices alone. Each sentence had to be constructed individually, with a sensitive control of its psychological effects and with a correspondingly careful choice of the exactly appropriate objective details. For example, he once described how he had spent hours trying to recall exactly what it was that had struck him so forcefully upon seeing a particular bullfighter gored in the ring. Finally he realized that it had been his sense of shock when he saw the clean whiteness of the man's thigh bone, which had been laid bare. One realizes that in writing about such an event Hemingway would have used this specific detail in order to provide the reader with the precise perception, and thus prompt in him similar feelings of surprise and horror. All of Hemingway's stories are intended to create such subjectively rounded accounts of the events they describe. Through most of his life he seems to have studied carefully everything he heard or saw in order to fix in his memory the authentic perceptions which were the bricks and mortar of his writing.

Inserted between the separate stories of *In Our Time* are a series of short prose pieces, printed in italics. All of these "short short stories" had been published previously under an uncapitalized version of the same title, *in our time*. They differ from most of the other stories in their brevity and their narrower field of vision. Half of them were not based on firsthand experiences but were composed by the painstaking reworking of events Hemingway had either read about or heard about from others. As a collection, the miniatures appear to represent a transitional stage in the evolution of Hemingway's fiction. They all aim at the same effects as his later fiction: to cause the reader to imagine a scene so effortlessly that it would have the subjective impact of an actual experience. It is a curious fact, discovered by Hemingway, that these effects are best achieved by means of a terse, impressionistic narrative and by laconic, allusive dialogue.

Many of the scenes in the miniatures from *in our time* are taken from executions, bullfights, and war. They combine to create an impression of the violence of "our time," and in this respect these inter-chapter pieces have a clearer unity as a group than the other short stories of *In Our Time* for which they act as a counterpoint.

These other stories range over a variety of more directly personal subjects. Some of them involve the fictional character, Nick Adams, in events closely related to Hemingway's boyhood. Others are related to the war in Italy or to events in the author's life even closer to 1925, the year the book was published. Almost all of these stories recapture the moods of complex psychological moments: the humiliation of a boy's father ("The Doctor and the Doctor's Wife"), an early apprehension of death ("Indian Camp"), a psychological convalescence ("Big Two-Hearted River"), a young wife's sense of isolation ("Cat in the Rain"). The essence of the stories lies in their emotional impact.

PART II centers on World War I and contains three works by Hemingway related to his life during that period. Certainly no other period made a greater contribution to his achievement as a writer. Actually, he spent only a little more than half a year in Italy: five months in wartime and two and one half months following the armistice. But the people he met there, the things he saw, and the things he learned provided material for his great novel, *A Farewell to Arms,* and several superb short stories.

Hemingway was eighteen years old when he volunteered for ambulance duty overseas with the American Red Cross. He went to the war directly from his job as a reporter for the *Kansas City Star,* which he had held for about six months. This newspaper experience had reinforced his natural curiosity and his inclination to be in the thick of things. It had also sharpened his eye for the details of an event. He was already hoping to become a writer and reacted to his various experiences with a writer's hunger for material. All of these things may help to explain the extraordinary richness and precision of his memories of this period. As a writer he was still a tyro in practice, but he had acquired the true writer's habits of mind.

On the day of his arrival in Milan a munitions factory blew up, and with the other volunteers in his contingent Hemingway was assigned to gathering up the remains of the dead. That incident provided details for his sardonic essay on "The Natural History of the Dead" included in this part of the book and originally published in *Death in the Afternoon.* Hemingway's attitude towards war changed at various times in his life, but he never closed his eyes to its horrors.

After a stint of more or less routine ambulance driving at Schio in the foothills of the Dolomites, he contrived to be assigned to an emergency canteen at Fossalta on the more active Piave river front facing the Austrians. There, only a month after his arrival in Italy, he was badly wounded in both legs at a forward post one night; first by an Austrian mortar shell and almost immediately afterwards by machine-gun fire while he was in the act of carrying a wounded Italian soldier to safety. This catastrophe marked the beginning of what must have been a very frightening and painful week: a temporary operation on his legs at a distribution center, five days in a field hospital, and then a grueling train trip to Milan, where he was taken to an American Red Cross hospital for further treatment.

In Milan things took a turn for the better. After successful surgery on his legs he began a stage of slow but almost certain recovery. He was an authentic war hero to the young American friends who came to see him. He had been recommended for an Italian medal for valor, and had received considerable attention in the press at home as the first American soldier to have been wounded in Italy. A photograph of Hemingway taken in his hospital room at this time catches an expression of profound happiness. He had passed a critical test of his mettle with honors. He had also fallen in love with one of the nurses.

Before long he was able to begin out-patient therapy at the Ospedale Maggiore, a routine which provided the physical details and the moods evoked in the haunting short story, "In Another Country," included in this part. In late October he returned briefly to the front as an observer but came down almost immediately with an attack of jaundice and had to return to the Red Cross Hospital. By the time he recovered, the armistice had been signed between Italy and Austria. He remained in Italy for a few more months, visiting with friends and trying to keep his wartime romance alive, mostly by letters. Finally in January he sailed back to the United States.

Even this bare outline of the events of the period between June, 1918 and January, 1919 makes clear how mistaken it would be to suppose that as a novelist Hemingway simply reported experiences without substantial change or invention. It is true that many of the details in the first two parts of *A Farewell to Arms* (published in 1929) probably correspond closely to what had actually occurred during the war, especially the accounts of the wounding of Lieutenant Henry and his hospitalization in Milan. But in these chapters there are also important differences in places, characters, and events. For instance, the love affair with the nurse progressed a great deal further in the book than it had in real life. There were many such changes, all of them obviously intended to create a more unified and dramatic story.

The last three parts of the novel, which include the retreat from

Caporetto, the escape by boat to Switzerland, and the final scenes of childbirth, were pure invention in terms of Hemingway's wartime experiences, although each of these episodes was based, at least in part, on Hemingway's experiences elsewhere.

A more accurate view of the role of invention in Hemingway's methods as a novelist would be that he did not hesitate to make up parts of the narrative whenever it suited his artistic purposes. Conversely, for the same purposes, he was often willing to stick closely to actual events. But he rarely ventured to create events or characters for which he could not draw upon a reservoir of actual perceptions appropriate to bringing these parts of the narrative fully to life. That is one reason why *A Farewell to Arms* as a whole is able to sustain the illusion of reality and why it has endured as a masterpiece.

HEMINGWAY saw his first bullfight in Madrid in 1923. He had made an excursion there from Paris, where he had made his home only a few months after his marriage to Hadley Richardson in 1921. On this occasion he saw in the company of two friends, Bob McAlmon and Bill Bird, each of whom was soon to publish a separate collection of Hemingway's writings. According to both men, he was overwhelmed by the bullfight experience; so much so that for a time he seemed to talk of nothing else. In fact, bullfighting continued to fascinate him the rest of his life. In 1959, two years before his death, he toured most of Spain following the fights of the matador Antonio Ordóñez and making notes for an article on modern bullfighting for *Life*.

He was a lifelong sportsman, enthusiastically involved in almost every sport with which he became familiar. But for Hemingway bullfighting was more than a sport. In his words it was "a tragedy." He appreciated the fact that each fight progressed inexorably through its separate stages, with the tragic certainty of death for the bull, however brave, and the ever-present risk of death for the man. Every detail of the spectacle captured his interest: he even observed and recorded the different ways in which people he knew reacted during a bullfight.

Almost immediately after seeing his first fight he began an exhaustive study of bullfighting, which resulted several years later in his famous treatise, *Death in the Afternoon*. He learned about all the current matadors—their lives, their personalities, and the distinctive features of their fighting styles—rating each man with the partisanship of an aficionado. He quickly became an expert on the tactics of the bullring and was able to explain them in relation to the natural fighting instincts of the bull, as modified by variations in bravery or behavior from one animal to another. In short, he taught himself to think like a bullfighter and to follow each move in a fight from a professional point of view. He also studied the history of bullfighting and its economics: the breeding and raising of the bulls, the personal finances of the toreros, and all the complex arrangements involved in scheduling the various corridas. He loved the ceremonies and customs of the festivals and participated whole-heartedly in the spirit of these occasions.

From one standpoint this intensive study in depth was very characteristic of Hemingway. He had a natural, sometimes almost competitive, tendency to find out everything he could about any subject that interested him, and was passionately determined to become a real "insider" when so many were satisfied with half-knowledge. It was remarkable how rapidly and how thoroughly he was able to educate himself in so many different fields. Too little attention has been paid by critics to the extraordinary level of his intelligence. He respected knowledge and he respected even more the moral courage of individuals who were willing to stake their careers on what they had learned. This helps to explain his admiration for professionals in every field, including bullfighting.

The energetic quest for information was also part of his job as a newspaper correspondent soon after World War I. At that time Hemingway's principal source of income was writing feature articles for the *Toronto Star*. He had begun this work in 1920, the year after he returned from Italy. Back in Europe again in 1921, he sent home both news-stories and feature articles, some of them on special assignment from the *Star* and others that arose from excursions of his own choosing.

It was part of his general assignment to produce sprightly, human-interest accounts of persons and places abroad. In doing this he almost always tried to get below the surface of what he saw in order to give his readers a true and complete picture. This might be called the "instructive" aspect of Hemingway's journalism. He stuck to that approach throughout his life in almost all his articles. "Pamplona in July," the first selection in the third part of this book, was such an article for the *Star*. On the recommendation of Gertrude Stein, he and his wife Hadley attended the Fiesta of San Fermín at Pamplona in July, 1923. It was their first visit to Pamplona, and his write-up of the festival makes a natural introduction for this part of the anthology.

But Hemingway was watching bullfights with more than a reporter's eye. He saw at once that the bullring was a rich source of material for his fiction. The necessity of courage and skill in bullfighting was almost as critical as in war. One of the earliest of the six miniatures of *in our time* described an incident in the bullring which Hemingway had been told about. But the five other bullfighting miniatures were all based on firsthand perceptions.

The Pamplona fiesta in 1925 provided the setting for the chapters we have included from *The Sun Also Rises*, Hemingway's first serious novel. It was the Hemingways' third fiesta, but this time they were there with a mixed bag of American and English friends, including Lady Duff Twysden, the model for the character of Brett Ashley.

It was a disappointing fiesta for Hemingway. He was put off by the crowds of wealthy tourists from the European resorts, and even more upsetting were the personal tensions developing within his own group. But the occasion offered rich material for a novelist, as he was able to show soon afterwards: remodeling the characters as appropriate, and changing the sequence of events in order to bring about the explosion touched off in the group by the young matador Pedro Romero. It is interesting to note that no character in the novel corresponds to Hadley Hemingway; and also that Jake Barnes, whose point of view has been adopted by the author, remains relatively detached from the action and is physically prevented from having an affair with Brett because of a war injury. By this device Hemingway was able to explain the restraints on the conduct of his alter ego in the novel. These inhibitions would not have required special explanation had he presented Jake Barnes, in a role closer to his own experience, as a married man attending the fiesta with his wife. But that note of conventionality would have made the book a very different one.

The last selection in this part, "The Undefeated," is a variation on a theme which Hemingway would render in different forms again and again in his career: the courage of a brave man whose luck has run out. The inability of the matador Manuel García to admit defeat in the course of a nightmarish bullfight is part of a simple strength of character, deeper than his will. Hemingway seemed to admire that in a man more than any other quality. Its most famous rendition is in his short novel *The Old Man and the Sea,* but "The Undefeated" is a beautiful story in its own right.

HEMINGWAY's first African safari (begun in December, 1933) had almost as great an impact on his life and his writing as the discovery of Spain and bullfighting ten years earlier. The whole safari lasted not much more than ten weeks, but his consciousness was so stimulated by his enthusiasm and interest that every event seems to have been etched in his memory with unusual clarity. Years later he was able to call up those memories and use them in his writings. The wealth of their detail creates the impression of a much longer stay in Africa than he actually had.

Green Hills of Africa, the book he wrote about the safari, is factual and autobiographical. Nevertheless, Hemingway wanted it to have the same psychological effect on his readers as a work of the imagination. He rearranged the sequence of the story accordingly, and constructed the scenes of each part with that artistic purpose in mind. Because this anthology includes only the first four chapters of *Green Hills of Africa* and thus omits some of the background information provided by the flashbacks in the later chapters, it will be helpful to say a few words about the safari and its members. It may also be of interest to know how Hemingway was able to make such an expedition in the first place.

In the year following the Pamplona fiesta of 1925 (described in *The Sun Also Rises*), Hemingway's marriage to Hadley began to fall apart. It ended in divorce early in 1927, and in May of that year he remarried in Paris. His second wife, Pauline Pfeiffer, had been a friend of both the Hemingways and was the daughter of a wealthy Arkansas family.

Later it was Pauline's millionaire uncle, Gus Pfeiffer, who not only bought the Hemingways a permanent home in Key West,

Florida, but also volunteered to bear all the costs of an African safari for them. In the time of the Depression that involved a staggering sum. But between the offer and the safari itself a number of things caused postponements, and Hemingway had three years in which to look forward to it, with some impatience.

For two intervening summers, in 1930 and 1932, the Hemingways lived on a dude ranch in northwestern Wyoming, beside the Clarks Fork Branch of the Yellowstone. There Hemingway was able to get some experience with big game on hunting trips for mountain sheep, elk, and bear. He also had a chance to try out the big Springfield hunting rifle that had been made to order for the safari.

He was a born hunter, with a passion for the sport. His father had taught him to shoot a rifle and a shotgun, and in spite of poor eyesight, later necessitating glasses, he became a fine shot with both. Dr. Hemingway preached the wrongness of killing for the sake of killing and insisted that one should eat any animal one shot. In later life Hemingway did not always comply with that particular rule, but he did not forget it, either. He believed without question that hunting had its own morality. In an article written for *Esquire* during the safari, he distinguished between "shootism" and "sport" on just such grounds.

Another side of Hemingway as a hunter was his competitiveness. He fought this tendency in himself, and usually he tried to conceal it, seldom with complete success. When his Key West friend, Charles Thompson, came out to Wyoming in 1932 to hunt big game, their hunting trips had a way of turning into contests. Charles Thompson was also invited along on the African safari the following year. He appears in *Green Hills of Africa* as Karl, and when the book opens, near the end of the safari, he has outshone Hemingway consistently in the size and quality of his big-game trophies. The latter is attempting to even up the score somewhat by killing a better kudu than Karl's. More or less on the sidelines are the other members of the party: Pauline (P.O.M. or Poor Old Mama), the white hunter Philip Percival (Jackson Phillips or Pop), and his assistant Ben Fourie (Dan). The African gunbearers, drivers, and trackers appear with their own names or nicknames. The campsite at that time was in eastern Tanganyika, off the road to Handeni.

The second two chapters of the selection flash back three weeks to their earlier hunting in the hill country south of the Ngorongoro

Crater. Hemingway had just returned to the safari after a sick leave for dysentery in Nairobi.

It is worth commenting on Hemingway's honesty as a writer in revealing so candidly to his readers his feelings of envy and frustration, however much he may have tried not to show those emotions at the time. But it is partly this underlying contest between him and Karl that gives the story its plot and suspense, in keeping with Hemingway's artistic intentions. Writers are sometimes criticized for being self-centered, yet they often have to be if they are going to take advantage of the material provided them in their own emotions. Tolstoy, whom Hemingway admired greatly as a novelist, was a master of that kind of self-expression.

In the course of the safari Hemingway often talked with Philip Percival about his experiences as a white hunter. He was gathering as much information as possible about the sport. A hunter of dangerous game sometimes faced formidable risks, especially if he abided by the rules of the sport: to shoot only on foot and to hunt down a wounded animal in order to dispatch it humanely. Situations could arise on a safari that called for courage; and Hemingway was profoundly interested in that particular trait: in itself and in its relations to pride and fear.

A brave man may lose his courage in special circumstances, and a coward may find courage suddenly and unexpectedly. War and the bullring had provided Hemingway with examples of such changes in individuals, and he was discovering others in discussions with Percival as well as in his own new experiences.

"The Short Happy Life of Francis Macomber" is one of the great short stories dealing with the theme of courage, and it has been included in this part of the anthology. Its plot is constructed around the relations among three characters: Macomber, his wife, and the white hunter. When the equilibrium among these three is disrupted by a change within Macomber a violent ending follows inevitably.

The final selection in this part, "Miss Mary's Lion," is a portion of a long book about Africa, left unfinished by Hemingway at the time of his death in 1961. Generally referred to now as his *African Journal,* the book deals with a second safari made in 1953 by Hemingway and his wife Mary, twenty years after the safari of *Green Hills of Africa.*

In this episode the party is encamped in southern Kenya. The white hunter—again Philip Percival—has had to leave the safari, and in doing so has placed special responsibilities on Hemingway, particularly in connection with hunting Mary's lion, which so far has eluded them. The Head Game Ranger of the area (G.C.) is on hand, and later a Kenya police officer, Harry Steele, shows up. But Hemingway is burdened by a double worry: to be sure that Mary will finally get a chance at her lion and that nothing will go wrong when she does.

The often rambling style of this journal is very different from most of Hemingway's other writing. Yet as a result of its informality it provides a delightful self-portrait of Hemingway, if not in his slippers, at least with his mosquito boots on, in front of the campfire with a scotch and soda. The narrative is zestful, self-disparaging, humorous, and at times outrageous. It also contains exquisitely sketched memories of the past.

THE Spanish Civil War was a crucial event in Hemingway's life. For almost two years it absorbed his whole attention and it led to some of his finest work as a writer. Several different things combined to make that war so important to him: his love for Spain and the Spanish people, his fear and hatred of fascism, his interest in war itself, the attraction of a big story for a former newspaperman, and, as a product of all these things, the impact of his experiences in Spain on his creative imagination as a writer.

The first of Hemingway's four visits to wartime Spain involved two professional assignments: to help in the filming of *The Spanish Earth,* a documentary motion picture promoting the Loyalist cause; and to serve as a war correspondent for the North American Newspaper Alliance. By then Hemingway was a writer of world renown. It was very valuable to the Loyalist leaders to have him on their side and he was treated accordingly. Doors opened for him. He met the men and women he wanted to see, and he was able to make special trips to battlefronts around Madrid. He was also provided with an automobile and chauffeur. An amusing dispatch he wrote about that has been included in this part of the anthology under the title "The Chauffeurs of Madrid." In spite of the strict distinction Hemingway tried to keep between his journalism and his imaginative writing, his gifts as a novelist affected almost everything he wrote. It is not surprising then, that some of his by-lined articles, like this one, have stood on an equal footing with his fiction and have been subsequently anthologized as short stories.

During his first two visits to Spain in 1937, Hemingway stayed at the Hotel Florida in Madrid, in the midst of an assorted population of fellow journalists from the United States and Europe. The city was under constant bombardment by Rebel artillery, and every aspect of life there was influenced by the war and the danger of death. He was able later to evoke the particular atmosphere of that time in one of his finest short stories, "The Butterfly and the Tank." He dealt with another side of the war in the battlefield story, "Under the Ridge." In it he showed the hatred of a Spanish soldier not only for the Russian battle police who take part in the action, but for all the foreigners intervening in the war, whether as enemies or as allies.

This story also shows something very important about Hemingway as a writer: the strength of his commitment to the truth. His strong sympathy for the Loyalist cause did not prevent him from describing the people he saw as they really were or from showing what they actually did. His conscience as an artist forced him to hold a point of view above any particular party line and to maintain a corresponding impartiality in seeing the good and the bad in individuals on both sides. During the period in question political views were strongly polarized and Hemingway was later criticized by the Left for writing about excesses on the Loyalist side. But the criticism did not influence his point of view. It could be fairly said about his writing what Tolstoy once said about his own: that its hero was the truth.

The stories and articles that Hemingway wrote about the Spanish Civil War can almost all be linked to firsthand experiences of the time, as can *The Fifth Column,* the play he wrote about Madrid under siege. One can also find immediate models for events and characters within parts of his novel, *For Whom the Bell Tolls.* But only in parts; for the book as a whole stands as one of the great imaginative creations of Hemingway's career. In writing it he relied upon his whole knowledge of Spain and the Spanish acquired during fifteen years, as well as upon the other observations and perceptions of a lifetime.

It is interesting that he should have chosen as his subject an

American saboteur working behind Rebel lines with a band of partisans. His own experiences in the war would not seem to have brought him that close to guerrilla operations. But one of the obvious advantages of choosing to write about this phase of the war was that it enabled him to describe a cast of authentically Spanish men and women, relatively isolated from the foreigners who had taken their side. The reader has been introduced to most of these characters by the end of the first two chapters included here and is able to see how fully they have been brought to life by the author.

Hemingway had to face a special problem in connection with such a group speaking their native language. He was not willing to try to render their speech by idiomatic spoken English but instead devised a special style in order to convey the construction and flavor of the original Spanish. Although this device has been criticized as artificial, a good case can be made for it on the grounds that a thought framed and spoken in Spanish often has no precise equivalent in spoken English. Particularly when writing about simple people whose thoughts have been largely shaped by their language, it is reasonable for the author to try to find some way of catching their characteristic expressions. It is doubtful whether these characters could otherwise have been rendered as authentically, unless of course their dialogue had been written wholly in Spanish.

A similar, but less important, problem arose in connection with the number of obscenities normal in the speech of the members of a guerrilla band like Pablo's. Here Hemingway came up against contemporary conventions prohibiting the publication of many common words and expressions. This problem would not have arisen twenty-four years later, but at the time he had to compromise by using circumlocutions. Practically speaking, the vocabulary of most present-day readers should be broad enough for them to be able to guess what would have been said.

THE last part of this book is called "On the Water" and contains three works of Hemingway's later years, all of them about the sea.

He had gone deep-sea fishing often in 1928, the year of his first visit to Key West, and the sport appealed to him so much that it was probably one of the reasons for the Hemingways' deciding to buy a house there. Some years afterwards, when he had separated from Pauline, he moved to a place outside Havana and there, too, he continued to live near the water. At first Hemingway had to charter boats for fishing trips, but in 1934 soon after his return from the African safari, he bought his own fishing boat, a 38-foot craft named the *Pilar*. To own such a boat bound him even closer to the sea, to the point where it became a major interest in his life.

Several of Hemingway's articles written in the thirties deal with experiences on board the *Pilar*. He was on it continually, sometimes taking groups of friends on excursions to Havana or Bimini for fishing in the Gulf Stream. He had thrown himself into the sport with his usual gusto and thoroughness, and as usual he passed on to readers what he had done and what he had learned, along with his personal theories on such subjects as the natural history of the marlin. "The Great Blue River," written for *Holiday* in 1949, is a later article in that vein. It describes a day of marlin fishing with Hemingway and Mary, and its lively, informative account shows him at his happiest.

But his masterpiece about the sea is the short novel, *The Old Man and the Sea*, published three years later and included here in its entirety. Part of its power comes from bringing together into one story so many of the themes of Hemingway's best work: his love of the sea, his tragic view of the contest between a brave man and a brave animal, his respect for the endurance and instinctive courage of simple people, and his compassion for the trials of old age. Rarely has so short a work held an emotional charge of such magnitude. More than any other story it seems to have given Hemingway a means of expressing his deepest beliefs about life.

The idea for the book had been planted in his mind, almost by chance, in a story he was told years before about an old Cuban fisherman in a small boat, who had killed a giant marlin after a similar struggle, only to lose it to sharks. Hemingway retold this story in a paragraph of one of his articles for *Esquire* in 1936, "On the Blue Water: A Gulf Stream Letter." Thereafter, the idea apparently lay dormant for long periods. In 1939 he mentioned it in a letter to Maxwell Perkins, his editor at Scribners, as the subject of a story he intended to write. But it was not until early in 1951 that he began the actual composition. It was finished in a little over a month.

Immediately after its publication, *The Old Man and the Sea* became a major success, critically and commercially. It was specifically referred to in the citation accompanying the author's Nobel Prize for Literature in 1954. Of all the praise the book received, the comment that pleased the author the most was made by the art-historian, Bernard Berenson:

> Hemingway's *The Old Man and the Sea* is an idyll of the sea as sea, as un-Byronic and un-Melvillian as Homer himself, and communicated in a prose as calm and compelling as Homer's verse. No real artist symbolizes or allegorizes—and Hemingway is a real artist —but every real work of art exhales symbols and allegories. So does this short but not small masterpiece.

The final selection in our anthology is taken from Hemingway's novel, *Islands in the Stream,* published several years after his death. Although it is only part of that book, it is a complete self-contained unit. The work describes a sea chase off the coast of Cuba in pursuit of the survivors of a destroyed German submarine in World War II. The events described are wholly fictional, but the story has a direct relation to the activities of Hemingway and some of his friends in the early part of the war. They had outfitted the *Pilar* with an arsenal of guns and explosives, and their plan was to use it as an improvised Q-boat; that is, to decoy and then attack enemy submarines in the area. Militarily the scheme was wholly unsuccessful, but from a literary standpoint it was more productive. For here we have Hemingway imagining what might have happened if on one of their missions they had engaged the enemy.

All the details of the setting of the story are closely based on experience. Hemingway knew the waters off the north coast of Cuba as well as he knew the inside of the *Pilar*. His descriptions of the wildlife and vegetation, the channels and beaches, landscapes and seascapes are sharp reproductions of things he had seen many times: not with a painter's eye, like his hero, Thomas Hudson, but just as acutely. On a level beneath the suspense of the plot, the thoughts of Thomas Hudson create a different mood: of resignation and nostalgia. At the very end, he hopes to endure only for the sake of his work as an artist. But he is aware of the limits on such hopes.

The need to endure was central in Hemingway's philosophy of life, and we have chosen the title *The Enduring Hemingway* in recognition of how important it was to him. Sometimes he expressed that idea in a favorite French motto: *"Il faut (d'abord) durer,"* or "One must, first of all, endure." As a writer he himself endured and created a large and precious legacy in the works of his imagination, now enduring with their author's name in that "life beyond life" to which all writers aspire.

CHARLES SCRIBNER, JR.

Acknowledgments

In Part IV of this anthology, the text of "Miss Mary's Lion" was taken from a version very ably edited by Ray Cave for *Sports Illustrated*. In connection with the biographical details in the Introduction, I have relied almost entirely on Carlos Baker's biography, *Ernest Hemingway, A Life Story*. It is as much a pleasure to acknowledge that indebtedness as it was a privilege to publish Dr. Baker's book.

C. S., JR.

❀ PART I ❀

IN OUR TIME

From A MOVEABLE FEAST

A Good Café on the Place St.-Michel
There Is Never Any End to Paris

IN OUR TIME

On the Quai at Smyrna
Indian Camp
The Doctor and the Doctor's Wife
The End of Something
The Three-Day Blow
The Battler
A Very Short Story
Soldier's Home
The Revolutionist
Mr. and Mrs. Elliot
Cat in the Rain
Out of Season
Cross-Country Snow
My Old Man
Big Two-Hearted River (PARTS I AND II)

A Good Café on
the Place St.-Michel

THEN there was the bad weather. It would come in one day when the fall was over. We would have to shut the windows in the night against the rain and the cold wind would strip the leaves from the trees in the Place Contrescarpe. The leaves lay sodden in the rain and the wind drove the rain against the big green autobus at the terminal and the Café des Amateurs was crowded and the windows misted over from the heat and the smoke inside. It was a sad, evilly run café where the drunkards of the quarter crowded together and I kept away from it because of the smell of dirty bodies and the sour smell of drunkenness. The men and women who frequented the Amateurs stayed drunk all of the time, or all of the time they could afford it, mostly on wine which they bought by the half-liter or liter. Many strangely named apéritifs were advertised, but few people could afford them except as a foundation to build their wine drunks on. The women drunkards were called *poivrottes* which meant female rummies.

The Café des Amateurs was the cesspool of the rue Mouffetard, that wonderful narrow crowded market street which led into the Place Contrescarpe. The squat toilets of the old apartment houses, one by the side of the stairs on each floor with the two cleated cement shoe-shaped elevations on each side of the aperture so a *locataire* would not slip, emptied into cesspools which were emptied by pumping into horse-drawn tank wagons at night. In the summer time, with all windows open, we would hear the pumping and the odor was very strong. The tank wagons were painted brown and saffron color and in the moonlight when they worked the rue Cardinal Lemoine their wheeled, horse-drawn cylinders looked like Braque paintings. No one emptied the Café des Amateurs though, and its yellowed poster stating the terms and penalties of the law against public drunkenness

3

was as flyblown and disregarded as its clients were constant and ill-smelling.

All of the sadness of the city came suddenly with the first cold rains of winter, and there were no more tops to the high white houses as you walked but only the wet blackness of the street and the closed doors of the small shops, the herb sellers, the stationery and the newspaper shops, the midwife—second class—and the hotel where Verlaine had died where I had a room on the top floor where I worked.

It was either six or eight flights up to the top floor and it was very cold and I knew how much it would cost for a bundle of small twigs, three wire-wrapped packets of short, half-pencil length pieces of split pine to catch fire from the twigs, and then the bundle of half-dried lengths of hard wood that I must buy to make a fire that would warm the room. So I went to the far side of the street to look up at the roof in the rain and see if any chimneys were going, and how the smoke blew. There was no smoke and I thought about how the chimney would be cold and might not draw and of the room possibly filling with smoke, and the fuel wasted, and the money gone with it, and I walked on in the rain. I walked down past the Lycée Henri Quatre and the ancient church of St.-Étienne-du-Mont and the windswept Place du Panthéon and cut in for shelter to the right and finally came out on the lee side of the Boulevard St.-Michel and worked on down it past the Cluny and the Boulevard St.-Germain until I came to a good café that I knew on the Place St.-Michel.

It was a pleasant café, warm and clean and friendly, and I hung up my old waterproof on the coat rack to dry and put my worn and weathered felt hat on the rack above the bench and ordered a *café au lait*. The waiter brought it and I took out a notebook from the pocket of the coat and a pencil and started to write. I was writing about up in Michigan and since it was a wild, cold, blowing day it was that sort of day in the story. I had already seen the end of fall come through boyhood, youth and young manhood, and in one place you could write about it better than in another. That was called transplanting yourself, I thought, and it could be as necessary with people as with other sorts of growing things. But in the story the boys were drinking and this made me thirsty and I ordered a rum St. James. This tasted wonderful on the cold day and I kept on writing, feeling very well and feeling the good Martinique rum warm me all through my body and my spirit.

A girl came in the café and sat by herself at a table near the window. She was very pretty with a face fresh as a newly minted coin if they minted coins in smooth flesh with rain-freshened skin, and her hair was black as a crow's wing and cut sharply and diagonally across her cheek.

I looked at her and she disturbed me and made me very excited. I wished I could put her in the story, or anywhere, but she had placed herself so she could watch the street and the entry and I knew she was waiting for someone. So I went on writing.

The story was writing itself and I was having a hard time keeping up with it. I ordered another rum St. James and I watched the girl whenever I looked up, or when I sharpened the pencil with a pencil sharpener with the shavings curling into the saucer under my drink.

I've seen you, beauty, and you belong to me now, whoever you are waiting for and if I never see you again, I thought. You belong to me and all Paris belongs to me and I belong to this notebook and this pencil.

Then I went back to writing and I entered far into the story and was lost in it. I was writing it now and it was not writing itself and I did not look up nor know anything about the time nor think where I was nor order any more rum St. James. I was tired of rum St. James without thinking about it. Then the story was finished and I was very tired. I read the last paragraph and then I looked up and looked for the girl and she had gone. I hope she's gone with a good man, I thought. But I felt sad.

I closed up the story in the notebook and put it in my inside pocket and I asked the waiter for a dozen *portugaises* and a half-carafe of the dry white wine they had there. After writing a story I was always empty and both sad and happy, as though I had made love, and I was sure this was a very good story although I would not know truly how good until I read it over the next day.

As I ate the oysters with their strong taste of the sea and their faint metallic taste that the cold white wine washed away, leaving only the sea taste and the succulent texture, and as I drank their cold liquid from each shell and washed it down with the crisp taste of the wine, I lost the empty feeling and began to be happy and to make plans.

Now that the bad weather had come, we could leave Paris for a while for a place where this rain would be snow coming down through the pines and covering the road and the high hillsides and at an altitude where we would hear it creak as we walked home at night. Below Les Avants there was a chalet where the pension was wonderful and where we would be together and have our books and at night be warm in bed together with the windows open and the stars bright. That was where we could go. Traveling third class on the train was not expensive. The pension cost very little more than we spent in Paris.

I would give up the room in the hotel where I wrote and there was only the rent of 74 rue Cardinal Lemoine which was nominal. I had written journalism for Toronto and the checks for that were due. I could write that anywhere under any circumstances and we had money to make the trip.

Maybe away from Paris I could write about Paris as in Paris I could write about Michigan. I did not know it was too early for that because I did not know Paris well enough. But that was how it worked out eventually. Anyway we would go if my wife wanted to, and I finished the oysters and the wine and paid my score in the café and made it the shortest way back up the Montagne Ste. Geneviève through the rain, that was now only local weather and not something that changed your life, to the flat at the top of the hill.

"I think it would be wonderful, Tatie," my wife said. She had a gently modeled face and her eyes and her smile lighted up at decisions as though they were rich presents. "When should we leave?"

"Whenever you want."

"Oh, I want to right away. Didn't you know?"

"Maybe it will be fine and clear when we come back. It can be very fine when it is clear and cold."

"I'm sure it will be," she said. "Weren't you good to think of going, too."

There Is Never Any End to Paris

WHEN there were the three of us instead of just the two, it was the cold and the weather that finally drove us out of Paris in the winter time. Alone there was no problem when you got used to it. I could always go to a café to write and could work all morning over a *café crème* while the waiters cleaned and swept out the café and it gradually grew warmer. My wife could go to work at the piano in a cold place and with enough sweaters keep warm playing and come home to nurse Bumby. It was wrong to take a baby to a café in the winter though; even a baby that never cried and watched everything that happened and was never bored. There were no baby-sitters then and Bumby would stay happy in his tall cage bed with his big, loving cat named F. Puss. There were people who said that it was dangerous to leave a cat with a baby. The most ignorant and prejudiced said that a cat would suck a baby's breath and kill him. Others said that a cat would lie on a baby and the cat's weight would smother him. F. Puss lay beside Bumby in the tall cage bed and watched the door with his big yellow eyes, and would let no one come near him when we were out and Marie, the *femme de ménage,* had to be away. There was no need for baby-sitters. F. Puss was the baby-sitter.

But when you are poor, and we were really poor when I had given up all journalism when we came back from Canada, and could sell no stories at all, it was too rough with a baby in Paris in the winter. At three months Mr. Bumby had crossed the North Atlantic on a twelve-day small Cunarder that sailed from New York via Halifax in January. He never cried on the trip and laughed happily when he would be barricaded in a bunk so he could not fall out when we were in heavy weather. But our Paris was too cold for him.

We went to Schruns in the Vorarlberg in Austria. After going through Switzerland you came to the Austrian frontier at Feldkirch. The train went through Liechtenstein and stopped at Bludenz where there was a small branch line that ran along a pebbly trout river

7

through a valley of farms and forest to Schruns, which was a sunny market town with sawmills, stores, inns and a good, year-around hotel called the Taube where we lived.

The rooms at the Taube were large and comfortable with big stoves, big windows and big beds with good blankets and feather coverlets. The meals were simple and excellent and the dining room and the wood-planked public bar were well heated and friendly. The valley was wide and open so there was good sun. The pension was about two dollars a day for the three of us, and as the Austrian schilling went down with inflation, our room and food were less all the time. There was no desperate inflation and poverty as there had been in Germany. The schilling went up and down, but its longer course was down.

There were no ski lifts from Schruns and no funiculars, but there were logging trails and cattle trails that led up different mountain valleys to the high mountain country. You climbed on foot carrying your skis and higher up, where the snow was too deep, you climbed on seal skins that you attached to the bottoms of the skis. At the tops of mountain valleys there were the big Alpine Club huts for summer climbers where you could sleep and leave payment for any wood you used. In some you had to pack up your own wood, or if you were going on a long tour in the high mountains and the glaciers, you hired someone to pack wood and supplies up with you, and established a base. The most famous of these high base huts were the Lindauer-Hütte, the Madlener-Haus and the Wiesbadener-Hütte.

In back of the Taube there was a sort of practice slope where you ran through orchards and fields and there was another good slope behind Tschagguns across the valley where there was a beautiful inn with an excellent collection of chamois horns on the walls of the drinking room. It was from behind the lumber village of Tschagguns, which was on the far edge of the valley, that the good skiing went all the way up until you could eventually cross the mountains and get over the Silvretta into the Klosters area.

Schruns was a healthy place for Bumby who had a dark-haired beautiful girl to take him out in the sun in his sleigh and look after him, and Hadley and I had all the new country to learn and the new villages, and the people of the town were very friendly. Herr Walther Lent who was a pioneer high-mountain skier and at one time had been a partner with Hannes Schneider, the great Arlberg skier, mak-

ing ski waxes for climbing and all snow conditions, was starting a
school for Alpine skiing and we both enrolled. Walther Lent's system
was to get his pupils off the practice slopes as soon as possible and into
the high mountains on trips. Skiing was not the way it is now, the
spiral fracture had not become common then, and no one could afford
a broken leg. There were no ski patrols. Anything you ran down
from, you had to climb up. That gave you legs that were fit to run
down with.

Walther Lent believed the fun of skiing was to get up into the
highest mountain country where there was no one else and where the
snow was untracked and then travel from one high Alpine Club hut
to another over the top passes and glaciers of the Alps. You must not
have a binding that could break your leg if you fell. The ski should
come off before it broke your leg. What he really loved was unroped
glacier skiing, but for that we had to wait until spring when the
crevasses were sufficiently covered.

Hadley and I had loved skiing since we had first tried it together
in Switzerland and later at Cortina d'Ampezzo in the Dolomites when
Bumby was going to be born and the doctor in Milan had given her
permission to continue to ski if I would promise that she would not
fall down. This took a very careful selection of terrain and of runs
and absolutely controlled running, but she had beautiful, wonderfully strong legs and fine control of her skis, and she did not fall. We
all knew the different snow conditions and everyone knew how to run
in deep powder snow.

We loved the Vorarlberg and we loved Schruns. We would go
there about Thanksgiving time and stay until nearly Easter. There
was always skiing even though Schruns was not high enough for a ski
resort except in a winter of heavy snow. But climbing was fun and
no one minded it in those days. You set a certain pace well under the
speed at which you could climb, and it was easy and your heart felt
good and you were proud of the weight of your rucksack. Part of the
climb up to the Madlener-Haus was steep and very tough. But the
second time you made that climb it was easier, and finally you made
it easily with double the weight you had carried at first.

We were always hungry and every meal time was a great event.
We drank light or dark beer and new wines and wines that were a
year old sometimes. The white wines were the best. For other drinks
there was kirsch made in the valley and Enzian *Schnapps* distilled

from mountain gentian. Sometimes for dinner there would be jugged hare with a rich red wine sauce, and sometimes venison with chestnut sauce. We would drink red wine with these even though it was more expensive than white wine, and the very best cost twenty cents a liter. Ordinary red wine was much cheaper and we packed it up in kegs to the Madlener-Haus.

We had a store of books that Sylvia Beach had let us take for the winter and we could bowl with the people of the town in the alley that gave onto the summer garden of the hotel. Once or twice a week there was a poker game in the dining room of the hotel with all the windows shuttered and the door locked. Gambling was forbidden in Austria then and I played with Herr Nels, the hotel keeper, Herr Lent of the Alpine ski school, a banker of the town, the public prosecutor and the captain of Gendarmerie. It was a stiff game and they were all good poker players except that Herr Lent played too wildly because the ski school was not making any money. The captain of Gendarmerie would raise his finger to his ear when he would hear the pair of gendarmes stop outside the door when they made their rounds, and we would be silent until they had gone on.

In the cold of the morning as soon as it was light the maid would come into the room and shut the windows and make a fire in the big porcelain stove. Then the room was warm, there was breakfast of fresh bread or toast with delicious fruit preserves and big bowls of coffee, fresh eggs and good ham if you wanted it. There was a dog named Schnauz that slept on the foot of the bed who loved to go on ski trips and to ride on my back or over my shoulder when I ran down hill. He was Mr. Bumby's friend too and would go for walks with him and his nurse beside the small sleigh.

Schruns was a good place to work. I know because I did the most difficult job of rewriting I have ever done there in the winter of 1925 and 1926, when I had to take the first draft of *The Sun Also Rises* which I had written in one sprint of six weeks, and make it into a novel. I cannot remember what stories I wrote there. There were several though that turned out well.

I remember the snow on the road to the village squeaking at night when we walked home in the cold with our skis and ski poles on our shoulders, watching the lights and then finally seeing the buildings, and how everyone on the road said, "Grüss Gott." There were always country men in the *Weinstube* with nailed boots and mountain clothes and the air was smoky and the wooden floors were scarred by the nails. Many of the young men had served in Austrian Alpine regiments and one named Hans, who worked in the sawmill, was a famous hunter and we were good friends because we had been in the same part of the mountains in Italy. We drank together and we all sang mountain songs.

I remember the trails up through the orchards and the fields of the hillside farms above the village and the warm farm houses with their great stoves and the huge wood piles in the snow. The women worked in the kitchens carding and spinning wool into grey and black yarn. The spinning wheels worked by a foot treadle and the yarn was not dyed. The black yarn was from the wool of black sheep. The wool was natural and the fat had not been removed, and the caps and sweaters and long scarves that Hadley knitted from it never became wet in the snow.

One Christmas there was a play by Hans Sachs that the school master directed. It was a good play and I wrote a review of it for the provincial paper that the hotel keeper translated. Another year a former German naval officer with a shaven head and scars came to give a lecture on the Battle of Jutland. The lantern slides showed the movements of the two battle fleets and the naval officer used a billiard cue for a pointer when he pointed out the cowardice of Jellicoe and sometimes he became so angry that his voice broke. The school master was afraid that he would stab the billiard cue through the screen. Afterwards the former naval officer could not quiet himself down and everyone was ill at ease in the *Weinstube*. Only the public prosecutor and the banker drank with him, and they were at a separate table. Herr Lent, who was a Rhinelander, would not attend the lecture. There was a couple from Vienna who had come for the skiing but who did not want to go to the high mountains and so were leaving for Zurs where, I heard, they were killed in an avalanche. The man said the lecturer was the type of swine who had ruined Germany and in twenty years they would do it again. The woman with him told him to shut up in French and said this is a small place and you never know.

That was the year that so many people were killed in avalanches. The first big loss was over the mountains from our valley in Lech in the Arlberg. A party of Germans wanted to come and ski with Herr Lent on their Christmas vacations. Snow was late that year and the hills and mountain slopes were still warm from the sun when a great

snowfall came. The snow was deep and powdery and it was not bound
to the earth at all. Conditions for skiing could not be more dangerous
and Herr Lent had wired the Berliners not to come. But it was their
vacation time and they were ignorant and had no fear of avalanches.
They arrived at Lech and Herr Lent refused to take them out. One
man called him a coward and they said they would ski by themselves.
Finally he took them to the safest slope he could find. He crossed it
himself and then they followed and the whole hillside came down in
a rush, rising over them as a tidal wave rises. Thirteen were dug out
and nine of them were dead. The Alpine ski school had not prospered
before this, and afterwards we were almost the only members. We
became great students of avalanches, the different types of avalanches,
how to avoid them and how to behave if you were caught in one.
Most of the writing that I did that year was in avalanche time.

The worst thing I remember of that avalanche winter was one
man who was dug out. He had squatted down and made a box with
his arms in front of his head, as we had been taught to do, so that
there would be air to breathe as the snow rose up over you. It was a
huge avalanche and it took a long time to dig everyone out, and this
man was the last to be found. He had not been dead long and his
neck was worn through so that the tendons and the bone were visible.
He had been turning his head from side to side against the pressure
of the snow. In this avalanche there must have been some old, packed
snow mixed in with the new light snow that had slipped. We could
not decide whether he had done it on purpose or if he had been out
of his head. He was refused burial in consecrated ground by the
local priest anyway, since there was no proof he was a Catholic.

When we lived in Schruns we used to make a long trip up the
valley to the inn where we slept before setting out on the climb to
the Madlener-Haus. It was a very beautiful old inn and the wood of
the walls of the room where we ate and drank were silky with the
years of polishing. So were the table and chairs. We slept close together in the big bed under the feather quilt with the window open
and the stars close and very bright. In the morning after breakfast
we all loaded to go up the road and started the climb in the dark with
the stars close and very bright, carrying our skis on our shoulders.
The porters' skis were short and they carried heavy loads. We com-
peted among ourselves as to who could climb with the heaviest loads,
but no one could compete with the porters, squat sullen peasants

who spoke only Montafon dialect, climbed steadily like pack horses
and at the top, where the Alpine Club hut was built on a shelf beside
the snow-covered glacier, shed their loads against the stone wall of
the hut, asked for more money than the agreed price, and, when
they had obtained a compromise, shot down and away on their short
skis like gnomes.

One of our friends was a German girl who skied with us. She
was a great mountain skier, small and beautifully built, who could
carry as heavy a rucksack as I could and carry it longer.

"Those porters always look at us as though they looked forward
to bringing us down as bodies," she said. "They set the price for the
climb and I've never known them not to ask for more."

In the winter in Schruns I wore a beard against the sun that
burned my face so badly on the high snow, and did not bother having
a haircut. Late one evening running on skis down the logging trails
Herr Lent told me that peasants I passed on those roads above
Schruns called me "the Black Christ." He said some, when they came
to the *Weinstube*, called me "the Black Kirsch-drinking Christ." But
to the peasants at the far upper end of the Montafon where we hired
porters to go up to the Madlener-Haus, we were all foreign devils
who went into the high mountains when people should stay out of
them. That we started before daylight in order not to pass avalanche
places when the sun could make them dangerous was not to our
credit. It only proved we were tricky as all foreign devils are.

I remember the smell of the pines and the sleeping on the
mattresses of beech leaves in the woodcutters' huts and the skiing
through the forest following the tracks of hares and of foxes. In the
high mountains above the tree line I remember following the track
of a fox until I came in sight of him and watching him stand with
his right forefoot raised and then go carefully to stop and then
pounce, and the whiteness and the clutter of a ptarmigan bursting
out of the snow and flying away and over the ridge.

I remember all the kinds of snow that the wind could make
and their different treacheries when you were on skis. Then there
were the blizzards when you were in the high Alpine hut and the
strange world that they would make where we had to make our route
as carefully as though we had never seen the country. We had not,
either, as it all was new. Finally towards spring there was the great
glacier run, smooth and straight, forever straight if our legs could

hold it, our ankles locked, we running so low, leaning into the speed, dropping forever and forever in the silent hiss of the crisp powder. It was better than any flying or anything else, and we built the ability to do it and to have it with the long climbs carrying the heavy rucksacks. We could not buy the trip up nor take a ticket to the top. It was the end we worked for all winter, and all the winter built to make it possible.

During our last year in the mountains new people came deep into our lives and nothing was ever the same again. The winter of the avalanches was like a happy and innocent winter in childhood compared to the next winter, a nightmare winter disguised as the greatest fun of all, and the murderous summer that was to follow. It was that year that the rich showed up.

The rich have a sort of pilot fish who goes ahead of them, some-times a little deaf, sometimes a little blind, but always smelling affable and hesitant ahead of them. The pilot fish talks like this: "Well I dont know. No of course not really. But I like them. I like them both. Yes, by God, Hem; I do like them. I see what you mean but I do like them truly and there's something damned fine about her." (He gives her name and pronounces it lovingly.) "No, Hem, dont be silly and dont be difficult. I like them truly. Both of them I swear it. You'll like him (using his baby-talk nickname) when you know him. I like them both, truly."

Then you have the rich and nothing is ever as it was again. The pilot fish leaves of course. He is always going somewhere, or coming from somewhere, and he is never around for very long. He enters and leaves politics or the theater in the same way he enters and leaves countries and people's lives in his early days. He is never caught and he is not caught by the rich. Nothing ever catches him and it is only those who trust him who are caught and killed. He has the irreplace-able early training of the bastard and a latent and long denied love of money. He ends up rich himself, having moved one dollar's width to the right with every dollar that he made.

These rich loved and trusted him because he was shy, comic, elusive, already in production, and because he was an unerring pilot fish.

When you have two people who love each other, are happy and gay and really good work is being done by one or both of them, people are drawn to them as surely as migrating birds are drawn at

night to a powerful beacon. If the two people were as solidly constructed as the beacon there would be little damage except to the
birds. Those who attract people by their happiness and their per-
formance are usually inexperienced. They do not know how not to be
overrun and how to go away. They do not always learn about the
good, the attractive, the charming, the soon-beloved, the generous,
the understanding rich who have no bad qualities and who give
each day the quality of a festival and who, when they have passed and
taken the nourishment they needed, leave everything deader than
the roots of any grass Attila's horses' hooves have ever scoured.

The rich came led by the pilot fish. A year before they would
never have come. There was no certainty then. The work was as good
and the happiness was greater but no novel had been written, so they
could not be sure. They never wasted their time nor their charm on
something that was not sure. Why should they? Picasso was sure and of
course had been before they had ever heard of painting. They were
very sure of another painter. Many others. But this year they were
sure and they had the word from the pilot fish who turned up too so
we would not feel that they were outlanders and that I would not be
difficult. The pilot fish was our friend of course.

In those days I trusted the pilot fish as I would trust the Corrected Hydrographic Office Sailing Directions for the Mediterranean,
say, or the tables in *Brown's Nautical Almanac*. Under the charm of
these rich I was as trusting and as stupid as a bird dog who wants to
go out with any man with a gun, or a trained pig in a circus who has
finally found someone who loves and appreciates him for himself
alone. That every day should be a fiesta seemed to me a marvelous
discovery. I even read aloud the part of the novel that I had rewritten,
which is about as low as a writer can get and much more dangerous
for him as a writer than glacier skiing unroped before the full winter
snowfall has set over the crevices.

When they said, "It's great, Ernest. Truly it's great. You cannot
know the thing it has," I wagged my tail in pleasure and plunged into
the fiesta concept of life to see if I could not bring some fine attractive
stick back, instead of thinking, "If these bastards like it what is wrong
with it?" That was what I would think if I had been functioning as a
professional although, if I had been functioning as a professional, I
would never have read it to them.

Before these rich had come we had already been infiltrated by another rich using the oldest trick there is. It is that an unmarried young woman becomes the temporary best friend of another young woman who is married, goes to live with the husband and wife and then unknowingly, innocently and unrelentingly sets out to marry the husband. When the husband is a writer and doing difficult work so that he is occupied much of the time and is not a good companion or partner to his wife for a big part of the day, the arrangement has advantages until you know how it works out. The husband has two attractive girls around when he has finished work. One is new and strange and if he has bad luck he gets to love them both.

Then, instead of the two of them and their child, there are three of them. First it is stimulating and fun and it goes on that way for a while. All things truly wicked start from an innocence. So you live day by day and enjoy what you have and do not worry. You lie and hate it and it destroys you and every day is more dangerous, but you live day to day as in a war.

It was necessary that I leave Schruns and go to New York to rearrange publishers. I did my business in New York and when I got back to Paris I should have caught the first train from the Gare de l'Est that would take me down to Austria. But the girl I was in love with was in Paris then, and I did not take the first train, or the second or the third.

When I saw my wife again standing by the tracks as the train came in by the piled logs at the station, I wished I had died before I ever loved anyone but her. She was smiling, the sun on her lovely face tanned by the snow and sun, beautifully built, her hair red gold in the sun, grown out all winter awkwardly and beautifully, and Mr. Bumby standing with her, blond and chunky and with winter cheeks looking like a good Vorarlberg boy.

"Oh Tatie," she said, when I was holding her in my arms, "you're back and you made such a fine successful trip. I love you and we've missed you so."

I loved her and I loved no one else and we had a lovely magic time while we were alone. I worked well and we made great trips, and I thought we were invulnerable again, and it wasn't until we were out of the mountains in late spring, and back in Paris that the other thing started again.

That was the end of the first part of Paris. Paris was never to be the same again although it was always Paris and you changed as it changed. We never went back to the Vorarlberg and neither did the rich.

There is never any ending to Paris and the memory of each person who has lived in it differs from that of any other. We always returned to it no matter who we were or how it was changed or with what difficulties, or ease, it could be reached. Paris was always worth it and you received return for whatever you brought to it. But this is how Paris was in the early days when we were very poor and very happy.

On the Quai at Smyrna

THE strange thing was, he said, how they screamed every night at midnight. I do not know why they screamed at that time. We were in the harbor and they were all on the pier and at midnight they started screaming. We used to turn the searchlight on them to quiet them. That always did the trick. We'd run the searchlight up and down over them two or three times and they stopped it. One time I was senior officer on the pier and a Turkish officer came up to me in a frightful rage because one of our sailors had been most insulting to him. So I told him the fellow would be sent on ship and be most severely punished. I asked him to point him out. So he pointed out a gunner's mate, most inoffensive chap. Said he'd been most frightfully and repeatedly insulting; talking to me through an interpreter. I couldn't imagine how the gunner's mate knew enough Turkish to be insulting. I called him over and said, "And just in case you should have spoken to any Turkish officers."

"I haven't spoken to any of them, sir."

"I'm quite sure of it," I said, "but you'd best go on board ship and not come ashore again for the rest of the day."

Then I told the Turk the man was being sent on board ship and would be most severely dealt with. Oh most rigorously. He felt topping about it. Great friends we were.

The worst, he said, were the women with dead babies. You couldn't get the women to give up their dead babies. They'd have babies dead for six days. Wouldn't give them up. Nothing you could do about it. Had to take them away finally. Then there was an old lady, most extraordinary case. I told it to a doctor and he said I was lying. We were clearing them off the pier, had to clear off the dead ones, and this old woman was lying on a sort of litter. They said, "Will you have a look at her, sir?" So I had a look at her and just then she died and went absolutely stiff. Her legs drew up and she drew up from the waist and went quite rigid. Exactly as though she had been dead over night. She was quite dead and absolutely rigid. I told a medical chap about it and he told me it was impossible.

They were all out there on the pier and it wasn't at all like an earthquake or that sort of thing because they never knew about the Turk. They never knew what the old Turk would do. You remember when they ordered us not to come in to take off any more? I had the wind up when we came in that morning. He had any amount of batteries and could have blown us clean out of the water. We were going to come in, run close along the pier, let go the front and rear anchors and then shell the Turkish quarter of the town. They would have blown us out of water but we would have blown the town simply to hell. They just fired a few blank charges at us as we came in. Kemal came down and sacked the Turkish commander. For exceeding his authority or some such thing. He got a bit above himself. It would have been the hell of a mess.

You remember the harbor. There were plenty of nice things floating around in it. That was the only time in my life I got so I dreamed about things. You didn't mind the women who were having babies as you did those with the dead ones. They had them all right. Surprising how few of them died. You just covered them over with something and let them go to it. They'd always pick out the darkest place in the hold to have them. None of them minded anything once they got off the pier.

The Greeks were nice chaps too. When they evacuated they had all their baggage animals they couldn't take off with them so they just broke their forelegs and dumped them into the shallow water. All those mules with their forelegs broken pushed over into the shallow water. It was all a pleasant business. My word yes a most pleasant business.

Chapter 1

Everybody was drunk. The whole battery was drunk going along the road in the dark. We were going to the Champagne. The lieutenant kept riding his horse out into the fields and saying to him, "I'm drunk, I tell you, mon vieux. Oh, I am so soused." We went along the road all night in the dark and the adjutant kept riding up alongside my kitchen and saying, "You must put it out. It is dangerous. It will be observed." We were fifty kilometers from the front but the adjutant worried about the fire in my kitchen. It was funny going along that road. That was when I was a kitchen corporal.

Indian Camp

AT the lake shore there was another rowboat drawn up. The two Indians stood waiting.

Nick and his father got in the stern of the boat and the Indians shoved it off and one of them got in to row. Uncle George sat in the stern of the camp rowboat. The young Indian shoved the camp boat off and got in to row Uncle George.

The two boats started off in the dark. Nick heard the oarlocks of the other boat quite a way ahead of them in the mist. The Indians rowed with quick choppy strokes. Nick lay back with his father's arm around him. It was cold on the water. The Indian who was rowing them was working very hard, but the other boat moved further ahead in the mist all the time.

"Where are we going, Dad?" Nick asked.

"Over to the Indian camp. There is an Indian lady very sick."

"Oh," said Nick.

Across the bay they found the other boat beached. Uncle George was smoking a cigar in the dark. The young Indian pulled the boat way up on the beach. Uncle George gave both the Indians cigars.

They walked up from the beach through a meadow that was soaking wet with dew, following the young Indian who carried a lantern. Then they went into the woods and followed a trail that led to the logging road that ran back into the hills. It was much lighter on the logging road as the timber was cut away on both sides. The young Indian stopped and blew out his lantern and they all walked on along the road.

They came around a bend and a dog came out barking. Ahead were the lights of the shanties where the Indian bark-peelers lived. More dogs rushed out at them. The two Indians sent them back to the shanties. In the shanty nearest the road there was a light in the window. An old woman stood in the doorway holding a lamp.

Inside on a wooden bunk lay a young Indian woman. She had been trying to have her baby for two days. All the old women in the

camp had been helping her. The men had moved off up the road
to sit in the dark and smoke out of range of the noise she made. She
screamed just as Nick and the two Indians followed his father and
Uncle George into the shanty. She lay in the lower bunk, very big
under a quilt. Her head was turned to one side. In the upper bunk
was her husband. He had cut his foot very badly with an ax three days
before. He was smoking a pipe. The room smelled very bad.

Nick's father ordered some water to be put on the stove, and
while it was heating he spoke to Nick.

"This lady is going to have a baby, Nick," he said.

"I know," said Nick.

"You don't know," said his father. "Listen to me. What she is
going through is called being in labor. The baby wants to be born
and she wants it to be born. All her muscles are trying to get the
baby born. That is what is happening when she screams."

"I see," Nick said.

Just then the woman cried out.

"Oh, Daddy, can't you give her something to make her stop
screaming?" asked Nick.

"No. I haven't any anæsthetic," his father said. "But her screams
are not important. I don't hear them because they are not important."

The husband in the upper bunk rolled over against the wall.

The woman in the kitchen motioned to the doctor that the
water was hot. Nick's father went into the kitchen and poured about
half of the water out of the big kettle into a basin. Into the water left
in the kettle he put several things he unwrapped from a handkerchief.

"Those must boil," he said, and began to scrub his hands in the
basin of hot water with a cake of soap he had brought from the camp.
Nick watched his father's hands scrubbing each other with the soap.
While his father washed his hands very carefully and thoroughly, he
talked.

"You see, Nick, babies are supposed to be born head first but
sometimes they're not. When they're not they make a lot of trouble
for everybody. Maybe I'll have to operate on this lady. We'll know
in a little while."

When he was satisfied with his hands he went in and went to
work.

"Pull back that quilt, will you, George?" he said. "I'd rather not
touch it."

Later when he started to operate Uncle George and three Indian men held the woman still. She bit Uncle George on the arm and Uncle George said, "Damn squaw bitch!" and the young Indian who had rowed Uncle George over laughed at him. Nick held the basin for his father. It all took a long time.

His father picked the baby up and slapped it to make it breathe and handed it to the old woman.

"See, it's a boy, Nick," he said. "How do you like being an interne?"

Nick said, "All right." He was looking away so as not to see what his father was doing.

"There. That gets it," said his father and put something into the basin.

Nick didn't look at it.

"Now," his father said, "there's some stitches to put in. You can watch this or not, Nick, just as you like. I'm going to sew up the incision I made."

Nick did not watch. His curiosity had been gone for a long time.

His father finished and stood up. Uncle George and the three Indian men stood up. Nick put the basin out in the kitchen.

Uncle George looked at his arm. The young Indian smiled reminiscently.

"I'll put some peroxide on that, George," the doctor said.

He bent over the Indian woman. She was quiet now and her eyes were closed. She looked very pale. She did not know what had become of the baby or anything.

"I'll be back in the morning," the doctor said, standing up. "The nurse should be here from St. Ignace by noon and she'll bring everything we need."

He was feeling exalted and talkative as football players are in the dressing room after a game.

"That's one for the medical journal, George," he said. "Doing a Cæsarian with a jack-knife and sewing it up with nine-foot, tapered gut leaders."

Uncle George was standing against the wall, looking at his arm.

"Oh, you're a great man, all right," he said.

"Ought to have a look at the proud father. They're usually the worst sufferers in these little affairs," the doctor said. "I must say he took it all pretty quietly."

He pulled back the blanket from the Indian's head. His hand came away wet. He mounted on the edge of the lower bunk with the lamp in one hand and looked in. The Indian lay with his face toward the wall. His throat had been cut from ear to ear. The blood had flowed down into a pool where his body sagged the bunk. His head rested on his left arm. The open razor lay, edge up, in the blankets.

"Take Nick out of the shanty, George," the doctor said.

There was no need of that. Nick, standing in the door of the kitchen, had a good view of the upper bunk when his father, the lamp in one hand, tipped the Indian's head back.

It was just beginning to be daylight when they walked along the logging road back toward the lake.

"I'm terribly sorry I brought you along, Nickie," said his father, all his post-operative exhilaration gone. "It was an awful mess to put you through."

"Do ladies always have such a hard time having babies?" Nick asked.

"No, that was very, very exceptional."

"Why did he kill himself, Daddy?"

"I don't know, Nick. He couldn't stand things, I guess."

"Do many men kill themselves, Daddy?"

"Not very many, Nick."

"Do many women?"

"Hardly ever."

"Don't they ever?"

"Oh, yes. They do sometimes."

"Daddy?"

"Yes."

"Where did Uncle George go?"

"He'll turn up all right."

"Is dying hard, Daddy?"

"No, I think it's pretty easy, Nick. It all depends."

They were seated in the boat, Nick in the stern, his father rowing. The sun was coming up over the hills. A bass jumped, making a circle in the water. Nick trailed his hand in the water. It felt warm in the sharp chill of the morning.

In the early morning on the lake sitting in the stern of the boat with his father rowing, he felt quite sure that he would never die.

Chapter 2

Minarets stuck up in the rain out of Adrianople across the mud flats. The carts were jammed for thirty miles along the Karagatch road. Water buffalo and cattle were hauling carts through the mud. No end and no beginning. Just carts loaded with everything they owned. The old men and women, soaked through, walked along keeping the cattle moving. The Maritza was running yellow almost up to the bridge. Carts were jammed solid on the bridge with camels bobbing along through them. Greek cavalry herded along the procession. Women and kids were in the carts crouched with mattresses, mirrors, sewing machines, bundles. There was a woman having a kid with a young girl holding a blanket over her and crying. Scared sick looking at it. It rained all through the evacuation.

The Doctor and the Doctor's Wife

DICK BOULTON came from the Indian camp to cut up logs for Nick's father. He brought his son Eddy and another Indian named Billy Tabeshaw with him. They came in through the back gate out of the woods, Eddy carrying the long cross-cut saw. It flopped over his shoulder and made a musical sound as he walked. Billy Tabeshaw carried two big cant-hooks. Dick had three axes under his arm.

He turned and shut the gate. The others went on ahead of him down to the lake shore where the logs were buried in the sand.

The logs had been lost from the big log booms that were towed down the lake to the mill by the steamer *Magic*. They had drifted up onto the beach and if nothing were done about them sooner or later the crew of the *Magic* would come along the shore in a rowboat, spot the logs, drive an iron spike with a ring on it into the end of each one and then tow them out into the lake to make a new boom. But the lumbermen might never come for them because a few logs were not worth the price of a crew to gather them. If no one came for them they would be left to waterlog and rot on the beach.

Nick's father always assumed that this was what would happen, and hired the Indians to come down from the camp and cut the logs up with the cross-cut saw and split them with a wedge to make cord wood and chunks for the open fireplace. Dick Boulton walked around past the cottage down to the lake. There were four big beech logs lying almost buried in the sand. Eddy hung the saw up by one of its handles in the crotch of a tree. Dick put the three axes down on the little dock. Dick was a half-breed and many of the farmers around the lake believed he was really a white man. He was very lazy but a great worker once he was started. He took a plug of tobacco out of his pocket, bit off a chew and spoke in Ojibway to Eddy and Billy Tabeshaw.

27

They sunk the ends of their cant-hooks into one of the logs and swung against it to loosen it in the sand. They swung their weight against the shafts of the cant-hooks. The log moved in the sand. Dick Boulton turned to Nick's father.

"Well, Doc," he said, "that's a nice lot of timber you've stolen."

"Don't talk that way, Dick," the doctor said. "It's driftwood."

Eddy and Billy Tabeshaw had rocked the log out of the wet sand and rolled it toward the water.

"Put it right in," Dick Boulton shouted.

"What are you doing that for?" asked the doctor.

"Wash it off. Clean off the sand on account of the saw. I want to see who it belongs to," Dick said.

The log was just awash in the lake. Eddy and Billy Tabeshaw leaned on their cant-hooks sweating in the sun. Dick kneeled down in the sand and looked at the mark of the scaler's hammer in the wood at the end of the log.

"It belongs to White and McNally," he said, standing up and brushing off his trousers knees.

The doctor was very uncomfortable.

"You'd better not saw it up then, Dick," he said, shortly.

"Don't get huffy, Doc," said Dick. "Don't get huffy. I don't care who you steal from. It's none of my business."

"If you think the logs are stolen, leave them alone and take your tools back to the camp," the doctor said. His face was red.

"Don't go off at half cock, Doc," Dick said. He spat tobacco juice on the log. It slid off, thinning in the water. "You know they're stolen as well as I do. It don't make any difference to me."

"All right. If you think the logs are stolen, take your stuff and get out."

"Now, Doc——"

"Take your stuff and get out."

"Listen, Doc."

"If you call me Doc once again, I'll knock your eye teeth down your throat."

"Oh, no, you won't, Doc."

Dick Boulton looked at the doctor. Dick was a big man. He knew how big a man he was. He liked to get into fights. He was happy. Eddy and Billy Tabeshaw leaned on their cant-hooks and looked at the doctor. The doctor chewed the beard on his lower lip and looked at

Dick Boulton. Then he turned away and walked up the hill to the cottage. They could see from his back how angry he was. They all watched him walk up the hill and go inside the cottage.

Dick said something in Ojibway. Eddy laughed but Billy Tabeshaw looked very serious. He did not understand English but he had sweat all the time the row was going on. He was fat with only a few hairs of mustache like a Chinaman. He picked up the two cant-hooks. Dick picked up the axes and Eddy took the saw down from the tree. They started off and walked up past the cottage and out the back gate into the woods. Dick left the gate open. Billy Tabeshaw went back and fastened it. They were gone through the woods.

In the cottage the doctor, sitting on the bed in his room, saw a pile of medical journals on the floor by the bureau. They were still in their wrappers unopened. It irritated him.

"Aren't you going back to work, dear?" asked the doctor's wife from the room where she was lying with the blinds drawn.

"No!"

"Was anything the matter?"

"I had a row with Dick Boulton."

"Oh," said his wife. "I hope you didn't lose your temper, Henry."

"No," said the doctor.

"Remember, that he who ruleth his spirit is greater than he that taketh a city," said his wife. She was a Christian Scientist. Her Bible, her copy of *Science and Health* and her *Quarterly* were on a table beside her bed in the darkened room.

Her husband did not answer. He was sitting on his bed now, cleaning a shotgun. He pushed the magazine full of the heavy yellow shells and pumped them out again. They were scattered on the bed.

"Henry," his wife called. Then paused a moment. "Henry!"

"Yes," the doctor said.

"You didn't say anything to Boulton to anger him, did you?"

"No," said the doctor.

"What was the trouble about, dear?"

"Nothing much."

"Tell me, Henry. Please don't try and keep anything from me. What was the trouble about?"

"Well, Dick owes me a lot of money for pulling his squaw through pneumonia and I guess he wanted a row so he wouldn't have to take it out in work."

His wife was silent. The doctor wiped his gun carefully with a rag. He pushed the shells back in against the spring of the magazine. He sat with the gun on his knees. He was very fond of it. Then he heard his wife's voice from the darkened room.

"Dear, I don't think, I really don't think that any one would really do a thing like that."

"No?" the doctor said.

"No. I can't really believe that any one would do a thing of that sort intentionally."

The doctor stood up and put the shotgun in the corner behind the dresser.

"Are you going out, dear?" his wife said.

"I think I'll go for a walk," the doctor said.

"If you see Nick, dear, will you tell him his mother wants to see him?" his wife said.

The doctor went out on the porch. The screen door slammed behind him. He heard his wife catch her breath when the door slammed.

"Sorry," he said, outside her window with the blinds drawn.

"It's all right, dear," she said.

He walked in the heat out the gate and along the path into the hemlock woods. It was cool in the woods even on such a hot day. He found Nick sitting with his back against a tree, reading.

"Your mother wants you to come and see her," the doctor said.

"I want to go with you," Nick said.

His father looked down at him.

"All right. Come on, then," his father said. "Give me the book, I'll put it in my pocket."

"I know where there's black squirrels, Daddy," Nick said.

"All right," said his father. "Let's go there."

Chapter 3

We were in a garden at Mons. Young Buckley came in with his patrol from across the river. The first German I saw climbed up over the garden wall. We waited till he got one leg over and then potted him. He had so much equipment on and looked awfully surprised and fell down into the garden. Then three more came over further down the wall. We shot them. They all came just like that.

The End of Something

In the old days Hortons Bay was a lumbering town. No one who lived in it was out of sound of the big saws in the mill by the lake. Then one year there were no more logs to make lumber. The lumber schooners came into the bay and were loaded with the cut of the mill that stood stacked in the yard. All the piles of lumber were carried away. The big mill building had all its machinery that was removable taken out and hoisted on board one of the schooners by the men who had worked in the mill. The schooner moved out of the bay toward the open lake carrying the two great saws, the travelling carriage that hurled the logs against the revolving, circular saws and all the rollers, wheels, belts and iron piled on a hull-deep load of lumber. Its open hold covered with canvas and lashed tight, the sails of the schooner filled and it moved out into the open lake, carrying with it everything that had made the mill a mill and Hortons Bay a town.

The one-story bunk houses, the eating-house, the company store, the mill offices, and the big mill itself stood deserted in the acres of sawdust that covered the swampy meadow by the shore of the bay.

Ten years later there was nothing of the mill left except the broken white limestone of its foundations showing through the swampy second growth as Nick and Marjorie rowed along the shore. They were trolling along the edge of the channel-bank where the bottom dropped off suddenly from sandy shallows to twelve feet of dark water. They were trolling on their way to the point to set night lines for rainbow trout.

"There's our old ruin, Nick," Marjorie said.

Nick, rowing, looked at the white stone in the green trees.

"There it is," he said.

"Can you remember when it was a mill?" Marjorie asked.

"I can just remember," Nick said.

"It seems more like a castle," Marjorie said.

Nick said nothing. They rowed on out of sight of the mill, following the shore line. Then Nick cut across the bay.

"They aren't striking," he said.

"No," Marjorie said. She was intent on the rod all the time they trolled, even when she talked. She loved to fish. She loved to fish with Nick.

Close beside the boat a big trout broke the surface of the water. Nick pulled hard on one oar so the boat would turn and the bait spinning far behind would pass where the trout was feeding. As the trout's back came up out of the water the minnows jumped wildly. They sprinkled the surface like a handful of shot thrown into the water. Another trout broke water, feeding on the other side of the boat.

"They're feeding," Marjorie said.

"But they won't strike," Nick said.

He rowed the boat around to troll past both the feeding fish, then headed it for the point. Marjorie did not reel in until the boat touched the shore.

They pulled the boat up the beach and Nick lifted out a pail of live perch. The perch swam in the water in the pail. Nick caught three of them with his hands and cut their heads off and skinned them while Majorie chased with her hands in the bucket, finally caught a perch, cut its head off and skinned it. Nick looked at her fish.

"You don't want to take the ventral fin out," he said. "It'll be all right for bait but it's better with the ventral fin in."

He hooked each of the skinned perch through the tail. There were two hooks attached to a leader on each rod. Then Marjorie rowed the boat out over the channel-bank, holding the line in her teeth, and looking toward Nick, who stood on the shore holding the rod and letting the line run out from the reel.

"That's about right," he called.

"Should I let it drop?" Marjorie called back, holding the line in her hand.

"Sure. Let it go." Marjorie dropped the line overboard and watched the baits go down through the water.

She came in with the boat and ran the second line out the same way. Each time Nick set a heavy slab of driftwood across the butt of the rod to hold it solid and propped it up at an angle with a small slab. He reeled in the slack line so the line ran taut out to where the bait rested on the sandy floor of the channel and set the click on the reel. When a trout, feeding on the bottom, took the bait it would run with it, taking line out of the reel in a rush and making the reel sing with the click on.

Marjorie rowed up the point a little way so she would not disturb the line. She pulled hard on the oars and the boat went way up the beach. Little waves came in with it. Marjorie stepped out of the boat and Nick pulled the boat high up the beach.

"What's the matter, Nick?" Marjorie asked.

"I don't know," Nick said, getting wood for a fire.

They made a fire with driftwood. Marjorie went to the boat and brought a blanket. The evening breeze blew the smoke toward the point, so Marjorie spread the blanket out between the fire and the lake.

Marjorie sat on the blanket with her back to the fire and waited for Nick. He came over and sat down beside her on the blanket. In back of them was the close second-growth timber of the point and in front was the bay with the mouth of Hortons Creek. It was not quite dark. The fire-light went as far as the water. They could both see the two steel rods at an angle over the dark water. The fire glinted on the reels.

Marjorie unpacked the basket of supper.

"I don't feel like eating," said Nick.

"Come on and eat, Nick."

"All right."

They ate without talking, and watched the two rods and the fire-light in the water.

"There's going to be a moon tonight," said Nick. He looked across the bay to the hills that were beginning to sharpen against the sky. Beyond the hills he knew the moon was coming up.

"I know it," Marjorie said happily.

"You know everything," Nick said.

"Oh, Nick, please cut it out! Please, please don't be that way!"

"I can't help it," Nick said. "You do. You know everything. That's the trouble. You know you do."

Marjorie did not say anything.

"I've taught you everything. You know you do. What don't you know, anyway?"

"Oh, shut up," Marjorie said. "There comes the moon."

They sat on the blanket without touching each other and watched the moon rise.

"You don't have to talk silly," Marjorie said. "What's really the matter?"

"I don't know."

"Of course you know."

"No I don't."

"Go on and say it."

Nick looked on at the moon, coming up over the hills.

"It isn't fun any more."

He was afraid to look at Marjorie. Then he looked at her. She sat there with her back toward him. He looked at her back. "It isn't fun any more. Not any of it."

She didn't say anything. He went on. "I feel as though everything was gone to hell inside of me. I don't know, Marge. I don't know what to say."

He looked on at her back.

"Isn't love any fun?" Marjorie said.

"No," Nick said. Marjorie stood up. Nick sat there, his head in his hands.

"I'm going to take the boat," Marjorie called to him. "You can walk back around the point."

"All right," Nick said. "I'll push the boat off for you."

"You don't need to," she said. She was afloat in the boat on the water with the moonlight on it. Nick went back and lay down with his face in the blanket by the fire. He could hear Marjorie rowing on the water.

He lay there for a long time. He lay there while he heard Bill come into the clearing walking around through the woods. He felt Bill coming up to the fire. Bill didn't touch him, either.

"Did she go all right?" Bill said.

"Yes," Nick said, lying, his face on the blanket.

"Have a scene?"

"No, there wasn't any scene."

"How do you feel?"

"Oh, go away, Bill! Go away for a while."

Bill selected a sandwich from the lunch basket and walked over to have a look at the rods.

Chapter 4

It was a frightfully hot day. We'd jammed an absolutely perfect barricade across the bridge. It was simply priceless. A big old wrought-iron grating from the front of a house. Too heavy to lift and you could shoot through it and they would have to climb over it. It was absolutely topping. They tried to get over it, and we potted them from forty yards. They rushed it, and officers came out alone and worked on it. It was an absolutely perfect obstacle. Their officers were very fine. We were frightfully put out when we heard the flank had gone, and we had to fall back.

The Three-Day Blow

THE rain stopped as Nick turned into the road that went up through the orchard. The fruit had been picked and the fall wind blew through the bare trees. Nick stopped and picked up a Wagner apple from beside the road, shiny in the brown grass from the rain. He put the apple in the pocket of his Mackinaw coat.

The road came out of the orchard on to the top of the hill. There was the cottage, the porch bare, smoke coming from the chimney. In back was the garage, the chicken coop and the second-growth timber like a hedge against the woods behind. The big trees swayed far over in the wind as he watched. It was the first of the autumn storms.

As Nick crossed the open field above the orchard the door of the cottage opened and Bill came out. He stood on the porch looking out.

"Well, Wemedge," he said.

"Hey, Bill," Nick said, coming up the steps.

They stood together, looking out across the country, down over the orchard, beyond the road, across the lower fields and the woods of the point to the lake. The wind was blowing straight down the lake. They could see the surf along Ten Mile point.

"She's blowing," Nick said.

"She'll blow like that for three days," Bill said.

"Is your dad in?" Nick said.

"No. He's out with the gun. Come on in."

Nick went inside the cottage. There was a big fire in the fireplace. The wind made it roar. Bill shut the door.

"Have a drink?" he said.

He went out to the kitchen and came back with two glasses and a pitcher of water. Nick reached the whisky bottle from the shelf above the fireplace.

"All right?" he said.

"Good," said Bill.

They sat in front of the fire and drank the Irish whisky and water.

"It's got a swell, smoky taste," Nick said, and looked at the fire through the glass.

"That's the peat," Bill said.

"You can't get peat into liquor," Nick said.

"That doesn't make any difference," Bill said.

"You ever seen any peat?" Nick asked.

"No," said Bill.

"Neither have I," Nick said.

His shoes, stretched out on the hearth, began to steam in front of the fire.

"Better take your shoes off," Bill said.

"I haven't got any socks on."

"Take them off and dry them and I'll get you some," Bill said. He went upstairs into the loft and Nick heard him walking about overhead. Upstairs was open under the roof and was where Bill and his father and he, Nick, sometimes slept. In back was a dressing room. They moved the cots back out of the rain and covered them with rubber blankets.

Bill came down with a pair of heavy wool socks.

"It's getting too late to go around without socks," he said.

"I hate to start them again," Nick said. He pulled the socks on and slumped back in the chair, putting his feet up on the screen in front of the fire.

"You'll dent in the screen," Bill said. Nick swung his feet over to the side of the fireplace.

"Got anything to read?" he asked.

"Only the paper."

"What did the Cards do?"

"Dropped a double header to the Giants."

"That ought to cinch it for them."

"It's a gift," Bill said. "As long as McGraw can buy every good ball player in the league there's nothing to it."

"He can't buy them all," Nick said.

"He buys all the ones he wants," Bill said. "Or he makes them discontented so they have to trade them to him."

"Like Heinie Zim," Nick agreed.

"That bonehead will do him a lot of good."

Bill stood up.

"He can hit," Nick offered. The heat from the fire was baking his legs.

"He's a sweet fielder, too," Bill said. "But he loses ball games."

"Maybe that's what McGraw wants him for," Nick suggested.

"Maybe," Bill agreed.

"There's always more to it than we know about," Nick said.

"Of course. But we've got pretty good dope for being so far away."

"Like how much better you can pick them if you don't see the horses."

"That's it."

Bill reached down the whisky bottle. His big hand went all the way around it. He poured the whisky into the glass Nick held out.

"How much water?"

"Just the same."

He sat down on the floor beside Nick's chair.

"It's good when the fall storms come, isn't it?" Nick said.

"It's swell."

"It's the best time of year," Nick said.

"Wouldn't it be hell to be in town?" Bill said.

"I'd like to see the World Series," Nick said.

"Well, they're always in New York or Philadelphia now," Bill said. "That doesn't do us any good."

"I wonder if the Cards will ever win a pennant?"

"Not in our lifetime," Bill said.

"Gee, they'd go crazy," Nick said.

"Do you remember when they got going that once before they had the train wreck?"

"Boy!" Nick said, remembering.

Bill reached over to the table under the window for the book that lay there, face down, where he had put it when he went to the door. He held his glass in one hand and the book in the other, leaning back against Nick's chair.

"What are you reading?"

"*Richard Feverel.*"

"I couldn't get into it."

"It's all right," Bill said. "It ain't a bad book, Wemedge."

"What else have you got I haven't read?" Nick asked.

"Did you read the *Forest Lovers?*"

"Yup. That's the one where they go to bed every night with the naked sword between them."

"That's a good book, Wemedge."

"It's a swell book. What I couldn't ever understand was what good the sword would do. It would have to stay edge up all the time because if it went over flat you could roll right over it and it wouldn't make any trouble."

"It's a symbol," Bill said.

"Sure," said Nick, "but it isn't practical."

"Did you ever read *Fortitude?*"

"It's fine," Nick said. "That's a real book. That's where his old man is after him all the time. Have you got any more by Walpole?"

"*The Dark Forest,*" Bill said. "It's about Russia."

"What does he know about Russia?" Nick asked.

"I don't know. You can't ever tell about those guys. Maybe he was there when he was a boy. He's got a lot of dope on it."

"I'd like to meet him," Nick said.

"I'd like to meet Chesterton," Bill said.

"I wish he was here now," Nick said. "We'd take him fishing to the 'Voix tomorrow."

"I wonder if he'd like to go fishing," Bill said.

"Sure," said Nick. "He must be about the best guy there is. Do you remember the *Flying Inn?*"

> " 'If an angel out of heaven
>   Gives you something else to drink,
>   Thank him for his kind intentions;
>   Go and pour them down the sink.' "

"That's right," said Nick. "I guess he's a better guy than Walpole."

"Oh, he's a better guy, all right," Bill said.

"But Walpole's a better writer."

"I don't know," Nick said. "Chesterton's a classic."

"Walpole's a classic, too," Bill insisted.

"I wish we had them both here," Nick said. "We'd take them both fishing to the 'Voix tomorrow."

"Let's get drunk," Bill said.

"All right," Nick agreed.

"My old man won't care," Bill said.

"Are you sure?" said Nick.

"I know it," Bill said.

"I'm a little drunk now," Nick said.

"You aren't drunk," Bill said.

He got up from the floor and reached for the whisky bottle. Nick held out his glass. His eyes fixed on it while Bill poured.

Bill poured the glass half full of whisky.

"Put in your own water," he said. "There's just one more shot."

"Got any more?" Nick asked.

"There's plenty more but dad only likes me to drink what's open."

"Sure," said Nick.

"He says opening bottles is what makes drunkards," Bill explained.

"That's right," said Nick. He was impressed. He had never thought of that before. He had always thought it was solitary drinking that made drunkards.

"How is your dad?" he asked respectfully.

"He's all right," Bill said. "He gets a little wild sometimes."

"He's a swell guy," Nick said. He poured water into his glass out of the pitcher. It mixed slowly with the whisky. There was more whisky than water.

"You bet your life he is," Bill said.

"My old man's all right," Nick said.

"You're damn right he is," said Bill.

"He claims he's never taken a drink in his life," Nick said, as though announcing a scientific fact.

"Well, he's a doctor. My old man's a painter. That's different."

"He's missed a lot," Nick said sadly.

"You can't tell," Bill said. "Everything's got its compensations."

"He says he's missed a lot himself," Nick confessed.

"Well, dad's had a tough time," Bill said.

"It all evens up," Nick said.

They sat looking into the fire and thinking of this profound truth.

"I'll get a chunk from the back porch," Nick said. He had noticed while looking into the fire that the fire was dying down. Also he wished to show he could hold his liquor and be practical. Even if his father had never touched a drop Bill was not going to get him drunk before he himself was drunk.

"Bring one of the big beech chunks," Bill said. He was also being consciously practical.

Nick came in with the log through the kitchen and in passing knocked a pan off the kitchen table. He laid the log down and picked up the pan. It had contained dried apricots, soaking in water. He carefully picked up all the apricots off the floor, some of them had gone under the stove, and put them back in the pan. He dipped some more water onto them from the pail by the table. He felt quite proud of himself. He had been thoroughly practical.

He came in carrying the log and Bill got up from the chair and helped him put it on the fire.

"That's a swell log," Nick said.

"I'd been saving it for the bad weather," Bill said. "A log like that will burn all night."

"There'll be coals left to start the fire in the morning," Nick said.

"That's right," Bill agreed. They were conducting the conversation on a high plane.

"Let's have another drink," Nick said.

"I think there's another bottle open in the locker," Bill said.

He kneeled down in the corner in front of the locker and brought out a square-faced bottle.

"It's Scotch," he said.

"I'll get some more water," Nick said. He went out into the kitchen again. He filled the pitcher with the dipper dipping cold spring water from the pail. On his way back to the living room he passed a mirror in the dining room and looked in it. His face looked strange. He smiled at the face in the mirror and it grinned back at him. He winked at it and went on. It was not his face but it didn't make any difference.

Bill had poured out the drinks.

"That's an awfully big shot," Nick said.

"Not for us, Wemedge," Bill said.

"What'll we drink to?" Nick asked, holding up the glass.

"Let's drink to fishing," Bill said.

"All right," Nick said. "Gentlemen, I give you fishing."

"All fishing," Bill said. "Everywhere."

"Fishing," Nick said. "That's what we drink to."

"It's better than baseball," Bill said.

"There isn't any comparison," said Nick. "How did we ever get talking about baseball?"

"It was a mistake," Bill said. "Baseball is a game for louts."

They drank all that was in their glasses.

"Now let's drink to Chesterton."

"And Walpole," Nick interposed.

Nick poured out the liquor. Bill poured in the water. They looked at each other. They felt very fine.

"Gentlemen," Bill said, "I give you Chesterton and Walpole."

"Exactly, gentlemen," Nick said.

They drank. Bill filled up the glasses. They sat down in the big chairs in front of the fire.

"You were very wise, Wemedge," Bill said.

"What do you mean?" asked Nick.

"To bust off that Marge business," Bill said.

"I guess so," said Nick.

"It was the only thing to do. If you hadn't, by now you'd be back home working trying to get enough money to get married."

Nick said nothing.

"Once a man's married he's absolutely bitched," Bill went on. "He hasn't got anything more. Nothing. Not a damn thing. He's done for. You've seen the guys that get married."

Nick said nothing.

"You can tell them," Bill said. "They get this sort of fat married look. They're done for."

"Sure," said Nick.

"It was probably bad busting it off," Bill said. "But you always fall for somebody else and then it's all right. Fall for them but don't let them ruin you."

"Yes," said Nick.

"If you'd have married her you would have had to marry the whole family. Remember her mother and that guy she married."

Nick nodded.

"Imagine having them around the house all the time and going to Sunday dinners at their house, and having them over to dinner and her telling Marge all the time what to do and how to act."

Nick sat quiet.

"You came out of it damned well," Bill said. "Now she can marry somebody of her own sort and settle down and be happy. You can't mix oil and water and you can't mix that sort of thing any more than if I'd marry Ida that works for Strattons. She'd probably like it, too."

Nick said nothing. The liquor had all died out of him and left him alone. Bill wasn't there. He wasn't sitting in front of the fire or going fishing tomorrow with Bill and his dad or anything. He wasn't drunk. It was all gone. All he knew was that he had once had Marjorie and that he had lost her. She was gone and he had sent her away. That was all that mattered. He might never see her again. Probably he never would. It was all gone, finished.

"Let's have another drink," Nick said.

Bill poured it out. Nick splashed in a little water.

"If you'd gone on that way we wouldn't be here now," Bill said.

That was true. His original plan had been to go down home and get a job. Then he had planned to stay in Charlevoix all winter so he could be near Marge. Now he did not know what he was going to do.

"Probably we wouldn't even be going fishing tomorrow," Bill said. "You had the right dope, all right."

"I couldn't help it," Nick said.

"I know. That's the way it works out," Bill said.

"All of a sudden everything was over," Nick said. "I don't know why it was. I couldn't help it. Just like when the three-day blows come now and rip all the leaves off the trees."

"Well, it's over. That's the point," Bill said.

"It was my fault," Nick said.

"It doesn't make any difference whose fault it was," Bill said.

"No, I suppose not," Nick said.

The big thing was that Marjorie was gone and that probably he would never see her again. He had talked to her about how they would go to Italy together and the fun they would have. Places they would be together. It was all gone now.

"So long as it's over that's all that matters," Bill said. "I tell you, Wemedge, I was worried while it was going on. You played it right. I understand her mother is sore as hell. She told a lot of people you were engaged."

"We weren't engaged," Nick said.

"It was all around that you were."

"I can't help it," Nick said. "We weren't."

"Weren't you going to get married?" Bill asked.

"Yes. But we weren't engaged," Nick said.

"What's the difference?" Bill asked judicially.

"I don't know. There's a difference."

"I don't see it," said Bill.

"All right," said Nick. "Let's get drunk."

"All right," Bill said. "Let's get really drunk."

"Let's get drunk and then go swimming," Nick said.

He drank off his glass.

"I'm sorry as hell about her but what could I do?" he said. "You know what her mother was like!"

"She was terrible," Bill said.

"All of a sudden it was over," Nick said. "I oughtn't to talk about it."

"You aren't," Bill said. "I talked about it and now I'm through. We won't ever speak about it again. You don't want to think about it. You might get back into it again."

Nick had not thought about that. It had seemed so absolute. That was a thought. That made him feel better.

"Sure," he said. "There's always that danger."

He felt happy now. There was not anything that was irrevocable. He might go into town Saturday night. Today was Thursday.

"There's always a chance," he said.

"You'll have to watch yourself," Bill said.

"I'll watch myself," he said.

He felt happy. Nothing was finished. Nothing was ever lost. He would go into town on Saturday. He felt lighter, as he had felt before Bill started to talk about it. There was always a way out.

"Let's take the guns and go down to the point and look for your dad," Nick said.

"All right."

Bill took down the two shotguns from the rack on the wall. He opened a box of shells. Nick put on his Mackinaw coat and his shoes. His shoes were stiff from the drying. He was still quite drunk but his head was clear.

"How do you feel?" Nick asked.

"Swell. I've just got a good edge on." Bill was buttoning up his sweater.

"There's no use getting drunk."

"No. We ought to get outdoors."

They stepped out the door. The wind was blowing a gale.

"The birds will lie right down in the grass with this," Nick said.

They struck down toward the orchard.

"I saw a woodcock this morning," Bill said.

"Maybe we'll jump him," Nick said.

"You can't shoot in this wind," Bill said.

Outside now the Marge business was no longer so tragic. It was not even very important. The wind blew everything like that away.

"It's coming right off the big lake," Nick said.

Against the wind they heard the thud of a shotgun.

"That's dad," Bill said. "He's down in the swamp."

"Let's cut down that way," Nick said.

"Let's cut across the lower meadow and see if we jump anything," Bill said.

"All right," Nick said.

None of it was important now. The wind blew it out of his head. Still he could always go into town Saturday night. It was a good thing to have in reserve.

Chapter 5

They shot the six cabinet ministers at half-past six in the morn-
ing against the wall of a hospital. There were pools of water in the
courtyard. There were wet dead leaves on the paving of the court-
yard. It rained hard. All the shutters of the hospital were nailed
shut. One of the ministers was sick with typhoid. Two soldiers car-
ried him downstairs and out into the rain. They tried to hold him
up against the wall but he sat down in a puddle of water. The other
five stood very quietly against the wall. Finally the officer told the
soldiers it was no good trying to make him stand up. When they
fired the first volley he was sitting down in the water with his head
on his knees.

The Battler

Nick stood up. He was all right. He looked up the track at the lights of the caboose going out of sight around the curve. There was water on both sides of the track, then tamarack swamp.

He felt of his knee. The pants were torn and the skin was barked. His hands were scraped and there were sand and cinders driven up under his nails. He went over to the edge of the track down the little slope to the water and washed his hands. He washed them carefully in the cold water, getting the dirt out from the nails. He squatted down and bathed his knee.

That lousy crut of a brakeman. He would get him some day. He would know him again. That was a fine way to act.

"Come here, kid," he said. "I got something for you."

He had fallen for it. What a lousy kid thing to have done. They would never suck him in that way again.

"Come here, kid, I got something for you." Then *wham* and he lit on his hands and knees beside the track.

Nick rubbed his eye. There was a big bump coming up. He would have a black eye, all right. It ached already. That son of a crutting brakeman.

He touched the bump over his eye with his fingers. Oh, well, it was only a black eye. That was all he had gotten out of it. Cheap at the price. He wished he could see it. Could not see it looking into the water, though. It was dark and he was a long way off from anywhere. He wiped his hands on his trousers and stood up, then climbed the embankment to the rails.

He started up the track. It was well ballasted and made easy walking, sand and gravel packed between the ties, solid walking. The smooth roadbed like a causeway went on ahead through the swamp. Nick walked along. He must get to somewhere.

Nick had swung on to the freight train when it slowed down for the yards outside of Walton Junction. The train, with Nick on it, had passed through Kalkaska as it started to get dark. Now he must be nearly to Mancelona. Three or four miles of swamp. He stepped along the track, walking so he kept on the ballast between the ties, the swamp ghostly in the rising mist. His eye ached and he was hungry. He kept on hiking, putting the miles of track back of him. The swamp was all the same on both sides of the track.

Ahead there was a bridge. Nick crossed it, his boots ringing hollow on the iron. Down below the water showed black between the slits of ties. Nick kicked a loose spike and it dropped into the water. Beyond the bridge were hills. It was high and dark on both sides of the track. Up the track Nick saw a fire.

He came up the track toward the fire carefully. It was off to one side of the track, below the railway embankment. He had only seen the light from it. The track came out through a cut and where the fire was burning the country opened out and fell away into woods. Nick dropped carefully down the embankment and cut into the woods to come up to the fire through the trees. It was a beechwood forest and the fallen beechnut burrs were under his shoes as he walked between the trees. The fire was bright now, just at the edge of the trees. There was a man sitting by it. Nick waited behind the tree and watched. The man looked to be alone. He was sitting there with his head in his hands looking at the fire. Nick stepped out and walked into the firelight.

The man sat there looking into the fire. When Nick stopped quite close to him he did not move.

"Hello!" Nick said.

The man looked up.

"Where did you get the shiner?" he said.

"A brakeman busted me."

"Off the through freight?"

"Yes."

"I saw the bastard," the man said. "He went through here 'bout an hour and a half ago. He was walking along the top of the cars slapping his arms and singing."

"The bastard!"

"It must have made him feel good to bust you," the man said seriously.

"I'll bust him."

"Get him with a rock sometime when he's going through," the man advised.

"I'll get him."

"You're a tough one, aren't you?"

"No," Nick answered.

"All you kids are tough."

"You got to be tough," Nick said.

"That's what I said."

The man looked at Nick and smiled. In the firelight Nick saw that his face was misshapen. His nose was sunken, his eyes were slits, he had queer-shaped lips. Nick did not perceive all this at once, he only saw the man's face was queerly formed and mutilated. It was like putty in color. Dead looking in the firelight.

"Don't you like my pan?" the man asked.

Nick was embarrassed.

"Sure," he said.

"Look here!" the man took off his cap.

He had only one ear. It was thickened and tight against the side of his head. Where the other ear should have been there was a stump.

"Ever see one like that?"

"No," said Nick. It made him a little sick.

"I could take it," the man said. "Don't you think I could take it, kid?"

"You bet!"

"They all bust their hands on me," the little man said. "They couldn't hurt me."

He looked at Nick. "Sit down," he said. "Want to eat?"

"Don't bother," Nick said. "I'm going on to the town."

"Listen!" the man said. "Call me Ad."

"Sure!"

"Listen," the little man said. "I'm not quite right."

"What's the matter?"

"I'm crazy."

He put on his cap. Nick felt like laughing.

"You're all right," he said.

"No, I'm not. I'm crazy. Listen, you ever been crazy?"

"No," Nick said. "How does it get you?"

"I don't know," Ad said. "When you got it you don't know about it. You know me, don't you?"

"No."

"I'm Ad Francis."

"Honest to God?"

"Don't you believe it?"

"Yes."

Nick knew it must be true.

"You know how I beat them?"

"No," Nick said.

"My heart's slow. It only beats forty a minute. Feel it."

Nick hesitated.

"Come on," the man took hold of his hand. "Take hold of my wrist. Put your fingers there."

The little man's wrist was thick and the muscles bulged above the bone. Nick felt the slow pumping under his fingers.

"Got a watch?"

"No."

"Neither have I," Ad said. "It ain't any good if you haven't got a watch."

Nick dropped his wrist.

"Listen," Ad Francis said. "Take ahold again. You count and I'll count up to sixty."

Feeling the slow hard throb under his fingers Nick started to count. He heard the little man counting slowly, one, two, three, four, five, and on—aloud.

"Sixty," Ad finished. "That's a minute. What did you make it?"

"Forty," Nick said.

"That's right," Ad said happily. "She never speeds up."

A man dropped down the railroad embankment and came across the clearing to the fire.

"Hello, Bugs!" Ad said.

"Hello!" Bugs answered. It was a negro's voice. Nick knew from the way he walked that he was a negro. He stood with his back to them, bending over the fire. He straightened up.

"This is my pal Bugs," Ad said. "He's crazy, too."

"Glad to meet you," Bugs said. "Where you say you're from?"

"Chicago," Nick said.

"That's a fine town," the negro said. "I didn't catch your name."

"Adams. Nick Adams."

"He says he's never been crazy, Bugs," Ad said.

"He's got a lot coming to him," the negro said. He was unwrapping a package by the fire.

"When are we going to eat, Bugs?" the prizefighter asked.

"Right away."

"Are you hungry, Nick?"

"Hungry as hell."

"Hear that, Bugs?"

"I hear most of what goes on."

"That ain't what I asked you."

"Yes. I heard what the gentleman said."

Into a skillet he was laying slices of ham. As the skillet grew hot the grease sputtered and Bugs, crouching on long nigger legs over the fire, turned the ham and broke eggs into the skillet, tipping it from side to side to baste the eggs with the hot fat.

"Will you cut some bread out of that bag, Mister Adams?" Bugs turned from the fire.

"Sure."

Nick reached in the bag and brought out a loaf of bread. He cut six slices. Ad watched him and leaned forward.

"Let me take your knife, Nick," he said.

"No, you don't," the negro said. "Hang onto your knife, Mister Adams."

The prizefighter sat back.

"Will you bring me the bread, Mister Adams?" Bugs asked. Nick brought it over.

"Do you like to dip your bread in the ham fat?" the negro asked.

"You bet!"

"Perhaps we'd better wait until later. It's better at the finish of the meal. Here."

The negro picked up a slice of ham and laid it on one of the pieces of bread, then slid an egg on top of it.

"Just close that sandwich, will you please, and give it to Mister Francis."

Ad took the sandwich and started eating.

"Watch out how that egg runs," the negro warned. "This is for you, Mister Adams. The remainder for myself."

Nick bit into the sandwich. The negro was sitting opposite him beside Ad. The hot fried ham and eggs tasted wonderful.

"Mister Adams is right hungry," the negro said. The little man whom Nick knew by name as a former champion fighter was silent. He had said nothing since the negro had spoken about the knife.

"May I offer you a slice of bread dipped in the hot ham fat?" Bugs said.

"Thanks a lot."

The little white man looked at Nick.

"Will you have some, Mister Adolph Francis?" Bugs offered from the skillet.

Ad did not answer. He was looking at Nick.

"Mister Francis?" came the nigger's soft voice.

Ad did not answer. He was looking at Nick.

"I spoke to you, Mister Francis," the nigger said softly.

Ad kept on looking at Nick. He had his cap down over his eyes. Nick felt nervous.

"How the hell do you get that way?" came out from under the cap sharply at Nick.

"Who the hell do you think you are? You're a snotty bastard. You come in here where nobody asks you and eat a man's food and when he asks to borrow a knife you get snotty."

He glared at Nick, his face was white and his eyes almost out of sight under the cap.

"You're a hot sketch. Who the hell asked you to butt in here?"

"Nobody."

"You're damn right nobody did. Nobody asked you to stay either. You come in here and act snotty about my face and smoke my cigars and drink my liquor and then talk snotty. Where the hell do you think you get off?"

Nick said nothing. Ad stood up.

"I'll tell you, you yellow-livered Chicago bastard. You're going to get your can knocked off. Do you get that?"

Nick stepped back. The little man came toward him slowly, stepping flat-footed forward, his left foot stepping forward, his right dragging up to it.

"Hit me," he moved his head. "Try and hit me."

"I don't want to hit you."

"You won't get out of it that way. You're going to take a beating, see? Come on and lead at me."

"Cut it out," Nick said.

"All right, then, you bastard."

The little man looked down at Nick's feet. As he looked down the negro, who had followed behind him as he moved away from the fire, set himself and tapped him across the base of the skull. He fell forward and Bugs dropped the cloth-wrapped blackjack on the grass. The little man lay there, his face in the grass. The negro picked him up, his head hanging, and carried him to the fire. He face looked bad, the eyes open. Bugs laid him down gently.

"Will you bring me the water in the bucket, Mister Adams," he said. "I'm afraid I hit him just a little hard."

The negro splashed water with his hand on the man's face and pulled his ears gently. The eyes closed.

Bugs stood up.

"He's all right," he said. "There's nothing to worry about. I'm sorry, Mister Adams."

"It's all right." Nick was looking down at the little man. He saw the blackjack on the grass and picked it up. It had a flexible handle and was limber in his hand. It was made of worn black leather with a handkerchief wrapped around the heavy end.

"That's a whalebone handle," the negro smiled. "They don't make them any more. I didn't know how well you could take care of yourself and, anyway, I didn't want you to hurt him or mark him up no more than he is."

The negro smiled again.

"You hurt him yourself."

"I know how to do it. He won't remember nothing of it. I have to do it to change him when he gets that way."

Nick was still looking down at the little man, lying, his eyes closed in the firelight. Bugs put some wood on the fire.

"Don't you worry about him none, Mister Adams. I seen him like this plenty of times before."

"What made him crazy?" Nick asked.

"Oh, a lot of things," the negro answered from the fire. "Would you like a cup of this coffee, Mister Adams?"

He handed Nick the cup and smoothed the coat he had placed under the unconscious man's head.

"He took too many beatings, for one thing," the negro sipped the coffee. "But that just made him sort of simple. Then his sister was his manager and they was always being written up in the papers all about brothers and sisters and how she loved her brother and how he loved his sister, and then they got married in New York and that made a lot of unpleasantness."

"I remember about it."

"Sure. Of course they wasn't brother and sister no more than a rabbit, but there was a lot of people didn't like it either way and they commenced to have disagreements, and one day she just went off and never come back."

He drank the coffee and wiped his lips with the pink palm of his hand.

"He just went crazy. Will you have some more coffee, Mister Adams?"

"Thanks."

"I seen her a couple of times," the negro went on. "She was an awful good-looking woman. Looked enough like him to be twins. He wouldn't be bad-looking without his face all busted."

He stopped. The story seemed to be over.

"Where did you meet him?" asked Nick.

"I met him in jail," the negro said. "He was busting people all the time after she went away and they put him in jail. I was in for cuttin' a man."

He smiled, and went on soft-voiced:

"Right away I liked him and when I got out I looked him up. He likes to think I'm crazy and I don't mind. I like to be with him and I like seeing the country and I don't have to commit no larceny to do it. I like living like a gentleman."

"What do you all do?" Nick asked.

"Oh, nothing. Just move around. He's got money."

"He must have made a lot of money."

"Sure. He spent all his money, though. Or they took it away from him. She sends him money."

He poked up the fire.

"She's a mighty fine woman," he said. "She looks enough like him to be his own twin."

The negro looked over at the little man, lying breathing heavily. His blond hair was down over his forehead. His mutilated face looked childish in repose.

"I can wake him up any time now, Mister Adams. If you don't mind I wish you'd sort of pull out. I don't like to not be hospitable, but it might disturb him back again to see you. I hate to have to

thump him and it's the only thing to do when he gets started. I have
to sort of keep him away from people. You don't mind, do you, Mister
Adams? No, don't thank me, Mister Adams. I'd have warned you
about him but he seemed to have taken such a liking to you and I
thought things were going to be all right. You'll hit a town about two
miles up the track. Mancelona they call it. Good-bye. I wish we could
ask you to stay the night but it's just out of the question. Would you
like to take some of that ham and some bread with you? No? You
better take a sandwich," all this in a low, smooth, polite nigger voice.

"Good. Well, good-bye, Mister Adams. Good-bye and good luck!"

Nick walked away from the fire across the clearing to the railway tracks. Out of the range of the fire he listened. The low soft
voice of the negro was talking. Nick could not hear the words. Then
he heard the little man say, "I got an awful headache, Bugs."

"You'll feel better, Mister Francis," the negro's voice soothed.
"Just you drink a cup of this hot coffee."

Nick climbed the embankment and started up the track. He
found he had a ham sandwich in his hand and put it in his pocket.
Looking back from the mounting grade before the track curved into
the hills he could see the firelight in the clearing.

Chapter 6

Nick sat against the wall of the church where they had dragged him to be clear of machine-gun fire in the street. Both legs stuck out awkwardly. He had been hit in the spine. His face was sweaty and dirty. The sun shone on his face. The day was very hot. Rinaldi, big backed, his equipment sprawling, lay face downward against the wall. Nick looked straight ahead brilliantly. The pink wall of the house opposite had fallen out from the roof, and an iron bedstead hung twisted toward the street. Two Austrian dead lay in the rubble in the shade of the house. Up the street were other dead. Things were getting forward in the town. It was going well. Stretcher bearers would be along any time now. Nick turned his head carefully and looked at Rinaldi. "Senta Rinaldi. Senta. You and me we've made a separate peace." Rinaldi lay still in the sun breathing with difficulty. "Not patriots." Nick turned his head carefully away smiling sweatily. Rinaldi was a disappointing audience.

A Very Short Story

ONE hot evening in Padua they carried him up onto the roof and he could look out over the top of the town. There were chimney swifts in the sky. After a while it got dark and the searchlights came out. The others went down and took the bottles with them. He and Luz could hear them below on the balcony. Luz sat on the bed. She was cool and fresh in the hot night.

Luz stayed on night duty for three months. They were glad to let her. When they operated on him she prepared him for the operating table; and they had a joke about friend or enema. He went under the anæsthetic holding tight on to himself so he would not blab about anything during the silly, talky time. After he got on crutches he used to take the temperatures so Luz would not have to get up from the bed. There were only a few patients, and they all knew about it. They all liked Luz. As he walked back along the halls he thought of Luz in his bed.

Before he went back to the front they went into the Duomo and prayed. It was dim and quiet, and there were other people praying. They wanted to get married, but there was not enough time for the banns, and neither of them had birth certificates. They felt as though they were married, but they wanted every one to know about it, and to make it so they could not lose it.

Luz wrote him many letters that he never got until after the armistice. Fifteen came in a bunch to the front and he sorted them by the dates and read them all straight through. They were all about the hospital, and how much she loved him and how it was impossible to get along without him and how terrible it was missing him at night.

After the armistice they agreed he should go home to get a job so they might be married. Luz would not come home until he had a good job and could come to New York to meet her. It was understood he would not drink, and he did not want to see his friends or any one in the States. Only to get a job and be married. On the train from

Padua to Milan they quarrelled about her not being willing to come home at once. When they had to say good-bye, in the station at Milan, they kissed good-bye, but were not finished with the quarrel. He felt sick about saying good-bye like that.

He went to America on a boat from Genoa. Luz went back to Pordenone to open a hospital. It was lonely and rainy there, and there was a battalion of arditi quartered in the town. Living in the muddy, rainy town in the winter, the major of the battalion made love to Luz, and she had never known Italians before, and finally wrote to the States that theirs had been only a boy and girl affair. She was sorry, and she knew he would probably not be able to understand, but might some day forgive her, and be grateful to her, and she expected, absolutely unexpectedly, to be married in the spring. She loved him as always, but she realized now it was only a boy and girl love. She hoped he would have a great career, and believed in him absolutely. She knew it was for the best.

The major did not marry her in the spring, or any other time. Luz never got an answer to the letter to Chicago about it. A short time after he contracted gonorrhea from a sales girl in a loop department store while riding in a taxicab through Lincoln Park.

Chapter 7

While the bombardment was knocking the trench to pieces at Fossalta, he lay very flat and sweated and prayed oh jesus christ get me out of here. Dear jesus please get me out. Christ please please please christ. If you'll only keep me from getting killed I'll do anything you say. I believe in you and I'll tell every one in the world that you are the only one that matters. Please please dear jesus. The shelling moved further up the line. We went to work on the trench and in the morning the sun came up and the day was hot and muggy and cheerful and quiet. The next night back at Mestre he did not tell the girl he went upstairs with at the Villa Rossa about Jesus. And he never told anybody.

Soldier's Home

KREBS went to the war from a Methodist college in Kansas. There is a picture which shows him among his fraternity brothers, all of them wearing exactly the same height and style collar. He enlisted in the Marines in 1917 and did not return to the United States until the second division returned from the Rhine in the summer of 1919.

There is a picture which shows him on the Rhine with two German girls and another corporal. Krebs and the corporal look too big for their uniforms. The German girls are not beautiful. The Rhine does not show in the picture.

By the time Krebs returned to his home town in Oklahoma the greeting of heroes was over. He came back much too late. The men from the town who had been drafted had all been welcomed elaborately on their return. There had been a great deal of hysteria. Now the reaction had set in. People seemed to think it was rather ridiculous for Krebs to be getting back so late, years after the war was over.

At first Krebs, who had been at Belleau Wood, Soissons, the Champagne, St. Mihiel and in the Argonne did not want to talk about the war at all. Later he felt the need to talk but no one wanted to hear about it. His town had heard too many atrocity stories to be thrilled by actualities. Krebs found that to be listened to at all he had to lie, and after he had done this twice he, too, had a reaction against the war and against talking about it. A distaste for everything that had happened to him in the war set in because of the lies he had told. All of the times that had been able to make him feel cool and clear inside himself when he thought of them; the times so long back when he had done the one thing, the only thing for a man to do, easily and naturally, when he might have done something else, now lost their cool, valuable quality and then were lost themselves.

His lies were quite unimportant lies and consisted in attributing to himself things other men had seen, done or heard of, and stating as facts certain apocryphal incidents familiar to all soldiers. Even his lies were not sensational at the pool room. His acquaintances, who had heard detailed accounts of German women found chained to machine guns in the Argonne forest and who could not comprehend, or were barred by their patriotism from interest in, any German machine gunners who were not chained, were not thrilled by his stories.

Krebs acquired the nausea in regard to experience that is the result of untruth or exaggeration, and when he occasionally met another man who had really been a soldier and they talked a few minutes in the dressing room at a dance he fell into the easy pose of the old soldier among other soldiers: that he had been badly, sickeningly frightened all the time. In this way he lost everything.

During this time, it was late summer, he was sleeping late in bed, getting up to walk down town to the library to get a book, eating lunch at home, reading on the front porch until he became bored and then walking down through the town to spend the hottest hours of the day in the cool dark of the pool room. He loved to play pool.

In the evening he practised on his clarinet, strolled down town, read and went to bed. He was still a hero to his two young sisters. His mother would have given him breakfast in bed if he had wanted it. She often came in when he was in bed and asked him to tell her about the war, but her attention always wandered. His father was noncommittal.

Before Krebs went away to the war he had never been allowed to drive the family motor car. His father was in the real estate business and always wanted the car to be at his command when he required it to take clients out into the country to show them a piece of farm property. The car always stood outside the First National Bank building where his father had an office on the second floor. Now, after the war, it was still the same car.

Nothing was changed in the town except that the young girls had grown up. But they lived in such a complicated world of already defined alliances and shifting feuds that Krebs did not feel the energy or the courage to break into it. He liked to look at them, though. There were so many good-looking young girls. Most of them had their hair cut short. When he went away only little girls wore their hair like that or girls that were fast. They all wore sweaters and shirt waists with round Dutch collars. It was a pattern. He liked to look at them from the front porch as they walked on the other side of the street. He liked to watch them walking under the shade of the trees. He liked the round Dutch collars above their sweaters. He liked their silk stockings and flat shoes. He liked their bobbed hair and the way they walked.

When he was in town their appeal to him was not very strong. He did not like them when he saw them in the Greek's ice cream parlor. He did not want them themselves really. They were too complicated. There was something else. Vaguely he wanted a girl but he did not want to have to work to get her. He would have liked to have a girl but he did not want to have to spend a long time getting her. He did not want to get into the intrigue and the politics. He did not want to have to do any courting. He did not want to tell any more lies. It wasn't worth it.

He did not want any consequences. He did not want any consequences ever again. He wanted to live along without consequences. Besides he did not really need a girl. The army had taught him that. It was all right to pose as though you had to have a girl. Nearly everybody did that. But it wasn't true. You did not need a girl. That was the funny thing. First a fellow boasted how girls mean nothing to him, that he never thought of them, that they could not touch him. Then a fellow boasted that he could not get along without girls, that he had to have them all the time, that he could not go to sleep without them.

That was all a lie. It was all a lie both ways. You did not need a girl unless you thought about them. He learned that in the army. Then sooner or later you always got one. When you were really ripe for a girl you always got one. You did not have to think about it. Sooner or later it would come. He had learned that in the army.

Now he would have liked a girl if she had come to him and not wanted to talk. But here at home it was all too complicated. He knew he could never get through it all again. It was not worth the trouble. That was the thing about French girls and German girls. There was not all this talking. You couldn't talk much and you did not need to talk. It was simple and you were friends. He thought about France and then he began to think about Germany. On the whole he had liked Germany better. He did not want to leave Germany. He did not want to come home. Still, he had come home. He sat on the front porch.

He liked the girls that were walking along the other side of the street. He liked the look of them much better than the French girls or the German girls. But the world they were in was not the world he was in. He would like to have one of them. But it was not worth it. They were such a nice pattern. He liked the pattern. It was exciting. But he would not go through all the talking. He did not want one badly enough. He liked to look at them all, though. It was not worth it. Not now when things were getting good again.

He sat there on the porch reading a book on the war. It was a history and he was reading about all the engagements he had been in. It was the most interesting reading he had ever done. He wished there were more maps. He looked forward with a good feeling to reading all the really good histories when they would come out with good detail maps. Now he was really learning about the war. He had been a good soldier. That made a difference.

One morning after he had been home about a month his mother came into his bedroom and sat on the bed. She smoothed her apron.

"I had a talk with your father last night, Harold," she said, "and he is willing for you to take the car out in the evenings."

"Yeah?" said Krebs, who was not fully awake. "Take the car out? Yeah?"

"Yes. Your father has felt for some time that you should be able to take the car out in the evenings whenever you wished but we only talked it over last night."

"I'll bet you made him," Krebs said.

"No. It was your father's suggestion that we talk the matter over."

"Yeah. I'll bet you made him," Krebs sat up in bed.

"Will you come down to breakfast, Harold?" his mother said.

"As soon as I get my clothes on," Krebs said.

His mother went out of the room and he could hear her frying something downstairs while he washed, shaved and dressed to go down into the dining-room for breakfast. While he was eating breakfast his sister brought in the mail.

"Well, Hare," she said. "You old sleepy-head. What do you ever get up for?"

Krebs looked at her. He liked her. She was his best sister.

"Have you got the paper?" he asked.

She handed him *The Kansas City Star* and he shucked off its brown wrapper and opened it to the sporting page. He folded *The Star* open and propped it against the water pitcher with his cereal dish to steady it, so he could read while he ate.

"Harold," his mother stood in the kitchen doorway, "Harold, please don't muss up the paper. Your father can't read his *Star* if it's been mussed."

"I won't muss it," Krebs said.

His sister sat down at the table and watched him while he read.

"We're playing indoor over at school this afternoon," she said. "I'm going to pitch."

"Good," said Krebs. "How's the old wing?"

"I can pitch better than lots of the boys. I tell them all you taught me. The other girls aren't much good."

"Yeah?" said Krebs.

"I tell them all you're my beau. Aren't you my beau, Hare?"

"You bet."

"Couldn't your brother really be your beau just because he's your brother?"

"I don't know."

"Sure you know. Couldn't you be my beau, Hare, if I was old enough and if you wanted to?"

"Sure. You're my girl now."

"Am I really your girl?"

"Sure."

"Do you love me?"

"Uh, huh."

"Will you love me always?"

"Sure."

"Will you come over and watch me play indoor?"

"Maybe."

"Aw, Hare, you don't love me. If you loved me, you'd want to come over and watch me play indoor."

Krebs's mother came into the dining-room from the kitchen. She carried a plate with two fried eggs and some crisp bacon on it and a plate of buckwheat cakes.

"You run along, Helen," she said. "I want to talk to Harold."

She put the eggs and bacon down in front of him and brought in a jug of maple syrup for the buckwheat cakes. Then she sat down across the table from Krebs.

"I wish you'd put down the paper a minute, Harold," she said.

Krebs took down the paper and folded it.

"Have you decided what you are going to do yet, Harold?" his mother said, taking off her glasses.

"No," said Krebs.

"Don't you think it's about time?" His mother did not say this in a mean way. She seemed worried.

"I hadn't thought about it," Krebs said.

"God has some work for every one to do," his mother said. "There can be no idle hands in His Kingdom."

"I'm not in His Kingdom," Krebs said.

"We are all of us in His Kingdom."

Krebs felt embarrassed and resentful as always.

"I've worried about you so much, Harold," his mother went on. "I know the temptations you must have been exposed to. I know how weak men are. I know what your own dear grandfather, my own father, told us about the Civil War and I have prayed for you. I pray for you all day long, Harold."

Krebs looked at the bacon fat hardening on his plate.

"Your father is worried, too," his mother went on. "He thinks you have lost your ambition, that you haven't got a definite aim in life. Charley Simmons, who is just your age, has a good job and is going to be married. The boys are all settling down; they're all determined to get somewhere; you can see that boys like Charley Simmons are on their way to being really a credit to the community."

Krebs said nothing.

"Don't look that way, Harold," his mother said. "You know we love you and I want to tell you for your own good how matters stand. Your father does not want to hamper your freedom. He thinks you should be allowed to drive the car. If you want to take some of the nice girls out riding with you, we are only too pleased. We want you to enjoy yourself. But you are going to have to settle down to work, Harold. Your father doesn't care what you start in at. All work is honorable as he says. But you've got to make a start at something. He asked me to speak to you this morning and then you can stop in and see him at his office."

"Is that all?" Krebs said.

"Yes. Don't you love your mother, dear boy?"

"No," Krebs said.

His mother looked at him across the table. Her eyes were shiny. She started crying.

"I don't love anybody," Krebs said.

It wasn't any good. He couldn't tell her, he couldn't make her see it. It was silly to have said it. He had only hurt her. He went over and took hold of her arm. She was crying with her head in her hands.

"I didn't mean it," he said. "I was just angry at something. I didn't mean I didn't love you."

His mother went on crying. Krebs put his arm on her shoulder.

"Can't you believe me, mother?"

His mother shook her head.

"Please, please, mother. Please believe me."

"All right," his mother said chokily. She looked up at him. "I believe you, Harold."

Krebs kissed her hair. She put her face up to him.

"I'm your mother," she said. "I held you next to my heart when you were a tiny baby."

Krebs felt sick and vaguely nauseated.

"I know, Mummy," he said. "I'll try and be a good boy for you."

"Would you kneel and pray with me, Harold?" his mother asked.

They knelt down beside the dining-room table and Krebs's mother prayed.

"Now, you pray, Harold," she said.

"I can't," Krebs said.

"Try, Harold."

"I can't."

"Do you want me to pray for you?"

"Yes."

So his mother prayed for him and then they stood up and Krebs kissed his mother and went out of the house. He had tried so to keep his life from being complicated. Still, none of it had touched him. He had felt sorry for his mother and she had made him lie. He would go to Kansas City and get a job and she would feel all right about it. There would be one more scene maybe before he got away. He would not go down to his father's office. He would miss that one. He wanted his life to go smoothly. It had just gotten going that way. Well, that was all over now, anyway. He would go over to the school-yard and watch Helen play indoor baseball.

Chapter 8

At two o'clock in the morning two Hungarians got into a cigar store at Fifteenth Street and Grand Avenue. Drevitts and Boyle drove up from the Fifteenth Street police station in a Ford. The Hungarians were backing their wagon out of an alley. Boyle shot one off the seat of the wagon and one out of the wagon box. Drevitts got frightened when he found they were both dead. Hell Jimmy, he said, you oughtn't to have done it. There's liable to be a hell of a lot of trouble.

—They're crooks, ain't they? said Boyle. They're wops, ain't they? Who the hell is going to make any trouble?

—That's all right maybe this time, said Drevitts, but how did you know they were wops when you bumped them?

Wops, said Boyle, I can tell wops a mile off.

The Revolutionist

IN 1919 he was travelling on the railroads in Italy, carrying a square of oilcloth from the headquarters of the party written in indelible pencil and saying here was a comrade who had suffered very much under the Whites in Budapest and requesting comrades to aid him in any way. He used this instead of a ticket. He was very shy and quite young and the train men passed him on from one crew to another. He had no money, and they fed him behind the counter in railway eating houses.

He was delighted with Italy. It was a beautiful country, he said. The people were all kind. He had been in many towns, walked much, and seen many pictures. Giotto, Masaccio, and Piero della Francesca he bought reproductions of and carried them wrapped in a copy of *Avanti*. Mantegna he did not like.

He reported at Bologna, and I took him with me up into the Romagna where it was necessary I go to see a man. We had a good trip together. It was early September and the country was pleasant. He was a Magyar, a very nice boy and very shy. Horthy's men had done some bad things to him. He talked about it a little. In spite of Hungary, he believed altogether in the world revolution.

"But how is the movement going in Italy?" he asked.

"Very badly," I said.

"But it will go better," he said. "You have everything here. It is the one country that every one is sure of. It will be the starting point of everything."

I did not say anything.

At Bologna he said good-bye to us to go on the train to Milano and then to Aosta to walk over the pass into Switzerland. I spoke to him about the Mantegnas in Milano. "No," he said, very shyly, he did not like Mantegna. I wrote out for him where to eat in Milano and the addresses of comrades. He thanked me very much, but his mind was already looking forward to walking over the pass. He was very eager to walk over the pass while the weather held good. He loved the mountains in the autumn. The last I heard of him the Swiss had him in jail near Sion.

Chapter 9

The first matador got the horn through his sword hand and the crowd hooted him. The second matador slipped and the bull caught him through the belly and he hung on to the horn with one hand and held the other tight against the place, and the bull rammed him wham against the wall and the horn came out, and he lay in the sand, and then got up like crazy drunk and tried to slug the men carrying him away and yelled for his sword but he fainted. The kid came out and had to kill five bulls because you can't have more than three matadors, and the last bull he was so tired he couldn't get the sword in. He couldn't hardly lift his arm. He tried five times and the crowd was quiet because it was a good bull and it looked like him or the bull and then he finally made it. He sat down in the sand and puked and they held a cape over him while the crowd hollered and threw things down into the bull ring.

Mr. and Mrs. Elliot

MR. AND MRS. ELLIOT tried very hard to have a baby. They tried as often as Mrs. Elliot could stand it. They tried in Boston after they were married and they tried coming over on the boat. They did not try very often on the boat because Mrs. Elliot was quite sick. She was sick and when she was sick she was sick as Southern women are sick. That is women from the Southern part of the United States. Like all Southern women Mrs. Elliot disintegrated very quickly under sea sickness, travelling at night, and getting up too early in the morning. Many of the people on the boat took her for Elliot's mother. Other people who knew they were married believed she was going to have a baby. In reality she was forty years old. Her years had been precipitated suddenly when she started travelling.

She had seemed much younger, in fact she had seemed not to have any age at all, when Elliot had married her after several weeks of making love to her after knowing her for a long time in her tea shop before he had kissed her one evening.

Hubert Elliot was taking postgraduate work in law at Harvard when he was married. He was a poet with an income of nearly ten thousand dollars a year. He wrote very long poems very rapidly. He was twenty-five years old and had never gone to bed with a woman until he married Mrs. Elliot. He wanted to keep himself pure so that he could bring to his wife the same purity of mind and body that he expected of her. He called it to himself living straight. He had been in love with various girls before he kissed Mrs. Elliot and always told them sooner or later that he had led a clean life. Nearly all the girls lost interest in him. He was shocked and really horrified at the way girls would become engaged to and marry men whom they must know had dragged themselves through the gutter. He once tried to warn a girl he knew against a man of whom he had almost proof that he had been a rotter at college and a very unpleasant incident had resulted.

Mrs. Elliot's name was Cornelia. She had taught him to call her Calutina, which was her family nickname in the South. His mother cried when he brought Cornelia home after their marriage but brightened very much when she learned they were going to live abroad.

Cornelia had said, "You dear sweet boy," and held him closer than ever when he had told her how he had kept himself clean for her. Cornelia was pure too. "Kiss me again like that," she said.

Hubert explained to her that he had learned that way of kissing from hearing a fellow tell a story once. He was delighted with his experiment and they developed it as far as possible. Sometimes when they had been kissing together a long time, Cornelia would ask him to tell her again that he had kept himself really straight for her. The declaration always set her off again.

At first Hubert had no idea of marrying Cornelia. He had never thought of her that way. She had been such a good friend of his, and then one day in the little back room of the shop they had been dancing to the gramophone while her girl friend was in the front of the shop and she had looked up into his eyes and he had kissed her. He could never remember just when it was decided that they were to be married. But they were married.

They spent the night of the day they were married in a Boston hotel. They were both disappointed but finally Cornelia went to sleep. Hubert could not sleep and several times went out and walked up and down the corridor of the hotel in his new Jaeger bathrobe that he had bought for his wedding trip. As he walked he saw all the pairs of shoes, small shoes and big shoes, outside the doors of the hotel rooms. This set his heart to pounding and he hurried back to his own room but Cornelia was asleep. He did not like to waken her and soon everything was quite all right and he slept peacefully.

The next day they called on his mother and the next day they sailed for Europe. It was possible to try to have a baby but Cornelia could not attempt it very often although they wanted a baby more than anything else in the world. They landed at Cherbourg and came to Paris. They tried to have a baby in Paris. Then they decided to go to Dijon where there was summer school and where a number of people who crossed on the boat with them had gone. They found there was nothing to do in Dijon. Hubert, however, was writing a great number of poems and Cornelia typed them for him. They were all very long poems. He was very severe about mistakes and would

make her re-do an entire page if there was one mistake. She cried a
good deal and they tried several times to have a baby before they left
Dijon.

They came to Paris and most of their friends from the boat came
back too. They were tired of Dijon and anyway would now be able to
say that after leaving Harvard or Columbia or Wabash they had
studied at the University of Dijon down in the Côte d'Or. Many of
them would have preferred to go to Languedoc, Montpellier or
Perpignan if there are universities there. But all those places are too
far away. Dijon is only four and a half hours from Paris and there is
a diner on the train.

So they all sat around the Café du Dome, avoiding the Rotonde
across the street because it is always so full of foreigners, for a few
days and then the Elliots rented a château in Touraine through an
advertisement in the New York *Herald*. Elliot had a number of
friends by now all of whom admired his poetry and Mrs. Elliot had
prevailed upon him to send over to Boston for her girl friend who had
been in the tea shop. Mrs. Elliot became much brighter after her
girl friend came and they had many good cries together. The girl
friend was several years older than Cornelia and called her Honey.
She too came from a very old Southern family.

The three of them, with several of Elliot's friends who called
him Hubie, went down to the château in Touraine. They found
Touraine to be a very flat hot country very much like Kansas. Elliot
had nearly enough poems for a book now. He was going to bring it
out in Boston and had already sent his check to, and made a contract
with, a publisher.

In a short time the friends began to drift back to Paris. Touraine
had not turned out the way it looked when it started. Soon all the
friends had gone off with a rich young and unmarried poet to a sea-
side resort near Trouville. There they were all very happy.

Elliot kept on at the château in Touraine because he had taken
it for all summer. He and Mrs. Elliot tried very hard to have a baby
in the big hot bedroom on the big, hard bed. Mrs. Elliot was learning
the touch system on the typewriter, but she found that while it increased the speed it made more mistakes. The girl friend was now
typing practically all of the manuscripts. She was very neat and
efficient and seemed to enjoy it.

Elliot had taken to drinking white wine and lived apart in his own room. He wrote a great deal of poetry during the night and in the morning looked very exhausted. Mrs. Elliot and the girl friend now slept together in the big mediæval bed. They had many a good cry together. In the evening they all sat at dinner together in the garden under a plane tree and the hot evening wind blew and Elliot drank white wine and Mrs. Elliot and the girl friend made conversation and they were all quite happy.

Chapter 10

They whack-whacked the white horse on the legs and he kneed himself up. The picador twisted the stirrups straight and pulled and hauled up into the saddle. The horse's entrails hung down in a blue bunch and swung backward and forward as he began to canter, the monos *whacking him on the back of his legs with the rods. He cantered jerkily along the barrera. He stopped stiff and one of the* monos *held his bridle and walked him forward. The picador kicked in his spurs, leaned forward and shook his lance at the bull. Blood pumped regularly from between the horse's front legs. He was nervously wobbly. The bull could not make up his mind to charge.*

Cat in the Rain

THERE were only two Americans stopping at the hotel. They did not know any of the people they passed on the stairs on their way to and from their room. Their room was on the second floor facing the sea. It also faced the public garden and the war monument. There were big palms and green benches in the public garden. In the good weather there was always an artist with his easel. Artists liked the way the palms grew and the bright colors of the hotels facing the gardens and the sea. Italians came from a long way off to look up at the war monument. It was made of bronze and glistened in the rain. It was raining. The rain dripped from the palm trees. Water stood in pools on the gravel paths. The sea broke in a long line in the rain and slipped back down the beach to come up and break again in a long line in the rain. The motor cars were gone from the square by the war monument. Across the square in the doorway of the café a waiter stood looking out at the empty square.

The American wife stood at the window looking out. Outside right under their window a cat was crouched under one of the dripping green tables. The cat was trying to make herself so compact that she would not be dripped on.

"I'm going down and get that kitty," the American wife said.

"I'll do it," her husband offered from the bed.

"No, I'll get it. The poor kitty out trying to keep dry under a table."

The husband went on reading, lying propped up with the two pillows at the foot of the bed.

"Don't get wet," he said.

The wife went downstairs and the hotel owner stood up and bowed to her as she passed the office. His desk was at the far end of the office. He was an old man and very tall.

"Il piove," the wife said. She liked the hotel-keeper.

"Si, si, Signora, brutto tempo. It's very bad weather."

He stood behind his desk in the far end of the dim room. The wife liked him. She liked the deadly serious way he received any complaints. She liked his dignity. She liked the way he wanted to serve her. She liked the way he felt about being a hotel-keeper. She liked his old, heavy face and big hands.

Liking him she opened the door and looked out. It was raining harder. A man in a rubber cape was crossing the empty square to the café. The cat would be around to the right. Perhaps she could go along under the eaves. As she stood in the doorway an umbrella opened behind her. It was the maid who looked after their room.

"You must not get wet," she smiled, speaking Italian. Of course, the hotel-keeper had sent her.

With the maid holding the umbrella over her, she walked along the gravel path until she was under their window. The table was there, washed bright green in the rain, but the cat was gone. She was suddenly disappointed. The maid looked up at her.

"Ha perduto qualque cosa, Signora?"

"There was a cat," said the American girl.

"A cat?"

"Si, il gatto."

"A cat?" the maid laughed. "A cat in the rain?"

"Yes," she said, "under the table." Then, "Oh, I wanted it so much. I wanted a kitty."

When she talked English the maid's face tightened.

"Come, Signora," she said. "We must get back inside. You will be wet."

"I suppose so," said the American girl.

They went back along the gravel path and passed in the door. The maid stayed outside to close the umbrella. As the American girl passed the office, the padrone bowed from his desk. Something felt very small and tight inside the girl. The padrone made her feel very small and at the same time really important. She had a momentary feeling of being of supreme importance. She went on up the stairs. She opened the door of the room. George was on the bed, reading.

"Did you get the cat?" he asked, putting the book down.

"It was gone."

"Wonder where it went to," he said, resting his eyes from reading.

She sat down on the bed.

"I wanted it so much," she said. "I don't know why I wanted

it so much. I wanted that poor kitty. It isn't any fun to be a poor kitty out in the rain."

George was reading again.

She went over and sat in front of the mirror of the dressing table looking at herself with the hand glass. She studied her profile, first one side and then the other. Then she studied the back of her head and her neck.

"Don't you think it would be a good idea if I let my hair grow out?" she asked, looking at her profile again.

George looked up and saw the back of her neck, clipped close like a boy's.

"I like it the way it is."

"I get so tired of it," she said. "I get so tired of looking like a boy."

George shifted his position in the bed. He hadn't looked away from her since she started to speak.

"You look pretty darn nice," he said.

She laid the mirror down on the dresser and went over to the window and looked out. It was getting dark.

"I want to pull my hair back tight and smooth and make a big knot at the back that I can feel," she said. "I want to have a kitty to sit on my lap and purr when I stroke her."

"Yeah?" George said from the bed.

"And I want to eat at a table with my own silver and I want candles. And I want it to be spring and I want to brush my hair out in front of a mirror and I want a kitty and I want some new clothes."

"Oh, shut up and get something to read," George said. He was reading again.

His wife was looking out of the window. It was quite dark now and still raining in the palm trees.

"Anyway, I want a cat," she said, "I want a cat. I want a cat now. If I can't have long hair or any fun, I can have a cat."

George was not listening. He was reading his book. His wife looked out of the window where the light had come on in the square.

Someone knocked at the door.

"Avanti," George said. He looked up from his book.

In the doorway stood the maid. She held a big tortoise-shell cat pressed tight against her and swung down against her body.

"Excuse me," she said, "the padrone asked me to bring this for the Signora."

Chapter 11

The crowd shouted all the time and threw pieces of bread down into the ring, then cushions and leather wine bottles, keeping up whistling and yelling. Finally the bull was too tired from so much bad sticking and folded his knees and lay down and one of the cuadrilla *leaned out over his neck and killed him with the* puntillo. *The crowd came over the barrera and around the torero and two men grabbed him and held him and some one cut off his pigtail and was waving it and a kid grabbed it and ran away with it. Afterwards I saw him at the café. He was very short with a brown face and quite drunk and he said after all it has happened before like that. I am not really a good bull fighter.*

Out of Season

ON the four lire Peduzzi had earned by spading the hotel garden he got quite drunk. He saw the young gentleman coming down the path and spoke to him mysteriously. The young gentleman said he had not eaten but would be ready to go as soon as lunch was finished. Forty minutes or an hour.

At the cantina near the bridge they trusted him for three more grappas because he was so confident and mysterious about his job for the afternoon. It was a windy day with the sun coming out from behind clouds and then going under in sprinkles of rain. A wonderful day for trout fishing.

The young gentleman came out of the hotel and asked him about the rods. Should his wife come behind with the rods? "Yes," said Peduzzi, "let her follow us." The young gentleman went back into the hotel and spoke to his wife. He and Peduzzi started down the road. The young gentleman had a musette over his shoulder. Peduzzi saw the wife, who looked as young as the young gentleman, and was wearing mountain boots and a blue beret, start out to follow them down the road, carrying the fishing rods, unjointed, one in each hand. Peduzzi didn't like her to be way back there. "Signorina," he called, winking at the young gentleman, "come up here and walk with us. Signora, come up here. Let us all walk together." Peduzzi wanted them all three to walk down the street of Cortina together.

The wife stayed behind, following rather sullenly. "Signorina," Peduzzi called tenderly, "come up here with us." The young gentleman looked back and shouted something. The wife stopped lagging behind and walked up.

Everyone they met walking through the main street of the town Peduzzi greeted elaborately. Buon' di, Arturo! Tipping his hat. The bank clerk stared at him from the door of the Fascist café. Groups of three and four people standing in front of the shops stared at the three. The workmen in their stone-powdered jackets working on the foundations of the new hotel looked up as they passed. Nobody spoke or gave any sign to them except the town beggar, lean and old, with a spittle-thickened beard, who lifted his hat as they passed.

Peduzzi stopped in front of a store with the window full of bottles and brought his empty grappa bottle from an inside pocket of his old military coat. "A little to drink, some marsala for the Signora, something, something to drink." He gestured with the bottle. It was a wonderful day. "Marsala, you like marsala, Signorina? A little marsala?"

The wife stood sullenly. "You'll have to play up to this," she said. "I can't understand a word he says. He's drunk, isn't he?"

The young gentleman appeared not to hear Peduzzi. He was thinking, what in hell makes him say marsala? That's what Max Beerbohm drinks.

"Geld," Peduzzi said finally, taking hold of the young gentleman's sleeve. "Lire." He smiled, reluctant to press the subject but needing to bring the young gentleman into action.

The young gentleman took out his pocketbook and gave him a ten-lira note. Peduzzi went up the steps to the door of the Specialty of Domestic and Foreign Wines shop. It was locked.

"It is closed until two," someone passing in the street said scornfully. Peduzzi came down the steps. He felt hurt. Never mind, he said, we can get it at the Concordia.

They walked down the road to the Concordia three abreast. On the porch of the Concordia, where the rusty bobsleds were stacked, the young gentleman said, "Was wollen sie?" Peduzzi handed him the ten-lira note folded over and over. "Nothing," he said, "anything." He was embarrassed. "Marsala, maybe. I don't know. Marsala?"

The door of the Concordia shut on the young gentleman and the wife. "Three marsalas," said the young gentleman to the girl behind the pastry counter. "Two, you mean?" she asked. "No," he said, "one for a vecchio." "Oh," she said, "a vecchio," and laughed, getting down the bottle. She poured out the three muddy looking drinks into three glasses. The wife was sitting at a table under the line of newspapers on sticks. The young gentleman put one of the marsalas in front of her. "You might as well drink it," he said, "maybe it'll make you feel better." She sat and looked at the glass. The young gentleman went outside the door with a glass for Peduzzi but could not see him.

"I don't know where he is," he said, coming back into the pastry room carrying the glass.

"He wanted a quart of it," said the wife.

"How much is a quarter litre?" the young gentleman asked the girl.

"Of the bianco? One lira."

"No, of the marsala. Put these two in, too," he said, giving her his own glass and the one poured for Peduzzi. She filled the quarter litre wine measure with a funnel. "A bottle to carry it," said the young gentleman.

She went to hunt for a bottle. It all amused her.

"I'm sorry you feel so rotten, Tiny," he said. "I'm sorry I talked the way I did at lunch. We were both getting at the same thing from different angles."

"It doesn't make any difference," she said. "None of it makes any difference."

"Are you too cold?" he asked. "I wish you'd worn another sweater."

"I've got on three sweaters."

The girl came in with a very slim brown bottle and poured the marsala into it. The young gentleman paid five lire more. They went out the door. The girl was amused. Peduzzi was walking up and down at the other end out of the wind and holding the rods.

"Come on," he said, "I will carry the rods. What difference does it make if anybody sees them? No one will trouble us. No one will make any trouble for me in Cortina. I know them at the municipio. I have been a soldier. Everybody in this town likes me. I sell frogs. What if it is forbidden to fish? Not a thing. Nothing. No trouble. Big trout, I tell you. Lots of them."

They were walking down the hill toward the river. The town was in back of them. The sun had gone under and it was sprinkling rain. "There," said Peduzzi, pointing to a girl in the doorway of a house they passed. "My daughter."

"His doctor," the wife said, "has he got to show us his doctor?"

"He said his daughter," said the young gentleman.

The girl went into the house as Peduzzi pointed.

They walked down the hill across the fields and then turned to follow the river bank. Peduzzi talked rapidly with much winking and knowingness. As they walked three abreast the wife caught his breath across the wind. Once he nudged her in the ribs. Part of the time he talked in d'Ampezzo dialect and sometimes in Tyroler German dialect. He could not make out which the young gentleman and his wife understood the best so he was being bilingual. But as the young gentleman said, Ja, Ja, Peduzzi decided to talk altogether in Tyroler. The young gentleman and the wife understood nothing.

"Everybody in the town saw us going through with these rods. We're probably being followed by the game police now. I wish we weren't in on this damn thing. This damned old fool is so drunk, too."

"Of course you haven't got the guts to just go back," said the wife. "Of course you have to go on."

"Why don't you go back? Go on back, Tiny."

"I'm going to stay with you. If you go to jail we might as well both go."

They turned sharp down the bank and Peduzzi stood, his coat blowing in the wind, gesturing at the river. It was brown and muddy. Off on the right there was a dump heap.

"Say it to me in Italian," said the young gentleman.

"Un' mezz' ora. Piu d' un' mezz' ora."

"He says it's at least a half hour more. Go on back, Tiny. You're cold in this wind anyway. It's a rotten day and we aren't going to have any fun, anyway."

"All right," she said, and climbed up the grassy bank.

Peduzzi was down at the river and did not notice her till she was almost out of sight over the crest. "Frau!" he shouted. "Frau! Fräulein! You're not going."

She went on over the crest of the hill.

"She's gone!" said Peduzzi. It shocked him.

He took off the rubber bands that held the rod segments together and commenced to joint up one of the rods.

"But you said it was half an hour further."

"Oh, yes. It is good half an hour down. It is good here, too."

"Really?"

"Of course. It is good here and good there, too."

The young gentleman sat down on the bank and jointed up a rod, put on the reel and threaded the line through the guides. He felt uncomfortable and afraid that any minute a gamekeeper or a posse of citizens would come over the bank from the town. He could

see the houses of the town and the campanile over the edge of the
hill. He opened his leader box. Peduzzi leaned over and dug his
flat, hard thumb and forefinger in and tangled the moistened leaders.

"Have you some lead?"

"No."

"You must have some lead." Peduzzi was excited. "You must have
piombo. Piombo. A little piombo. Just here. Just above the hook or
your bait will float on the water. You must have it. Just a little
piombo."

"Have you got some?"

"No." He looked through his pockets desperately. Sifting
through the cloth dirt in the linings of his inside military pockets. "I
haven't any. We must have piombo."

"We can't fish then," said the young gentleman, and unjointed
the rod, reeling the line back through the guides. "We'll get some
piombo and fish tomorrow."

"But listen, caro, you must have piombo. The line will lie flat on
the water." Peduzzi's day was going to pieces before his eyes. "You
must have piombo. A little is enough. Your stuff is all clean and new
but you have no lead. I would have brought some. You said you had
everything."

The young gentleman looked at the stream discolored by the
melting snow. "I know," he said, "we'll get some piombo and fish
tomorrow."

"At what hour in the morning? Tell me that."

"At seven."

The sun came out. It was warm and pleasant. The young gentleman felt relieved. He was no longer breaking the law. Sitting on the
bank he took the bottle of marsala out of his pocket and passed it to
Peduzzi. Peduzzi passed it back. The young gentleman took a drink
of it and passed it to Peduzzi again. Peduzzi passed it back again.
"Drink," he said, "drink. It's your marsala." After another short drink
the young gentleman handed the bottle over. Peduzzi had been
watching it closely. He took the bottle very hurriedly and tipped it
up. The gray hairs in the folds of his neck oscillated as he drank, his
eyes fixed on the end of the narrow brown bottle. He drank it all.
The sun shone while he drank. It was wonderful. This was a great
day, after all. A wonderful day.

"Senta, caro! In the morning at seven." He had called the young gentleman caro several times and nothing had happened. It was good marsala. His eyes glistened. Days like this stretched out ahead. It would begin at seven in the morning.

They started to walk up the hill toward the town. The young gentleman went on ahead. He was quite a way up the hill. Peduzzi called to him.

"Listen, caro, can you let me take five lire for a favor?"

"For today?" asked the young gentleman frowning.

"No, not today. Give it to me today for tomorrow. I will provide everything for tomorrow. Pane, salami, formaggio, good stuff for all of us. You and I and the Signora. Bait for fishing, minnows, not worms only. Perhaps I can get some marsala. All for five lire. Five lire for a favor."

The young gentleman looked through his pocketbook and took out a two-lira note and two ones.

"Thank you, caro. Thank you," said Peduzzi, in the tone of one member of the Carleton Club accepting the *Morning Post* from another. This was living. He was through with the hotel garden, breaking up frozen manure with a dung fork. Life was opening out.

"Until seven o'clock then, caro," he said, slapping the young gentleman on the back. "Promptly at seven."

"I may not be going," said the young gentleman putting his purse back in his pocket.

"What," said Peduzzi, "I will have minnows, Signor. Salami, everything. You and I and the Signora. The three of us."

"I may not be going," said the young gentleman, "very probably not. I will leave word with the padrone at the hotel office."

Chapter 12

If it happened right down close in front of you, you could see Villalta snarl at the bull and curse him, and when the bull charged he swung back firmly like an oak when the wind hits it, his legs tight together, the muleta trailing and the sword following the curve behind. Then he cursed the bull, flopped the muleta at him, and swung back from the charge his feet firm, the muleta curving and at each swing the crowd roaring.

When he started to kill it was all in the same rush. The bull looking at him straight in front, hating. He drew out the sword from the folds of the muleta and sighted with the same movement and called to the bull, Toro! Toro! and the bull charged and Villalta charged and just for a moment they became one. Villalta became one with the bull and then it was over. Villalta standing straight and the red hilt of the sword sticking out dully between the bull's shoulders. Villalta, his hand up at the crowd and the bull roaring blood, looking straight at Villalta and his legs caving.

Cross-Country Snow

THE funicular car bucked once more and then stopped. It could not go farther, the snow drifted solidly across the track. The gale scouring the exposed surface of the mountain had swept the snow surface into a wind-board crust. Nick, waxing his skis in the baggage car, pushed his boots into the toe irons and shut the clamp tight. He jumped from the car sideways onto the hard wind-board, made a jump turn and crouching and trailing his sticks slipped in a rush down the slope.

On the white below George dipped and rose and dipped out of sight. The rush and the sudden swoop as he dropped down a steep undulation in the mountain side plucked Nick's mind out and left him only the wonderful flying, dropping sensation in his body. He rose to a slight up-run and then the snow seemed to drop out from under him as he went down, down, faster and faster in a rush down the last, long steep slope. Crouching so he was almost sitting back on his skis, trying to keep the center of gravity low, the snow driving like a sand-storm, he knew the pace was too much. But he held it. He would not let go and spill. Then a patch of soft snow, left in a hollow by the wind, spilled him and he went over and over in a clashing of skis, feeling like a shot rabbit, then stuck, his legs crossed, his skis sticking straight up and his nose and ears jammed full of snow.

George stood a little farther down the slope, knocking the snow from his wind jacket with big slaps.

"You took a beauty, Mike," he called to Nick. "That's lousy soft snow. It bagged me the same way."

"What's it like over the khud?" Nick kicked his skis around as he lay on his back and stood up.

"You've got to keep to your left. It's a good fast drop with a Christy at the bottom on account of a fence."

"Wait a sec and we'll take it together."

"No, you come on and go first. I like to see you take the khuds."

Nick Adams came up past George, big back and blond head still faintly snowy, then his skis started slipping at the edge and he swooped down, hissing in the crystalline powder snow and seeming to float up and drop down as he went up and down the billowing khuds. He held to his left and at the end, as he rushed toward the fence, keeping his knees locked tight together and turning his body like tightening a screw brought his skis sharply around to the right in a smother of snow and slowed into a loss of speed parallel to the hillside and the wire fence.

He looked up the hill. George was coming down in telemark position, kneeling; one leg forward and bent, the other trailing; his sticks hanging like some insect's thin legs, kicking up puffs of snow as they touched the surface and finally the whole kneeling, trailing figure coming around in a beautiful right curve, crouching, the legs shot forward and back, the body leaning out against the swing, the sticks accenting the curve like points of light, all in a wild cloud of snow.

"I was afraid to Christy," George said, "the snow was too deep. You made a beauty."

"I can't telemark with my leg," Nick said.

Nick held down the top strand of the wire fence with his ski and George slid over. Nick followed him down to the road. They thrust bent-kneed along the road into a pine forest. The road became polished ice, stained orange and a tobacco yellow from the teams hauling logs. The skiers kept to the stretch of snow along the side. The road dipped sharply to a stream and then ran straight up-hill. Through the woods they could see a long low-eaved, weather-beaten building. Through the trees it was a faded yellow. Closer the window frames were painted green. The paint was peeling. Nick knocked his clamps loose with one of his ski sticks and kicked off the skis.

"We might as well carry them up here," he said.

He climbed the steep road with the skis on his shoulder, kicking his heel nails into the icy footing. He heard George breathing and kicking in his heels just behind him. They stacked the skis against the side of the inn and slapped the snow off each other's trousers, stamped their boots clean, and went in.

Inside it was quite dark. A big porcelain stove shone in the corner of the room. There was a low ceiling. Smooth benches back of dark, wine-stained tables were along each side of the rooms. Two Swiss sat over their pipes and two decies of cloudy new wine next to the stove. The boys took off their jackets and sat against the wall on the other side of the stove. A voice in the next room stopped singing and a girl in a blue apron came in through the door to see what they wanted to drink.

"A bottle of Sion," Nick said. "Is that all right, Gidge?"

"Sure," said George. "You know more about wine than I do. I like any of it."

The girl went out.

"There's nothing really can touch skiing, is there?" Nick said. "The way it feels when you first drop off on a long run."

"Huh," said George. "It's too swell to talk about."

The girl brought the wine in and they had trouble with the cork. Nick finally opened it. The girl went out and they heard her singing in German in the next room.

"Those specks of cork in it don't matter," said Nick.

"I wonder if she's got any cake."

"Let's find out."

The girl came in and Nick noticed that her apron covered swellingly her pregnancy. I wonder why I didn't see that when she first came in, he thought.

"What were you singing?" he asked her.

"Opera, German opera." She did not care to discuss the subject. "We have some apple strudel if you want it."

"She isn't so cordial, is she?" said George.

"Oh, well. She doesn't know us and she thought we were going to kid her about her singing, maybe. She's from up where they speak German probably and she's touchy about being here and then she's got that baby coming without being married and she's touchy."

"How do you know she isn't married?"

"No ring. Hell, no girls get married around here till they're knocked up."

The door came open and a gang of woodcutters from up the road came in, stamping their boots and steaming in the room. The waitress brought in three litres of new wine for the gang and they sat at the two tables, smoking and quiet, with their hats off, leaning back against the wall or forward on the table. Outside the horses on the wood sledges made an occasional sharp jangle of bells as they tossed their heads.

George and Nick were happy. They were fond of each other. They knew they had the run back home ahead of them.

"When have you got to go back to school?" Nick asked.

"Tonight," George answered. "I've got to get the ten-forty from Montreux."

"I wish you could stick over and we could do the Dent du Lys tomorrow."

"I got to get educated," George said. "Gee, Mike, don't you wish we could just bum together? Take our skis and go on the train to where there was good running and then go on and put up at pubs and go right across the Oberland and up the Valais and all through the Engadine and just take repair kit and extra sweaters and pyjamas in our rucksacks and not give a damn about school or anything."

"Yes, and go through the Schwarzwald that way. Gee, the swell places."

"That's where you went fishing last summer, isn't it?"

"Yes."

They ate the strudel and drank the rest of the wine.

George leaned back against the wall and shut his eyes.

"Wine always makes me feel this way," he said.

"Feel bad?" Nick asked.

"No. I feel good, but funny."

"I know," Nick said.

"Sure," said George.

"Should we have another bottle?" Nick asked.

"Not for me," George said.

They sat there, Nick leaning his elbows on the table, George slumped back against the wall.

"Is Helen going to have a baby?" George said, coming down to the table from the wall.

"Yes."

"When?"

"Late next summer."

"Are you glad?"

"Yes. Now."

"Will you go back to the States?"

"I guess so."

"Do you want to?"

"No."

"Does Helen?"

"No."

George sat silent. He looked at the empty bottle and the empty glasses.

"It's hell, isn't it?" he said.

"No. Not exactly," Nick said.

"Why not?"

"I don't know," Nick said.

"Will you ever go skiing together in the States?" George said.

"I don't know," said Nick.

"The mountains aren't much," George said.

"No," said Nick. "They're too rocky. There's too much timber and they're too far away."

"Yes," said George, "that's the way it is in California."

"Yes," Nick said, "that's the way it is everywhere I've ever been."

"Yes," said George, "that's the way it is."

The Swiss got up and paid and went out.

"I wish we were Swiss," George said.

"They've all got goiter," said Nick.

"I don't believe it," George said.

"Neither do I," said Nick.

They laughed.

"Maybe we'll never go skiing again, Nick," George said.

"We've got to," said Nick. "It isn't worth while if you can't."

"We'll go, all right," George said.

"We've got to," Nick agreed.

"I wish we could make a promise about it," George said.

Nick stood up. He buckled his wind jacket tight. He leaned over George and picked up the two ski poles from against the wall. He stuck one of the ski poles into the floor.

"There isn't any good in promising," he said.

They opened the door and went out. It was very cold. The snow had crusted hard. The road ran up the hill into the pine trees.

They took down their skis from where they leaned against the wall in the inn. Nick put on his gloves. George was already started up the road, his skis on his shoulder. Now they would have the run home together.

Chapter 13

I heard the drums coming down the street and then the fifes and the pipes and then they came around the corner, all dancing. The street was full of them. Maera saw him and then I saw him. When they stopped the music for the crouch he hunched down in the street with them all and when they started it again he jumped up and went dancing down the street with them. He was drunk all right.

You go down after him, said Maera, he hates me.

So I went down and caught up with them and grabbed him while he was crouched down waiting for the music to break loose and said, Come on Luis. For Christ's sake you've got bulls this afternoon. He didn't listen to me, he was listening so hard for the music to start.

I said, Don't be a damn fool Luis. Come on back to the hotel.

Then the music started up again and he jumped up and twisted away from me and started dancing. I grabbed his arm and he pulled loose and said, Oh leave me alone. You're not my father.

I went back to the hotel and Maera was on the balcony looking out to see if I'd be bringing him back. He went inside when he saw me and came downstairs disgusted.

Well, I said, after all he's just an ignorant Mexican savage.

Yes, Maera said, and who will kill his bulls after he gets a cogida?

We, I suppose, I said.

Yes, we, said Maera. We kills the savages' bulls, and the drunkards' bulls, and the riau-riau *dancers' bulls. Yes. We kill them. We kill them all right. Yes. Yes. Yes.*

93

My Old Man

I GUESS looking at it, now, my old man was cut out for a fat guy, one of those regular little roly fat guys you see around, but he sure never got that way, except a little toward the last, and then it wasn't his fault, he was riding over the jumps only and he could afford to carry plenty of weight then. I remember the way he'd pull on a rubber shirt over a couple of jerseys and a big sweat shirt over that, and get me to run with him in the forenoon in the hot sun. He'd have, maybe, taken a trial trip with one of Razzo's skins early in the morning after just getting in from Torino at four o'clock in the morning and beating it out to the stables in a cab and then with the dew all over everything and the sun just starting to get going, I'd help him pull off his boots and he'd get into a pair of sneakers and all these sweaters and we'd start out.

"Come on, kid," he'd say, stepping up and down on his toes in front of the jock's dressing room, "let's get moving."

Then we'd start off jogging around the infield once, maybe, with him ahead, running nice, and then turn out the gate and along one of those roads with all the trees along both sides of them that run out from San Siro. I'd go ahead of him when we hit the road and I could run pretty good and I'd look around and he'd be jogging easy just behind me and after a little while I'd look around again and he'd begun to sweat. Sweating heavy and he'd just be dogging it along with his eyes on my back, but when he'd catch me looking at him he'd grin and say, "Sweating plenty?" When my old man grinned, nobody could help but grin too. We'd keep right on running out toward the mountains and then my old man would yell, "Hey, Joe!" and I'd look back and he'd be sitting under a tree with a towel he'd had around his waist wrapped around his neck.

I'd come back and sit down beside him and he'd pull a rope out of his pocket and start skipping rope out in the sun with the sweat pouring off his face and him skipping rope out in the white dust

94

with the rope going cloppetty, cloppetty, clop, clop, clop, and the sun hotter, and him working harder up and down a patch of the road. Say, it was a treat to see my old man skip rope, too. He could whirr it fast or lop it slow and fancy. Say, you ought to have seen wops look at us sometimes, when they'd come by, going into town walking along with big white steers hauling the cart. They sure looked as though they thought the old man was nuts. He'd start the rope whirring till they'd stop dead still and watch him, then give the steers a cluck and a poke with the goad and get going again.

When I'd sit watching him working out in the hot sun I sure felt fond of him. He sure was fun and he done his work so hard and he'd finish up with a regular whirring that'd drive the sweat out on his face like water and then sling the rope at the tree and come over and sit down with me and lean back against the tree with the towel and a sweater wrapped around his neck.

"Sure is hell keeping it down, Joe," he'd say and lean back and shut his eyes and breathe long and deep, "it ain't like when you're a kid." Then he'd get up and before he started to cool we'd jog along back to the stables. That's the way it was keeping down to weight. He was worried all the time. Most jocks can just about ride off all they want to. A jock loses about a kilo every time he rides, but my old man was sort of dried out and he couldn't keep down his kilos without all that running.

I remember once at San Siro, Regoli, a little wop, that was riding for Buzoni, came out across the paddock going to the bar for something cool; and flicking his boots with his whip, after he'd just weighed in and my old man had just weighed in too, and came out with the saddle under his arm looking red-faced and tired and too big for his silks and he stood there looking at young Regoli standing up to the outdoors bar, cool and kid-looking, and I said, "What's the matter, Dad?" 'cause I thought maybe Regoli had bumped him or something and he just looked at Regoli and said, "Oh, to hell with it," and went on to the dressing room.

Well, it would have been all right, maybe, if we'd stayed in Milan and ridden at Milan and Torino, 'cause if there ever were any easy courses, it's those two. "Pianola, Joe," my old man said when he dismounted in the winning stall after what the wops thought was a hell of a steeplechase. I asked him once. "This course rides itself. It's the pace you're going at, that makes riding the jumps dangerous, Joe.

We ain't going any pace here, and they ain't really bad jumps either. But it's the pace always—not the jumps—that makes the trouble."

San Siro was the swellest course I'd ever seen but the old man said it was a dog's life. Going back and forth between Mirafiore and San Siro and riding just about every day in the week with a train ride every other night.

I was nuts about the horses, too. There's something about it, when they come out and go up the track to the post. Sort of dancy and tight looking with the jock keeping a tight hold on them and maybe easing off a little and letting them run a little going up. Then once they were at the barrier it got me worse than anything. Especially at San Siro with that big green infield and the mountains way off and the fat wop starter with his big whip and the jocks fiddling them around and then the barrier snapping up and that bell going off and them all getting off in a bunch and then commencing to string out. You know the way a bunch of skins gets off. If you're up in the stand with a pair of glasses all you see is them plunging off and then that bell goes off and it seems like it rings for a thousand years and then they come sweeping round the turn. There wasn't ever anything like it for me.

But my old man said one day, in the dressing room, when he was getting into his street clothes, "None of these things are horses, Joe. They'd kill that bunch of skates for their hides and hoofs up at Paris." That was the day he'd won the Premio Commercio with Lantorna shooting her out of the field the last hundred meters like pulling a cork out of a bottle.

It was right after the Premio Commercio that we pulled out and left Italy. My old man and Holbrook and a fat wop in a straw hat that kept wiping his face with a handkerchief were having an argument at a table in the Galleria. They were all talking French and the two of them was after my old man about something. Finally he didn't say anything any more but just sat there and looked at Holbrook, and the two of them kept after him, first one talking and then the other, and the fat wop always butting in on Holbrook.

"You go out and buy me a *Sportsman,* will you, Joe?" my old man said, and handed me a couple of soldi without looking away from Holbrook.

So I went out of the Galleria and walked over to in front of the Scala and bought a paper, and came back and stood a little way away because I didn't want to butt in and my old man was sitting back in his chair looking down at his coffee and fooling with a spoon and Holbrook and the big wop were standing and the big wop was wiping his face and shaking his head. And I came up and my old man acted just as though the two of them weren't standing there and said, "Want an ice, Joe?" Holbrook looked down at my old man and said slow and careful, "You son of a bitch," and he and the fat wop went out through the tables.

My old man sat there and sort of smiled at me, but his face was white and he looked sick as hell and I was scared and felt sick inside because I knew something had happened and I didn't see how anybody could call my old man a son of a bitch, and get away with it. My old man opened up the *Sportsman* and studied the handicaps for a while and then he said, "You got to take a lot of things in this world, Joe." And three days later we left Milan for good on the Turin train for Paris, after an auction sale out in front of Turner's stables of everything we couldn't get into a trunk and a suit case.

We got into Paris early in the morning in a long, dirty station the old man told me was the Gare de Lyon. Paris was an awful big town after Milan. Seems like in Milan everybody is going somewhere and all the trams run somewhere and there ain't any sort of a mix-up, but Paris is all balled up and they never do straighten it out. I got to like it, though, part of it, anyway, and say, it's got the best race courses in the world. Seems as though that were the thing that keeps it all going and about the only thing you can figure on is that every day the buses will be going out to whatever track they're running at, going right out through everything to the track. I never really got to know Paris well, because I just came in about once or twice a week with the old man from Maisons and he always sat at the Café de la Paix on the Opera side with the rest of the gang from Maisons and I guess that's one of the busiest parts of the town. But, say, it is funny that a big town like Paris wouldn't have a Galleria, isn't it?

Well, we went out to live at Maisons-Lafitte, where just about everybody lives except the gang at Chantilly, with a Mrs. Meyers that runs a boarding house. Maisons is about the swellest place to live I've ever seen in all my life. The town ain't so much, but there's a lake and a swell forest that we used to go off bumming in all day, a couple of us kids, and my old man made me a sling shot and we got a lot of things with it but the best one was a magpie. Young Dick

Atkinson shot a rabbit with it one day and we put it under a tree and were all sitting around and Dick had some cigarettes and all of a sudden the rabbit jumped up and beat it into the brush and we chased it but we couldn't find it. Gee, we had fun at Maisons. Mrs. Meyers used to give me lunch in the morning and I'd be gone all day. I learned to talk French quick. It's an easy language.

As soon as we got to Maisons, my old man wrote to Milan for his license and he was pretty worried till it came. He used to sit around the Café de Paris in Maisons with the gang, there were lots of guys he'd known when he rode up at Paris, before the war, lived at Maisons, and there's a lot of time to sit around because the work around a racing stable, for the jocks, that is, is all cleaned up by nine o'clock in the morning. They take the first bunch of skins out to gallop them at 5:30 in the morning and they work the second lot at 8 o'clock. That means getting up early all right and going to bed early, too. If a jock's riding for somebody too, he can't go boozing around because the trainer always has an eye on him if he's a kid and if he ain't a kid he's always got an eye on himself. So mostly if a jock ain't working he sits around the Café de Paris with the gang and they can all sit around about two or three hours in front of some drink like a vermouth and seltz and they talk and tell stories and shoot pool and it's sort of like a club or the Galleria in Milan. Only it ain't really like the Galleria because there everybody is going by all the time and there's everybody around at the tables.

Well, my old man got his license all right. They sent it through to him without a word and he rode a couple of times. Amiens, up country and that sort of thing, but he didn't seem to get any engagement. Everybody liked him and whenever I'd come into the Café in the forenoon I'd find somebody drinking with him because my old man wasn't tight like most of these jockeys that have got the first dollar they made riding at the World's Fair in St. Louis in nineteen ought four. That's what my old man would say when he'd kid George Burns. But it seemed like everybody steered clear of giving my old man any mounts.

We went out to wherever they were running every day with the car from Maisons and that was the most fun of all. I was glad when the horses came back from Deauville and the summer. Even though it meant no more bumming in the woods, 'cause then we'd ride to Enghien or Tremblay or St. Cloud and watch them from the trainers' and jockeys' stand. I sure learned about racing from going out with that gang and the fun of it was going every day.

I remember once out at St. Cloud. It was a big two hundred thousand franc race with seven entries and Kzar a big favorite. I went around to the paddock to see the horses with my old man and you never saw such horses. This Kzar is a great big yellow horse that looks like just nothing but run. I never saw such a horse. He was being led around the paddocks with his head down and when he went by me I felt all hollow inside he was so beautiful. There never was such a wonderful, lean, running built horse. And he went around the paddock putting his feet just so and quiet and careful and moving easy like he knew just what he had to do and not jerking and standing up on his legs and getting wild eyed like you see these selling platers with a shot of dope in them. The crowd was so thick I couldn't see him again except just his legs going by and some yellow and my old man started out through the crowd and I followed him over to the jock's dressing room back in the trees and there was a big crowd around there, too, but the man at the door in a derby nodded to my old man and we got in and everybody was sitting around and getting dressed and pulling shirts over their heads and pulling boots on and it all smelled hot and sweaty and linimenty and outside was the crowd looking in.

The old man went over and sat down beside George Gardner that was getting into his pants and said, "What's the dope, George?" just in an ordinary tone of voice 'cause there ain't any use him feeling around because George either can tell him or he can't tell him.

"He won't win," George says very low, leaning over and buttoning the bottoms of his breeches.

"Who will?" my old man says, leaning over close so nobody can hear.

"Kircubbin," George says, "and if he does, save me a couple of tickets."

My old man says something in a regular voice to George and George says, "Don't ever bet on anything I tell you," kidding like, and we beat it out and through all the crowd that was looking in, over to the 100 franc mutuel machine. But I knew something big was up because George is Kzar's jockey. On the way he gets one of the yellow odds-sheets with the starting prices on and Kzar is only paying 5 for 10, Cefisidote is next at 3 to 1 and fifth down the list this Kircubbin at 8 to 1. My old man bets five thousand on Kircubbin to win and puts on a thousand to place and we went around back of the grandstand to go up the stairs and get a place to watch the race.

We were jammed in tight and first a man in a long coat with a gray tall hat and a whip folded up in his hand came out and then one after another the horses, with the jocks up and a stable boy holding the bridle on each side and walking along, followed the old guy. That big yellow horse Kzar came first. He didn't look so big when you first looked at him until you saw the length of his legs and the whole way he's built and the way he moves. Gosh, I never saw such a horse. George Gardner was riding him and they moved along slow, back of the old guy in the gray tall hat that walked along like he was a ring master in a circus. Back of Kzar, moving along smooth and yellow in the sun, was a good looking black with a nice head with Tommy Archibald riding him; and after the black was a string of five more horses all moving along slow in a procession past the grandstand and the pesage. My old man said the black was Kircubbin and I took a good look at him and he was a nice-looking horse, all right, but nothing like Kzar.

Everybody cheered Kzar when he went by and he sure was one swell-looking horse. The procession of them went around on the other side past the pelouse and then back up to the near end of the course and the circus master had the stable boys turn them loose one after another so they could gallop by the stands on their way up to the post and let everybody have a good look at them. They weren't at the post hardly any time at all when the gong started and you could see them way off across the infield all in a bunch starting on the first swing like a lot of little toy horses. I was watching them through the glasses and Kzar was running well back, with one of the bays making the pace. They swept down and around and came pounding past and Kzar was way back when they passed us and this Kircubbin horse in front and going smooth. Gee, it's awful when they go by you and then you have to watch them go farther away and get smaller and smaller and then all bunched up on the turns and then come around towards into the stretch and you feel like swearing and goddamming worse and worse. Finally they made the last turn and came into the straightaway with this Kircubbin horse way out in front. Everybody was looking funny and saying "Kzar" in sort of a sick way and them pounding nearer down the stretch, and then something came out of the pack right into my glasses like a horse-headed yellow streak and everybody began to yell "Kzar" as though they were crazy. Kzar came on faster than I'd ever seen anything in my life and pulled up on Kircubbin that was going fast as any black horse could go with the jock flogging hell out of him with the gad and they were right dead neck and neck for a second but Kzar seemed going about twice as fast with those great jumps and that head out—but it was while they were neck and neck that they passed the winning post and when the numbers went up in the slots the first one was 2 and that meant that Kircubbin had won.

I felt all trembly and funny inside, and then we were all jammed in with the people going downstairs to stand in front of the board where they'd post what Kircubbin paid. Honest, watching the race I'd forgot how much my old man had bet on Kircubbin. I'd wanted Kzar to win so damned bad. But now it was all over it was swell to know we had the winner.

"Wasn't it a swell race, Dad?" I said to him.

He looked at me sort of funny with his derby on the back of his head. "George Gardner's a swell jockey, all right," he said. "It sure took a great jock to keep that Kzar horse from winning."

Of course I knew it was funny all the time. But my old man saying that right out like that sure took the kick all out of it for me and I didn't get the real kick back again ever, even when they posted the numbers upon the board and the bell rang to pay off and we saw that Kircubbin paid 67.50 for 10. All round people were saying, "Poor Kzar! Poor Kzar!" And I thought, I wish I were a jockey and could have rode him instead of that son of a bitch. And that was funny, thinking of George Gardner as a son of a bitch because I'd always liked him and besides he'd given us the winner, but I guess that's what he is, all right.

My old man had a big lot of money after that race and he took to coming into Paris oftener. If they raced at Tremblay he'd have them drop him in town on their way back to Maisons and he and I'd sit out in front of the Café de la Paix and watch the people go by. It's funny sitting there. There's streams of people going by and all sorts of guys come up and want to sell you things, and I loved to sit there with my old man. That was when we'd have the most fun. Guys would come by selling funny rabbits that jumped if you squeezed a bulb and they'd come up to us and my old man would kid with them. He could talk French just like English and all those kind of guys knew him 'cause you can always tell a jockey—and then we always sat at the same table and they got used to seeing us there. There were guys selling matrimonial papers and girls selling rubber eggs that when you squeezed them a rooster came out of them and one old wormy-looking guy that went by with post-cards of Paris, showing them to everybody, and, of course, nobody ever bought any, and then he would come back and show the under side of the pack and they would all be smutty post-cards and lots of people would dig down and buy them.

Gee, I remember the funny people that used to go by. Girls around supper time looking for somebody to take them out to eat and they'd speak to my old man and he'd make some joke at them in French and they'd pat me on the head and go on. Once there was an American woman sitting with her kid daughter at the next table to us and they were both eating ices and I kept looking at the girl and she was awfully good looking and I smiled at her and she smiled at me but that was all that ever came of it because I looked for her mother and her every day and I made up ways that I was going to speak to her and I wondered if I got to know her if her mother would let me take her out to Auteuil or Tremblay but I never saw either of them again. Anyway, I guess it wouldn't have been any good, anyway, because looking back on it I remember the way I thought out would be best to speak to her was to say, "Pardon me, but perhaps I can give you a winner at Enghien today?" and, after all, maybe she would have thought I was a tout instead of really trying to give her a winner.

We'd sit at the Café de la Paix, my old man and me, and we had a big drag with the waiter because my old man drank whisky and it cost five francs, and that meant a good tip when the saucers were counted up. My old man was drinking more than I'd ever seen him, but he wasn't riding at all now and besides he said that whisky kept his weight down. But I noticed he was putting it on, all right, just the same. He'd busted away from his old gang out at Maisons and seemed to like just sitting around on the boulevard with me. But he was dropping money every day at the track. He'd feel sort of doleful after the last race, if he'd lost on the day, until we'd get to our table and he'd have his first whisky and then he'd be fine.

He'd be reading the *Paris-Sport* and he'd look over at me and say, "Where's your girl, Joe?" to kid me on account I had told him about the girl that day at the next table. And I'd get red, but I liked being kidded about her. It gave me a good feeling. "Keep your eye peeled for her, Joe," he'd say, "she'll be back."

He'd ask me questions about things and some of the things I'd say he'd laugh. And then he'd get started talking about things. About riding down in Egypt, or at St. Moritz on the ice before my mother died, and about during the war when they had regular races down in the south of France without any purses, or betting or crowd or anything just to keep the breed up. Regular races with the jocks riding hell out of the horses. Gee, I could listen to my old man talk by the hour, especially when he'd had a couple or so of drinks. He'd tell me about when he was a boy in Kentucky and going coon hunting, and the old days in the States before everything went on the bum there. And he'd say, "Joe, when we've got a decent stake, you're going back there to the States and go to school."

"What've I got to go back there to go to school for when everything's on the bum there?" I'd ask him.

"That's different," he'd say and get the waiter over and pay the pile of saucers and we'd get a taxi to the Gare St. Lazare and get on the train out to Maisons.

One day at Auteuil, after a selling steeplechase, my old man bought in the winner for 30,000 francs. He had to bid a little to get him but the stable let the horse go finally and my old man had his permit and his colors in a week. Gee, I felt proud when my old man was an owner. He fixed it up for stable space with Charles Drake and cut out coming in to Paris, and started his running and sweating out again, and him and I were the whole stable gang. Our horse's name was Gilford, he was Irish bred and a nice, sweet jumper. My old man figured that training him and riding him, himself, he was a good investment. I was proud of everything and I thought Gilford was as good a horse as Kzar. He was a good, solid jumper, a bay, with plenty of speed on the flat, if you asked him for it, and he was a nice-looking horse, too.

Gee, I was fond of him. The first time he started with my old man up, he finished third in a 2500 meter hurdle race and when my old man got off him, all sweating and happy in the place stall, and went in to weigh, I felt as proud of him as though it was the first race he'd ever placed in. You see, when a guy ain't been riding for a long time, you can't make yourself really believe that he has ever rode. The whole thing was different now, 'cause down in Milan, even big races never seemed to make any difference to my old man, if he won he wasn't ever excited or anything, and now it was so I couldn't hardly sleep the night before a race and I knew my old man was excited, too, even if he didn't show it. Riding for yourself makes an awful difference.

Second time Gilford and my old man started, was a rainy Sunday at Auteuil, in the Prix du Marat, a 4500 meter steeplechase. As soon as he'd gone out I beat it up in the stand with the new glasses my old man had bought for me to watch them. They started way over at the far end of the course and there was some trouble at the barrier. Something with goggle blinders on was making a great fuss and rearing around and busted the barrier once, but I could see my old man in our black jacket, with a white cross and a black cap, sitting up on Gilford, and patting him with his hand. Then they were off in a jump and out of sight behind the trees and the gong going for dear life and the pari-mutuel wickets rattling down. Gosh, I was so excited, I was afraid to look at them, but I fixed the glasses on the place where they would come out back of the trees and then out they came with the old black jacket going third and they all sailing over the jump like birds. Then they went out of sight again and then they came pounding out and down the hill and all going nice and sweet and easy and taking the fence smooth in a bunch, and moving away from us all solid. Looked as though you could walk across on their backs they were all so bunched and going so smooth. Then they bellied over the big double Bullfinch and something came down. I couldn't see who it was, but in a minute the horse was up and galloping free and the field, all bunched still, sweeping around the long left turn into the straightaway. They jumped the stone wall and came jammed down the stretch toward the big water-jump right in front of the stands. I saw them coming and hollered at my old man as he went by, and he was leading by about a length and riding way out, and light as a monkey, and they were racing for the water-jump. They took off over the big hedge of the water-jump in a pack and then there was a crash, and two horses pulled sideways out off it, and kept on going, and three others were piled up. I couldn't see my old man anywhere. One horse kneed himself up and the jock had hold of the bridle and mounted and went slamming on after the place money. The other horse was up and away by himself, jerking his head and galloping with the bridle rein hanging and the jock staggered over to one side of the track against the fence. Then Gilford rolled over to one side off my old man and got up and started to run on three legs with his front off hoof dangling and there was my old man laying there on the grass flat out with his face up and blood all over the side of his head. I ran down the stand and bumped into a jam of people and got to the rail and a cop grabbed me and held me and two big stretcher-bearers were going out after my old man and around on the other side of the course I saw three horses, strung way out, coming out of the trees and taking the jump.

My old man was dead when they brought him in and while a doctor was listening to his heart with a thing plugged in his ears, I heard a shot up the track that meant they'd killed Gilford. I lay down beside my old man, when they carried the stretcher into the hospital room, and hung onto the stretcher and cried and cried, and he looked so white and gone and so awfully dead, and I couldn't help feeling that if my old man was dead maybe they didn't need to have shot Gilford. His hoof might have got well. I don't know. I loved my old man so much.

Then a couple of guys came in and one of them patted me on the back and then went over and looked at my old man and then pulled a sheet off the cot and spread it over him; and the other was telephoning in French for them to send the ambulance to take him out to Maisons. And I couldn't stop crying, crying and choking, sort of, and George Gardner came in and sat down beside me on the floor and put his arm around me and says, "Come on, Joe, old boy. Get up and we'll go out and wait for the ambulance."

George and I went out to the gate and I was trying to stop bawling and George wiped off my face with his handkerchief and we were standing back a little ways while the crowd was going out of the gate and a couple of guys stopped near us while we were waiting for the crowd to get through the gate and one of them was counting a bunch of mutuel tickets and he said, "Well, Butler got his, all right."

The other guy said, "I don't give a good goddam if he did, the crook. He had it coming to him on the stuff he's pulled."

"I'll say he had," said the other guy, and tore the bunch of tickets in two.

And George Gardner looked at me to see if I'd heard and I had all right and he said, "Don't you listen to what those bums said, Joe. Your old man was one swell guy."

But I don't know. Seems like when they get started they don't leave a guy nothing.

Chapter 14

Maera lay still, his head on his arms, his face in the sand. He felt warm and sticky from the bleeding. Each time he felt the horn coming. Sometimes the bull only bumped him with his head. Once the horn went all the way through him and he felt it go into the sand. Some one had the bull by the tail. They were swearing at him and flopping the cape in his face. Then the bull was gone. Some men picked Maera up and started to run with him toward the barriers through the gate out the passageway around under the grandstand to the infirmary. They laid Maera down on a cot and one of the men went out for the doctor. The others stood around. The doctor came running from the corral where he had been sewing up picador horses. He had to stop and wash his hands. There was a great shouting going on in the grandstand overhead. Maera felt everything getting larger and larger and then smaller and smaller. Then it got larger and larger and larger and then smaller and smaller. Then everything commenced to run faster and faster as when they speed up a cinematograph film. Then he was dead.

Big Two-Hearted River: Part I

THE train went on up the track out of sight, around one of the hills of burnt timber. Nick sat down on the bundle of canvas and bedding the baggage man had pitched out of the door of the baggage car. There was no town, nothing but the rails and the burned-over country. The thirteen saloons that had lined the one street of Seney had not left a trace. The foundations of the Mansion House hotel stuck up above the ground. The stone was chipped and split by the fire. It was all that was left of the town of Seney. Even the surface had been burned off the ground.

Nick looked at the burned-over stretch of hillside, where he had expected to find the scattered houses of the town and then walked down the railroad track to the bridge over the river. The river was there. It swirled against the log spiles of the bridge. Nick looked down into the clear, brown water, colored from the pebbly bottom, and watched the trout keeping themselves steady in the current with wavering fins. As he watched them they changed their positions by quick angles, only to hold steady in the fast water again. Nick watched them a long time.

He watched them holding themselves with their noses into the current, many trout in deep, fast moving water, slightly distorted as he watched far down through the glassy convex surface of the pool, its surface pushing and swelling smooth against the resistance of the log-driven piles of the bridge. At the bottom of the pool were the big trout. Nick did not see them at first. Then he saw them at the bottom of the pool, big trout looking to hold themselves on the gravel bottom in a varying mist of gravel and sand, raised in spurts by the current.

Nick looked down into the pool from the bridge. It was a hot day. A kingfisher flew up the stream. It was a long time since Nick had looked into a stream and seen trout. They were very satisfactory. As the shadow of the kingfisher moved up the stream, a big trout shot upstream in a long angle, only his shadow marking the angle, then lost his shadow as he came through the surface of the water, caught the sun, and then, as he went back into the stream under the surface, his shadow seemed to float down the stream with the current, unresisting, to his post under the bridge where he tightened facing up into the current.

Nick's heart tightened as the trout moved. He felt all the old feeling.

He turned and looked down the stream. It stretched away, pebbly-bottomed with shallows and big boulders and a deep pool as it curved away around the foot of a bluff.

Nick walked back up the ties to where his pack lay in the cinders beside the railway track. He was happy. He adjusted the pack harness around the bundle, pulling straps tight, slung the pack on his back, got his arms through the shoulder straps and took some of the pull off his shoulders by leaning his forehead against the wide band of the tump-line. Still, it was too heavy. It was much too heavy. He had his leather rod-case in his hand and leaning forward to keep the weight of the pack high on his shoulders he walked along the road that paralleled the railway track, leaving the burned town behind in the heat, and then turned off around a hill with a high, fire-scarred hill on either side onto a road that went back into the country. He walked along the road feeling the ache from the pull of the heavy pack. The road climbed steadily. It was hard work walking up-hill. His muscles ached and the day was hot, but Nick felt happy. He felt he had left everything behind, the need for thinking, the need to write, other needs. It was all back of him.

From the time he had gotten down off the train and the baggage man had thrown his pack out of the open car door things had been different. Seney was burned, the country was burned over and changed, but it did not matter. It could not all be burned. He knew that. He hiked along the road, sweating in the sun, climbing to cross the range of hills that separated the railway from the pine plains.

The road ran on, dipping occasionally, but always climbing. Nick went on up. Finally the road after going parallel to the burnt hillside reached the top. Nick leaned back against a stump and slipped out of the pack harness. Ahead of him, as far as he could see, was the pine plain. The burned country stopped off at the left with the range of hills. On ahead islands of dark pine trees rose out of the plain. Far off to the left was the line of the river. Nick followed it with his eye and caught glints of the water in the sun.

There was nothing but the pine plain ahead of him, until the far blue hills that marked the Lake Superior height of land. He could hardly see them, faint and far away in the heat-light over the plain. If he looked too steadily they were gone. But if he only half-looked they were there, the far-off hills of the height of land.

Nick sat down against the charred stump and smoked a cigarette. His pack balanced on the top of the stump, harness holding ready, a hollow molded in it from his back. Nick sat smoking, looking out over the country. He did not need to get his map out. He knew where he was from the position of the river.

As he smoked, his legs stretched out in front of him, he noticed a grasshopper walk along the ground and up onto his woolen sock. The grasshopper was black. As he had walked along the road, climbing, he had started many grasshoppers from the dust. They were all black. They were not the big grasshoppers with yellow and black or red and black wings whirring out from their black wing sheathing as they fly up. These were just ordinary hoppers, but all a sooty black in color. Nick had wondered about them as he walked, without really thinking about them. Now, as he watched the black hopper that was nibbling at the wool of his sock with its fourway lip, he realized that they had all turned black from living in the burned-over land. He realized that the fire must have come the year before, but the grasshoppers were all black now. He wondered how long they would stay that way.

Carefully he reached his hand down and took hold of the hopper by the wings. He turned him up, all his legs walking in the air, and looked at his jointed belly. Yes, it was black too, iridescent where the back and head were dusty.

"Go on, hopper," Nick said, speaking out loud for the first time. "Fly away somewhere."

He tossed the grasshopper up into the air and watched him sail away to a charcoal stump across the road.

Nick stood up. He leaned his back against the weight of his pack where it rested upright on the stump and got his arms through the shoulder straps. He stood with the pack on his back on the brow of the hill looking out across the country, toward the distant river and then struck down the hillside away from the road. Underfoot the ground was good walking. Two hundred yards down the hillside the fire line stopped. Then it was sweet fern, growing ankle high, to walk through, and clumps of jack pines; a long undulating country with frequent rises and descents, sandy underfoot and the country alive again.

Nick kept his direction by the sun. He knew where he wanted to strike the river and he kept on through the pine plain, mounting small rises to see other rises ahead of him and sometimes from the top of a rise a great solid island of pines off to his right or his left. He broke off some sprigs of the heathery sweet fern, and put them under his pack straps. The chafing crushed it and he smelled it as he walked.

He was tired and very hot, walking across the uneven, shadeless pine plain. At any time he knew he could strike the river by turning off to his left. It could not be more than a mile away. But he kept on toward the north to hit the river as far upstream as he could go in one day's walking.

For some time as he walked Nick had been in sight of one of the big islands of pine standing out above the rolling high ground he was crossing. He dipped down and then as he came slowly up to the crest of the bridge he turned and made toward the pine trees.

There was no underbrush in the island of pine trees. The trunks of the trees went straight up or slanted toward each other. The trunks were straight and brown without branches. The branches were high above. Some interlocked to make a solid shadow on the brown forest floor. Around the grove of trees was a bare space. It was brown and soft underfoot as Nick walked on it. This was the over-lapping of the pine needle floor, extending out beyond the width of the high branches. The trees had grown tall and the branches moved high, leaving in the sun this bare space they had once covered with shadow. Sharp at the edge of this extension of the forest floor commenced the sweet fern.

Nick slipped off his pack and lay down in the shade. He lay on his back and looked up into the pine trees. His neck and back and the small of his back rested as he stretched. The earth felt good against his back. He looked up at the sky, through the branches, and then shut his eyes. He opened them and looked up again. There was a wind high up in the branches. He shut his eyes again and went to sleep.

Nick woke stiff and cramped. The sun was nearly down. His pack was heavy and the straps painful as he lifted it on. He leaned over with the pack on and picked up the leather rod-case and started out from the pine trees across the sweet fern swale, toward the river He knew it could not be more than a mile.

He came down a hillside covered with stumps into a meadow At the edge of the meadow flowed the river. Nick was glad to get to the river. He walked upstream through the meadow. His trousers were soaked with the dew as he walked. After the hot day, the dew had come quickly and heavily. The river made no sound. It was too fast and smooth. At the edge of the meadow, before he mounted to a piece of high ground to make camp, Nick looked down the river at the trout rising. They were rising to insects come from the swamp on the other side of the stream when the sun went down. The trout jumped out of water to take them. While Nick walked through the little stretch of meadow alongside the stream, trout had jumped high out of water. Now as he looked down the river, the insects must be settling on the surface, for the trout were feeding steadily all down the stream. As far down the long stretch as he could see, the trout were rising, making circles all down the surface of the water, as though it were starting to rain.

The ground rose, wooded and sandy, to overlook the meadow, the stretch of river and the swamp. Nick dropped his pack and rod-case and looked for a level piece of ground. He was very hungry and he wanted to make his camp before he cooked. Between two jack pines, the ground was quite level. He took the ax out of the pack and chopped out two projecting roots. That leveled a piece of ground large enough to sleep on. He smoothed out the sandy soil with his hand and pulled all the sweet fern bushes by their roots. His hands smelled good from the sweet fern. He smoothed the uprooted earth. He did not want anything making lumps under the blankets. When he had the ground smooth, he spread his three blankets. One he folded double, next to the ground. The other two he spread on top.

With the ax he slit off a bright slab of pine from one of the stumps and split it into pegs for the tent. He wanted them long and solid to hold in the ground. With the tent unpacked and spread on the ground, the pack, leaning against a jackpine, looked much smaller. Nick tied the rope that served the tent for a ridge-pole to the trunk of one of the pine trees and pulled the tent up off the ground with the other end of the rope and tied it to the other pine. The tent hung on the rope like a canvas blanket on a clothesline. Nick poked a pole he had cut up under the back peak of the canvas and then made it a tent by pegging out the sides. He pegged the sides out taut and drove the pegs deep, hitting them down into the ground with the flat of the ax until the rope loops were buried and the canvas was drum tight.

Across the open mouth of the tent Nick fixed cheesecloth to keep out mosquitoes. He crawled inside under the mosquito bar with various things from the pack to put at the head of the bed under the slant of the canvas. Inside the tent the light came through the brown canvas. It smelled pleasantly of canvas. Already there was something mysterious and homelike. Nick was happy as he crawled inside the tent. He had not been unhappy all day. This was different though. Now things were done. There had been this to do. Now it was done. It had been a hard trip. He was very tired. That was done. He had made his camp. He was settled. Nothing could touch him. It was a good place to camp. He was there, in the good place. He was in his home where he had made it. Now he was hungry.

He came out, crawling under the cheesecloth. It was quite dark outside. It was lighter in the tent.

Nick went over to the pack and found, with his fingers, a long nail in a paper sack of nails, in the bottom of the pack. He drove it into the pine tree, holding it close and hitting it gently with the flat of the ax. He hung the pack up on the nail. All his supplies were in the pack. There were off the ground and sheltered now.

Nick was hungry. He did not believe he had ever been hungrier. He opened and emptied a can of pork and beans and a can of spaghetti into the frying pan.

"I've got a right to eat this kind of stuff, if I'm willing to carry it," Nick said. His voice sounded strange in the darkening woods. He did not speak again.

He started a fire with some chunks of pine he got with the ax from a stump. Over the fire he stuck a wire grill, pushing the four legs down into the ground with his boot. Nick put the frying pan on the grill over the flames. He was hungrier. The beans and spaghetti warmed. Nick stirred them and mixed them together. They began to bubble, making little bubbles that rose with difficulty to the surface. There was a good smell. Nick got out a bottle of tomato catchup and cut four slices of bread. The little bubbles were coming faster now. Nick sat down beside the fire and lifted the frying pan off. He poured about half the contents out into the tin plate. It spread slowly on the plate. Nick knew it was too hot. He poured on some tomato catchup. He knew the beans and spaghetti were still too hot. He looked at the fire, then at the tent, he was not going to spoil it all by burning his tongue. For years he had never enjoyed fried bananas because he had never been able to wait for them to cool. His tongue was very sensitive. He was very hungry. Across the river in the swamp, in the almost dark, he saw a mist rising. He looked at the tent once more. All right. He took a full spoonful from the plate.

"Chrise," Nick said, "Geezus Chrise," he said happily.

He ate the whole plateful before he remembered the bread. Nick finished the second plateful with the bread, mopping the plate shiny. He had not eaten since a cup of coffee and a ham sandwich in the station restaurant at St. Ignace. It had been a very fine experience. He had been that hungry before, but had not been able to satisfy it. He could have made camp hours before if he had wanted to. There were plenty of good places to camp on the river. But this was good.

Nick tucked two big chips of pine under the grill. The fire flared up. He had forgotten to get water for the coffee. Out of the pack he got a folding canvas bucket and walked down the hill, across the edge of the meadow, to the stream. The other bank was in the white mist. The grass was wet and cold as he knelt on the bank and dipped the canvas bucket into the stream. It bellied and pulled hard in the current. The water was ice cold. Nick rinsed the bucket and carried it full up to the camp. Up away from the stream it was not so cold.

Nick drove another big nail and hung up the bucket full of water. He dipped the coffee pot half full, put some more chips under the grill onto the fire and put the pot on. He could not remember which way he made coffee. He could remember an argument about it with Hopkins, but not which side he had taken. He decided to bring it to a boil. He remembered now that was Hopkins's way. He had once argued about everything with Hopkins. While he waited for the coffee to boil, he opened a small can of apricots. He liked to open cans. He emptied the can of apricots out into a tin cup. While he watched the coffee on the fire, he drank the juice syrup of the apricots, carefully at first to keep from spilling, then meditatively, sucking the apricots down. They were better than fresh apricots.

The coffee boiled as he watched. The lid came up and coffee and grounds ran down the side of the pot. Nick took it off the grill. It was a triumph for Hopkins. He put sugar in the empty apricot cup and poured some of the coffee out to cool. It was too hot to pour and he used his hat to hold the handle of the coffee pot. He would not let it steep in the pot at all. Not the first cup. It should be straight Hopkins all the way. Hop deserved that. He was a very serious coffee drinker. He was the most serious man Nick had ever known. Not heavy, serious. That was a long time ago. Hopkins spoke without moving his lips. He had played polo. He made millions of dollars in Texas. He had borrowed carfare to go to Chicago, when the wire came that his first big well had come in. He could have wired for money. That would have been too slow. They called Hop's girl the Blonde Venus. Hop did not mind because she was not his real girl. Hopkins said very confidently that none of them would make fun of his real girl. He was right. Hopkins went away when the telegram came. That was on the Black River. It took eight days for the telegram to reach him. Hopkins gave away his .22 caliber Colt automatic pistol to Nick. He gave his camera to Bill. It was to remember him always by. They were all going fishing again next summer. The Hop Head was rich. He would get a yacht and they would all cruise along the north shore of Lake Superior. He was excited but serious. They said good-bye and all felt bad. It broke up the trip. They never saw Hopkins again. That was a long time ago on the Black River.

Nick drank the coffee, the coffee according to Hopkins. The coffee was bitter. Nick laughed. It made a good ending to the story. His mind was starting to work. He knew he could choke it because he was tired enough. He spilled the coffee out of the pot and shook the grounds loose into the fire. He lit a cigarette and went inside the tent. He took off his shoes and trousers, sitting on the blankets, rolled the shoes up inside the trousers for a pillow and got in between the blankets.

Out through the front of the tent he watched the glow of the fire, when the night wind blew on it. It was a quiet night. The swamp was perfectly quiet. Nick stretched under the blanket comfortably. A mosquito hummed close to his ear. Nick sat up and lit a match.

The mosquito was on the canvas, over his head. Nick moved the match quickly up to it. The mosquito made a satisfactory hiss in the flame. The match went out. Nick lay down again under the blanket. He turned on his side and shut his eyes. He was sleepy. He felt sleep coming. He curled up under the blanket and went to sleep.

Chapter 15

They hanged Sam Cardinella at six o'clock in the morning in the corridor of the county jail. The corridor was high and narrow with tiers of cells on either side. All the cells were occupied. The men had been brought in for the hanging. Five men sentenced to be hanged were in the five top cells. Three of the men to be hanged were negroes. They were very frightened. One of the white men sat on his cot with his head in his hands. The other lay flat on his cot with a blanket wrapped around his head.

They came out onto the gallows through a door in the wall. There were seven of them including two priests. They were carrying Sam Cardinella. He had been like that since about four o'clock in the morning.

While they were strapping his legs together two guards held him up and the two priests were whispering to him. "Be a man, my son," said one priest. When they came toward him with the cap to go over his head Sam Cardinella lost control of his sphincter muscle. The guards who had been holding him up both dropped him. They were both disgusted. "How about a chair, Will?" asked one of the guards. "Better get one," said a man in a derby hat.

When they all stepped back on the scaffolding back of the drop, which was very heavy, built of oak and steel and swung on ball bearings, Sam Cardinella was left sitting there strapped tight, the younger of the two priests kneeling beside the chair. The priest skipped back onto the scaffolding just before the drop fell.

117

Big Two-Hearted River: Part II

In the morning the sun was up and the tent was starting to get hot, Nick crawled out under the mosquito netting stretched across the mouth of the tent, to look at the morning. The grass was wet on his hands as he came out. He held his trousers and his shoes in his hands. The sun was just up over the hill. There was the meadow, the river and the swamp. There were birch trees in the green of the swamp on the other side of the river.

The river was clear and smoothly fast in the early morning. Down about two hundred yards were three logs all the way across the stream. They made the water smooth and deep above them. As Nick watched, a mink crossed the river on the logs and went into the swamp. Nick was excited. He was excited by the early morning and the river. He was really too hurried to eat breakfast, but he knew he must. He built a little fire and put on the coffee pot.

While the water was heating in the pot he took an empty bottle and went down over the edge of the high ground to the meadow. The meadow was wet with dew and Nick wanted to catch grasshoppers for bait before the sun dried the grass. He found plenty of good grasshoppers. They were at the base of the grass stems. Sometimes they clung to a grass stem. They were cold and wet with the dew, and could not jump until the sun warmed them. Nick picked them up, taking only the medium-sized brown ones, and put them into the bottle. He turned over a log and just under the shelter of the edge were several hundred hoppers. It was a grasshopper lodging house. Nick put about fifty of the medium browns into the bottle. While he was picking up the hoppers the others warmed in the sun and commenced to hop away. They flew when they hopped. At first they made one flight and stayed stiff when they landed, as though they were dead.

Nick knew that by the time he was through with breakfast they would be as lively as ever. Without dew in the grass it would take him all day to catch a bottle full of good grasshoppers and he would have to crush many of them, slamming at them with his hat. He washed his hands at the stream. He was excited to be near it. Then he walked up to the tent. The hoppers were already jumping stiffly in the grass. In the bottle, warmed by the sun, they were jumping in a mass. Nick put in a pine stick as a cork. It plugged the mouth of the bottle enough, so the hoppers could not get out and left plenty of air passage.

He had rolled the log back and knew he could get grasshoppers there every morning.

Nick laid the bottle full of jumping grasshoppers against a pine trunk. Rapidly he mixed some buckwheat flour with water and stirred it smooth, one cup of flour, one cup of water. He put a handful of coffee in the pot and dipped a lump of grease out of a can and slid it sputtering across the hot skillet. On the smoking skillet he poured smoothly the buckwheat batter. It spread like lava, the grease spitting sharply. Around the edges the buckwheat cake began to firm, then brown, then crisp. The surface was bubbling slowly to porousness. Nick pushed under the browned under surface with a fresh pine chip. He shook the skillet sideways and the cake was loose on the surface. I won't try and flop it, he thought. He slid the chip of clean wood all the way under the cake, and flopped it over onto its face. It sputtered in the pan.

When it was cooked Nick regreased the skillet. He used all the batter. It made another big flapjack and one smaller one.

Nick ate a big flapjack and a smaller one, covered with apple butter. He put apple butter on the third cake, folded it over twice, wrapped it in oiled paper and put it in his shirt pocket. He put the apple butter jar back in the pack and cut bread for two sandwiches.

In the pack he found a big onion. He sliced it in two and peeled the silky outer skin. Then he cut one half into slices and made onion sandwiches. He wrapped them in oiled paper and buttoned them in the other pocket of his khaki shirt. He turned the skillet upside down on the grill, drank the coffee, sweetened and yellow brown with the condensed milk in it, and tidied up the camp. It was a good camp.

Nick took his fly rod out of the leather rod-case, jointed it, and shoved the rod-case back into the tent. He put on the reel and threaded the line through the guides. He had to hold it from hand to hand, as he threaded it, or it would slip back through its own weight. It was a heavy, double tapered fly line. Nick had paid eight dollars for it a long time ago. It was made heavy to lift back in the air and come forward flat and heavy and straight to make it possible to cast a fly which has no weight. Nick opened the aluminum leader box. The leaders were coiled between the damp flannel pads. Nick had wet the pads at the water cooler on the train up to St. Ignace. In the damp pads the gut leaders had softened and Nick unrolled one and tied it by a loop at the end to the heavy fly line. He fastened a hook on the end of the leader. It was a small hook; very thin and springy.

Nick took it from his hook book, sitting with the rod across his laps. He tested the knot and the spring of the rod by pulling the line taut. It was a good feeling. He was careful not to let the hook bite into his finger.

He started down to the stream, holding his rod, the bottle of grasshoppers hung from his neck by a thong tied in half hitches around the neck of the bottle. His landing net hung by a hook from his belt. Over his shoulder was a long flour sack tied at each corner into an ear. The cord went over his shoulder. The sack flapped against his legs.

Nick felt awkward and professionally happy with all his equipment hanging from him. The grasshopper bottle swung against his chest. In his shirt the breast pockets bulged against him with the lunch and his fly book.

He stepped into the stream. It was a shock. His trousers clung tight to his legs. His shoes felt the gravel. The water was a rising cold shock.

Rushing, the current sucked against his legs. Where he stepped in, the water was over his knees. He waded with the current. The gravel slid under his shoes. He looked down at the swirl of water below each leg and tipped up the bottle to get a grasshopper.

The first grasshopper gave a jump in the neck of the bottle and went out into the water. He was sucked under in the whirl by Nick's right leg and came to the surface a little way down stream. He floated rapidly, kicking. In a quick circle, breaking the smooth surface of the water, he disappeared. A trout had taken him.

Another hopper poked his face out of the bottle. His antennæ wavered. He was getting his front legs out of the bottle to jump. Nick took him by the head and held him while he threaded the slim

hook under his chin, down through his thorax and into the last
segments of his abdomen. The grasshopper took hold of the hook
with his front feet, spitting tobacco juice on it. Nick dropped him
into the water.

Holding the rod in his right hand he let out line against the
pull of the grasshopper in the current. He stripped off line from the
reel with his left hand and let it run free. He could see the hopper
in the little waves of the current. It went out of sight.

There was a tug on the line. Nick pulled against the taut line.
It was his first strike. Holding the now living rod across the current,
he brought in the line with his left hand. The rod bent in jerks, the
trout pumping against the current. Nick knew it was a small one.
He lifted the rod straight up in the air. It bowed with the pull.

He saw the trout in the water jerking with his head and body
against the shifting tangent of the line in the stream.

Nick took the line in his left hand and pulled the trout, thump-
ing tiredly against the current, to the surface. His back was mottled
the clear, water-over-gravel color, his side flashing in the sun. The rod
under his right arm, Nick stooped, dipping his right hand into the
current. He held the trout, never still, with his moist right hand,
while he unhooked the barb from his mouth, then dropped him back
into the stream.

He hung unsteadily in the current, then settled to the bottom
beside a stone. Nick reached down his hand to touch him, his arm to
the elbow under water. The trout was steady in the moving stream,
resting on the gravel, beside a stone. As Nick's fingers touched him,
touched his smooth, cool, underwater feeling he was gone, gone in a
shadow across the bottom of the stream.

He's all right, Nick thought. He was only tired.

He had wet his hand before he touched the trout, so he would
not disturb the delicate mucus that covered him. If a trout was
touched with a dry hand, a white fungus attacked the unprotected
spot. Years before when he had fished crowded streams, with fly
fishermen ahead of him and behind him, Nick had again and again
come on dead trout, furry with white fungus, drifted against a rock,
or floating belly up in some pool. Nick did not like to fish with other
men on the river. Unless they were of your party, they spoiled it.

He wallowed down the stream, above his knees in the current,
through the fifty yards of shallow water above the pile of logs that

crossed the stream. He did not rebait his hook and held it in his hand as he waded. He was certain he could catch small trout in the shallows, but he did not want them. There would be no big trout in the shallows this time of day.

Now the water deepened up his thighs sharply and coldly. Ahead was the smooth dammed-back flood of water above the logs. The water was smooth and dark; on the left, the lower edge of the meadow; on the right the swamp.

Nick leaned back against the current and took a hopper from the bottle. He threaded the hopper on the hook and spat on him for good luck. Then he pulled several yards of line from the reel and tossed the hopper out ahead onto the fast, dark water. It floated down towards the logs, then the weight of the line pulled the bait under the surface. Nick held the rod in his right hand, letting the line run out through his fingers.

There was a long tug. Nick struck and the rod came alive and dangerous, bent double, the line tightening, coming out of water, tightening, all in a heavy, dangerous, steady pull. Nick felt the moment when the leader would break if the strain increased and let the line go.

The reel ratcheted into a mechanical shriek as the line went out in a rush. Too fast. Nick could not check it, the line rushing out, the reel note rising as the line ran out.

With the core of the reel showing, his heart feeling stopped with the excitement, leaning back against the current that mounted icily his thighs, Nick thumbed the reel hard with his left hand. It was awkward getting his thumb inside the fly reel frame.

As he put on pressure the line tightened into sudden hardness and beyond the logs a huge trout went high out of water. As he jumped, Nick lowered the tip of the rod. But he felt, as he dropped the tip to ease the strain, the moment when the strain was too great; the hardness too tight. Of course, the leader had broken. There was no mistaking the feeling when all spring left the line and it became dry and hard. Then it went slack.

His mouth dry, his heart down, Nick reeled in. He had never seen so big a trout. There was a heaviness, a power not to be held, and then the bulk of him, as he jumped. He looked as broad as a salmon.

Nick's hand was shaky. He reeled in slowly. The thrill had been

too much. He felt, vaguely, a little sick, as though it would be better
to sit down.

The leader had broken where the hook was tied to it. Nick took
it in his hand. He thought of the trout somewhere on the bottom,
holding himself steady over the gravel, far down below the light,
under the logs, with the hook in his jaw. Nick knew the trout's teeth
would cut through the snell of the hook. The hook would imbed
itself in his jaw. He'd bet the trout was angry. Anything that size
would be angry. That was a trout. He had been solidly hooked. Solid
as a rock. He felt like a rock, too, before he started off. By God, he
was a big one. By God, he was the biggest one I ever heard of.

Nick climbed out onto the meadow and stood, water running
down his trousers and out of his shoes, his shoes squlchy. He went
over and sat on the logs. He did not want to rush his sensations any.

He wriggled his toes in the water, in his shoes, and got out a
cigarette from his breast pocket. He lit it and tossed the match into
the fast water below the logs. A tiny trout rose at the match, as it
swung around in the fast current. Nick laughed. He would finish
the cigarette.

He sat on the logs, smoking, drying in the sun, the sun warm
on his back, the river shallow ahead entering the woods, curving into
the woods, shallows, light glittering, big water-smooth rocks, cedars
along the bank and white birches, the logs warm in the sun, smooth
to sit on, without bark, gray to the touch; slowly the feeling of disappointment left him. It went away slowly, the feeling of disappoint-
ment that came sharply after the thrill that made his shoulders ache.
It was all right now. His rod lying out on the logs, Nick tied a new
hook on the leader, pulling the gut tight until it grimped into itself
in a hard knot.

He baited up, then picked up the rod and walked to the far end
of the logs to get into the water, where it was not too deep. Under
and beyond the logs was a deep pool. Nick walked around the shallow
shelf near the swamp shore until he came out on the shallow bed of
the stream.

On the left, where the meadow ended and the woods began, a
great elm tree was uprooted. Gone over in a storm, it lay back into
the woods, its roots clotted with dirt, grass growing in them, rising a
solid bank beside the stream. The river cut to the edge of the uprooted tree. From where Nick stood he could see deep channels, like

ruts, cut in the shallow bed of the stream by the flow of the current. Pebbly where he stood and pebbly and full of boulders beyond; where it curved near the tree roots, the bed of the stream was marly and between the ruts of deep water green weed fronds swung in the current.

Nick swung the rod back over his shoulder and forward, and the line, curving forward, laid the grasshopper down on one of the deep channels in the weeds. A trout struck and Nick hooked him.

Holding the rod far out toward the uprooted tree and sloshing backward in the current, Nick worked the trout, plunging, the rod bending alive, out of the danger of the weeds into the open river. Holding the rod, pumping alive against the current, Nick brought the trout in. He rushed, but always came, the spring of the rod yielding to the rushes, sometimes jerking under water, but always bringing him in. Nick eased downstream with the rushes. The rod above his head he led the trout over the net, then lifted.

The trout hung heavy in the net, mottled trout back and silver sides in the meshes. Nick unhooked him; heavy sides, good to hold, big undershot jaw, and slipped him, heaving and big sliding, into the long sack that hung from his shoulders in the water.

Nick spread the mouth of the sack against the current and it filled, heavy with water. He held it up, the bottom in the stream, and the water poured out through the sides. Inside at the bottom was the big trout, alive in the water.

Nick moved downstream. The sack out ahead of him sunk heavy in the water, pulling from his shoulders.

It was getting hot, the sun hot on the back of his neck.

Nick had one good trout. He did not care about getting many trout. Now the stream was shallow and wide. There were trees along both banks. The trees of the left bank made short shadows on the current in the forenoon sun. Nick knew there were trout in each shadow. In the afternoon, after the sun had crossed toward the hills, the trout would be in the cool shadows on the other side of the stream.

The very biggest ones would lie up close to the bank. You could always pick them up there on the Black. When the sun was down they all moved out into the current. Just when the sun made the water blinding in the glare before it went down, you were liable to strike a big trout anywhere in the current. It was almost impossible to fish then, the surface of the water was blinding as a mirror in the sun. Of course, you could fish upstream, but in a stream like the Black, or this, you had to wallow against the current and in a deep place, the water piled up on you. It was no fun to fish upstream with this much current.

Nick moved along through the shallow stretch watching the banks for deep holes. A beech tree grew close beside the river, so that the branches hung down into the water. The stream went back in under the leaves. There were always trout in a place like that.

Nick did not care about fishing that hole. He was sure he would get hooked in the branches.

It looked deep though. He dropped the grasshopper so the current took it under water, back in under the overhanging branch. The line pulled hard and Nick struck. The trout threshed heavily, half out of water in the leaves and branches. The line was caught. Nick pulled hard and the trout was off. He reeled in and holding the hook in his hand, walked down the stream.

Ahead, close to the left bank, was a big log. Nick saw it was hollow; pointing up river the current entered it smoothly, only a little ripple spread each side of the log. The water was deepening. The top of the hollow log was gray and dry. It was partly in the shadow.

Nick took the cork out of the grasshopper bottle and a hopper clung to it. He picked him off, hooked him and tossed him out. He held the rod far out so that the hopper on the water moved into the current flowing into the hollow log. Nick lowered the rod and the hopper floated in. There was a heavy strike. Nick swung the rod against the pull. It felt as though he were hooked into the log itself, except for the live feeling.

He tried to force the fish out into the current. It came, heavily.

The line went slack and Nick thought the trout was gone. Then he saw him, very near, in the current, shaking his head, trying to get the hook out. His mouth was clamped shut. He was fighting the hook in the clear flowing current.

Looping in the line with his left hand, Nick swung the rod to make the line taut and tried to lead the trout toward the net, but he was gone, out of sight, the line pumping. Nick fought him against the current, letting him thump in the water against the spring of the rod. He shifted the rod to his left hand, worked the trout upstream, holding his weight, fighting on the rod, and then let him down into the net. He lifted him clear of the water, a heavy half circle in the net, the net dripping, unhooked him and slid him into the sack.

He spread the mouth of the sack and looked down in at the two big trout alive in the water.

Through the deepening water, Nick waded over to the hollow log. He took the sack off, over his head, the trout flopping as it came out of water, and hung it so the trout were deep in the water. Then he pulled himself up on the log and sat, the water from his trouser and boots running down into the stream. He laid his rod down, moved along to the shady end of the log and took the sandwiches out of his pocket. He dipped the sandwiches in the cold water. The current carried away the crumbs. He ate the sandwiches and dipped his hat full of water to drink, the water running out through his hat just ahead of his drinking.

It was cool in the shade, sitting on the log. He took a cigarette out and struck a match to light it. The match sunk into the gray wood, making a tiny furrow. Nick leaned over the side of the log, found a hard place and lit the match. He sat smoking and watching the river.

Ahead the river narrowed and went into a swamp. The river became smooth and deep and the swamp looked solid with cedar trees, their trunks close together, their branches solid. It would not be possible to walk through a swamp like that. The branches grew so low. You would have to keep almost level with the ground to move at all. You could not crash through the branches. That must be why the animals that lived in swamps were built the way they were, Nick thought.

He wished he had brought something to read. He felt like reading. He did not feel like going on into the swamp. He looked down the river. A big cedar slanted all the way across the stream. Beyond that the river went into the swamp.

Nick did not want to go in there now. He felt a reaction against deep wading with the water deepening up under his armpits, to hook big trout in places impossible to land them. In the swamp the banks were bare, the big cedars came together overhead, the sun did not come through, except in patches; in the fast deep water, in the half light, the fishing would be tragic. In the swamp fishing was a tragic adventure. Nick did not want it. He did not want to go down the stream any further today.

He took out his knife, opened it and stuck it in the log. Then he pulled up the sack, reached into it and brought out one of the trout. Holding him near the tail, hard to hold, alive, in his hand, he whacked him against the log. The trout quivered, rigid. Nick laid him on the log in the shade and broke the neck of the other fish the same way. He laid them side by side on the log. They were fine trout.

Nick cleaned them, slitting them from the vent to the tip of the jaw. All the insides and the gills and tongue came out in one piece. They were both males; long gray-white strips of milt, smooth and clean. All the insides clean and compact, coming out all together. Nick tossed the offal ashore for the minks to find.

He washed the trout in the stream. When he held them back up in the water they looked like live fish. Their color was not gone yet. He washed his hands and dried them on the log. Then he laid the trout on the sack spread out on the log, rolled them up in it, tied the bundle and put it in the landing net. His knife was still standing, blade stuck in the log. He cleaned it on the wood and put it in his pocket.

Nick stood up on the log, holding his rod, the landing net hanging heavy, then stepped into the water and splashed ashore. He climbed the bank and cut up into the woods, toward the high ground. He was going back to camp. He looked back. The river just showed through the trees. There were plenty of days coming when he could fish the swamp.

L'Envoi

The king was working in the garden. He seemed very glad to see me. We walked through the garden. This is the queen, he said. She was clipping a rose bush. Oh how do you do, she said. We sat down at a table under a big tree and the king ordered whiskey and soda. We have good whiskey anyway, he said. The revolutionary committee, he told me, would not allow him to go outside the palace grounds. Plastiras is a very good man I believe, he said, but frightfully difficult. I think he did right though shooting those chaps. If Kerensky had shot a few men things might have been altogether different. Of course the great thing in this sort of an affair is not to be shot oneself!

It was very jolly. We talked for a long time. Like all Greeks he wanted to go to America.

❈ PART II ❈

THE GREAT WAR

A Natural History of the Dead

İt has always seemed to me that the war has been omitted as a field for the observations of the naturalist. We have charming and sound accounts of the flora and fauna of Patagonia by the late W. H. Hudson, the Reverend Gilbert White has written most interestingly of the Hoopoe on its occasional and not at all common visits to Selborne, and Bishop Stanley has given us a valuable, although popular, *Familiar History of Birds.* Can we not hope to furnish the reader with a few rational and interesting facts about the dead? I hope so.

When that persevering traveller, Mungo Park, was at one period of his course fainting in the vast wilderness of an African desert, naked and alone, considering his days as numbered and nothing appearing to remain for him to do but to lie down and die, a small moss-flower of extraordinary beauty caught his eye. "Though the whole plant," says he, "was no larger than one of my fingers, I could not contemplate the delicate conformation of its roots, leaves and capsules without admiration. Can that Being who planted, watered and brought to perfection, in this obscure part of the world, a thing which appears of so small importance, look with unconcern upon the situation and suffering of creatures formed after his own image? Surely not. Reflections like these would not allow me to despair; I started up and, disregarding both hunger and fatigue, travelled forward, assured that relief was at hand; and I was not disappointed."

With a disposition to wonder and adore in like manner, as Bishop Stanley says, can any branch of Natural History be studied without increasing that faith, love and hope which we also, every one of us, need in our journey through the wilderness of life? Let us therefore see what inspiration we may derive from the dead.

In war the dead are usually the male of the human species although this does not hold true with animals, and I have frequently seen dead mares among the horses. An interesting aspect of war, too, is that it is only there that the naturalist has an opportunity to observe the dead of mules. In twenty years of observation in civil life I had never seen a dead mule and had begun to entertain doubts as to whether these animals were really mortal. On rare occasions I had seen what I took to be dead mules, but on close approach these always proved to be living creatures who seemed to be dead through their quality of complete repose. But in war these animals succumb in much the same manner as the more common and less hardy horse.

Most of those mules that I saw dead were along mountain roads or lying at the foot of steep declivities whence they had been pushed to rid the road of their encumbrance. They seemed a fitting enough sight in the mountains where one was accustomed to their presence and looked less incongruous there than they did later, at Smyrna, where the Greeks broke the legs of all their baggage animals and pushed them off the quay into the shallow water to drown. The numbers of broken-legged mules and horses drowning in the shallow water called for a Goya to depict them. Although, speaking literally, one can hardly say that they called for a Goya since there has only been one Goya, long dead, and it is extremely doubtful if these animals, were they able to call, would call for pictorial representation of their plight but, more likely, would, if they were articulate, call for some one to alleviate their condition.

Regarding the sex of the dead it is a fact that one becomes so accustomed to the sight of all the dead being men that the sight of a dead woman is quite shocking. I first saw inversion of the usual sex of the dead after the explosion of a munition factory which had been situated in the countryside near Milan, Italy. We drove to the scene of the disaster in trucks along poplar-shaded roads, bordered with ditches containing much minute animal life, which I could not clearly observe because of the great clouds of dust raised by the trucks. Arriving where the munition plant had been, some of us were put to patrolling about those large stocks of munitions which for some reason had not exploded, while others were put at extinguishing a fire which had gotten into the grass of an adjacent field; which task being concluded, we were ordered to search the immediate vicinity and surrounding fields for bodies. We found and carried to an improvised mortuary a good number of these and, I must admit, frankly, the shock it was to find that these dead were women rather than men. In those days women had not yet commenced to wear their hair cut short, as they did later for several years in Europe and America, and the most disturbing thing, perhaps because it was the most unaccustomed, was the presence and, even more disturbing, the occasional absence of this long hair. I remember that after we had searched quite thoroughly for the complete dead we collected fragments. Many of these were detached from a heavy, barbed-wire fence which had surrounded the position of the factory and from the still existent portions of which we picked many of these detached bits which illustrated only too well the tremendous energy of high explosive. Many fragments we found a considerable distance away in the fields, they being carried farther by their own weight.

On our return to Milan I recall one or two of us discussing the occurrence and agreeing that the quality of unreality and the fact that there were no wounded did much to rob the disaster of a horror which might have been much greater. Also the fact that it had been so immediate and that the dead were in consequence still as little unpleasant as possible to carry and deal with made it quite removed from the usual battlefield experience. The pleasant, though dusty, ride through the beautiful Lombard countryside also was a compensation for the unpleasantness of the duty and on our return, while we exchanged impressions, we all agreed that it was indeed fortunate that the fire which broke out just before we arrived had been brought under control as rapidly as it had and before it had attained any of the seemingly huge stocks of unexploded munitions. We agreed too that the picking up of the fragments had been an extraordinary business; it being amazing that the human body should be blown into pieces which exploded along no anatomical lines, but rather divided as capriciously as the fragmentation in the burst of a high explosive shell.

A naturalist, to obtain accuracy of observation, may confine himself in his observations to one limited period and I will take first that following the Austrian offensive of June, 1918, in Italy as one in which the dead were present in their greatest numbers, a withdrawal having been forced and an advance later made to recover the ground lost so that the positions after the battle were the same as before except for the presence of the dead. Until the dead are buried they change somewhat in appearance each day. The color change in Caucasian races is from white to yellow, to yellow-green, to black. If left long enough in the heat the flesh comes to resemble coal-tar, especially where it has been broken or torn, and it has quite a visible tarlike iridescence. The dead grow larger each day until sometimes they become quite too big for their uniforms, filling these until they seem blown tight enough to burst. The individual members may increase in girth to an unbelievable extent and faces fill as taut and globular as balloons. The surprising thing, next to their progressive corpulence, is the amount of paper that is scattered about the dead. Their ultimate position, before there is any question of burial, depends on the location of the pockets in the uniform. In the Austrian army these pockets were in the back of the breeches and the dead, after a short time, all consequently lay on their faces, the two hip pockets pulled out and, scattered around them in the grass, all those papers their pockets had contained. The heat, the flies, the indicative positions of the bodies in the grass, and the amount of paper scattered are the impressions one retains. The smell of a battlefield in hot weather one cannot recall. You can remember that there was such a smell, but nothing ever happens to you to bring it back. It is unlike the smell of a regiment, which may come to you suddenly while riding in the street car and you will look across and see the man who has brought it to you. But the other thing is gone as completely as when you have been in love; you remember things that happened, but the sensation cannot be recalled.

One wonders what that persevering traveller, Mungo Park, would have seen on a battlefield in hot weather to restore his confidence. There were always poppies in the wheat in the end of June and in July, and the mulberry trees were in full leaf and one could see the heat waves rise from the barrels of the guns where the sun struck them through the screens of leaves; the earth was turned a bright yellow at the edge of holes where mustard gas shells had been and the average broken house is finer to see than one that has never been shelled, but few travellers would take a good full breath of that early summer air and have any such thoughts as Mungo Park about those formed in His own image.

The first thing that you found about the dead was that, hit badly enough, they died like animals. Some quickly from a little

wound you would not think would kill a rabbit. They died from
little wounds as rabbits die sometimes from three or four small
grains of shot that hardly seem to break the skin. Others would
die like cats; a skull broken in and iron in the brain, they lie alive
two days like cats that crawl into the coal bin with a bullet in the
brain and will not die until you cut their heads off. Maybe cats do
not die then, they say they have nine lives, I do not know, but most
men die like animals, not men. I'd never seen a natural death, so
called, and so I blamed it on the war and like the persevering traveller, Mungo Park, knew that there was something else, that always
absent something else, and then I saw one.

The only natural death I've ever seen, outside of loss of blood,
which isn't bad, was death from Spanish influenza. In this you drown
in mucus, choking, and how you know the patient's dead is: at
the end he turns to be a little child again, though with his manly
force, and fills the sheets as full as any diaper with one vast, final,
yellow cataract that flows and dribbles on after he's gone. So now
I want to see the death of any self-called Humanist* because a persevering traveller like Mungo Park or me lives on and maybe yet
will live to see the actual death of members of this literary sect and
watch the noble exits that they make. In my musings as a naturalist
it has occurred to me that while decorum is an excellent thing
some must be indecorous if the race is to be carried on since the
position prescribed for procreation is indecorous, highly indecorous,
and it occurred to me that perhaps that is what these people are,
or were: the children of decorous cohabitation. But regardless of
how they started I hope to see the finish of a few, and speculate how
worms will try that long preserved sterility; with their quaint pam-
phlets gone to bust and into foot-notes all their lust.

While it is, perhaps, legitimate to deal with these self-desig-
nated citizens in a natural history of the dead, even though the
designation may mean nothing by the time this work is published,
yet it is unfair to the other dead, who were not dead in their youth
of choice, who owned no magazines, many of whom had doubtless

* The reader's indulgence is requested for this mention of an extinct phe-
nomenon. The reference, like all references to fashions, dates the story but it is
retained because of its mild historical interest and because its omission would
spoil the rhythm.

never even read a review, that one has seen in the hot weather with a half-pint of maggots working where their mouths have been. It was not always hot weather for the dead, much of the time it was the rain that washed them clean when they lay in it and made the earth soft when they were buried in it and sometimes then kept on until the earth was mud and washed them out and you had to bury them again. Or in the winter in the mountains you had to put them in the snow and when the snow melted in the spring some one else had to bury them. They had beautiful burying grounds in the mountains, war in the mountains is the most beautiful of all war, and in one of them, at a place called Pocol, they buried a general who was shot through the head by a sniper. This is where those writers are mistaken who write books called *Generals Die in Bed,* because this general died in a trench dug in snow, high in the mountains, wearing an Alpini hat with an eagle feather in it and a hole in front you couldn't put your little finger in and a hole in back you could put your fist in, if it were a small fist and you wanted to put it there, and much blood in the snow. He was a damned fine general, and so was General von Behr who commanded the Bavarian Alpenkorps troops at the battle of Caporetto and was killed in his staff car by the Italian rearguard as he drove into Udine ahead of his troops, and the titles of all such books should be *Generals Usually Die in Bed,* if we are to have any sort of accuracy in such things.

In the mountains too, sometimes, the snow fell on the dead outside the dressing station on the side that was protected by the mountain from any shelling. They carried them into a cave that had been dug into the mountainside before the earth froze. It was in this cave that a man whose head was broken as a flower-pot may be broken, although it was all held together by membranes and a skillfully applied bandage now soaked and hardened, with the structure of his brain disturbed by a piece of broken steel in it, lay a day, a night, and a day. The stretcher-bearers asked the doctor to go in and have a look at him. They saw him each time they made a trip and even when they did not look at him they heard him breathing. The doctor's eyes were red and the lids swollen, almost shut from tear gas. He looked at the man twice; once in daylight, once with a flashlight. That too would have made a good etching for Goya, the visit with the flashlight, I mean. After looking at him the second time the doctor believed the stretcher-bearers when they said the soldier was still alive.

"What do you want me to do about it?" he asked.

There was nothing they wanted done. But after a while they asked permission to carry him out and lay him with the badly wounded.

"No. No. No!" said the doctor, who was busy. "What's the matter? Are you afraid of him?"

"We don't like to hear him in there with the dead."

"Don't listen to him. If you take him out of there you will have to carry him right back in."

"We wouldn't mind that, Captain Doctor."

"No," said the doctor. "No. Didn't you hear me say no?"

"Why don't you give him an overdose of morphine?" asked an artillery officer who was waiting to have a wound in his arm dressed.

"Do you think that is the only use I have for morphine? Would you like me to have to operate without morphine? You have a pistol, go out and shoot him yourself."

"He's been shot already," said the officer. "If some of you doctors were shot you'd be different."

"Thank you very much," said the doctor waving a forceps in the air. "Thank you a thousand times. What about these eyes?" He pointed the forceps at them. "How would you like these?"

"Tear gas. We call it lucky if it's tear gas."

"Because you leave the line," said the doctor. "Because you come running here with your tear gas to be evacuated. You rub onions in your eyes."

"You are beside yourself. I do not notice your insults. You are crazy."

The stretcher-bearers came in.

"Captain Doctor," one of them said.

"Get out of here!" said the doctor.

They went out.

"I will shoot the poor fellow," the artillery officer said. "I am a humane man. I will not let him suffer."

"Shoot him then," said the doctor. "Shoot him. Assume the responsibility. I will make a report. Wounded shot by lieutenant of artillery in first curing post. Shoot him. Go ahead shoot him."

"You are not a human being."

"My business is to care for the wounded, not to kill them. That is for gentlemen of the artillery."

"Why don't you care for him then?"

"I have done so. I have done all that can be done."

"Why don't you send him down on the cable railway?"

"Who are you to ask me questions? Are you my superior officer? Are you in command of this dressing post? Do me the courtesy to answer."

The lieutenant of artillery said nothing. The others in the room were all soldiers and there were no other officers present.

"Answer me," said the doctor holding a needle up in his forceps. "Give me a response."

"F— yourself," said the artillery officer.

"So," said the doctor. "So, you said that. All right. All right. We shall see."

The lieutenant of artillery stood up and walked toward him.

"F— yourself," he said. "F— yourself. F— your mother. F— your sister. . . ."

The doctor tossed the saucer full of iodine in his face. As he came toward him, blinded, the lieutenant fumbled for his pistol. The doctor skipped quickly behind him, tripped him and, as he fell to the floor, kicked him several times and picked up the pistol in his rubber gloves. The lieutenant sat on the floor holding his good hand to his eyes.

"I'll kill you!" he said. "I'll kill you as soon as I can see."

"I am the boss," said the doctor. "All is forgiven since you know I am the boss. You cannot kill me because I have your pistol. Sergeant! Adjutant! Adjutant!"

"The adjutant is at the cable railway," said the sergeant.

"Wipe out this officer's eyes with alcohol and water. He has got iodine in them. Bring me the basin to wash my hands. I will take this officer next."

"You won't touch me."

"Hold him tight. He is a little delirious."

One of the stretcher-bearers came in.

"Captain Doctor."

"What do you want?"

"The man in the dead-house——"

"Get out of here."

"Is dead, Captain Doctor. I thought you would be glad to know."

"See, my poor lieutenant? We dispute about nothing. In time of war we dispute about nothing."

"F— you," said the lieutenant of artillery. He still could not see. "You've blinded me."

"It is nothing," said the doctor. "Your eyes will be all right. It is nothing. A dispute about nothing."

"Ayee! Ayee! Ayee!" suddenly screamed the lieutenant. "You have blinded me! You have blinded me!"

"Hold him tight," said the doctor. "He is in much pain. Hold him very tight."

A FAREWELL TO ARMS

BOOK ONE

1

IN the late summer of that year we lived in a house in a village that looked across the river and the plain to the mountains. In the bed of the river there were pebbles and boulders, dry and white in the sun, and the water was clear and swiftly moving and blue in the channels. Troops went by the house and down the road and the dust they raised powdered the leaves of the trees. The trunks of the trees too were dusty and the leaves fell early that year and we saw the troops marching along the road and the dust rising and leaves, stirred by the breeze, falling and the soldiers marching and afterward the road bare and white except for the leaves.

The plain was rich with crops; there were many orchards of fruit trees and beyond the plain the mountains were brown and bare. There was fighting in the mountains and at night we could see the flashes from the artillery. In the dark it was like summer lightning, but the nights were cool and there was not the feeling of a storm coming.

Sometimes in the dark we heard the troops marching under the window and guns going past pulled by motor-tractors. There was much traffic at night and many mules on the roads with boxes of ammunition on each side of their pack-saddles and gray motor trucks that carried men, and other trucks with loads covered with canvas that moved slower in the traffic. There were big guns too that passed in the day drawn by tractors, the long barrels of the guns covered with green branches and green leafy branches and vines laid over the tractors. To the north we could look across a valley and see a forest of chestnut trees and behind it another mountain on this side of the river. There was fighting for that mountain too, but it was not successful, and in the fall when the rains came the leaves all fell from the chestnut trees and the branches were bare and the

141

trunks black with rain. The vineyards were thin and bare-branched too and all the country wet and brown and dead with the autumn. There were mists over the river and clouds on the mountain and the trucks splashed mud on the road and the troops were muddy and wet in their capes; their rifles were wet and under their capes the two leather cartridge-boxes on the front of the belts, gray leather boxes heavy with the packs of clips of thin, long 6.5 mm. cartridges, bulged forward under the capes so that the men, passing on the road, marched as though they were six months gone with child.

There were small gray motor cars that passed going very fast; usually there was an officer on the seat with the driver and more officers in the back seat. They splashed more mud than the camions even and if one of the officers in the back was very small and sitting between two generals, he himself so small that you could not see his face but only the top of his cap and his narrow back, and if the car went especially fast it was probably the King. He lived in Udine and came out in this way nearly every day to see how things were going, and things went very badly.

At the start of the winter came the permanent rain and with the rain came the cholera. But it was checked and in the end only seven thousand died of it in the army.

2

THE next year there were many victories. The mountain that was beyond the valley and the hillside where the chestnut forest grew was captured and there were victories beyond the plain on the plateau to the south and we crossed the river in August and lived in a house in Gorizia that had a fountain and many thick shady trees in a walled garden and a wistaria vine purple on the side of the house. Now the fighting was in the next mountains beyond and was not a mile away. The town was very nice and our house was very fine. The river ran behind us and the town had been captured very handsomely but the mountains beyond it could not be taken and I was very glad the Austrians seemed to want to come back to the town some time, if the war should end, because they did not bombard it to destroy it but only a little in a military way. People lived on in it and there were hospitals and cafés and artillery up side streets and two

bawdy houses, one for troops and one for officers, and with the end
of the summer, the cool nights, the fighting in the mountains beyond
the town, the shell-marked iron of the railway bridge, the smashed
tunnel by the river where the fighting had been, the trees around
the square and the long avenue of trees that led to the square; these
with there being girls in the town, the King passing in his motor
car, sometimes now seeing his face and little long necked body and
gray beard like a goat's chin tuft; all these with the sudden interiors
of houses that had lost a wall through shelling, with plaster and
rubble in their gardens and sometimes in the street, and the whole
thing going well on the Carso made the fall very different from the
last fall when we had been in the country. The war was changed too.

The forest of oak trees on the mountain beyond the town was
gone. The forest had been green in the summer when we had come
into the town but now there were the stumps and the broken trunks
and the ground torn up, and one day at the end of the fall when I
was out where the oak forest had been I saw a cloud coming over
the mountain. It came very fast and the sun went a dull yellow and
then everything was gray and the sky was covered and the cloud
came on down the mountain and suddenly we were in it and it was
snow. The snow slanted across the wind, the bare ground was covered, the stumps of trees projected, there was snow on the guns and
there were paths in the snow going back to the latrines behind
trenches.

Later, below in the town, I watched the snow falling, looking
out of the window of the bawdy house, the house for officers, where
I sat with a friend and two glasses drinking a bottle of Asti, and,
looking out at the snow falling slowly and heavily, we knew it
was all over for that year. Up the river the mountains had not been
taken; none of the mountains beyond the river had been taken.
That was all left for next year. My friend saw the priest from our
mess going by in the street, walking carefully in the slush, and
pounded on the window to attract his attention. The priest looked
up. He saw us and smiled. My friend motioned for him to come
in. The priest shook his head and went on. That night in the mess
after the spaghetti course, which every one ate very quickly and
seriously, lifting the spaghetti on the fork until the loose strands
hung clear then lowering it into the mouth, or else using a continuous lift and sucking into the mouth, helping ourselves to wine

from the grass-covered gallon flask; it swung in a metal cradle and you pulled the neck of the flask down with the forefinger and the wine, clear red, tannic and lovely, poured out into the glass held with the same hand; after this course, the captain commenced picking on the priest.

The priest was young and blushed easily and wore a uniform like the rest of us but with a cross in dark red velvet above the left breast pocket of his gray tunic. The captain spoke pidgin Italian for my doubtful benefit, in order that I might understand perfectly, that nothing should be lost.

"Priest to-day with girls," the captain said looking at the priest and at me. The priest smiled and blushed and shook his head. This captain baited him often.

"Not true?" asked the captain. "To-day I see priest with girls."

"No," said the priest. The other officers were amused at the baiting.

"Priest not with girls," went on the captain. "Priest never with girls," he explained to me. He took my glass and filled it, looking at my eyes all the time, but not losing sight of the priest.

"Priest every night five against one." Every one at the table laughed. "You understand? Priest every night five against one." He made a gesture and laughed loudly. The priest accepted it as a joke.

"The Pope wants the Austrians to win the war," the major said. "He loves Franz Joseph. That's where the money comes from. I am an atheist."

"Did you ever read the 'Black Pig'?" asked the lieutenant. "I will get you a copy. It was that which shook my faith."

"It is a filthy and vile book," said the priest. "You do not really like it."

"It is very valuable," said the lieutenant. "It tells you about those priests. You will like it," he said to me. I smiled at the priest and he smiled back across the candle-light. "Don't you read it," he said.

"I will get it for you," said the lieutenant.

"All thinking men are atheists," the major said. "I do not believe in the Free Masons however."

"I believe in the Free Masons," the lieutenant said. "It is a noble organization." Some one came in and as the door opened I could see the snow falling.

"There will be no more offensive now that the snow has come," I said.

"Certainly not," said the major. "You should go on leave. You should go to Rome, Naples, Sicily——"

"He should visit Amalfi," said the lieutenant. "I will write you cards to my family in Amalfi. They will love you like a son."

"He should go to Palermo."

"He ought to go to Capri."

"I would like you to see Abruzzi and visit my family at Capracotta," said the priest.

"Listen to him talk about the Abruzzi. There's more snow there than here. He doesn't want to see peasants. Let him go to centres of culture and civilization."

"He should have fine girls. I will give you the addresses of places in Naples. Beautiful young girls—accompanied by their mothers. Ha! Ha! Ha!" The captain spread his hand open, the thumb up and fingers outspread as when you make shadow pictures. There was a shadow from his hand on the wall. He spoke again in pidgin Italian. "You go away like this," he pointed to the thumb, "and come back like this," he touched the little finger. Every one laughed.

"Look," said the captain. He spread the hand again. Again the candle-light made its shadows on the wall. He started with the upright thumb and named in their order the thumb and four fingers, "soto-tenente (the thumb), tenente (first finger), capitano (next finger), maggiore (next to the little finger), and tenente-colonello (the little finger). You go away soto-tenente! You come back soto-colonello!" They all laughed. The captain was having a great success with finger games. He looked at the priest and shouted, "Every night priest five against one!" They all laughed again.

"You must go on leave at once," the major said.

"I would like to go with you and show you things," the lieutenant said.

"When you come back bring a phonograph."

"Bring good opera disks."

"Bring Caruso."

"Don't bring Caruso. He bellows."

"Don't you wish you could bellow like him?"

"He bellows. I say he bellows!"

"I would like you to go to Abruzzi," the priest said. The others were shouting. "There is good hunting. You would like the people and though it is cold it is clear and dry. You could say with my family. My father is a famous hunter."

"Come on," said the captain. "We go whorehouse before it shuts."

"Good-night," I said to the priest.

"Good-night," he said.

3

WHEN I came back to the front we still lived in that town. There were many more guns in the country around and the spring had come. The fields were green and there were small green shoots on the vines, the trees along the road had small leaves and a breeze came from the sea. I saw the town with the hill and the old castle above it in a cup in the hills with the mountains beyond, brown mountains with a little green on their slopes. In the town there were more guns, there were some new hospitals, you met British men and sometimes women, on the street, and a few more houses had been hit by shell fire. It was warm and like the spring and I walked down the alleyway of trees, warmed from the sun on the wall, and found we still lived in the same house and that it all looked the same as when I had left it. The door was open, there was a soldier sitting on a bench outside in the sun, an ambulance was waiting by the side door and inside the door, as I went in, there was the smell of marble floors and hospital. It was all as I had left it except that now it was spring. I looked in the door of the big room and saw the major sitting at his desk, the window open and the sunlight coming into the room. He did not see me and I did not know whether to go in and report or go upstairs first and clean up. I decided to go on upstairs.

The room I shared with the lieutenant Rinaldi looked out on the courtyard. The window was open, my bed was made up with blankets and my things hung on the wall, the gas mask in an ob-

long tin can, the steel helmet on the same peg. At the foot of the
bed was my flat trunk, and my winter boots, the leather shiny with
oil, were on the trunk. My Austrian sniper's rifle with its blued
octagon barrel and the lovely dark walnut, cheek-fitted, *schutzen*
stock, hung over the two beds. The telescope that fitted it was, I
remembered, locked in the trunk. The lieutenant, Rinaldi, lay
asleep on the other bed. He woke when he heard me in the room
and sat up.

"Ciaou!" he said. "What kind of time did you have?"

"Magnificent."

We shook hands and he put his arm around my neck and kissed
me.

"Oughf," I said.

"You're dirty," he said. "You ought to wash. Where did you go
and what did you do? Tell me everything at once."

"I went everywhere. Milan, Florence, Rome, Naples, Villa San
Giovanni, Messina, Taormina——"

"You talk like a time-table. Did you have any beautiful adventures?"

"Yes."

"Where?"

"Milano, Firenze, Roma, Napoli——"

"That's enough. Tell me really what was the best."

"In Milano."

"That was because it was first. Where did you meet her? In the
Cova? Where did you go? How did you feel? Tell me everything
at once. Did you stay all night?"

"Yes."

"That's nothing. Here now we have beautiful girls. New girls
never been to the front before."

"Wonderful."

"You don't believe me? We will go now this afternoon and see.
And in the town we have beautiful English girls. I am now in love
with Miss Barkley. I will take you to call. I will probably marry Miss
Barkley."

"I have to get washed and report. Doesn't anybody work now?"

"Since you are gone we have nothing but frostbites, chilblains,
jaundice, gonorrhea, self-inflicted wounds, pneumonia and hard
and soft chancres. Every week some one gets wounded by rock frag-

ments. There are a few real wounded. Next week the war starts again. Perhaps it start again. They say so. Do you think I would do right to marry Miss Barkley—after the war of course?"

"Absolutely," I said and poured the basin full of water.

"To-night you will tell me everything," said Rinaldi. "Now I must go back to sleep to be fresh and beautiful for Miss Barkley."

I took off my tunic and shirt and washed in the cold water in the basin. While I rubbed myself with a towel I looked around the room and out the window and at Rinaldi lying with his eyes closed on the bed. He was good-looking, was my age, and he came from Amalfi. He loved being a surgeon and we were great friends. While I was looking at him he opened his eyes.

"Have you any money?"

"Yes."

"Loan me fifty lire."

I dried my hands and took out my pocket-book from the inside of my tunic hanging on the wall. Rinaldi took the note, folded it without rising from the bed and slid it in his breeches pocket. He smiled, "I must make on Miss Barkley the impression of a man of sufficient wealth. You are my great and good friend and financial protector."

"Go to hell," I said.

That night at the mess I sat next to the priest and he was disappointed and suddenly hurt that I had not gone to the Abruzzi. He had written to his father that I was coming and they had made preparations. I myself felt as badly as he did and could not understand why I had not gone. It was what I had wanted to do and I tried to explain how one thing had led to another and finally he saw it and understood that I had really wanted to go and it was almost all right. I had drunk much wine and afterward coffee and Strega and I explained, winefully, how we did not do the things we wanted to do; we never did such things.

We two were talking while the others argued. I had wanted to go to Abruzzi. I had gone to no place where the roads were frozen and hard as iron, where it was clear cold and dry and the snow was dry and powdery and hare-tracks in the snow and the peasants took off their hats and called you Lord and there was good hunting. I had gone to no such place but to the smoke of cafés and nights when the room whirled and you needed to look at the wall to make it stop, nights in bed, drunk, when you knew that that was all there was, and the strange excitement of waking and not knowing who it was with you, and the world all unreal in the dark and so exciting that you must resume again unknowing and not caring in the night, sure that this was all and all and all and not caring. Suddenly to care very much and to sleep to wake with it sometimes morning and all that had been there gone and everything sharp and hard and clear and sometimes a dispute about the cost. Sometimes still pleasant and fond and warm and breakfast and lunch. Sometimes all niceness gone and glad to get out on the street but always another day starting and then another night. I tried to tell about the night and the difference between the night and the day and how the night was better unless the day was very clean and cold and I could not tell it; as I cannot tell it now. But if you have had it you know. He had not had it but he understood that I had really wanted to go to the Abruzzi but had not gone and we were still friends, with many tastes alike, but with the difference between us. He had always known what I did not know and what, when I learned it, I was always able to forget. But I did not know that then, although I learned it later. In the meantime we were all at the mess, the meal was finished, and the argument went on. We two stopped talking and the captain shouted, "Priest not happy. Priest not happy without girls."

"I am happy," said the priest.

"Priest not happy. Priest wants Austrians to win the war," the captain said. The others listened. The priest shook his head.

"No," he said.

"Priest wants us never to attack. Don't you want us never to attack?"

"No. If there is a war I suppose we must attack."

"Must attack. Shall attack!"

The priest nodded.

"Leave him alone," the major said. "He's all right."

"He can't do anything about it anyway," the captain said. We all got up and left the table.

4

THE battery in the next garden woke me in the morning and I saw
the sun coming through the window and got out of the bed. I went
to the window and looked out. The gravel paths were moist and
the grass was wet with dew. The battery fired twice and the air
came each time like a blow and shook the window and made the
front of my pajamas flap. I could not see the guns but they were
evidently firing directly over us. It was a nuisance to have them
there but it was a comfort that they were no bigger. As I looked
out at the garden I heard a motor truck starting on the road. I
dressed, went downstairs, had some coffee in the kitchen and went
out to the garage.

Ten cars were lined up side by side under the long shed. They
were top-heavy, blunt-nosed ambulances, painted gray and built
like moving-vans. The mechanics were working on one out in the
yard. Three others were up in the mountains at dressing stations.

"Do they ever shell that battery?" I asked one of the mechanics.

"No, Signor Tenente. It is protected by the little hill."

"How's everything?"

"Not so bad. This machine is no good but the others march."
He stopped working and smiled. "Were you on permission?"

"Yes."

He wiped his hands on his jumper and grinned. "You have a
good time?" The others all grinned too.

"Fine," I said. "What's the matter with this machine?"

"It's no good. One thing after another."

"What's the matter now?"

"New rings."

I left them working, the car looking disgraced and empty with
the engine open and parts spread on the work bench, and went in
under the shed and looked at each of the cars. They were moderately clean, a few freshly washed, the others dusty. I looked at the
tires carefully, looking for cuts or stone bruises. Everything seemed
in good condition. It evidently made no difference whether I was
there to look after things or not. I had imagined that the condition
of the cars, whether or not things were obtainable, the smooth functioning of the business of removing wounded and sick from the

dressing stations, hauling them back from the mountains to the clearing station and then distributing them to the hospitals named on their papers, depended to a considerable extent on myself. Evidently it did not matter whether I was there or not.

"Has there been any trouble getting parts?" I asked the sergeant mechanic.

"No, Signor Tenente."

"Where is the gasoline park now?"

"At the same place."

"Good," I said and went back to the house and drank another bowl of coffee at the mess table. The coffee was a pale gray and sweet with condensed milk. Outside the window it was a lovely spring morning. There was that beginning of a feeling of dryness in the nose that meant the day would be hot later on. That day I visited the posts in the mountains and was back in town late in the afternoon.

The whole thing seemed to run better while I was away. The offensive was going to start again I heard. The division for which we worked were to attack at a place up the river and the major told me that I would see about the posts for during the attack. The attack would cross the river up above the narrow gorge and spread up the hillside. The posts for the cars would have to be as near the river as they could get and keep covered. They would, of course, be selected by the infantry but we were supposed to work it out. It was one of those things that gave you a false feeling of soldiering.

I was very dusty and dirty and went up to my room to wash. Rinaldi was sitting on the bed with a copy of Hugo's English grammar. He was dressed, wore his black boots, and his hair shone.

"Splendid," he said when he saw me. "You will come with me to see Miss Barkley."

"No."

"Yes. You will please come and make me a good impression on her."

"All right. Wait till I get cleaned up."

"Wash up and come as you are."

I washed, brushed my hair and we started.

"Wait a minute," Rinaldi said. "Perhaps we should have a drink." He opened his trunk and took out a bottle.

"Not Strega," I said.

"No. Grappa."

"All right."

He poured two glasses and we touched them, first fingers extended. The grappa was very strong.

"Another?"

"All right," I said. We drank the second grappa, Rinaldi put away the bottle and we went down the stairs. It was hot walking through the town but the sun was starting to go down and it was very pleasant. The British hospital was a big villa built by Germans before the war. Miss Barkley was in the garden. Another nurse was with her. We saw their white uniforms through the trees and walked toward them. Rinaldi saluted. I saluted too but more moderately.

"How do you do?" Miss Barkley said. "You're not an Italian, are you?"

"Oh, no."

Rinaldi was talking with the other nurse. They were laughing.

"What an odd thing—to be in the Italian army."

"It's not really the army. It's only the ambulance."

"It's very odd though. Why did you do it?"

"I don't know," I said. "There isn't always an explanation for everything."

"Oh, isn't there? I was brought up to think there was."

"That's awfully nice."

"*Do* we have to go on and talk this way?"

"No," I said.

"That's a relief. Isn't it?"

"What is the stick?" I asked. Miss Barkley was quite tall. She wore what seemed to me to be a nurse's uniform, was blonde and had a tawny skin and gray eyes. I thought she was very beautiful. She was carrying a thin rattan stick like a toy riding-crop, bound in leather.

"It belonged to a boy who was killed last year."

"I'm awfully sorry."

"He was a very nice boy. He was going to marry me and he was killed in the Somme."

"It was a ghastly show."

"Were you there?"

"No."

"I've heard about it," she said. "There's not really any war of that sort down here. They sent me the little stick. His mother sent it to me. They returned it with his things."

"Had you been engaged long?"

"Eight years. We grew up together."

"And why didn't you marry?"

"I don't know," she said. "I was a fool not to. I could have given him that anyway. But I thought it would be bad for him."

"I see."

"Have you ever loved any one?"

"No," I said.

We sat down on a bench and I looked at her.

"You have beautiful hair," I said.

"Do you like it?"

"Very much."

"I was going to cut it all off when he died."

"No."

"I wanted to do something for him. You see I didn't care about the other thing and he could have had it all. He could have had anything he wanted if I would have known. I would have married him or anything. I know all about it now. But then he wanted to go to war and I didn't know."

I did not say anything.

"I didn't know about anything then. I thought it would be worse for him. I thought perhaps he couldn't stand it and then of course he was killed and that was the end of it."

"I don't know."

"Oh, yes," she said. "That's the end of it."

We looked at Rinaldi talking with the other nurse.

"What is her name?"

"Ferguson. Helen Ferguson. Your friend is a doctor, isn't he?"

"Yes. He's very good."

"That's splendid. You rarely find any one any good this close to the front. This is close to the front, isn't it?"

"Quite."

"It's a silly front," she said. "But it's very beautiful. Are they going to have an offensive?"

"Yes."

"Then we'll have to work. There's no work now."

"Have you done nursing long?"

"Since the end of 'fifteen. I started when he did. I remember having a silly idea he might come to the hospital where I was. With a sabre cut, I suppose, and a bandage around his head. Or shot through the shoulder. Something picturesque."

"This is the picturesque front," I said.

"Yes," she said. "People can't realize what France is like. If they did, it couldn't all go on. He didn't have a sabre cut. They blew him all to bits."

I didn't say anything.

"Do you suppose it will always go on?"

"No."

"What's to stop it?"

"It will crack somewhere."

"We'll crack. We'll crack in France. They can't go on doing things like the Somme and not crack."

"They won't crack here," I said.

"You think not?"

"No. They did very well last summer."

"They may crack," she said. "Anybody may crack."

"The Germans too."

"No," she said. "I think not."

We went over toward Rinaldi and Miss Ferguson.

"You love Italy?" Rinaldi asked Miss Ferguson in English.

"Quite well."

"No understand," Rinaldi shook his head.

"Abbastanza bene," I translated. He shook his head.

"That is not good. You love England?"

"Not too well. I'm Scotch, you see."

Rinaldi looked at me blankly.

"She's Scotch, so she loves Scotland better than England," I said in Italian.

"But Scotland is England."

I translated this for Miss Ferguson.

"Pas encore," said Miss Ferguson.

"Not really?"

"Never. We do not like the English."

"Not like the English? Not like Miss Barkley?"

"Oh, that's different. You mustn't take everything so literally."

After a while we said good-night and left. Walking home Rinaldi said, "Miss Barkley prefers you to me. That is very clear. But the little Scotch one is very nice."

"Very," I said. I had not noticed her. "You like her?"

"No," said Rinaldi.

5

THE next afternoon I went to call on Miss Barkley again. She was not in the garden and I went to the side door of the villa where the ambulances drove up. Inside I saw the head nurse, who said Miss Barkley was on duty—"there's a war on, you know."

I said I knew.

"You're the American in the Italian army?" she asked.

"Yes, ma'am."

"How did you happen to do that? Why didn't you join up with us?"

"I don't know," I said. "Could I join now?"

"I'm afraid not now. Tell me. Why did you join up with the Italians?"

"I was in Italy," I said, "and I spoke Italian."

"Oh," she said. "I'm learning it. It's beautiful language."

"Somebody said you should be able to learn it in two weeks."

"Oh, I'll not learn it in two weeks. I've studied it for months now. You may come and see her after seven o'clock if you wish. She'll be off then. But don't bring a lot of Italians."

"Not even for the beautiful language?"

"No. Nor for the beautiful uniforms."

"Good evening," I said.

"A rivederci, Tenente."

"A rivederla." I saluted and went out. It was impossible to salute foreigners as an Italian, without embarrassment. The Italian salute never seemed made for export.

The day had been hot. I had been up the river to the bridge-head at Plava. It was there that the offensive was to begin. It had been impossible to advance on the far side the year before because there was only one road leading down from the pass to the pontoon bridge and it was under machine-gun and shell fire for nearly a mile.

It was not wide enough either to carry all the transport for an offensive and the Austrians could make a shambles out of it. But the Italians had crossed and spread out a little way on the far side to hold about a mile and a half on the Austrian side of the river. It was a nasty place and the Austrians should not have let them hold it. I suppose it was mutual tolerance because the Austrians still kept a bridgehead further down the river. The Austrian trenches were above on the hillside only a few yards from the Italian lines. There had been a little town but it was all rubble. There was what was left of a railway station and a smashed permanent bridge that could not be repaired and used because it was in plain sight.

I went along the narrow road down toward the river, left the car at the dressing station under the hill, crossed the pontoon bridge, which was protected by a shoulder of the mountain, and went through the trenches in the smashed-down town and along the edge of the slope. Everybody was in the dugouts. There were racks of rockets standing to be touched off to call for help from the artillery or to signal with if the telephone wires were cut. It was quiet, hot and dirty. I looked across the wire at the Austrian lines. Nobody was in sight. I had a drink with a captain that I knew in one of the dugouts and went back across the bridge.

A new wide road was being finished that would go over the mountain and zig-zag down to the bridge. When this road was finished the offensive would start. It came down through the forest in sharp turns. The system was to bring everything down the new road and take the empty trucks, carts and loaded ambulances and all returning traffic up the old narrow road. The dressing station was on the Austrian side of the river under the edge of the hill and stretcher-bearers would bring the wounded back across the pontoon bridge. It would be the same when the offensive started. As far as I could make out the last mile or so of the new road where it started to level out would be able to be shelled steadily by the Austrians. It looked as though it might be a mess. But I found a place where the cars would be sheltered after they passed that last bad-looking bit and could wait for the wounded to be brought across the pontoon bridge. I would have liked to drive over the new road but it was not yet finished. It looked wide and well made with a good grade and the turns looked very impressive where you could see them through openings in the forest on the mountain side. The cars would

be all right with their good metal-to-metal brakes and anyway, coming down, they would not be loaded. I drove back up the narrow
road.

Two carabinieri held the car up. A shell had fallen and while
we waited three others fell up the road. They were seventy-sevens
and came with a whishing rush of air, a hard bright burst and flash
and then gray smoke that blew across the road. The carabinieri waved
us to go on. Passing where the shells had landed I avoided the small
broken places and smelled the high explosive and the smell of
blasted clay and stone and freshly shattered flint. I drove back to
Gorizia and our villa and, as I said, went to call on Miss Barkley,
who was on duty.

At dinner I ate very quickly and left for the villa where the
British had their hospital. It was really very large and beautiful and
there were fine trees in the grounds. Miss Barkley was sitting on a
bench in the garden. Miss Ferguson was with her. They seemed
glad to see me and in a little while Miss Ferguson excused herself
and went away.

"I'll leave you two," she said. "You get along very well without
me."

"Don't go, Helen," Miss Barkley said.

"I'd really rather. I must write some letters."

"Good-night," I said.

"Good-night, Mr. Henry."

"Don't write anything that will bother the censor."

"Don't worry. I only write about what a beautiful place we live
in and how brave the Italians are."

"That way you'll be decorated."

"That will be nice. Good-night, Catherine."

"I'll see you in a little while," Miss Barkley said. Miss Ferguson
walked away in the dark.

"She's nice," I said.

"Oh, yes, she's very nice. She's a nurse."

"Aren't you a nurse?"

"Oh, no. I'm something called a V. A. D. We work very hard
but no one trusts us."

"Why not?"

"They don't trust us when there's nothing going on. When
there is really work they trust us."

"What is the difference?"

"A nurse is like a doctor. It takes a long time to be. A V. A. D. is a short cut."

"I see."

"The Italians didn't want women so near the front. So we're all on very special behavior. We don't go out."

"I can come here though."

"Oh, yes. We're not cloistered."

"Let's drop the war."

"It's very hard. There's no place to drop it."

"Let's drop it anyway."

"All right."

We looked at each other in the dark. I thought she was very beautiful and I took her hand. She let me take it and I held it and put my arm around under her arm.

"No," she said. I kept my arm where it was.

"Why not?"

"No."

"Yes," I said. "Please." I leaned forward in the dark to kiss her and there was a sharp stinging flash. She had slapped my face hard. Her hand had hit my nose and eyes, and tears came in my eyes from the reflex.

"I'm so sorry," she said. I felt I had a certain advantage.

"You were quite right."

"I'm dreadfully sorry," she said. "I just couldn't stand the nurse's-evening-off aspect of it. I didn't mean to hurt you. I did hurt you, didn't I?"

She was looking at me in the dark. I was angry and yet certain, seeing it all ahead like the moves in a chess game.

"You did exactly right," I said. "I don't mind at all."

"Poor man."

"You see I've been leading a sort of a funny life. And I never even talk English. And then you are so very beautiful." I looked at her.

"You don't need to say a lot of nonsense. I said I was sorry. We do get along."

"Yes," I said. "And we have gotten away from the war."

She laughed. It was the first time I had ever heard her laugh. I watched her face.

"You are sweet," she said.

"No, I'm not."

"Yes. You are a dear. I'd be glad to kiss you if you don't mind."

I looked in her eyes and put my arm around her as I had before and kissed her. I kissed her hard and held her tight and tried to open her lips; they were closed tight. I was still angry and as I held her suddenly she shivered. I held her close against me and could feel her heart beating and her lips opened and her head went back against my hand and then she was crying on my shoulder.

"Oh, darling," she said. "You will be good to me, won't you?"

What the hell, I thought. I stroked her hair and patted her shoulder. She was crying.

"You will, won't you?" She looked up at me. "Because we're going to have a strange life."

After a while I walked with her to the door of the villa and she went in and I walked home. Back at the villa I went upstairs to the room. Rinaldi was lying on his bed. He looked at me.

"So you make progress with Miss Barkley?"

"We are friends."

"You have that pleasant air of a dog in heat."

I did not understand the word.

"Of a what?"

He explained.

"You," I said, "have that pleasant air of a dog who——"

"Stop it," he said. "In a little while we would say insulting things." He laughed.

"Good-night," I said.

"Good-night, little puppy."

I knocked over his candle with the pillow and got into bed in the dark.

Rinaldi picked up the candle, lit it and went on reading.

6

I was away for two days at the posts. When I got home it was too late and I did not see Miss Barkley until the next evening. She was not in the garden and I had to wait in the office of the hospital until she came down. There were many marble busts on painted wooden pillars along the walls of the room they used for an office. The hall too, that the office opened on, was lined with them. They had the complete marble quality of all looking alike. Sculpture had always seemed a dull business—still, bronzes looked like something. But marble busts all looked like a cemetery. There was one fine cemetery though—the one at Pisa. Genoa was the place to see the bad marbles. This had been the villa of a very wealthy German and the busts must have cost him plenty. I wondered who had done them and how much he got. I tried to make out whether they were members of the family or what; but they were all uniformly classical. You could not tell anything about them.

I sat on a chair and held my cap. We were supposed to wear steel helmets even in Gorizia but they were uncomfortable and too bloody theatrical in a town where the civilian inhabitants had not been evacuated. I wore one when we went up to the posts and carried an English gas mask. We were just beginning to get some of them. They were a real mask. Also we were required to wear an automatic pistol; even doctors and sanitary officers. I felt it against the back of the chair. You were liable to arrest if you did not have one worn in plain sight. Rinaldi carried a holster stuffed with toilet paper. I wore a real one and felt like a gunman until I practised firing it. It was an Astra 7.65 caliber with a short barrel and it jumped so sharply when you let it off that there was no question of hitting anything. I practised with it, holding below the target and trying to master the jerk of the ridiculous short barrel until I could hit within a yard of where I aimed at twenty paces and then the ridiculousness of carrying a pistol at all came over me and I soon forgot it and carried it flopping against the small of my back with no feeling at all except a vague sort of shame when I met English-speaking people. I sat now in the chair and an orderly of some sort looked at me disapprovingly from behind a desk while I looked at the marble floor, the pillars with the marble busts, and the frescoes on the wall and waited for Miss Barkley. The frescoes were not bad. Any frescoes were good when they started to peel and flake off.

I saw Catherine Barkley coming down the hall, and stood up. She did not seem tall walking toward me but she looked very lovely.

"Good-evening, Mr. Henry," she said.

"How do you do?" I said. The orderly was listening behind the desk.

"Shall we sit here or go out in the garden?"

"Let's go out. It's much cooler."

I walked behind her out into the garden, the orderly looking after us. When we were out on the gravel drive she said, "Where have you been?"

"I've been out on post."

"You couldn't have sent me a note?"

"No," I said. "Not very well. I thought I was coming back."

"You ought to have let me know, darling."

We were off the driveway, walking under the trees. I took her hands, then stopped and kissed her.

"Isn't there anywhere we can go?"

"No," she said. "We have to just walk here. You've been away a long time."

"This is the third day. But I'm back now."

She looked at me, "And you do love me?"

"Yes."

"You did say you loved me, didn't you?"

"Yes," I lied. "I love you." I had not said it before.

"And you call me Catherine?"

"Catherine." We walked on a way and were stopped under a tree.

"Say, 'I've come back to Catherine in the night.' "

"I've come back to Catherine in the night."

"Oh, darling, you have come back, haven't you?"

"Yes."

"I love you so and it's been awful. You won't go away?"

"No. I'll always come back."

"Oh, I love you so. Please put your hand there again."

"It's not been away." I turned her so I could see her face when I kissed her and I saw that her eyes were shut. I kissed both her shut eyes. I thought she was probably a little crazy. It was all right if she was. I did not care what I was getting into. This was better than going every evening to the house for officers where the girls climbed all over you and put your cap on backward as a sign of affection between their trips upstairs with brother officers. I knew I did not love Catherine Barkley nor had any idea of loving her. This was a game, like bridge, in which you said things instead of playing cards. Like bridge you had to pretend you were playing for money or playing for some stakes. Nobody had mentioned what the stakes were. It was all right with me.

"I wish there was some place we could go," I said. I was experiencing the masculine difficulty of making love very long standing up.

"There isn't any place," she said. She came back from wherever she had been.

"We might sit there just for a little while."

We sat on the flat stone bench and I held Catherine Barkley's hand. She would not let me put my arm around her.

"Are you very tired?" she asked.

"No."

She looked down at the grass.

"This is a rotten game we play, isn't it?"

"What game?"

"Don't be dull."

"I'm not, on purpose."

"You're a nice boy," she said. "And you play it as well as you know how. But it's a rotten game."

"Do you always know what people think?"

"Not always. But I do with you. You don't have to pretend you love me. That's over for the evening. Is there anything you'd like to talk about?"

"But I do love you."

"Please let's not lie when we don't have to. I had a very fine little show and I'm all right now. You see I'm not mad and I'm not gone off. It's only a little sometimes."

I pressed her hand, "Dear Catherine."

"It sounds very funny now—Catherine. You don't pronounce it very much alike. But you're very nice. You're a very good boy."

"That's what the priest said."

"Yes, you're very good. And you will come and see me?"

"Of course."

"And you don't have to say you love me. That's all over for a while." She stood up and put out her hand. "Good-night."

I wanted to kiss her.

"No," she said. "I'm awfully tired."

"Kiss me, though," I said.

"I'm awfully tired, darling."

"Kiss me."

"Do you want to very much?"

"Yes."

We kissed and she broke away suddenly. "No. Good-night, please, darling." We walked to the door and I saw her go in and down the hall. I liked to watch her move. She went on down the hall. I went on home. It was a hot night and there was a good deal going on up in the mountains. I watched the flashes on San Gabriele.

I stopped in front of the Villa Rossa. The shutters were up but it was still going on inside. Somebody was singing. I went on home. Rinaldi came in while I was undressing.

"Ah, ha!" he said. "It does not go so well. Baby is puzzled."

"Where have you been?"

"At the Villa Rossa. It was very edifying, baby. We all sang. Where have you been?"

"Calling on the British."

"Thank God I did not become involved with the British."

7

I CAME back the next afternoon from our first mountain post and stopped the car at the *smistimento* where the wounded and sick were sorted by their papers and the papers marked for the different hospitals. I had been driving and I sat in the car and the driver took the papers in. It was a hot day and the sky was very bright and blue and the road was white and dusty. I sat in the high seat of the Fiat and thought about nothing. A regiment went by in the road and I watched them pass. The men were hot and sweating. Some wore their steel helmets but most of them carried them slung from their packs. Most of the helmets were too big and came down almost over the ears of the men who wore them. The officers all wore helmets; better-fitting helmets. It was half of the brigata Basilicata. I identified them by their red and white striped collar mark. There were stragglers going by long after the regiment had passed—men who could not keep up with their platoons. They were sweaty, dusty and tired. Some looked pretty bad. A soldier came along after the last of the stragglers. He was walking with a limp. He stopped and sat down beside the road. I got down and went over.

"What's the matter?"

He looked at me, then stood up.

"I'm going on."

"What's the trouble?"

"—— the war."

"What's wrong with your leg?"

"It's not my leg. I got a rupture."

"Why don't you ride with the transport?" I asked. "Why don't you go to the hospital?"

"They won't let me. The lieutenant said I slipped the truss on purpose."

"Let me feel it."

"It's way out."

"Which side is it on?"

"Here."

I felt it.

"Cough," I said.

"I'm afraid it will make it bigger. It's twice as big as it was this morning."

"Sit down," I said. "As soon as I get the papers on these wounded I'll take you along the road and drop you with your medical officers."

"He'll say I did it on purpose."

"They can't do anything," I said. "It's not a wound. You've had it before, haven't you?"

"But I lost the truss."

"They'll send you to a hospital."

"Can't I stay here, Tenente?"

"No, I haven't any papers for you."

The driver came out of the door with the papers for the wounded in the car.

"Four for 105. Two for 132," he said. They were hospitals beyond the river.

"You drive," I said. I helped the soldier with the rupture up on the seat with us.

"You speak English?" he asked.

"Sure."

"How you like this goddam war?"

"Rotten."

"I say it's rotten. Jesus Christ, I say it's rotten."

"Were you in the States?"

"Sure. In Pittsburgh. I know you was an American."

"Don't I talk Italian good enough?"

"I knew you was an American all right."

"Another American," said the driver in Italian looking at the hernia man.

"Listen, lootenant. Do you have to take me to that regiment?"

"Yes."

"Because the captain doctor knew I had this rupture. I threw away the goddam truss so it would get bad and I wouldn't have to go to the line again."

"I see."

"Couldn't you take me no place else?"

"If it was closer to the front I could take you to a first medical post. But back here you've got to have papers."

"If I go back they'll make me get operated on and then they'll put me in the line all the time."

I thought it over.

"You wouldn't want to go in the line all the time, would you?" he asked.

"No."

"Jesus Christ, ain't this a goddam war?"

"Listen," I said. "You get out and fall down by the road and get a bump on your head and I'll pick you up on our way back and take you to a hospital. We'll stop by the road here, Aldo." We stopped at the side of the road. I helped him down.

"I'll be right here, lieutenant," he said.

"So long," I said. We went on and passed the regiment about a mile ahead, then crossed the river, cloudy with snow-water and running fast through the spiles of the bridge, to ride along the road across the plain and deliver the wounded at the two hospitals. I drove coming back and went fast with the empty car to find the man from Pittsburgh. First we passed the regiment, hotter and slower than ever: then the stragglers. Then we saw a horse ambulance stopped by the road. Two men were lifting the hernia man to put him in. They had come back for him. He shook his

head at me. His helmet was off and his forehead was bleeding below the hair line. His nose was skinned and there was dust on the
bloody patch and dust in his hair.

"Look at the bump, lieutenant!" he shouted. "Nothing to do.
They come back for me."

When I got back to the villa it was five o'clock and I went out
where we washed the cars, to take a shower. Then I made out my
report in my room, sitting in my trousers and an undershirt in front
of the open window. In two days the offensive was to start and I
would go with the cars to Plava. It was a long time since I had
written to the States and I knew I should write but I had let it go
so long that it was almost impossible to write now. There was nothing to write about. I sent a couple of army Zona di Guerra post-
cards, crossing out everything except, I am well. That should handle
them. Those post-cards would be very fine in America; strange and
mysterious. This was a strange and mysterious war zone but I supposed it was quite well run and grim compared to other wars with
the Austrians. The Austrian army was created to give Napoleon victories; any Napoleon. I wished we had a Napoleon, but instead
we had Il Generale Cadorna, fat and prosperous and Vittorio Em-
manuele, the tiny man with the long thin neck and the goat beard.
Over on the right they had the Duke of Aosta. Maybe he was too
good-looking to be a great general but he looked like a man. Lots of
them would have liked him to be king. He looked like a king. He
was the King's uncle and commanded the third army. We were in
the second army. There were some British batteries up with the
third army. I had met two gunners from that lot, in Milan. They
were very nice and we had a big evening. They were big and shy
and embarrassed and very appreciative together of anything that
happened. I wish that I was with the British. It would have been
much simpler. Still I would probably have been killed. Not in this
ambulance business. Yes, even in the ambulance business. British
ambulance drivers were killed sometimes. Well, I knew I would
not be killed. Not in this war. It did not have anything to do with
me. It seemed no more dangerous to me myself than war in the
movies. I wished to God it was over though. Maybe it would finish
this summer. Maybe the Austrians would crack. They had always
cracked in other wars. What was the matter with this war? Every-

body said the French were through. Rinaldi said that the French had mutinied and troops marched on Paris. I asked him what happened and he said, "Oh, they stopped them." I wanted to go to Austria without war. I wanted to go to the Black Forest. I wanted to go to the Hartz Mountains. Where were the Hartz Mountains anyway? They were fighting in the Carpathians. I did not want to go there anyway. It might be good though. I could go to Spain if there was no war. The sun was going down and the day was cooling off. After supper I would go and see Catherine Barkley. I wish she were here now. I wished I were in Milan with her. I would like to eat at the Cova and then walk down the Via Manzoni in the hot evening and cross over and turn off along the canal and go to the hotel with Catherine Barkley. Maybe she would. Maybe she would pretend that I was her boy that was killed and we would go in the front door and the porter would take off his cap and I would stop at the concierge's desk and ask for the key and she would stand by the elevator and then we would get in the elevator and it would go up very slowly clicking at all the floors and then our floor and the boy would open the door and stand there and she would step out and I would step out and we would walk down the hall and I would put the key in the door and open it and go in and then take down the telephone and ask them to send a bottle of capri bianca in a silver bucket full of ice and you would hear the ice against the pail coming down the corridor and the boy would knock and I would say leave it outside the door please. Because we would not wear any clothes because it was so hot and the window open and the swallows flying over the roofs of the houses and when it was dark afterward and you went to the window very small bats hunting over the houses and close down over the trees and we would drink the capri and the door locked and it hot and only a sheet and the whole night and we would both love each other all night in the hot night in Milan. That was how it ought to be. I would eat quickly and go and see Catherine Barkley.

They talked too much at the mess and I drank wine because to-night we were not all brothers unless I drank a little and talked with the priest about Archbishop Ireland who was, it seemed, a noble man and with whose injustice, the injustices he had received and in which I participated as an American, and of which I had never heard, I feigned acquaintance. It would have been impolite not to have known something of them when I had listened to such a splendid explanation of their causes which were, after all, it seemed, misunder-standings. I thought he had a fine name and he came from Minnesota which made a lovely name: Ireland of Minnesota, Ireland of Wisconsin, Ireland of Michigan. What made it pretty was that it sounded like Island. No that wasn't it. There was more to it than that. Yes, father. That is true, father. Perhaps, father. No, father. Well, maybe yes, father. You know more about it than I do, father. The priest was good but dull. The officers were not good but dull. The King was good but dull. The wine was bad but not dull. It took the enamel off your teeth and left it on the roof of your mouth.

"And the priest was locked up," Rocca said, "because they found the three per cent bonds on his person. It was in France of course. Here they would never have arrested him. He denied all knowledge of the five per cent bonds. This took place at Béziers. I was there and reading of it in the paper, went to the jail and asked to see the priest. It was quite evident he had stolen the bonds."

"I don't believe a word of this," Rinaldi said.

"Just as you like," Rocca said. "But I am telling it for our priest here. It is very informative. He is a priest; he will appreciate it."

The priest smiled. "Go on," he said. "I am listening."

"Of course some of the bonds were not accounted for but the priest had all of the three per cent bonds and several local obligations, I forget exactly what they were. So I went to the jail, now this is the point of the story, and I stood outside his cell and I said as though I were going to confession, 'Bless me, father, for you have sinned.' "

There was great laughter from everybody.

"And what did he say?" asked the priest. Rocca ignored this and went on to explain the joke to me. "You see the point, don't you?" It seemed it was a very funny joke if you understood it properly. They poured me more wine and I told the story about the English private soldier who was placed under the shower bath. Then the major told the story of the eleven Czecho-slovaks and the Hungarian corporal. After some more wine I told the story of the jockey who found the penny. The major said there was an Italian story something like that about the duchess who could not sleep at night. At this point the priest left and I told the story about the travelling salesman who arrived at five o'clock in the morning at Marseilles when the mistral was blowing. The major said he had heard a report that I could drink. I denied this. He said it was true and by the corpse of Bacchus we would test whether it was true or not. Not Bacchus, I said. Not Bacchus. Yes, Bacchus, he said I should drink cup for cup and glass for glass with Bassi, Fillipo Vincenza. Bassi said no that was no test because he had already drunk twice as much as I. I said that was a foul lie and, Bacchus or no Bacchus, Fillipo Vincenza Bassi or Bassi Fillippo Vicenza had never touched a drop all evening and what was his name anyway? He said was my name Frederico Enrico or Enrico Federico? I said let the best man win, Bacchus barred, and the major started us with red wine in mugs. Half-way through the wine I did not want any more. I remembered where I was going.

"Bassi wins," I said. "He's a better man than I am. I have to go."

"He does really," said Rinaldi. "He has a rendezvous. I know all about it."

"I have to go."

"Another night," said Bassi. "Another night when you feel stronger." He slapped me on the shoulder. There were lighted candles on the table. All the officers were very happy. "Good-night, gentlemen," I said.

Rinaldi went out with me. We stood outside the door on the patch and he said, "You better not go up there drunk."

"I'm not drunk, Rinin. Really."

"You'd better chew some coffee."

"Nonsense."

"I'll get some, baby. You walk up and down." He came back with a handful of roasted coffee beans. "Chew those, baby, and God be with you."

"Bacchus," I said.

"I'll walk down with you."

"I'm perfectly all right."

We walked along together through the town and I chewed the coffee. At the gate of the driveway that led up to the British villa, Rinaldi said good-night.

"Good-night," I said. "Why don't you come in?"

He shook his head. "No," he said. "I like the simpler pleasures."

"Thank you for the coffee beans."

"Nothing, baby. Nothing."

I started down the driveway. The outlines of the cypresses that lined it were sharp and clear. I looked back and saw Rinaldi standing watching me and waved to him.

I sat in the reception hall of the villa, waiting for Catherine Barkley to come down. Some one was coming down the hallway. I stood up, but it was not Catherine. It was Miss Ferguson.

"Hello," she said. "Catherine asked me to tell you she was sorry she couldn't see you this evening."

"I'm so sorry. I hope she's not ill."

"She's not awfully well."

"Will you tell her how sorry I am?"

"Yes, I will."

"Do you think it would be any good to try and see her to-morrow?"

"Yes, I do."

"Thank you very much," I said. "Good-night."

I went out the door and suddenly I felt lonely and empty. I had treated seeing Catherine very lightly, I had gotten somewhat drunk and had nearly forgotten to come but when I could not see her there I was feeling lonely and hollow.

8

THE next afternoon we heard there was to be an attack up the river that night and that we were to take four cars there. Nobody knew anything about it although they all spoke with great positiveness and strategical knowledge. I was riding in the first car and as we passed the entry to the British hospital I told the driver to stop. The other cars pulled up. I got out and told the driver to go on and that if we had not caught up to them at the junction of the road to Cormons to wait there. I hurried up the driveway and inside the reception hall I asked for Miss Barkley.

"She's on duty."

"Could I see her just for a moment?"

They sent an orderly to see and she came back with him.

"I stopped to ask if you were better. They told me you were on duty, so I asked to see you."

"I'm quite well," she said, "I think the heat knocked me over yesterday."

"I have to go."

"I'll just step out the door a minute."

"And you're all right?" I asked outside.

"Yes, darling. Are you coming to-night?"

"No. I'm leaving now for a show up above Plava."

"A show?"

"I don't think it's anything."

"And you'll be back?"

"To-morrow."

She was unclasping something from her neck. She put it in my hand. "It's a Saint Anthony," she said. "And come to-morrow night."

"You're not a Catholic, are you?"

"No. But they say a Saint Anthony's very useful."

"I'll take care of him for you. Good-by."

"No," she said, "not good-by."

"All right."

"Be a good boy and be careful. No, you can't kiss me here. You can't."

"All right."

I looked back and saw her standing on the steps. She waved and I kissed my hand and held it out. She waved again and then I was out of the driveway and climbing up into the seat of the ambulance and we started. The Saint Anthony was in a little white metal capsule. I opened the capsule and spilled him out into my hand.

"Saint Anthony?" asked the driver.

"Yes."

"I have one." His right hand left the wheel and opened a button on his tunic and pulled it out from under his shirt.

"See?"

I put my Saint Anthony back in the capsule, spilled the thin gold chain together and put it all in my breast pocket.

"You don't wear him?"

"No."

"It's better to wear him. That's what it's for."

"All right," I said. I undid the clasp of the gold chain and put it around my neck and clasped it. The saint hung down on the outside of my uniform and I undid the throat of my tunic, unbuttoned the shirt collar and dropped him in under the shirt. I felt him in his metal box against my chest while we drove. Then I forgot about him. After I was wounded I never found him. Some one probably got it at one of the dressing stations.

We drove fast when we were over the bridge and soon we saw
the dust of the other cars ahead down the road. The road curved and
we saw the three cars looking quite small, the dust rising from the
wheels and going off through the trees. We caught them and passed
them and turned off on a road that climbed up into the hills. Driving
in convoy is not unpleasant if you are the first car and I settled back
in the seat and watched the country. We were in the foot-hills on
the near side of the river and as the road mounted there were the
high mountains off to the north with snow still on the tops. I looked
back and saw the three cars all climbing, spaced by the interval of
their dust. We passed a long column of loaded mules, the drivers
walking along beside the mules wearing red fezzes. They were
bersaglieri.

Beyond the mule train the road was empty and we climbed
through the hills and then went down over the shoulder of a long
hill into a river-valley. There were trees along both sides of the road
and through the right line of trees I saw the river, the water clear,
fast and shallow. The river was low and there were stretches of sand
and pebbles with a narrow channel of water and sometimes the
water spread like a sheen over the pebbly bed. Close to the bank I
saw deep pools, the water blue like the sky. I saw arched stone
bridges over the river where tracks turned off from the road and we
passed stone farmhouses with pear trees candelabraed against their
south walls and low stone walls in the fields. The road went up the
valley a long way and then we turned off and commenced to climb
into the hills again. The road climbed steeply going up and back and
forth through chestnut woods to level finally along a ridge. I could
look down through the woods and see, far below, with the sun on it,
the line of the river that separated the two armies. We went along
the rough new military road that followed the crest of the ridge and
I looked to the north at the two ranges of mountains, green and dark
to the snow-line and then white and lovely in the sun. Then, as the
road mounted along the ridge, I saw a third range of mountains,
higher snow mountains, that looked chalky white and furrowed, with
strange planes, and then there were mountains far off beyond all ·
these that you could hardly tell if you really saw. Those were all the
Austrians' mountains and we had nothing like them. Ahead there
was a rounded turn-off in the road to the right and looking down I
could see the road dropping through the trees. There were troops on

this road and motor trucks and mules with mountain guns and as we went down, keeping to the side, I could see the river far down below, the line of ties and rails running along it, the old bridge where the railway crossed to the other side and across, under a hill beyond the river, the broken houses of the little town that was to be taken.

It was nearly dark when we came down and turned onto the main road that ran beside the river.

9

THE road was crowded and there were screens of corn-stalk and straw matting on both sides and matting over the top so that it was like the entrance at a circus or a native village. We drove slowly in this matting-covered tunnel and came out onto a bare cleared space where the railway station had been. The road here was below the level of the river bank and all along the side of the sunken road there were holes dug in the bank with infantry in them. The sun was going down and looking up along the bank as we drove I saw the Austrian observation balloons above the hills on the other side dark against the sunset. We parked the cars beyond a brickyard. The ovens and some deep holes had been equipped as dressing stations. There were three doctors that I knew. I talked with the major and learned that when it should start and our cars should be loaded we would drive them back along the screened road and up to the main road along the ridge where there would be a post and other cars to clear them. He hoped the road would not jam. It was a one-road show. The road was screened because it was in sight of the Austrians across the river. Here at the brickyard we were sheltered from rifle or machine-gun fire by the river bank. There was one smashed bridge across the river. They were going to put over another bridge when the bombardment started and some troops were to cross at the shallows up above at the bend of the river. The major was a little man with upturned mustaches. He had been in the war in Libya and wore two wound-stripes. He said that if the thing went well he would see that I was decorated. I said I hoped it would go well but that he was too kind. I asked him if there was a big dugout where the drivers could stay and he sent a soldier to show me. I went with him and found the dugout, which was very good. The drivers were pleased with it and I left them there. The major asked me to have a drink with him and two other officers. We drank rum and it was very friendly. Outside it was getting dark. I asked what time the attack was to be and they said as soon as it was dark. I went back to the drivers. They were sitting in the dugout talking and when I came in they stopped. I gave them each a package of cigarettes, Macedonias, loosely packed cigarettes that spilled tobacco and needed to have the ends twisted before you smoked them. Manera lit his lighter and passed it around. The lighter was shaped like a Fiat radiator. I told them what I had heard.

"Why didn't we see the post when we came down?" Passini asked.

"It was just beyond where we turned off."

"That road will be a dirty mess," Manera said.

"They'll shell the —— out of us."

"Probably."

"What about eating, lieutenant? We won't get a chance to eat after this thing starts."

"I'll go and see now," I said.

"You want us to stay here or can we look around?"

"Better stay here."

I went back to the major's dugout and he said the field kitchen would be along and the drivers could come and get their stew. He would loan them mess tins if they did not have them. I said I thought they had them. I went back and told the drivers I would get them as soon as the food came. Manera said he hoped it would come before the bombardment started. They were silent until I went out. They were all mechanics and hated the war.

I went out to look at the cars and see what was going on and then came back and sat down in the dugout with the four drivers. We sat on the ground with our backs against the wall and smoked. Outside it was nearly dark. The earth of the dugout was warm and dry and I let my shoulders back against the wall, sitting on the small of my back, and relaxed.

"Who goes to the attack?" asked Gavuzzi.

"Bersaglieri."

"All bersaglieri?"

"I think so."

"There aren't enough troops here for a real attack."

"It is probably to draw attention from where the real attack will be."

"Do the men know that who attack?"

"I don't think so."

"Of course they don't," Manera said. "They wouldn't attack if they did."

"Yes, they would," Passini said. "Bersaglieri are fools."

"They are brave and have good discipline," I said.

"They are big through the chest by measurement, and healthy. But they are still fools."

"The granatieri are tall," Manera said. This was a joke. They all laughed.

"Were you there, Tenente, when they wouldn't attack and they shot every tenth man?"

"No."

"It is true. They lined them up afterward and took every tenth man. Carabinieri shot them."

"Carabinieri," said Passini and spat on the floor. "But those grenadiers; all over six feet. They wouldn't attack."

"If everybody would not attack the war would be over," Manera said.

"It wasn't that way with the granatieri. They were afraid. The officers all came from such good families."

"Some of the officers went alone."

"A sergeant shot two officers who would not get out."

"Some troops went out."

"Those that went out were not lined up when they took the tenth men."

"One of those shot by the carabinieri is from my town," Passini said. "He was a big smart tall boy to be in the granatieri. Always in Rome. Always with the girls. Always with the carabinieri." He laughed. "Now they have a guard outside his house with a bayonet and nobody can come to see his mother and father and sisters and his father loses his civil rights and cannot even vote. They are all without law to protect them. Anybody can take their property."

"If it wasn't that that happens to their families nobody would go to the attack."

"Yes. Alpini would. These V. E. soldiers would. Some bersaglieri."

"Bersaglieri have run too. Now they try to forget it."

"You should not let us talk this way, Tenente. Evviva l'esercito," Passini said sarcastically.

"I know how you talk," I said. "But as long as you drive the cars and behave——"

"——and don't talk so other officers can hear," Manera finished.

"I believe we should get the war over," I said. "It would not finish it if one side stopped fighting. It would only be worse if we stopped fighting."

"It could not be worse," Passini said respectfully. "There is nothing worse than war."

"Defeat is worse."

"I do not believe it," Passini said still respectfully. "What is defeat? You go home."

"They come after you. They take your home. They take your sisters."

"I don't believe it," Passini said. "They can't do that to every-body. Let everybody defend his home. Let them keep their sisters in the house."

"They hang you. They come and make you be a soldier again. Not in the auto-ambulance, in the infantry."

"They can't hang every one."

"An outside nation can't make you be a soldier," Manera said. "At the first battle you all run."

"Like the Tchecos."

"I think you do not know anything about being conquered and so you think it is not bad."

"Tenente," Passini said. "We understand you let us talk. Listen. There is nothing as bad as war. We in the auto-ambulance cannot even realize at all how bad it is. When people realize how bad it is they cannot do anything to stop it because they go crazy. There are some people who never realize. There are people who are afraid of their officers. It is with them the war is made."

"I know it is bad but we must finish it."

"It doesn't finish. There is no finish to a war."

"Yes there is."

Passini shook his head.

"War is not won by victory. What if we take San Gabriele? What if we take the Carso and Monfalcone and Trieste? Where are we then? Did you see all the far mountains to-day? Do you think we could take all them too? Only if the Austrians stop fighting. One side must stop fighting. Why don't we stop fighting? If they come down into Italy they will get tired and go away. They have their own country. But no, instead there is a war."

"You're an orator."

"We think. We read. We are not peasants. We are mechanics. But even the peasants know better than to believe in a war. Everybody hates this war."

"There is a class that controls a country that is stupid and does not realize anything and never can. That is why we have this war."

"Also they make money out of it."

"Most of them don't," said Passini. "They are too stupid. They do it for nothing. For stupidity."

"We must shut up," said Manera. "We talk too much even for the Tenente."

"He likes it," said Passini. "We will convert him."

"But now we will shut up," Manera said.

"Do we eat yet, Tenente?" Gavuzzi asked.

"I will go and see," I said. Gordini stood up and went outside with me.

"Is there anything I can do, Tenente? Can I help in any way?" He was the quietest one of the four. "Come with me if you want," I said, "and we'll see."

It was dark outside and the long light from the search-lights was moving over the mountains. There were big search-lights on that front mounted on camions that you passed sometimes on the roads at night, close behind the lines, the camion stopped a little off the road, an officer directing the light and the crew scared. We crossed the brickyard, and stopped at the main dressing station. There was a little shelter of green branches outside over the entrance and in the dark the night wind rustled the leaves dried by the sun. Inside there was a light. The major was at the telephone sitting on a box. One of the medical captains said the attack had been put forward an hour. He offered me a glass of cognac. I looked at the board tables, the instruments shining in the light, the basins and the stoppered bottles. Gordini stood behind me. The major got up from the telephone.

"It starts now," he said. "It has been put back again."

I looked outside, it was dark and the Austrian search-lights were moving on the mountains behind us. It was quiet for a moment still, then from all the guns behind us the bombardment started.

"Savoia," said the major.

"About the soup, major," I said. He did not hear me. I repeated it.

"It hasn't come up."

A big shell came in and burst outside in the brickyard. Another burst and in the noise you could hear the smaller noise of the brick and dirt raining down.

"What is there to eat?"

"We have a little pasta asciutta," the major said.

"I'll take what you can give me."

The major spoke to an orderly who went out of sight in the back and came back with a metal basin of cold cooked macaroni. I handed it to Gordini.

"Have you any cheese?"

The major spoke grudgingly to the orderly who ducked back into the hole again and came out with a quarter of a white cheese.

"Thank you very much," I said.

"You'd better not go out."

Outside something was set down beside the entrance. One of the two men who had carried it looked in.

"Bring him in," said the major. "What's the matter with you? Do you want us to come outside and get him?"

The two stretcher-bearers picked up the man under the arms and by the legs and brought him in.

"Slit the tunic," the major said.

He held a forceps with some gauze in the end. The two captains took off their coats. "Get out of here," the major said to the two stretcher-bearers.

"Come on," I said to Gordini.

"You better wait until the shelling is over," the major said over his shoulder.

"They want to eat," I said.

"As you wish."

Outside we ran across the brickyard. A shell burst short near the river bank. Then there was one that we did not hear coming until the sudden rush. We both went flat and with the flash and bump of the burst and the smell heard the singing off of the fragments and the rattle of falling brick. Gordini got up and ran for the dugout. I was after him, holding the cheese, its smooth surface covered with brick dust. Inside the dugout were the three drivers sitting against the wall, smoking.

"Here, you patriots," I said.

"How are the cars?" Manera asked.

"All right."

"Did they scare you, Tenente?"

"You're damned right," I said.

I took out my knife, opened it, wiped off the blade and pared off the dirty outside surface of the cheese. Gavuzzi handed me the basin of macaroni.

"Start in to eat, Tenente."

"No," I said. "Put it on the floor. We'll all eat."

"There are no forks."

"What the hell," I said in English.

I cut the cheese into pieces and laid them on the macaroni.

"Sit down to it," I said. They sat down and waited. I put thumb and fingers into the macaroni and lifted. A mass loosened.

"Lift it high, Tenente."

I lifted it to arm's length and the strands cleared. I lowered it into the mouth, sucked and snapped in the ends, and chewed, then took a bite of cheese, chewed, and then a drink of wine. It tasted of rusty metal. I handed the canteen back to Passini.

"It's rotten," he said. "It's been in there too long. I had it in the car."

They were all eating, holding their chins close over the basin, tipping their heads back, sucking in the ends. I took another mouthful and some cheese and a rinse of wine. Something landed outside that shook the earth.

"Four hundred twenty or minnenwerfer," Gavuzzi said.

"There aren't any four hundred twenties in the mountains," I said.

"They have big Skoda guns. I've seen the holes."

"Three hundred fives."

We went on eating. There was a cough, a noise like a railway engine starting and then an explosion that shook the earth again.

"This isn't a deep dugout," Passini said.

"That was a big trench mortar."

"Yes, sir."

I ate the end of my piece of cheese and took a swallow of wine. Through the other noise I heard a cough, then came the chuh-chuh-chuh-chuh—then there was a flash, as when a blast-furnace door is swung open, and a roar that started white and went red and on and on in a rushing wind. I tried to breathe but my breath would not come and I felt myself rush bodily out of myself and out and out and out and all the time bodily in the wind. I went out swiftly, all of myself, and I knew I was dead and that it had all been a mistake to think you just died. Then I floated, and instead of going on I felt myself slide back. I breathed and I was back. The ground was torn up and in front of my head there was a splintered beam of wood. In the jolt of my head I heard somebody crying. I thought somebody was screaming. I tried to move but I could not move. I heard the machine-guns and rifles firing across the river and all along the river. There was a great splashing and I saw the star-shells go up and burst and float whitely and rockets going up and heard the bombs, all this in a moment, and then I heard close to me some one saying "Mama Mia! Oh, mama Mia!" I pulled and twisted and got my legs loose finally and turned around and touched him. It was Passini and when I touched him he screamed. His legs were toward me and I saw in the dark and the light that they were both smashed above the knee. One leg was gone and the other was held by tendons and part of the trouser and the stump twitched and jerked as though it were not connected. He bit his arm and moaned, "Oh mama mia, mama Mia," then, "Dio te salve, Maria. Dio te salve, Maria. Oh Jesus shoot me Christ shoot me mama mia mama Mia oh purest lovely Mary shoot me. Stop it. Stop it. Stop it. Oh Jesus lovely Mary stop it. Oh oh oh oh," then choking, "Mama mama mia." Then he was quiet, biting his arm, the stump of his leg twitching.

"Porta feriti!" I shouted holding my hands cupped. "Porta feriti!" I tried to get closer to Passini to try to put a tourniquet on the legs but I could not move. I tried again and my legs moved a little. I could pull backward along with my arms and elbows. Passini was quiet now. I sat beside him, undid my tunic and tried to rip the tail of my shirt. It would not rip and I bit the edge of the cloth to start it. Then I thought of his puttees. I had on wool stockings but Passini wore puttees. All the drivers wore puttees but Passini had only one leg. I unwound the puttee and while I was doing it I saw there was no need to try and make a tourniquet because he was dead already. I made sure he was dead. There were three others to locate. I sat up straight and as I did so something inside my head moved like the weights on a doll's eyes and it hit me inside in back of my eyeballs. My legs felt warm and wet and my shoes were wet and warm inside. I knew that I was hit and leaned over and put my hand on my knee. My knee wasn't there. My hand went in and my knee was down on my shin. I wiped my hand on my shirt and another floating light came very slowly down and I looked at my leg and was very afraid. Oh, God, I said, get me out of here. I knew, however, that there had been three others. There were four drivers. Passini was dead. That left three. Some one took hold of me under the arms and somebody else lifted my legs.

"There are three others," I said. "One is dead."

"It's Manera. We went for a stretcher but there wasn't any. How are you, Tenente?"

"Where is Gordini and Gavuzzi?"

"Gordini's at the post getting bandaged. Gavuzzi has your legs. Hold on to my neck, Tenente. Are you badly hit?"

"In the leg. How is Gordini?"

"He's all right. It was a big trench mortar shell."

"Passini's dead."

"Yes. He's dead."

A shell fell close and they both dropped to the ground and dropped me. "I'm sorry, Tenente," said Manera. "Hang onto my neck."

"If you drop me again."

"It was because we were scared."

"Are you unwounded?"

"We are both wounded a little."

"Can Gordini drive?"

"I don't think so."

They dropped me once more before we reached the post.

"You sons of bitches," I said.

"I am sorry, Tenente," Manera said. "We won't drop you again."

Outside the post a great many of us lay on the ground in the dark. They carried wounded in and brought them out. I could see the light come out from the dressing station when the curtain opened and they brought some one in or out. The dead were off to one side.

The doctors were working with their sleeves up to their shoulders and were red as butchers. There were not enough stretchers. Some of the wounded were noisy but most were quiet. The wind blew the leaves in the bower over the door of the dressing station and the night was getting cold. Stretcher-bearers came in all the time, put their stretchers down, unloaded them and went away. As soon as I got to the dressing station Manera brought a medical sergeant out and he put bandages on both my legs. He said there was so much dirt blown into the wound that there had not been much hemorrhage. They would take me as soon as possible. He went back inside. Gordini could not drive, Manera said. His shoulder was smashed and his head was hurt. He had not felt bad but now the shoulder had stiffened. He was sitting up beside one of the brick walls. Manera and Gavuzzi each went off with a load of wounded. They could drive all right. The British had come with three ambulances and they had two men on each ambulance. One of their drivers came over to me, brought by Gordini who looked very white and sick. The Britisher leaned over.

"Are you hit badly?" he asked. He was a tall man and wore steel-rimmed spectacles.

"In the legs."

"It's not serious I hope. Will you have a cigarette?"

"Thanks."

"They tell me you've lost two drivers."

"Yes. One killed and the fellow that brought you."

"What rotten luck. Would you like us to take the cars?"

"That's what I wanted to ask you."

"We'd take quite good care of them and return them to the villa. 206 aren't you?"

"Yes."

"It's a charming place. I've seen you about. They tell me you're an American."

"Yes."

"I'm English."

"No!"

"Yes, English. Did you think I was Italian? There were some Italians with one of our units."

"It would be fine if you would take the cars," I said.

"We'll be most careful of them," he straightened up. "This chap of yours was very anxious for me to see you." He patted Gordini on the shoulder. Gordini winced and smiled. The Englishman broke into voluble and perfect Italian. "Now everything is arranged. I've seen your Tenente. We will take over the two cars. You won't worry now." He broke off, "I must do something about getting you out of here. I'll see the medical wallahs. We'll take you back with us."

He walked across to the dressing station, stepping carefully among the wounded. I saw the blanket open, the light came out and he went in.

"He will look after you, Tenente," Gordini said.

"How are you, Franco?"

"I am all right." He sat down beside me. In a moment the blanket in front of the dressing station opened and two stretcher-bearers came out followed by the tall Englishman. He brought them over to me.

"Here is the American Tenente," he said in Italian.

"I'd rather wait," I said. "There are much worse wounded than me. I'm all right."

"Come, come," he said. "Don't be a bloody hero." Then in Italian: "Lift him very carefully about the legs. His legs are very painful. He is the legitimate son of President Wilson." They picked me up and took me into the dressing room. Inside they were operating on all the tables. The little major looked at us furious. He recognized me and waved a forceps.

"Ça va bien?"

"Ça va."

"I have brought him in," the tall Englishman said in Italian. "The only son of the American Ambassador. He can be here until you are ready to take him. Then I will take him with my first load." He bent over me. "I'll look up their adjutant to do your papers and it will all go much faster." He stooped to go under the doorway and went out. The major was unhooking the forceps now, dropping them in a basin. I followed his hands with my eyes. Now he was bandaging. Then the stretcher-bearers took the man off the table.

"I'll take the American Tenente," one of the captains said. They lifted me onto the table. It was hard and slippery. There were many strong smells, chemical smells and the sweet smell of blood. They took off my trousers and the medical captain commenced dictating to the sergeant-adjutant while he worked, "Multiple superficial wounds of the left and right thigh and left and right knee and right foot. Profound wounds of right knee and foot. Lacerations of the scalp (he probed—Does that hurt?—Christ, yes!) with possible fracture of the skull. Incurred in the line of duty. That's what keeps you from being court-martialled for self-inflicted wounds," he said. "Would you like a drink of brandy? How did you run into this thing anyway? What were you trying to do? Commit suicide? Antitetanus please, and mark a cross on both legs. Thank you. I'll clean this up a little, wash it out, and put on a dressing. Your blood coagulates beautifully."

The adjutant, looking up from the paper, "What inflicted the wounds?"

The medical captain, "What hit you?"

Me, with the eyes shut, "A trench mortar shell."

The captain, doing things that hurt sharply and severing tissue—"Are you sure?"

Me—trying to lie still and feeling my stomach flutter when the flesh was cut, "I think so."

Captain doctor—(interested in something he was finding), "Fragments of enemy trench-mortar shell. Now I'll probe for some of this if you like but it's not necessary. I'll paint all this and—Does that sting? Good, that's nothing to how it will feel later. The pain hasn't started yet. Bring him a glass of brandy. The shock dulls the pain; but this is all right, you have nothing to worry about if it doesn't infect and it rarely does now. How is your head?"

"Good Christ!" I said.

"Better not drink too much brandy then. If you've got a fracture you don't want inflammation. How does that feel?"

Sweat ran all over me.

"Good Christ!" I said.

"I guess you've got a fracture all right. I'll wrap you up and don't bounce your head around." He bandaged, his hands moving very fast and the bandage coming taut and sure. "All right, good luck and Vive la France."

"He's an American," one of the other captains said.

"I thought you said he was a Frenchman. He talks French," the captain said. "I've known him before. I always thought he was French." He drank a half tumbler of cognac. "Bring on something serious. Get some more of that Antitetanus." The captain waved to me. They lifted me and the blanket-flap went across my face as we went out. Outside the sergeant-adjutant knelt down beside me where I lay, "Name?" he asked softly. "Middle name? First name? Rank? Where born? What class? What corps?" and so on. "I'm sorry for your head, Tenente. I hope you feel better. I'm sending you now with the English ambulance."

"I'm all right," I said. "Thank you very much." The pain that the major had spoken about had started and all that was happening was without interest or relation. After a while the English ambulance came up and they put me onto a stretcher and lifted the stretcher up to the ambulance level and shoved it in. There was another stretcher by the side with a man on it whose nose I could see, waxy-looking, out of the bandages. He breathed very heavily. There were stretchers lifted and slid into the slings above. The tall English driver came around and looked in, "I'll take it very easily," he said. "I hope you'll be comfy." I felt the engine start, felt him climb up into the front seat, felt the brake come off and the clutch go in, then we started. I lay still and let the pain ride.

As the ambulance climbed along the road, it was slow in the traffic, sometimes it stopped, sometimes it backed on a turn, then finally it climbed quite fast. I felt something dripping. At first it dropped slowly and regularly, then it pattered into a stream. I shouted to the driver. He stopped the car and looked in through the hole behind his seat.

"What is it?"

"The man on the stretcher over me has a hemorrhage."

"We're not far from the top. I wouldn't be able to get the stretcher out alone." He started the car. The stream kept on. In the dark I could not see where it came from the canvas overhead. I tried to move sideways so that it did not fall on me. Where it had run down under my shirt it was warm and sticky. I was cold and my leg hurt so that it made me sick. After a while the stream from the stretcher above lessened and started to drip again and I heard and felt the canvas above move as the man on the stretcher settled more comfortably.

"How is he?" the Englishman called back. "We're almost up."

"He's dead I think," I said.

The drops fell very slowly, as they fall from an icicle after the sun has gone. It was cold in the car in the night as the road climbed. At the post on the top they took the stretcher out and put another in and we went on.

10

IN the ward at the field hospital they told me a visitor was coming to see me in the afternoon. It was a hot day and there were many flies in the room. My orderly had cut paper into strips and tied the strips to a stick to make a brush that swished the flies away. I watched them settle on the ceiling. When he stopped swishing and fell asleep they came down and I blew them away and finally covered my face with my hands and slept too. It was very hot and when I woke my legs itched. I waked the orderly and he poured mineral water on the dressings. That made the bed damp and cool. Those of us that were awake talked across the ward. The afternoon was a quiet time. In the morning they came to each bed in turn, three men nurses and a doctor and picked you up out of bed and carried you into the dressing room so that the beds could be made while we were having our wounds dressed. It was not a pleasant trip to the dressing room and I did not know until later that beds could be made with men in them. My orderly had finished pouring water and the bed felt cool and lovely and I was telling him where to scratch on the soles of my feet against the itching when one of the doctors brought in Rinaldi. He came in very fast and bent down over the bed and kissed me. I saw he wore gloves.

"How are you, baby? How do you feel? I bring you this—" It was a bottle of cognac. The orderly brought a chair and he sat down, "and good news. You will be decorated. They want to get you the medaglia d'argento but perhaps they can get only the bronze."

"What for?"

"Because you are gravely wounded. They say if you can prove you did any heroic act you can get the silver. Otherwise it will be the bronze. Tell me exactly what happened. Did you do any heroic act?"

"No," I said. "I was blown up while we were eating cheese."

"Be serious. You must have done something heroic either before or after. Remember carefully."

"I did not."

"Didn't you carry anybody on your back? Gordini says you carried several people on your back but the medical major at the first post declares it is impossible. He had to sign the proposition for the citation."

"I didn't carry anybody. I couldn't move."

"That doesn't matter," said Rinaldi.

He took off his gloves.

"I think we can get you the silver. Didn't you refuse to be medically aided before the others?"

"Not very firmly."

"That doesn't matter. Look how you are wounded. Look at your valorous conduct in asking to go always to the first line. Besides, the operation was successful."

"Did they cross the river all right?"

"Enormously. They take nearly a thousand prisoners. It's in the bulletin. Didn't you see it?"

"No."

"I'll bring it to you. It is a successful coup de main."

"How is everything?"

"Splendid. We are all splendid. Everybody is proud of you. Tell me just exactly how it happened. I am positive you will get the silver. Go on tell me. Tell me all about it." He paused and thought. "Maybe you will get an English medal too. There was an English there. I'll go and see him and ask if he will recommend you. He ought to be able to do something. Do you suffer much? Have a drink. Orderly, go get a corkscrew. Oh you should see what I did in the removal of three metres of small intestine and better now than ever. It is one for *The Lancet*. You do me a translation and I will send it to *The Lancet*. Every day I am better. Poor dear baby, how do you feel? Where is that damn corkscrew? You are so brave and quiet I forget you are suffering." He slapped his gloves on the edge of the bed.

"Here is the corkscrew, Signor Tenente," the orderly said.

"Open the bottle. Bring a glass. Drink that, baby. How is your poor head? I looked at your papers. You haven't any fracture. That major at the first post was a hog-butcher. I would take you and never hurt you. I never hurt anybody. I learn how to do it. Every day I learn to do things smoother and better. You must forgive me for talking so much, baby. I am very moved to see you badly wounded. There, drink that. It's good. It cost fifteen lire. It ought to be good.

Five stars. After I leave here I'll go see that English and he'll get you an English medal."

"They don't give them like that."

"You are so modest. I will send the liaison officer. He can handle the English."

"Have you seen Miss Barkley?"

"I will bring her here. I will go now and bring her here."

"Don't go," I said. "Tell me about Gorizia. How are the girls?"

"There are no girls. For two weeks now they haven't changed them. I don't go there any more. It is disgraceful. They aren't girls; they are old war comrades."

"You don't go at all?"

"I just go to see if there is anything new. I stop by. They all ask for you. It is a disgrace that they should stay so long that they become friends."

"Maybe girls don't want to go to the front any more."

"Of course they do. They have plenty of girls. It is just bad administration. They are keeping them for the pleasure of dugout hiders in the rear."

"Poor Rinaldi," I said. "All alone at the war with no new girls."

Rinaldi poured himself another glass of the cognac.

"I don't think it will hurt you, baby. You take it."

I drank the cognac and felt it warm all the way down. Rinaldi poured another glass. He was quieter now. He held up the glass. "To your valorous wounds. To the silver medal. Tell me, baby, when you lie here all the time in the hot weather don't you get excited?"

"Sometimes."

"I can't imagine lying like that. I would go crazy."

"You are crazy."

"I wish you were back. No one to come in at night from adventures. No one to make fun of. No one to lend me money. No blood brother and roommate. Why do you get yourself wounded?"

"You can make fun of the priest."

"That priest. It isn't me that makes fun of him. It is the captain. I like him. If you must have a priest have that priest. He's coming to see you. He makes big preparations."

"I like him."

"Oh, I knew it. Sometimes I think you and he are a little that way. You know."

"No, you don't."

"Yes, I do sometimes. A little that way like the number of the first regiment of the Brigata Ancona."

"Oh, go to hell."

He stood up and put on his gloves.

"Oh I love to tease you, baby. With your priest and your English girl, and really you are just me underneath."

"No, I'm not."

"Yes, we are. You are really an Italian. All fire and smoke and nothing inside. You only pretend to be American. We are brothers and we love each other."

"Be good while I'm gone," I said.

"I will send Miss Barkley. You are better with her without me. You are purer and sweeter."

"Oh, go to hell."

"I will send her. Your lovely cool goddess. English goddess. My God what would a man do with a woman like that except worship her? What else is an Englishwoman good for?"

"You are an ignorant foul-mouthed dago."

"A what?"

"An ignorant wop."

"Wop. You are a frozen-faced . . . wop."

"You are ignorant. Stupid." I saw that word pricked him and kept on. "Uninformed. Inexperienced, stupid from inexperience."

"Truly? I tell you something about your good women. Your goddesses. There is only one difference between taking a girl who has always been good and a woman. With a girl it is painful. That's all I know." He slapped the bed with his glove. "And you never know if the girl will really like it."

"Don't get angry."

"I'm not angry. I just tell you, baby, for your own good. To save you trouble."

"That the only difference?"

"Yes. But millions of fools like you don't know it."

"You were sweet to tell me."

"We won't quarrel, baby. I love you too much. But don't be a fool."

"No. I'll be wise like you."

"Don't be angry, baby. Laugh. Take a drink. I must go, really."

"You're a good old boy."

"Now you see. Underneath we are the same. We are war brothers.
Kiss me good-by."

"You're sloppy."

"No. I am just more affectionate."

I felt his breath come toward me. "Good-by. I come to see you
again soon." His breath went away. "I won't kiss you if you don't
want. I'll send your English girl. Good-by, baby. The cognac is under
the bed. Get well soon."

He was gone.

11

IT was dusk when the priest came. They had brought the soup and
afterward taken away the bowls and I was lying looking at the rows of
beds and out the window at the tree-top that moved a little in the
evening breeze. The breeze came in through the window and it was
cooler with the evening. The flies were on the ceiling now and on the
electric light bulbs that hung on wires. The lights were only turned
on when some one was brought in at night or when something was
being done. It made me feel very young to have the dark come after
the dusk and then remain. It was like being put to bed after early
supper. The orderly came down between the beds and stopped.
Some one was with him. It was the priest. He stood there small,
brown-faced, and embarrassed.

"How do you do?" he asked. He put some packages down by the
bed, on the floor.

"All right, father."

He sat down in the chair that had been brought for Rinaldi and
looked out of the window embarrassedly. I noticed his face looked
very tired.

"I can only stay a minute," he said. "It is late."

"It's not late. How is the mess?"

He smiled. "I am still a great joke," he sounded tired too.
"Thank God they are all well.

"I am so glad you are all right," he said. "I hope you don't
suffer." He seemed very tired and I was not used to seeing him tired.

"Not any more."

"I miss you at the mess."

"I wish I were there. I always enjoyed our talking."

"I brought you a few little things," he said. He picked up the packages. "This is mosquito netting. This is a bottle of vermouth. You like vermouth? These are English papers."

"Please open them."

He was pleased and undid them. I held the mosquito netting in my hands. The vermouth he held up for me to see and then put it on the floor beside the bed. I held up one of the sheaf of English papers. I could read the headlines by turning it so the half-light from the window was on it. It was *The News of the World.*

"The others are illustrated," he said.

"It will be a great happiness to read them. Where did you get them?"

"I sent for them to Mestre. I will have more."

"You were very good to come, father. Will you drink a glass of vermouth?"

"Thank you. You keep it. It's for you."

"No, drink a glass."

"All right. I will bring you more then."

The orderly brought the glasses and opened the bottle. He broke off the cork and the end had to be shoved down into the bottle. I could see the priest was disappointed but he said, "That's all right. It's no matter."

"Here's to your health, father."

"To your better health."

Afterward he held the glass in his hand and we looked at one another. Sometimes we talked and were good friends but to-night it was difficult.

"What's the matter, father? You seem very tired."

"I am tired but I have no right to be."

"It's the heat."

"No. This is only the spring. I feel very low."

"You have the war disgust."

"No. But I hate the war."

"I don't enjoy it," I said. He shook his head and looked out of the window.

"You do not mind it. You do not see it. You must forgive me. I know you are wounded."

"That is an accident."

"Still even wounded you do not see it. I can tell. I do not see it myself but I feel it a little."

"When I was wounded we were talking about it. Passini was talking."

The priest put down the glass. He was thinking about something else.

"I know them because I am like they are," he said.

"You are different though."

"But really I am like they are."

"The officers don't see anything."

"Some of them do. Some are very delicate and feel worse than any of us."

"They are mostly different."

"It is not education or money. It is something else. Even if they had education or money men like Passini would not wish to be officers. I would not be an officer."

"You rank as an officer. I am an officer."

"I am not really. You are not even an Italian. You are a foreigner. But you are nearer the officers than you are to the men."

"What is the difference?"

"I cannot say it easily. There are people who would make war. In this country there are many like that. There are other people who would not make war."

"But the first ones make them do it."

"Yes."

"And I help them."

"You are a foreigner. You are a patriot."

"And the ones who would not make war? Can they stop it?"

"I do not know."

He looked out of the window again. I watched his face.

"Have they ever been able to stop it?"

"They are not organized to stop things and when they get organized their leaders sell them out."

"Then it's hopeless?"

"It is never hopeless. But sometimes I cannot hope. I try always to hope but sometimes I cannot."

"Maybe the war will be over."

"I hope so."

"What will you do then?"

"If it is possible I will return to the Abruzzi."

His brown face was suddenly very happy.

"You love the Abruzzi?"

"Yes, I love it very much."

"You ought to go there then."

"I would be too happy. If I could live there and love God and serve Him."

"And be respected," I said.

"Yes and be respected. Why not?"

"No reason not. You should be respected."

"It does not matter. But there in my country it is understood that a man may love God. It is not a dirty joke."

"I understand."

He looked at me and smiled.

"You understand but you do not love God."

"No."

"You do not love Him at all?" he asked.

"I am afraid of Him in the night sometimes."

"You should love Him."

"I don't love much."

"Yes," he said. "You do. What you tell me about in the nights. That is not love. That is only passion and lust. When you love you wish to do things for. You wish to sacrifice for. You wish to serve."

"I don't love."

"You will. I know you will. Then you will be happy."

"I'm happy. I've always been happy."

"It is another thing. You cannot know about it unless you have it."

"Well," I said. "If I ever get it I will tell you."

"I stay too long and talk too much." He was worried that he really did.

"No. Don't go. How about loving women? If I really loved some woman would it be like that?"

"I don't know about that. I never loved any woman."

"What about your mother?"

"Yes, I must have loved my mother."

"Did you always love God?"

"Ever since I was a little boy."

"Well," I said. I did not know what to say. "You are a fine boy," I said.

"I am a boy," he said. "But you call me father."

"That's politeness."

He smiled.

"I must go, really," he said. "You do not want me for anything?" he asked hopefully.

"No. Just to talk."

"I will take your greetings to the mess."

"Thank you for the many fine presents."

"Nothing."

"Come and see me again."

"Yes. Good-by," he patted my hand.

"So long," I said in dialect.

"Ciaou," he repeated.

It was dark in the room and the orderly, who had sat by the foot of the bed, got up and went out with him. I liked him very much and I hoped he would get back to the Abruzzi some time. He had a rotten life in the mess and he was fine about it but I thought how he would be in his own country. At Capracotta, he had told me, there were trout in the stream below the town. It was forbidden to play the flute at night. When the young men serenaded only the flute was forbidden. Why, I had asked. Because it was bad for the girls to hear the flute at night. The peasants all called you "Don" and when you met them they took off their hats. His father hunted every day and stopped to eat at the houses of peasants. They were always honored. For a foreigner to hunt he must present a certificate that he had never been arrested. There were bears on the Gran Sasso D'Italia but it was a long way. Aquila was a fine town. It was cool in the summer at night and the spring in Abruzzi was the most beautiful in Italy. But what was lovely was the fall to go hunting through the chestnut woods. The birds were all good because they fed on grapes and you never took a lunch because the peasants were always honored if you would eat with them at their houses. After a while I went to sleep.

12

THE room was long with windows on the right-hand side and a door
at the far end that went into the dressing room. The row of beds that
mine was in faced the windows and another row, under the windows,
faced the wall. If you lay on your left side you could see the dressing-
room door. There was another door at the far end that people sometimes came in by. If any one were going to die they put a screen
around the bed so you could not see them die, but only the shoes and
puttees of doctors and men nurses showed under the bottom of the
screen and sometimes at the end there would be whispering. Then
the priest would come out from behind the screen and afterward the
men nurses would go back behind the screen to come out again carrying the one who was dead with a blanket over him down the corridor
between the beds and some one folded the screen and took it away.

That morning the major in charge of the ward asked me if I felt
that I could travel the next day. I said I could. He said then they
would ship me out early in the morning. He said I would be better
off making the trip now before it got too hot.

When they lifted you up out of bed to carry you into the dressing
room you could look out of the window and see the new graves in
the garden. A soldier sat outside the door that opened onto the
garden making crosses and painting on them the names, rank, and
regiment of the men who were buried in the garden. He also ran
errands for the ward and in his spare time made me a cigarette lighter
out of an empty Austrian rifle cartridge. The doctors were very nice
and seemed very capable. They were anxious to ship me to Milan
where there were better X-ray facilities and where, after the operation, I could take mechano-therapy. I wanted to go to Milan too.
They wanted to get us all out and back as far as possible because all
the beds were needed for the offensive, when it should start.

The night before I left the field hospital Rinaldi came in to see
me with the major from our mess. They said that I would go to an
American hospital in Milan that had just been installed. Some American ambulance units were to be sent down and this hospital would
look after them and any other Americans on service in Italy. There
were many in the Red Cross. The States had declared war on Germany but not on Austria.

The Italians were sure America would declare war on Austria too and they were very excited about any Americans coming down, even the Red Cross. They asked me if I thought President Wilson would declare war on Austria and I said it was only a matter of days. I did not know what we had against Austria but it seemed logical that they should declare war on her if they did on Germany. They asked me if we would declare war on Turkey. I said that was doubtful. Turkey, I said, was our national bird but the joke translated so badly and they were so puzzled and suspicious that I said yes, we would probably declare war on Turkey. And on Bulgaria? We had drunk several glasses of brandy and I said yes by God on Bulgaria too and on Japan. But, they said, Japan is an ally of England. You can't trust the bloody English. The Japanese want Hawaii, I said. Where is Hawaii? It is in the Pacific Ocean. Why do the Japanese want it? They don't really want it, I said. That is all talk. The Japanese are a wonderful little people fond of dancing and light wines. Like the French, said the major. We will get Nice and Savoia from the French. We will get Corsica and all the Adriatic coast-line, Rinaldi said. Italy will return to the splendors of Rome, said the major. I don't like Rome, I said. It is hot and full of fleas. You don't like Rome? Yes, I love Rome. Rome is the mother of nations. I will never forget Romulus suckling the Tiber. What? Nothing. Let's all go to Rome. Let's go to Rome to-night and never come back. Rome is a beautiful city, said the major. The mother and father of nations, I said. Roma is feminine, said Rinaldi. It cannot be the father. Who is the father, then, the Holy Ghost? Don't blaspheme. I wasn't blaspheming, I was asking for information. You are drunk, baby. Who made me drunk? I made you drunk, said the major. I made you drunk because I love you and because America is in the war. Up to the hilt, I said. You go away in the morning, baby, Rinaldi said. To Rome, I said. No, to Milan. To Milan, said the major, to the Crystal Palace, to the Cova, to Campari's, to Biffi's, to the galleria. You lucky boy. To the Gran Italia, I said, where I will borrow money from George. To the Scala, said Rinaldi. You will go to the Scala. Every night, I said. You won't be able to afford it every night, said the major.

The tickets are very expensive. I will draw a sight draft on my grandfather, I said. A what? A sight draft. He has to pay or I go to jail. Mr. Cunningham at the bank does it. I live by sight drafts. Can a grandfather jail a patriotic grandson who is dying that Italy may live? Live the American Garibaldi, said Rinaldi. Viva the sight drafts, I said. We must be quiet, said the major. Already we have been asked many times to be quiet. Do you go to-morrow really, Federico? He goes to the American hospital I tell you, Rinaldi said. To the beautiful nurses. Not the nurses with beards of the field hospital. Yes, yes, said the major, I know he goes to the American hospital. I don't mind their beards, I said. If any man wants to raise a beard let him. Why don't you raise a beard, Signor Maggiore? It could not go in a gas mask. Yes it could. Anything can go in a gas mask. I've vomited into a gas mask. Don't be so loud, baby, Rinaldi said. We all know you have been at the front. Oh, you fine baby, what will I do while you are gone? We must go, said the major. This becomes sentimental. Listen, I have a surprise for you. Your English. You know? The English you go to see every night at their hospital? She is going to Milan too. She goes with another to be at the American hospital. They had not got nurses yet from America. I talked to-day with the head of their riparto. They have too many women here at the front. They send some back. How do you like that, baby? All right. Yes? You go to live in a big city and have your English there to cuddle you. Why don't I get wounded? Maybe you will, I said. We must go, said the major. We drink and make noise and disturb Federico. Don't go. Yes, we must go. Good-by. Good luck. Many things. Ciaou. Ciaou. Ciaou. Come back quickly, baby. Rinaldi kissed me. You smell of lysol. Good-by, baby. Good-by. Many things. The major patted my shoulder. They tiptoed out. I found I was quite drunk but went to sleep.

The next day in the morning we left for Milan and arrived forty-eight hours later. It was a bad trip. We were sidetracked for a long time this side of Mestre and children came and peeked in. I got a little boy to go for a bottle of cognac but he came back and said he could only get grappa. I told him to get it and when it came I gave him the change and the man beside me and I got drunk and slept until past Vicenza where I woke up and was very sick on the floor. It did not matter because the man on that side had been very sick on the floor several times before. Afterward I thought I could not stand the thirst and in the yards outside of Verona I called to a soldier who was walking up and down beside the train and he got me a drink of

water. I woke Georgetti, the other boy who was drunk, and offered
him some water. He said to pour it on his shoulder and went back to
sleep. The soldier would not take the penny I offered him and
brought me a pulpy orange. I sucked on that and spit out the pith
and watched the soldier pass up and down past a freight-car outside
and after a while the train gave a jerk and started.

BOOK TWO

13

WE got into Milan early in the morning and they unloaded us in the freight yard. An ambulance took me to the American hospital. Riding in the ambulance on a stretcher I could not tell what part of town we were passing through but when they unloaded the stretcher I saw a market-place and an open wine shop with a girl sweeping out. They were watering the street and it smelled of the early morning. They put the stretcher down and went in. The porter came out with them. He had gray mustaches, wore a doorman's cap and was in his shirt sleeves. The stretcher would not go into the elevator and they discussed whether it was better to lift me off the stretcher and go up in the elevator or carry the stretcher up the stairs. I listened to them discussing it. They decided on the elevator. They lifted me from the stretcher. "Go easy," I said. "Take it softly."

In the elevator we were crowded and as my legs bent the pain was very bad. "Straighten out the legs," I said.

"We can't, Signor Tenente. There isn't room." The man who said this had his arm around me and my arm was around his neck. His breath came in my face metallic with garlic and red wine.

"Be gentle," the other man said.

"Son of a bitch who isn't gentle!"

"Be gentle I say," the man with my feet repeated.

I saw the doors of the elevator closed, and the grill shut and the fourth-floor button pushed by the porter. The porter looked worried. The elevator rose slowly.

"Heavy?" I asked the man with the garlic.

"Nothing," he said. His face was sweating and he grunted. The elevator rose steadily and stopped. The man holding the feet opened the door and stepped out. We were on a balcony. There were several doors with brass knobs. The man carrying the feet pushed a button

199

that rang a bell. We heard it inside the doors. No one came. Then the porter came up the stairs.

"Where are they?" the stretcher-bearers asked.

"I don't know," said the porter. "They sleep down stairs."

"Get somebody."

The porter rang the bell, then knocked on the door, then he opened the door and went in. When he came back there was an elderly woman wearing glasses with him. Her hair was loose and half-falling and she wore a nurse's dress.

"I can't understand," she said. "I can't understand Italian."

"I can speak English," I said. "They want to put me somewhere."

"None of the rooms are ready. There isn't any patient expected." She tucked at her hair and looked at me near-sightedly.

"Show they any room where they can put me."

"I don't know," she said. "There's no patient expected. I couldn't put you in just any room."

"Any room will do," I said. Then to the porter in Italian, "Find an empty room."

"They are all empty," said the porter. "You are the first patient." He held his cap in his hand and looked at the elderly nurse.

"For Christ's sweet sake take me to some room." The pain had gone on and on with the legs bent and I could feel it going in and out of the bone. The porter went in the door, followed by the gray-haired woman, then came hurrying back. "Follow me," he said. They carried me down a long hallway and into a room with drawn blinds. It smelled of new furniture. There was a bed and a big wardrobe with a mirror. They laid me down on the bed.

"I can't put on sheets," the woman said. "The sheets are locked up."

I did not speak to her. "There is money in my pocket," I said to the porter. "In the buttoned-down pocket." The porter took out the money. The two stretcher-bearers stood beside the bed holding their caps. "Give them five lire apiece and five lire for yourself. My papers are in the other pocket. You may give them to the nurse."

The stretcher-bearers saluted and said thank you. "Good-by," I said. "And many thanks." They saluted again and went out.

"Those papers," I said to the nurse, "describe my case and the treatment already given."

The woman picked them up and looked at them through her

glasses. There were three papers and they were folded. "I don't know what to do," she said. "I can't read Italian. I can't do anything without the doctor's orders." She commenced to cry and put the papers in her apron pocket. "Are you an American?" she asked crying.

"Yes. Please put the papers on the table by the bed."

It was dim and cool in the room. As I lay on the bed I could see the big mirror on the other side of the room but could not see what it reflected. The porter stood by the bed. He had a nice face and was very kind.

"You can go," I said to him. "You can go too," I said to the nurse. "What is your name?"

"Mrs. Walker."

"You can go, Mrs. Walker. I think I will go to sleep."

I was alone in the room. It was cool and did not smell like a hospital. The mattress was firm and comfortable and I lay without moving, hardly breathing, happy in feeling the pain lessen. After a while I wanted a drink of water and found the bell on a cord by the bed and rang it but nobody came. I went to sleep.

When I woke I looked around. There was sunlight coming in through the shutters. I saw the big armoire, the bare walls, and two chairs. My legs in the dirty bandages, stuck straight out in the bed. I was careful not to move them. I was thirsty and I reached for the bell and pushed the button. I heard the door open and looked and it was a nurse. She looked young and pretty.

"Good-morning," I said.

"Good-morning," she said and came over to the bed. "We haven't been able to get the doctor. He's gone to Lake Como. No one knew there was a patient coming. What's wrong with you anyway?"

"I'm wounded. In the legs and feet and my head is hurt."

"What's your name?"

"Henry. Frederic Henry."

"I'll wash you up. But we can't do anything to the dressings until the doctor comes."

"Is Miss Barkley here?"

"No. There's no one by that name here."

"Who was the woman who cried when I came in?"

The nurse laughed. "That's Mrs. Walker. She was on night duty and she'd been asleep. She wasn't expecting any one."

While we were talking she was undressing me, and when I was

undressed, except for the bandages, she washed me, very gently and smoothly. The washing felt very good. There was a bandage on my head but she washed all around the edge.

"Where were you wounded?"

"On the Isonze north of Plava."

"Where is that?"

"North of Gorizia."

I could see that none of the places meant anything to her.

"Do you have a lot of pain?"

"No. Not much now."

She put a thermometer in my mouth.

"The Italians put it under the arm," I said.

"Don't talk."

When she took the thermometer out she read it and then shook it.

"What's the temperature?"

"You're not supposed to know that."

"Tell me what it is."

"It's almost normal."

"I never have any fever. My legs are full of old iron too."

"What do you mean?"

"They're full of trench-mortar fragments, old screws and bed-springs and things."

She shook her head and smiled.

"If you had any foreign bodies in your legs they would set up an inflammation and you'd have fever."

"All right," I said. "We'll see what comes out."

She went out of the room and came back with the old nurse of the early morning. Together they made the bed with me in it. That was new to me and an admirable proceeding.

"Who is in charge here?"

"Miss Van Campen."

"How many nurses are there?"

"Just us two."

"Won't there be more?"

"Some more are coming."

"When will they get here?"

"I don't know. You ask a great many questions for a sick boy."

"I'm not sick," I said. "I'm wounded."

They had finished making the bed and I lay with a clean smooth sheet under me and another sheet over me. Mrs. Walker went out and came back with a pajama jacket. They put that on me and I felt very clean and dressed.

"You're awfully nice to me," I said. The nurse called Miss Gage giggled. "Could I have a drink of water?" I asked.

"Certainly. Then you can have breakfast."

"I don't want breakfast. Can I have the shutters opened please?"

The light had been dim in the room and when the shutters were opened it was bright sunlight and I looked out on a balcony and beyond were the tile roofs of houses and chimneys. I looked out over the tiled roofs and saw white clouds and the sky very blue.

"Don't you know when the other nurses are coming?"

"Why? Don't we take good care of you?"

"You're very nice."

"Would you like to use the bedpan?"

"I might try."

They helped me and held me up but it was not any use. Afterward I lay and looked out the open doors onto the balcony.

"When does the doctor come?"

"When he gets back. We've tried to telephone to Lake Como for him."

"Aren't there any other doctors?"

"He's the doctor for the hospital."

Miss Gage brought a pitcher of water and a glass. I drank three glasses and then they left me and I looked out the window a while and went back to sleep. I ate some lunch and in the afternoon Miss Van Campen, the superintendent, came up to see me. She did not like me and I did not like her. She was small and neatly suspicious and too good for her position. She asked many questions and seemed to think it was somewhat disgraceful that I was with the Italians.

"Can I have wine with the meals?" I asked her.

"Only if the doctor prescribes it."

"I can't have it until he comes?"

"Absolutely not."

"You plan on having him come eventually?"

"We've telephoned him at Lake Como."

She went out and Miss Gage came back.

"Why were you rude to Miss Van Campen?" she asked after she had done something for me very skilfully.

"I didn't mean to be. But she was snooty."

"She said you were domineering and rude."

"I wasn't. But what's the idea of a hospital without a doctor?"

"He's coming. They've telephoned for him to Lake Como."

"What does he do there? Swim?"

"No. He has a clinic there."

"Why don't they get another doctor?"

"Hush. Hush. Be a good boy and he'll come."

I sent for the porter and when he came I told him in Italian to get me a bottle of Cinzano at the wine shop, a fiasco of chianti and the evening papers. He went away and brought them wrapped in newspaper, unwrapped them and, when I asked him to, drew the corks and put the wine and vermouth under the bed. They left me alone and I lay in bed and read the papers awhile, the news from the front, and the list of dead officers with their decorations and then reached down and brought up the bottle of Cinzano and held it straight up on my stomach, the cool glass against my stomach, and took little drinks making rings on my stomach from holding the bottle there between drinks, and watched it get dark outside over the roofs of the town. The swallows circled around and I watched them and the night-hawks flying above the roofs and drank the Cinzano. Miss Gage brought up a glass with some eggnog in it. I lowered the vermouth bottle to the other side of the bed when she came in.

"Miss Van Campen had some sherry put in this," she said. "You shouldn't be rude to her. She's not young and this hospital is a big responsibility for her. Mrs. Walker's too old and she's no use to her."

"She's a splendid woman," I said. "Thank her very much."

"I'm going to bring your supper right away."

"That's all right," I said. "I'm not hungry."

When she brought the tray and put it on the bed table I thanked her and ate a little of the supper. Afterward it was dark outside and I could see the beams of the search-lights moving in the sky. I watched for a while and then went to sleep. I slept heavily except once I woke sweating and scared and then went back to sleep trying to stay outside of my dream. I woke for good long before it was light and heard roosters crowing and stayed on awake until it began to be light. I was tired and once it was really light I went back to sleep again.

14

IT was bright sunlight in the room when I woke. I thought I was back at the front and stretched out in bed. My legs hurt me and I looked down at them still in the dirty bandages, and seeing them knew where I was. I reached up for the bell-cord and pushed the button. I heard it buzz down the hall and then some one coming on rubber soles along the hall. It was Miss Gage and she looked a little older in the bright sunlight and not so pretty.

"Good-morning," she said. "Did you have a good night?"

"Yes. Thanks very much," I said. "Can I have a barber?"

"I came in to see you and you were asleep with this in the bed with you."

She opened the armoire door and held up the vermouth bottle. It was nearly empty. "I put the other bottle from under the bed in there too," she said. "Why didn't you ask me for a glass?"

"I thought maybe you wouldn't let me have it."

"I'd have had some with you."

"You're a fine girl."

"It isn't good for you to drink alone," she said. "You mustn't do it."

"All right."

"Your friend Miss Barkley's come," she said.

"Really?"

"Yes. I don't like her."

"You will like her. She's awfully nice."

She shook her head. "I'm sure she's fine. Can you move just a little to this side? That's fine. I'll clean you up for breakfast." She washed me with a cloth and soap and warm water. "Hold your shoulder up," she said. "That's fine."

"Can I have the barber before breakfast?"

"I'll send the porter for him." She went out and came back. "He's gone for him," she said and dipped the cloth she held in the basin of water.

The barber came with the porter. He was a man of about fifty with an upturned mustache. Miss Gage was finished with me and went out and the barber lathered my face and shaved. He was very solemn and refrained from talking.

"What's the matter? Don't you know any news?" I asked.

"What news?"

"Any news. What's happened in the town?"

"It is time of war," he said. "The enemy's ears are everywhere."

I looked up at him. "Please hold your face still," he said and went on shaving. "I will tell nothing."

"What's the matter with you?" I asked.

"I am an Italian. I will not communicate with the enemy."

I let it go at that. If he was crazy, the sooner I could get out from under the razor the better. Once I tried to get a good look at him. "Beware," he said. "The razor is sharp."

I paid him when it was over and tipped him half a lira. He returned the coins.

"I will not. I am not at the front. But I am an Italian."

"Get the hell out of here."

"With your permission," he said and wrapped his razors in newspaper. He went out leaving the five copper coins on the table beside the bed. I rang the bell. Miss Gage came in. "Would you ask the porter to come please?"

"All right."

The porter came in. He was trying to keep from laughing.

"Is that barber crazy?"

"No, signorino. He made a mistake. He doesn't understand very well and he thought I said you were an Austrian officer."

"Oh," I said.

"Ho ho ho," the porter laughed. "He was funny. One move from you he said and he would have—" he drew his forefinger across his throat.

"Ho ho ho," he tried to keep from laughing. "When I tell him you were not an Austrian. Ho ho ho."

"Ho ho ho," I said bitterly. "How funny if he would cut my throat. Ho ho ho."

"No, signorino. No, no. He was so frightened of an Austrian. Ho ho ho."

"Ho ho ho," I said. "Get out of here."

He went out and I heard him laughing in the hall. I heard some one coming down the hallway. I looked toward the door. It was Catherine Barkley.

She came in the room and over to the bed.

"Hello, darling," she said. She looked fresh and young and very beautiful. I thought I had never seen any one so beautiful.

"Hello," I said. When I saw her I was in love with her. Everything turned over inside of me. She looked toward the door, saw there was no one, then she sat on the side of the bed and leaned over and kissed me. I pulled her down and kissed her and felt her heart beating.

"You sweet," I said. "Weren't you wonderful to come here?"

"It wasn't very hard. It may be hard to stay."

"You've got to stay," I said. "Oh, you're wonderful." I was crazy about her. I could not believe she was really there and held her tight to me.

"You mustn't," she said. "You're not well enough."

"Yes, I am. Come on."

"No. You're not strong enough."

"Yes. I am. Yes. Please."

"You do love me?"

"I really love you. I'm crazy about you. Come on please."

"Feel our hearts beating."

"I don't care about our hearts. I want you. I'm just mad about you."

"You really love me?"

"Don't keep on saying that. Come on. Please. Please, Catherine."

"All right but only for a minute."

"All right," I said. "Shut the door."

"You can't. You shouldn't."

"Come on. Don't talk. Please come on."

Catherine sat in a chair by the bed. The door was open into the hall. The wildness was gone and I felt finer than I had ever felt.

She asked, "Now do you believe I love you?"

"Oh, you're lovely," I said. "You've got to stay. They can't send you away. I'm crazy in love with you."

"We'll have to be awfully careful. That was just madness. We can't do that."

"We can at night."

"We'll have to be awfully careful. You'll have to be careful in front of other people."

"I will."

"You'll have to be. You're sweet. You do love me, don't you?"

"Don't say that again. You don't know what that does to me."

"I'll be careful then. I don't want to do anything more to you. I have to go now, darling, really."

"Come back right away."

"I'll come when I can."

"Good-by."

"Good-by, sweet."

She went out. God knows I had not wanted to fall in love with her. I had not wanted to fall in love with any one. But God knows I had and I lay on the bed in the room of the hospital in Milan and all sorts of things went through my head but I felt wonderful and finally Miss Gage came in.

"The doctor's coming," she said. "He telephoned from Lake Como."

"When does he get here?"

"He'll be here this afternoon."

15

NOTHING happened until afternoon. The doctor was a thin quiet little man who seemed disturbed by the war. He took out a number of small steel splinters from my thighs with delicate and refined distaste. He used a local anæsthetic called something or other "snow," which froze the tissue and avoided pain until the probe, the scalpel or the forceps got below the frozen portion. The anæsthetized area was clearly defined by the patient and after a time the doctor's fragile delicacy was exhausted and he said it would be better to have an X-ray. Probing was unsatisfactory, he said.

The X-ray was taken at the Ospedale Maggiore and the doctor who did it was excitable, efficient and cheerful. It was arranged by holding up the shoulders, that the patient should see personally some of the larger foreign bodies through the machine. The plates were to be sent over. The doctor requested me to write in his pocket note-book, my name, and regiment and some sentiment. He declared that the foreign bodies were ugly, nasty, brutal. The Austrians were sons of bitches. How many had I killed? I had not killed any but I was anxious to please—and I said I had killed plenty. Miss Gage was with me and the doctor put his arm around her and said she was more beautiful than Cleopatra. Did she understand that? Cleopatra the former queen of Egypt. Yes, by God she was. We returned to the little hospital in the ambulance and after a while and much lifting I was upstairs and in bed again. The plates came that afternoon, the doctor had said by God he would have them that afternoon and he did. Catherine Barkley showed them to me. They were in red envelopes and she took them out of the envelopes and held them up to the light and we both looked.

"That's your right leg," she said, then put the plate back in the envelope. "This is your left."

"Put them away," I said, "and come over to the bed."

"I can't," she said. "I just brought them in for a second to show you."

She went out and I lay there. It was a hot afternoon and I was sick of lying in bed. I sent the porter for the papers, all the papers he could get.

Before he came back three doctors came into the room. I have noticed that doctors who fail in the practice of medicine have a tendency to seek one another's company and aid in consultation. A doctor who cannot take out your appendix properly will recommend to you a doctor who will be unable to remove your tonsils with success. These were three such doctors.

"This is the young man," said the house doctor with the delicate hands.

"How do you do?" said the tall gaunt doctor with the beard. The third doctor, who carried the X-ray plates in their red envelopes, said nothing.

"Remove the dressings?" questioned the bearded doctor.

"Certainly. Remove the dressings, please, nurse," the house doctor said to Miss Gage. Miss Gage removed the dressings. I looked down at the legs. At the field hospital they had the look of not too freshly ground hamburger steak. Now they were crusted and the knee was swollen and discolored and the calf sunken but there was no pus.

"Very clean," said the house doctor. "Very clean and nice."

"Um," said the doctor with the beard. The third doctor looked over the house doctor's shoulder.

"Please move the knee," said the bearded doctor.

"I can't."

"Test the articulation?" the bearded doctor questioned. He had a stripe beside the three stars on his sleeve. That meant he was a first captain.

"Certainly," the house doctor said. Two of them took hold of my right leg very gingerly and bent it.

"That hurts," I said.

"Yes. Yes. A little further, doctor."

"That's enough. That's as far as it goes," I said.

"Partial articulation," said the first captain. He straightened up. "May I see the plates again, please, doctor?" The third doctor handed him one of the plates. "No. The left leg, please."

"That is the left leg, doctor."

"You are right. I was looking from a different angle." He returned the plate. The other plate he examined for some time. "You see, doctor?" he pointed to one of the foreign bodies which showed spherical and clear against the light. They examined the plate for some time.

"Only one thing I can say," the first captain with the beard said. "It is a question of time. Three months, six months probably."

"Certainly the synovial fluid must re-form."

"Certainly. It is a question of time. I could not conscientiously open a knee like that before the projectile was encysted."

"I agree with you, doctor."

"Six months for what?" I asked.

"Six months for the projectile to encyst before the knee can be opened safely."

"I don't believe it," I said.

"Do you want to keep your knee, young man?"

"No," I said.

"What?"

"I want it cut off," I said, "so I can wear a hook on it."

"What do you mean? A hook?"

"He is joking," said the house doctor. He patted my shoulder very delicately. "He wants to keep his knee. This is a very brave young man. He has been proposed for the silver medal of valor."

"All my felicitations," said the first captain. He shook my hand.

"I can only say that to be on the safe side you should wait at least six months before opening such a knee. You are welcome of course to another opinion."

"Thank you very much," I said. "I value your opinion."

The first captain looked at his watch.

"We must go," he said. "All my best wishes."

"All my best wishes and many thanks," I said. I shook hands with the third doctor. "Capitano Varini—Tenente Enry," and they all three went out of the room.

"Miss Gage," I called. She came in. "Please ask the house doctor to come back a minute."

He came in holding his cap and stood by the bed. "Did you wish to see me?"

"Yes. I can't wait six months to be operated on. My God, doctor, did you ever stay in bed six months?"

"You won't be in bed all the time. You must first have the wounds exposed to the sun. Then afterward you can be on crutches."

"For six months and then have an operation?"

"That is the safe way. The foreign bodies must be allowed to encyst and the synovial fluid will re-form. Then it will be safe to open up the knee."

"Do you really think yourself I will have to wait that long?"

"That is the safe way."

"Who is that first captain?"

"He is a very excellent surgeon of Milan."

"He's a first captain, isn't he?"

"Yes, but he is an excellent surgeon."

"I don't want my leg fooled with by a first captain. If he was any good he would be made a major. I know what a first captain is, doctor."

"He is an excellent surgeon and I would rather have his judgment than any surgeon I know."

"Could another surgeon see it?"

"Certainly if you wish. But I would take Dr. Varella's opinion myself."

"Could you ask another surgeon to come and see it?"

"I will ask Valentini to come."

"Who is he?"

"He is a surgeon of the Ospedale Maggiore."

"Good. I appreciate it very much. You understand, doctor, I couldn't stay in bed six months."

"You would not be in bed. You would first take a sun cure. Then you could have light exercise. Then when it was encysted we would operate."

"But I can't wait six months."

The doctor spread his delicate fingers on the cap he held and smiled. "You are in such a hurry to get back to the front?"

"Why not?"

"It is very beautiful," he said. "You are a noble young man." He stooped over and kissed me very delicately on the forehead. "I will send for Valentini. Do not worry and excite yourself. Be a good boy."

"Will you have a drink?" I asked.

"No thank you. I never drink alcohol."

"Just have one." I rang for the porter to bring glasses.

"No. No thank you. They are waiting for me."

"Good-by," I said.

"Good-by."

Two hours later Dr. Valentini came into the room. He was in a great hurry and the points of his mustache stood straight up. He was a major, his face was tanned and he laughed all the time.

"How did you do it, this rotten thing?" he asked. "Let me see the plates. Yes. Yes. That's it. You look healthy as a goat. Who's the pretty girl. Is she your girl? I thought so. Isn't this a bloody war? How does that feel? You are a fine boy. I'll make you better than new. Does that hurt? You bet it hurts. How they love to hurt you, these doctors. What have they done for you so far? Can't that girl talk Italian? She should learn. What a lovely girl. I could teach her. I will be a patient here myself. No, but I will do all your maternity work free. Does she understand that? She will make you a fine boy. A fine blonde like she is. That's fine. That's all right. What a lovely girl. Ask her if she eats supper with me. No I won't take her away from you. Thank you. Thank you very much, Miss. That's all."

"That's all I want to know." He patted me on the shoulder. "Leave the dressings off."

"Will you have a drink, Dr. Valentini?"

"A drink? Certainly. I will have ten drinks. Where are they?"

"In the armoire. Miss Barkley will get the bottle."

"Cheery oh. Cheery oh to you, Miss. What a lovely girl. I will bring you better cognac than that." He wiped his mustache.

"When do you think it can be operated on?"

"To-morrow morning. Not before. Your stomach must be emptied. You must be washed out. I will see the old lady downstairs and leave instructions. Good-by. I see you to-morrow. I'll bring you better cognac than that. You are very comfortable here. Good-by. Until to-morrow. Get a good sleep. I'll see you early." He waved from the doorway, his mustaches went straight up, his brown face was smiling. There was a star in a box on his sleeve because he was a major.

16

THAT night a bat flew into the room through the open door that led onto the balcony and through which we watched the night over the roofs of the town. It was dark in our room except for the small light of the night over the town and the bat was not frightened but hunted in the room as though he had been outside. We lay and watched him and I do not think he saw us because we lay so still. After he went out we saw a searchlight come on and watched the beam move across the sky and then go off and it was dark again. A breeze came in the night and we heard the men of the anti-aircraft gun on the next roof talking. It was cool and they were putting on their capes. I worried in the night about some one coming up but Catherine said they were all asleep. Once in the night we went to sleep and when I woke she was not there but I heard her coming along the hall and the door opened and she came back to the bed and said it was all right she had been downstairs and they were all asleep. She had been outside Miss Van Campen's door and heard her breathing in her sleep. She brought crackers and we ate them and drank some vermouth. We were very hungry but she said that would all have to be gotten out of me in the morning. I went to sleep again in the morning when it was light and when I was awake I found she was gone again. She came in looking fresh and lovely and sat on the bed and the sun rose while I had the thermometer in my mouth and we smelled the dew on the roofs and then the coffee of the men at the gun on the next roof.

"I wish we could go for a walk," Catherine said. "I'd wheel you if we had a chair."

"How would I get into the chair?"

"We'd do it."

"We could go out to the park and have breakfast outdoors." I looked out the open doorway.

"What we'll really do," she said, "is get you ready for your friend Dr. Valentini."

"I thought he was grand."

"I didn't like him as much as you did. But I imagine he's very good."

"Come back to bed, Catherine. Please," I said.

"I can't. Didn't we have a lovely night?"

"And can you be on night duty to-night?"

"I probably will. But you won't want me."

"Yes, I will."

"No, you won't. You've never been operated on. You don't know how you'll be."

"I'll be all right."

"You'll be sick and I won't be anything to you."

"Come back then now."

"No," she said. "I have to do the chart, darling, and fix you up."

"You don't really love me or you'd come back again."

"You're such a silly boy." She kissed me. "That's all right for the chart. Your temperature's always normal. You've such a lovely temperature."

"You've got a lovely everything."

"Oh no. You have the lovely temperature. I'm awfully proud of your temperature."

"Maybe all our children will have fine temperatures."

"Our children will probably have beastly temperatures."

"What do you have to do to get me ready for Valentini?"

"Not much. But quite unpleasant."

"I wish you didn't have to do it."

"I don't. I don't want any one else to touch you. I'm silly. I get furious if they touch you."

"Even Ferguson?"

"Especially Ferguson and Gage and the other, what's her name?"

"Walker?"

"That's it. They've too many nurses here now. There must be some more patients or they'll send us away. They have four nurses now."

"Perhaps there'll be some. They need that many nurses. It's quite a big hospital."

"I hope some will come. What would I do if they sent me away? They will unless there are more patients."

"I'd go too."

"Don't be silly. You can't go yet. But get well quickly, darling, and we will go somewhere."

"And then what?"

"Maybe the war will be over. It can't always go on."

"I'll get well," I said. "Valentini will fix me."

"He should with those mustaches. And, darling, when you're going under the ether just think about something else—not us. Because people get very blabby under an anæsthetic."

"What should I think about?"

"Anything. Anything but us. Think about your people. Or even any other girl."

"No."

"Say your prayers then. That ought to create a splendid impression."

"Maybe I won't talk."

"That's true. Often people don't talk."

"I won't talk."

"Don't brag, darling. Please don't brag. You're so sweet and you don't have to brag."

"I won't talk a word."

"Now you're bragging, darling. You know you don't need to brag. Just start your prayers or poetry or something when they tell you to breathe deeply. You'll be lovely that way and I'll be so proud of you. I'm very proud of you anyway. You have such a lovely temperature and you sleep like a little boy with your arm around the pillow and think it's me. Or is it some other girl? Some fine Italian girl?"

"It's you."

"Of course it's me. Oh I do love you and Valentini will make you a fine leg. I'm glad I don't have to watch it."

"And you'll be on night duty to-night."

"Yes. But you won't care."

"You wait and see."

"There, darling. Now you're all clean inside and out. Tell me. How many people have you ever loved?"

"Nobody."

"Not me even?"

"Yes, you."

"How many others really?"

"None."

"How many have you—how do you say it?—stayed with?"

"None."

"You're lying to me."

"Yes."

"It's all right. Keep right on lying to me. That's what I want you to do. Were they pretty?"

"I never stayed with any one."

"That's right. Were they very attractive?"

"I don't know anything about it."

"You're just mine. That's true and you've never belonged to any one else. But I don't care if you have. I'm not afraid of them. But don't tell me about them. When a man stays with a girl when does she say how much it costs?"

"I don't know."

"Of course not. Does she say she loves him? Tell me that. I want to know that."

"Yes. If he wants her to."

"Does he say he loves her? Tell me please. It's important."

"He does if he wants to."

"But you never did? Really?"

"No."

"Not really. Tell me the truth."

"No," I lied.

"You wouldn't," she said. "I knew you wouldn't. Oh, I love you, darling."

Outside the sun was up over the roofs and I could see the points of the cathedral with the sunlight on them. I was clean inside and outside and waiting for the doctor.

"And that's it?" Catherine said. "She says just what he wants her to?"

"Not always."

"But I will. I'll say just what you wish and I'll do what you wish and then you will never want any other girls, will you?" She looked at me very happily. "I'll do what you want and say what you want and then I'll be a great success, won't I?"

"Yes."

"What would you like me to do now that you're all ready?"

"Come to the bed again."

"All right. I'll come."

"Oh, darling, darling, darling," I said.

"You see," she said. "I do anything you want."

"You're so lovely."

"I'm afraid I'm not very good at it yet."

"You're lovely."

"I want what you want. There isn't any me any more. Just what you want."

"You sweet."

"I'm good. Aren't I good? You don't want any other girls, do you?"

"No."

"You see? I'm good. I do what you want."

17

WHEN I was awake after the operation I had not been away. You do not go away. They only choke you. It is not like dying it is just a chemical choking so you do not feel, and afterward you might as well have been drunk except that when you throw up nothing comes but bile and you do not feel better afterward. I saw sandbags at the end of the bed. They were on pipes that came out of the cast. After a while I saw Miss Gage and she said, "How is it now?"

"Better," I said.

"He did a wonderful job on your knee."

"How long did it take?"

"Two hours and a half."

"Did I say anything silly?"

"Not a thing. Don't talk. Just be quiet."

I was sick and Catherine was right. It did not make any difference who was on night duty.

There were three other patients in the hospital now, a thin boy in the Red Cross from Georgia with malaria, a nice boy, also thin, from New York, with malaria and jaundice, and a fine boy who had tried to unscrew the fuse-cap from a combination shrapnel and high explosive shell for a souvenir. This was a shrapnel shell used by the Austrians in the mountains with a nose-cap which went on after the burst and exploded on contact.

Catherine Barkley was greatly liked by the nurses because she would do night duty indefinitely. She had quite a little work with the malaria people, the boy who had unscrewed the nose-cap was a friend of ours and never rang at night, unless it was necessary but between the times of working we were together. I loved her very much and she loved me. I slept in the daytime and we wrote notes during the day when we were awake and sent them by Ferguson. Ferguson was a fine girl. I never learned anything about her except that she had a brother in the Fifty-Second Division and a brother in Mesopotamia and she was very good to Catherine Barkley.

"Will you come to our wedding, Fergy?" I said to her once.

"You'll never get married."

"We will."

"No you won't."

"Why not?"

"You'll fight before you'll marry."

"We never fight."

"You've time yet."

"We don't fight."

"You'll die then. Fight or die. That's what people do. They don't marry."

I reached for her hand. "Don't take hold of me," she said. "I'm not crying. Maybe you'll be all right you two. But watch out you don't get her in trouble. You get her in trouble and I'll kill you."

"I won't get her in trouble."

"Well watch out then. I hope you'll be all right. You have a good time."

"We have a fine time."

"Don't fight then and don't get her into trouble."

"I won't."

"Mind you watch out. I don't want her with any of these war babies."

"You're a fine girl, Fergy."

"I'm not. Don't try to flatter me. How does your leg feel?"

"Fine."

"How is your head?" She touched the top of it with her fingers. It was sensitive like a foot that had gone to sleep. "It's never bothered me."

"A bump like that could make you crazy. It never bothers you?"

"No."

"You're a lucky young man. Have you the letter done? I'm going down."

"It's here," I said.

"You ought to ask her not to do night duty for a while. She's getting very tired."

"All right. I will."

"I want to do it but she won't let me. The others are glad to let her have it. You might give her just a little rest."

"All right."

"Miss Van Campen spoke about you sleeping all the forenoons."

"She would."

"It would be better if you let her stay off nights a little while."

"I want her to."

"You do not. But if you would make her I'd respect you for it."

"I'll make her."

"I don't believe it." She took the note and went out. I rang the bell and in a little while Miss Gage came in.

"What's the matter?"

"I just wanted to talk to you. Don't you think Miss Barkley ought to go off night duty for a while? She looks awfully tired. Why does she stay on so long?"

Miss Gage looked at me.

"I'm a friend of yours," she said. "You don't have to talk to me like that."

"What do you mean?"

"Don't be silly. Was that all you wanted?"

"Do you want a vermouth?"

"All right. Then I have to go." She got out the bottle from the armoire and brought a glass.

"You take the glass," I said. "I'll drink out of the bottle."

"Here's to you," said Miss Gage.

"What did Van Campen say about me sleeping late in the mornings?"

"She just jawed about it. She calls you our privileged patient."

"To hell with her."

"She isn't mean," Miss Gage said. "She's just old and cranky. She never liked you."

"No."

"Well, I do. And I'm your friend. Don't forget that."

"You're awfully damned nice."

"No. I know who you think is nice. But I'm your friend. How does your leg feel?"

"Fine."

"I'll bring some cold mineral water to pour over it. It must itch under the cast. It's hot outside."

"You're awful nice."

"Does it itch much?"

"No. It's fine."

"I'll fix those sandbags better." She leaned over. "I'm your friend."

"I know you are."

"No you don't. But you will some day."

Catherine Barkley took three nights off night duty and then she came back on again. It was as though we met again after each of us had been away on a long journey.

18

WE had a lovely time that summer. When I could go out we rode in a carriage in the park. I remember the carriage, the horse going slowly, and up ahead the back of the driver with his varnished high hat, and Catherine Barkley sitting beside me. If we let our hands touch, just the side of my hand touching hers, we were excited. Afterward when I could get around on crutches we went to dinner at

Biffi's or the Gran Italia and sat at the tables outside on the floor of
the galleria. The waiters came in and out and there were people
going by and candles with shades on the tablecloths and after we decided that we liked the Gran Italia best, George, the headwaiter,
saved us a table. He was a fine waiter and we let him order the meal
while we looked at the people, and the great galleria in the dusk, and
each other. We drank dry white capri iced in a bucket; although we
tried many of the other wines, fresa, barbera and the sweet white
wines. They had no wine waiter because of the war and George would
smile ashamedly when I asked about wines like fresa.

"If you imagine a country that makes a wine because it tastes
like strawberries," he said.

"Why shouldn't it?" Catherine asked. "It sounds splendid."

"You try it, lady," said George, "if you want to. But let me bring
a little bottle of margaux for the Tenente."

"I'll try it too, George."

"Sir, I can't recommend you to. It doesn't even taste like strawberries."

"It might," said Catherine. "It would be wonderful if it did."

"I'll bring it," said George, "and when the lady is satisfied I'll
take it away."

It was not much of a wine. As he said, it did not even taste like
strawberries. We went back to capri. One evening I was short of
money and George loaned me a hundred lire. "That's all right,
Tenente," he said. "I know how it is. I know how a man gets short.
If you or the lady need money I've always got money."

After dinner we walked through the galleria, past the other
restaurants and the shops with their steel shutters down, and stopped
at the little place where they sold sandwiches; ham and lettuce
sandwiches and anchovy sandwiches made of very tiny brown glazed
rolls and only about as long as your finger. They were to eat in the
night when we were hungry. Then we got into an open carriage outside the galleria in front of the cathedral and rode to the hospital.
At the door of the hospital the porter came out to help with the
crutches. I paid the driver, and then we rode upstairs in the elevator.
Catherine got off at the lower floor where the nurses lived and I
went on up and went down the hall on crutches to my room; sometimes I undressed and got into bed and sometimes I sat out on the
balcony with my leg up on another chair and watched the swallows

over the roofs and waited for Catherine. When she came upstairs it
was as though she had been away on a long trip and I went along the
hall with her on the crutches and carried the basins and waited outside the doors, or went in with her; it depending on whether they
were friends of ours or not, and when she had done all there was to be
done we sat out on the balcony outside my room. Afterward I went
to bed and when they were all asleep and she was sure they would not
call she came in. I loved to take her hair down and she sat on the bed
and kept very still, except suddenly she would dip down to kiss me
while I was doing it, and I would take out the pins and lay them
on the sheet and it would be loose and I would watch her while she
kept very still and then take out the last two pins and it would all
come down and she would drop her head and we would both be inside of it, and it was the feeling of inside a tent or behind a falls.

She had wonderfully beautiful hair and I would lie sometimes
and watch her twisting it up in the light that came in the open door
and it shone even in the night as water shines sometimes just before
it is really daylight. She had a lovely face and body and lovely smooth
skin too. We would be lying together and I would touch her cheeks
and her forehead and under her eyes and her chin and throat with
the tips of my fingers and say, "Smooth as piano keys," and she would
stroke my chin with her finger and say, "Smooth as emery paper
and very hard on piano keys."

"Is it rough?"

"No, darling. I was just making fun of you."

It was lovely in the nights and if we could only touch each other
we were happy. Besides all the big times we had many small ways of
making love and we tried putting thoughts in the other one's head
while we were in different rooms. It seemed to work sometimes but
that was probably because we were thinking the same thing anyway.

We said to each other that we were married the first day she had
come to the hospital and we counted months from our wedding day.
I wanted to be really married but Catherine said that if we were
they would send her away and if we merely started on the formalities
they would watch her and would break us up. We would have to
be married under Italian law and the formalities were terrific. I
wanted us to be married really because I worried about having a
child if I thought about it, but we pretended to ourselves we were

married and did not worry much and I suppose I enjoyed not being married, really. I know one night we talked about it and Catherine said, "But, darling, they'd send me away."

"Maybe they wouldn't."

"They would. They'd send me home and then we would be apart until after the war."

"I'd come on leave."

"You couldn't get to Scotland and back on a leave. Besides, I won't leave you. What good would it do to marry now? We're really married. I couldn't be any more married."

"I only wanted to for you."

"There isn't any me. I'm you. Don't make up a separate me."

"I thought girls always wanted to be married."

"They do. But, darling, I am married. I'm married to you. Don't I make you a good wife?"

"You're a lovely wife."

"You see, darling, I had one experience of waiting to be married."

"I don't want to hear about it."

"You know I don't love any one but you. You shouldn't mind because some one else loved me."

"I do."

"You shouldn't be jealous of some one who's dead when you have everything."

"No, but I don't want to hear about it."

"Poor darling. And I know you've been with all kinds of girls and it doesn't matter to me."

"Couldn't we be married privately some way? Then if anything happened to me or if you had a child."

"There's no way to be married except by church or state. We are married privately. You see, darling, it would mean everything to me if I had any religion. But I haven't any religion."

"You gave me the Saint Anthony."

"That was for luck. Some one gave it to me."

"Then nothing worries you?"

"Only being sent away from you. You're my religion. You're all I've got."

"All right. But I'll marry you the day you say."

"Don't talk as though you had to make an honest woman of me, darling. I'm a very honest woman. You can't be ashamed of something if you're only happy and proud of it. Aren't you happy?"

"But you won't ever leave me for some one else."

"No, darling. I won't ever leave you for some one else. I suppose all sorts of dreadful things will happen to us. But you don't have to worry about that."

"I don't. But I love you so much and you did love some one else before."

"And what happened to him?"

"He died."

"Yes and if he hadn't I wouldn't have met you. I'm not unfaithful, darling. I've plenty of faults but I'm very faithful. You'll be sick of me I'll be so faithful."

"I'll have to go back to the front pretty soon."

"We won't think about that until you go. You see I'm happy, darling, and we have a lovely time. I haven't been happy for a long time and when I met you perhaps I was nearly crazy. Perhaps I was crazy. But now we're happy and we love each other. Do let's please just be happy. You are happy, aren't you? Is there anything I do you don't like? Can I do anything to please you? Would you like me to take down my hair? Do you want to play?"

"Yes and come to bed."

"All right. I'll go and see the patients first."

19

THE summer went that way. I do not remember much about the days, except that they were hot and that there were many victories in the papers. I was very healthy and my legs healed quickly so that it was not very long after I was first on crutches before I was through with them and walking with a cane. Then I started treatments at the Ospedale Maggiore for bending the knees, mechanical treatments, baking in a box of mirrors with violet rays, massage, and baths. I went over there afternoons and afterward stopped at the café and had a drink and read the papers. I did not roam around the town; but wanted to get home to the hospital from the café. All I wanted was to see Catherine. The rest of the time I was glad to kill. Mostly I slept in the mornings, and in the afternoons, sometimes, I went to the races, and late to the mechano-therapy treatments. Sometimes I stopped in at the Anglo-American Club and sat in a deep leather-cushioned chair in front of the window and read the magazines. They would not let us go out together when I was off crutches because it was unseemly for a nurse to be seen unchaperoned with a patient who did not look as though he needed attendance, so we were not together much in the afternoons. Although sometimes we could go out to dinner if Ferguson went along. Miss Van Campen had accepted the status that we were great friends because she got a great amount of work out of Catherine. She thought Catherine came from very good people and that prejudiced her in her favor finally. Miss Van Campen admired family very much and came from an excellent family herself. The hospital was quite busy, too, and that kept her occupied. It was a hot summer and I knew many people in Milan but always was anxious to get back home to the hospital as soon as the afternoon was over. At the front they were advancing on the Carso, they had taken Kuk across from Plava and were taking the Bainsizza plateau. The West front did not sound so good. It looked as though the war were going on for a long time. We were in the war now but I thought it would take a year to get any great amount of troops over and train them for combat. Next year would be a bad year, or a good year maybe. The Italians were using up an awful amount of men. I did not see how it could go on. Even if they took all the Bainsizza and Monte San Gabriele there were plenty of mountains beyond for the Austrians. I had seen them. All the highest mountains were beyond. On the Carso they were going forward but there were marshes and swamps down by the sea. Napoleon would have whipped the Austrians on the plains. He never would have fought them in the mountains. He would have let them come down and whipped them around Verona. Still nobody was whipping any one on the Western front. Perhaps wars weren't won any more. Maybe they went on forever. Maybe it was another Hundred Years' War. I put the paper back on the rack and left the club. I went down the steps carefully and walked up the Via Manzoni. Outside the Gran Hotel I met old Meyers and his wife getting out of a carriage. They were coming back from the races. She was a big-busted woman in black satin. He was short and old, with a white mustache and walked flat-footed with a cane.

"How do you do? How do you do?" She shook hands. "Hello," said Meyers.

"How were the races?"

"Fine. They were just lovely. I had three winners."

"How did you do?" I asked Meyers.

"All right. I had a winner."

"I never know how he does," Mrs. Meyers said. "He never tells me."

"I do all right," Meyers said. He was being cordial. "You ought to come out." While he talked you had the impression that he was not looking at you or that he mistook you for some one else.

"I will," I said.

"I'm coming up to the hospital to see you," Mrs. Meyers said. "I have some things for my boys. You're all my boys. You certainly are my dear boys."

"They'll be glad to see you."

"Those dear boys. You too. You're one of my boys."

"I have to get back," I said.

"You give my love to all those dear boys. I've got lots of things to bring. I've some fine marsala and cakes."

"Good-by," I said. "They'll be awfully glad to see you."

"Good-by," said Meyers. "You come around to the galleria. You know where my table is. We're all there every afternoon." I went on up the street. I wanted to buy something at the Cova to take to Catherine. Inside, at the Cova, I bought a box of chocolate and while the girl wrapped it up I walked over to the bar. There were a couple of British and some aviators. I had a martini alone, paid for it, picked up the box of chocolate at the outside counter and walked on home toward the hospital. Outside the little bar up the street from the Scala there were some people I knew, a vice-consul, two fellows who studied singing, and Ettore Moretti, an Italian from San Francisco who was in the Italian army. I had a drink with them. One of the singers was named Ralph Simmons, and he was singing under the name of Enrico DelCredo. I never knew how well he could sing but he was always on the point of something very big happening. He was fat and looked shopworn around the nose and mouth as though he had hayfever. He had come back from singing in Piacenza. He had sung Tosca and it had been wonderful.

"Of course you've never heard me sing," he said.

"When will you sing here?"

"I'll be at the Scala in the fall."

"I'll bet they throw the benches at you," Ettore said. "Did you hear how they threw the benches at him in Modena?"

"It's a damned lie."

"They threw the benches at him," Ettore said. "I was there. I threw six benches myself."

"You're just a wop from Frisco."

"He can't pronounce Italian," Ettore said. "Everywhere he goes they throw the benches at him."

"Piacenza's the toughest house to sing in the north of Italy," the other tenor said. "Believe me that's a tough little house to sing." This tenor's name was Edgar Saunders, and he sang under the name of Edouardo Giovanni.

"I'd like to be there to see them throw the benches at you," Ettore said. "You can't sing Italian."

"He's a nut," said Edgar Saunders. "All he knows how to say is throw benches."

"That's all they know how to do when you two sing," Ettore said. "Then when you go to America you'll tell about your triumphs at the Scala. They wouldn't let you get by the first note at the Scala."

"I'll sing at the Scala," Simmons said. "I'm going to sing Tosca in October."

"We'll go, won't we, Mac?" Ettore said to the vice-consul. "They'll need somebody to protect them."

"Maybe the American army will be there to protect them," the vice-consul said. "Do you want another drink, Simmons? You want a drink, Saunders?"

"All right," said Saunders.

"I hear you're going to get the silver medal," Ettore said to me. "What kind of citation you going to get?"

"I don't know. I don't know I'm going to get it."

"You're going to get it. Oh boy, the girls at the Cova will think you're fine then. They'll all think you killed two hundred Austrians or captured a whole trench by yourself. Believe me, I got to work for my decorations."

"How many have you got, Ettore?" asked the vice-consul.

"He's got everything," Simmons said. "He's the boy they're running the war for."

"I've got the bronze twice and three silver medals," said Ettore. "But the papers on only one have come through."

"What's the matter with the others?" asked Simmons.

"The action wasn't successful," said Ettore. "When the action isn't successful they hold up all the medals."

"How many times have you been wounded, Ettore?"

"Three times bad. I got three wound stripes. See?" He pulled his sleeve around. The stripes were parallel silver lines on a black background sewed to the cloth of the sleeve about eight inches below the shoulder.

"You got one too," Ettore said to me. "Believe me they're fine to have. I'd rather have them than medals. Believe me, boy, when you get three you've got something. You only get one for a wound that puts you three months in the hospital."

"Where were you wounded, Ettore?" asked the vice-consul.

Ettore pulled up his sleeve. "Here," he showed the deep smooth red scar. "Here on my leg. I can't show you that because I got puttees on; and in the foot. There's dead bone in my foot that stinks right now. Every morning I take new little pieces out and it stinks all the time."

"What hit you?" asked Simmons.

"A hand-grenade. One of those potato mashers. It just blew the whole side of my foot off. You know those potato mashers?" He turned to me.

"Sure."

"I saw the son of a bitch throw it," Ettore said. "It knocked me down and I thought I was dead all right but those damn potato mashers haven't got anything in them. I shot the son of a bitch with my rifle. I always carry a rifle so they can't tell I'm an officer."

"How did he look?" asked Simmons.

"That was the only one he had," Ettore said. "I don't know why he threw it. I guess he always wanted to throw one. He never saw any real fighting probably. I shot the son of a bitch all right."

"How did he look when you shot him?" Simmons asked.

"Hell, how should I know?" said Ettore. "I shot him in the belly. I was afraid I'd miss him if I shot him in the head."

"How long have you been an officer, Ettore?" I asked.

"Two years. I'm going to be a captain. How long have you been a lieutenant?"

"Going on three years."

"You can't be a captain because you don't know the Italian language well enough," Ettore said. "You can talk but you can't read and write well enough. You got to have an education to be a captain. Why don't you go in the American army?"

"Maybe I will."

"I wish to God I could. Oh, boy, how much does a captain get, Mac?"

"I don't know exactly. Around two hundred and fifty dollars, I think."

"Jesus Christ what I could do with two hundred and fifty dollars. You better get in the American army quick, Fred. See if you can't get me in."

"All right."

"I can command a company in Italian. I could learn it in English easy."

"You'd be a general," said Simmons.

"No, I don't know enough to be a general. A general's got to know a hell of a lot. You guys think there ain't anything to war. You ain't got brains enough to be a second-class corporal."

"Thank God I don't have to be," Simmons said.

"Maybe you will if they round up all you slackers. Oh, boy, I'd like to have you two in my platoon. Mac too. I'd make you my orderly, Mac."

"You're a great boy, Ettore," Mac said. "But I'm afraid you're a militarist."

"I'll be a colonel before the war's over," Ettore said.

"If they don't kill you."

"They won't kill me." He touched the stars at his collar with his thumb and forefinger. "See me do that? We always touch our stars if anybody mentions getting killed."

"Let's go, Sim," said Saunders standing up.

"All right."

"So long," I said. "I have to go too." It was a quarter to six by the clock inside the bar. "Ciaou, Ettore."

"Ciaou, Fred," said Ettore. "That's pretty fine you're going to get the silver medal."

"I don't know I'll get it."

"You'll get it all right, Fred. I heard you were going to get it all right."

"Well, so long," I said. "Keep out of trouble, Ettore."

"Don't worry about me. I don't drink and I don't run around. I'm no boozer and whorehound. I know what's good for me."

"So long," I said. "I'm glad you're going to be promoted captain."

"I don't have to wait to be promoted. I'm going to be a captain for merit of war. You know. Three stars with the crossed swords and crown above. That's me."

"Good luck."

"Good luck. When you going back to the front?"

"Pretty soon."

"Well, I'll see you around."

"So long."

"So long. Don't take any bad nickels."

I walked on down a back street that led to a cross-cut to the hospital. Ettore was twenty-three. He had been brought up by an uncle in San Francisco and was visiting his father and mother in Torino when war was declared. He had a sister, who had been sent to America with him at the same time to live with the uncle, who would graduate from normal school this year. He was a legitimate hero who bored every one he met. Catherine could not stand him.

"We have heroes too," she said. "But usually, darling, they're much quieter."

"I don't mind him."

"I wouldn't mind him if he wasn't so conceited and didn't bore me, and bore me, and bore me."

"He bores me."

"You're sweet to say so, darling. But you don't need to. You can picture him at the front and you know he's useful but he's so much the type of boy I don't care for."

"I know."

"You're awfully sweet to know, and I try and like him but he's a dreadful, dreadful boy really."

"He said this afternoon he was going to be a captain."

"I'm glad," said Catherine. "That should please him."

"Wouldn't you like me to have some more exalted rank?"

"No, darling. I only want you to have enough rank so that we're admitted to the better restaurants."

"That's just the rank I have."

"You have a splendid rank. I don't want you to have any more rank. It might go to your head. Oh, darling, I'm awfully glad you're not conceited. I'd have married you even if you were conceited but it's very restful to have a husband who's not conceited."

We were talking softly out on the balcony. The moon was supposed to rise but there was a mist over the town and it did not come up and in a little while it started to drizzle and we came in. Outside the mist turned to rain and in a little while it was raining hard and we heard it drumming on the roof. I got up and stood at the door to see if it was raining in but it wasn't, so I left the door open.

"Who else did you see?" Catherine asked.

"Mr. and Mrs. Meyers."

"They're a strange lot."

"He's supposed to have been in the penitentiary at home. They let him out to die."

"And he lived happily in Milan forever after."

"I don't know how happily."

"Happily enough after jail I should think."

"She's bringing some things here."

"She brings splendid things. Were you her dear boy?"

"One of them."

"You are all her dear boys," Catherine said. "She prefers the dear boys. Listen to it rain."

"It's raining hard."

"And you'll always love me, won't you?"

"Yes."

"And the rain won't make any difference?"

"No."

"That's good. Because I'm afraid of the rain."

"Why?" I was sleepy. Outside the rain was falling steadily.

"I don't know, darling. I've always been afraid of the rain."

"I like it."

"I like to walk in it. But it's very hard on loving."

"I'll love you always."

"I'll love you in the rain and in the snow and in the hail and— what else is there?"

"I don't know. I guess I'm sleepy."

"Go to sleep, darling, and I'll love you no matter how it is."

"You're not really afraid of the rain are you?"

"Not when I'm with you."

"Why are you afraid of it?"

"I don't know."

"Tell me."

"Don't make me."

"Tell me."

"No."

"Tell me."

"All right. I'm afraid of the rain because sometimes I see me dead in it."

"No."

"And sometimes I see you dead in it."

"That's more likely."

"No, it's not, darling. Because I can keep you safe. I know I can. But nobody can help themselves."

"Please stop it. I don't want you to get Scotch and crazy to-night. We won't be together much longer."

"No, but I am Scotch and crazy. But I'll stop it. It's all nonsense."

"Yes it's all nonsense."

"It's all nonsense. It's only nonsense. I'm not afraid of the rain. I'm not afraid of the rain. Oh, oh, God, I wish I wasn't." She was crying. I comforted her and she stopped crying. But outside it kept on raining.

20

ONE day in the afternoon we went to the races. Ferguson went too and Crowell Rodgers, the boy who had been wounded in the eyes by the explosion of the shell nose-cap. The girls dressed to go after lunch while Crowell and I sat on the bed in his room and read the past performances of the horses and the predictions in the racing paper. Crowell's head was bandaged and he did not care much about these races but read the racing paper constantly and kept track of all the horses for something to do. He said the horses were a terrible lot but they were all the horses we had. Old Meyers liked him and gave him tips. Meyers won on nearly every race but disliked to give tips because it brought down the prices. The racing was very crooked. Men who had been ruled off the turf everywhere else were racing in Italy. Meyers' information was good but I hated to ask him because sometimes he did not answer, and always you could see it hurt him to tell you, but he felt obligated to tell us for some reason and he hated less to tell Crowell. Crowell's eyes had been hurt, one was hurt badly, and Meyers had trouble with his eyes and so he liked Crowell. Meyers never told his wife what horses he was playing and she won or lost, mostly lost, and talked all the time.

We four drove out to San Siro in an open carriage. It was a lovely day and we drove out through the park and out along the tramway and out of town where the road was dusty. There were villas with iron fences and big overgrown gardens and ditches with water flowing and green vegetable gardens with dust on the leaves. We could look across the plain and see farmhouses and the rich green farms with their irrigation ditches and the mountains to the north. There were many carriages going into the race track and the men at the gate let us in without cards because we were in uniform. We left the carriage, bought programmes, and walked across the infield and then across the smooth thick turf of the course to the paddock. The grand-stands were old and made of wood and the betting booths were under the stands and in a row out near the stables. There was a crowd of soldiers along the fence in the infield. The paddock was fairly well filled with people and they were walking the horses around in a ring under the trees behind the grand-stand. We saw people we knew and got chairs for Ferguson and Catherine and watched the horses.

They went around, one after the other, their heads down, the grooms leading them. One horse, a purplish black, Crowell swore was dyed that color. We watched him and it seemed possible. He had only come out just before the bell rang to saddle. We looked him up in the programme from the number on the groom's arm and it was listed a black gelding named Japalac. The race was for horses that had never won a race worth one thousand lire or more. Catherine was sure his color had been changed. Ferguson said she could not tell. I thought he looked suspicious. We all agreed we ought to back him and pooled one hundred lire. The odds sheets showed he would pay thirty-five to one. Crowell went over and bought the tickets while we watched the jockeys ride around once more and then go out under the trees to the track and gallop slowly up to the turn where the start was to be.

We went up in the grand-stand to watch the race. They had no elastic barrier at San Siro then and the starter lined up all the horses, they looked very small way up the track, and then sent them off with a crack of his long whip. They came past us with the black horse well in front and on the turn he was running away from the others. I watched them on the far side with the glasses and saw the jockey fighting to hold him in but he could not hold him and when they came around the turn and into the stretch the black horse was fifteen lengths ahead of the others. He went way on up and around the turn after the finish.

"Isn't it wonderful," Catherine said. "We'll have over three thousand lire. He must be a splendid horse."

"I hope his color doesn't run," Crowell said, "before they pay off."

"He was really a lovely horse," Catherine said. "I wonder if Mr. Meyers backed him."

"Did you have the winner?" I called to Meyers. He nodded.

"I didn't," Mrs. Meyers said. "Who did you children bet on?"

"Japalac."

"Really? He's thirty-five to one!"

"We liked his color."

"I didn't. I thought he looked seedy. They told me not to back him."

"He won't pay much," Meyers said.

"He's marked thirty-five to one in the quotas," I said.

"He won't pay much. At the last minute," Meyers said, "they put a lot of money on him."

"Who?"

"Kempton and the boys. You'll see. He won't pay two to one."

"Then we won't get three thousand lire," Catherine said. "I don't like this crooked racing!"

"We'll get two hundred lire."

"That's nothing. That doesn't do us any good. I thought we were going to get three thousand."

"It's crooked and disgusting," Ferguson said.

"Of course," said Catherine, "if it hadn't been crooked we'd never have backed him at all. But I would have liked the three thousand lire."

"Let's go down and get a drink and see what they pay," Crowell said. We went out to where they posted the numbers and the bell rang to pay off and they put up 18.50 after Japalac to win. That meant he paid less than even money on a ten-lira bet.

We went to the bar under the grand-stand and had a whiskey and soda apiece. We ran into a couple of Italians we knew and McAdams, the vice-consul, and they came up with us when we joined the girls. The Italians were full of manners and McAdams talked to Catherine while we went down to bet again. Mr. Meyers was standing near the pari-mutuel.

"Ask him what he played," I said to Crowell.

"What are you on, Mr. Meyers?" Crowell asked. Meyers took out his programme and pointed to the number five with his pencil.

"Do you mind if we play him too?" Crowell asked.

"Go ahead. Go ahead. But don't tell my wife I gave it to you."

"Will you have a drink?" I asked.

"No thanks. I never drink."

We put a hundred lire on number five to win and a hundred to place and then had another whiskey and soda apiece. I was feeling very good and we picked up a couple more Italians, who each had a drink with us, and went back to the girls. These Italians were also very mannered and matched manners with the two we had collected before. In a little while no one could sit down. I gave the tickets to Catherine.

"What horse is it?"

"I don't know. Mr. Meyers' choice."

"Don't you even know the name?"

"No. You can find it on the programme. Number five I think."

"You have touching faith," she said. The number five won but did not pay anything. Mr. Meyers was angry.

"You have to put up two hundred lire to make twenty," he said. "Twelve lire for ten. It's not worth it. My wife lost twenty lire."

"I'll go down with you," Catherine said to me. The Italians all stood up. We went downstairs and out to the paddock.

"Do you like this?" Catherine asked.

"Yes. I guess I do."

"It's all right, I suppose," she said. "But, darling, I can't stand to see so many people."

"We don't see many."

"No. But those Meyers and the man from the bank with his wife and daughters——"

"He cashes my sight drafts," I said.

"Yes but some one else would if he didn't. Those last four boys were awful."

"We can stay out here and watch the race from the fence."

"That will be lovely. And, darling, let's back a horse we've never heard of and that Mr. Meyers won't be backing."

"All right."

We backed a horse named Light For Me that finished fourth in a field of five. We leaned on the fence and watched the horses go by, their hoofs thudding as they went past, and saw the mountains off in the distance and Milan beyond the trees and the fields.

"I feel so much cleaner," Catherine said. The horses were coming back, through the gate, wet and sweating, the jockeys quieting them and riding up to dismount under the trees.

"Wouldn't you like a drink? We could have one out here and see the horses."

"I'll get them," I said.

"The boy will bring them," Catherine said. She put her hand up and the boy came out from the Pagoda bar beside the stables. We sat down at a round iron table.

"Don't you like it better when we're alone?"

"Yes," I said.

"I felt very lonely when they were all there."

"It's grand here," I said.

"Yes. It's really a pretty course."

"It's nice."

"Don't let me spoil your fun, darling. I'll go back whenever you want."

"No," I said. "We'll stay here and have our drink. Then we'll go down and stand at the water jump for the steeplechase."

"You're awfully good to me," she said.

After we had been alone awhile we were glad to see the others again. We had a good time.

21

IN September the first cool nights came, then the days were cool and the leaves on the trees in the park began to turn color and we knew the summer was gone. The fighting at the front went very badly and they could not take San Gabriele. The fighting on the Bainsizza plateau was over and by the middle of the month the fighting for San Gabriele was about over too. They could not take it. Ettore was gone back to the front. The horses were gone to Rome and there was no more racing. Crowell had gone to Rome too, to be sent back to America. There were riots twice in the town against the war and bad rioting in Turin. A British major at the club told me the Italians had lost one hundred and fifty thousand men on the Bainsizza plateau and on San Gabriele. He said they had lost forty thousand on the Carso besides. We had a drink and he talked. He said the fighting was over for the year down here and that the Italians had bitten off more than they could chew. He said the offensive in Flanders was going to the bad. If they killed men as they did this fall the Allies would be cooked in another year. He said we were all cooked but we were all right as long as we did not know it. We were all cooked. The thing was not to recognize it. The last country to realize they were cooked would win the war. We had another drink. Was I on somebody's staff? No. He was. It was all balls. We were alone in the club sitting back in one of the big leather sofas. His boots were smoothly polished dull leather. They were beautiful boots. He said it was all balls. They thought only in divisions and man-power. They all squabbled about divisions and only killed them when they got them. They were all cooked. The Germans won the victories. By God they were soldiers. The old Hun was a soldier. But they were cooked too. We were all cooked. I asked about Russia. He said they were cooked already. I'd soon see they were cooked. Then the Austrians were cooked too. If they got some Hun divisions they could do it. Did he think they would attack this fall? Of course they would. The Italians were cooked. Everybody knew they were cooked. The old Hun would come down through the Trentino and cut the railway at Vicenza and then where would the Italians be? They tried that in 'sixteen, I said. Not with Germans. Yes, I said. But they probably wouldn't do that, he said. It was too simple. They'd try something complicated

and get royally cooked. I had to go, I said. I had to get back to the
hospital. "Good-by," he said. Then cheerily, "Every sort of luck!"
There was a great contrast between his world pessimism and personal
cheeriness.

I stopped at a barber shop and was shaved and went home to
the hospital. My leg was as well as it would get for a long time. I had
been up for examination three days before. There were still some
treatments to take before my course at the Ospedale Maggiore was
finished and I walked along the side street practising not limping.
An old man was cutting silhouettes under an arcade. I stopped to
watch him. Two girls were posing and he cut their silhouettes together, snipping very fast and looking at them, his head on one side.
The girls were giggling. He showed me the silhouettes before he
pasted them on white paper and handed them to the girls.

"They're beautiful," he said. "How about you, Tenente?"

The girls went away looking at their silhouettes and laughing.
They were nice-looking girls. One of them worked in the wine shop
across from the hospital.

"All right," I said.

"Take your cap off."

"No. With it on."

"It will not be so beautiful," the old man said. "But," he brightened, "it will be more military."

He snipped away at the black paper, then separated the two
thicknesses and pasted the profiles on a card and handed them to me.

"How much?"

"That's all right." He waved his hand. "I just made them for
you."

"Please." I brought out some coppers. "For pleasure."

"No. I did them for a pleasure. Give them to your girl."

"Many thanks until we meet."

"Until I see thee."

I went on to the hospital. There were some letters, an official
one, and some others. I was to have three weeks' convalescent leave
and then return to the front. I read it over carefully. Well, that was
that. The convalescent leave started October fourth when my course
was finished. Three weeks was twenty-one days. That made October
twenty-fifth. I told them I would not be in and went to the restaurant
a little way up the street from the hospital for supper and read my

letters and the *Corriere Della Sera* at the table. There was a letter from my grandfather, containing family news, patriotic encouragement, a draft for two hundred dollars, and a few clippings; a dull letter from the priest at our mess, a letter from a man I knew who was flying with the French and had gotten in with a wild gang and was telling about it, and a note from Rinaldi asking me how long I was going to skulk in Milano and what was all the news? He wanted me to bring him phonograph records and enclosed a list. I drank a small bottle of chianti with the meal, had a coffee afterward with a glass of cognac, finished the paper, put my letters in my pocket, left the paper on the table with the tip and went out. In my room at the hospital I undressed, put on pajamas and a dressing-gown, pulled down the curtains on the door that opened onto the balcony and sitting up in bed read Boston papers from a pile Mrs. Meyers had left for her boys at the hospital. The Chicago White Sox were winning the American League pennant and the New York Giants were leading the National League. Babe Ruth was a pitcher then playing for Boston. The papers were dull, the news was local and stale, and the war news was all old. The American news was all training camps. I was glad I wasn't in a training camp. The baseball news was all I could read and I did not have the slightest interest in it. A number of papers together made it impossible to read with interest. It was not very timely but I read at it for a while. I wondered if America really got into the war, if they would close down the major leagues. They probably wouldn't. There was still racing in Milan and the war could not be much worse. They had stopped racing in France. That was where our horse Japalac came from. Catherine was not due on duty until nine o'clock. I heard her passing along the floor when she first came on duty and once saw her pass in the hall. She went to several other rooms and finally came into mine.

"I'm late, darling," she said. "There was a lot to do. How are you?"

I told her about my papers and the leave.

"That's lovely," she said. "Where do you want to go?"

"Nowhere. I want to stay here."

"That's silly. You pick a place to go and I'll come too."

"How will you work it?"

"I don't know. But I will."

"You're pretty wonderful."

"No I'm not. But life isn't hard to manage when you've nothing to lose."

"How do you mean?"

"Nothing. I was only thinking how small obstacles seemed that once were so big."

"I should think it might be hard to manage."

"No it won't, darling. If necessary I'll simply leave. But it won't come to that."

"Where should we go?"

"I don't care. Anywhere you want. Anywhere we don't know people."

"Don't you care where we go?"

"No. I'll like any place."

She seemed upset and taut.

"What's the matter, Catherine?"

"Nothing. Nothing's the matter."

"Yes there is."

"No nothing. Really nothing."

"I know there is. Tell me, darling. You can tell me."

"It's nothing."

"Tell me."

"I don't want to. I'm afraid I'll make you unhappy or worry you."

"No it won't."

"You're sure? It doesn't worry me but I'm afraid to worry you."

"It won't if it doesn't worry you."

"I don't want to tell."

"Tell it."

"Do I have to?"

"Yes."

"I'm going to have a baby, darling. It's almost three months along. You're not worried, are you? Please please don't. You mustn't worry."

"All right."

"Is it all right?"

"Of course."

"I did everything. I took everything but it didn't make any difference."

"I'm not worried."

"I couldn't help it, darling, and I haven't worried about it. You mustn't worry or feel badly."

"I only worry about you."

"That's it. That's what you mustn't do. People have babies all the time. Everybody has babies. It's a natural thing."

"You're pretty wonderful."

"No I'm not. But you mustn't mind, darling. I'll try and not make trouble for you. I know I've made trouble now. But haven't I been a good girl until now? You never knew it, did you?"

"No."

"It will all be like that. You simply mustn't worry. I can see you're worrying. Stop it. Stop it right away. Wouldn't you like a drink, darling? I know a drink always makes you feel cheerful."

"No. I feel cheerful. And you're pretty wonderful."

"No I'm not. But I'll fix everything to be together if you pick out a place for us to go. It ought to be lovely in October. We'll have a lovely time, darling, and I'll write you every day while you're at the front."

"Where will you be?"

"I don't know yet. But somewhere splendid. I'll look after all that."

We were quiet awhile and did not talk. Catherine was sitting on the bed and I was looking at her but we did not touch each other. We were apart as when some one comes into a room and people are self-conscious. She put out her hand and took mine.

"You aren't angry are you, darling?"

"No."

"And you don't feel trapped?"

"Maybe a little. But not by you."

"I didn't mean by me. You mustn't be stupid. I meant trapped at all."

"You always feel trapped biologically."

She went away a long way without stirring or removing her hand.

" 'Always' isn't a pretty word."

"I'm sorry."

"It's all right. But you see I've never had a baby and I've never even loved any one. And I've tried to be the way you wanted and then you talk about 'always.' "

"I could cut off my tongue," I offered.

"Oh, darling!" she came back from wherever she had been. "You mustn't mind me." We were both together again and the self-consciousness was gone. "We really are the same one and we mustn't misunderstand on purpose."

"We won't."

"But people do. They love each other and they misunderstand on purpose and they fight and then suddenly they aren't the same one."

"We won't fight."

"We mustn't. Because there's only us two and in the world there's all the rest of them. If anything comes between us we're gone and then they have us."

"They won't get us," I said. "Because you're too brave. Nothing ever happens to the brave."

"They die of course."

"But only once."

"I don't know. Who said that?"

"The coward dies a thousand deaths, the brave but one?"

"Of course. Who said it?"

"I don't know."

"He was probably a coward," she said. "He knew a great deal about cowards but nothing about the brave. The brave dies perhaps two thousands deaths if he's intelligent. He simply doesn't mention them."

"I don't know. It's hard to see inside the head of the brave."

"Yes. That's how they keep that way."

"You're an authority."

"You're right, darling. That was deserved."

"You're brave."

"No," she said. "But I would like to be."

"I'm not," I said. "I know where I stand. I've been out long enough to know. I'm like a ball-player that bats two hundred and thirty and knows he's no better."

"What is a ball-player that bats two hundred and thirty? It's awfully impressive."

"It's not. It means a mediocre hitter in baseball."

"But still a hitter," she prodded me.

"I guess we're both conceited," I said. "But you are brave."

"No. But I hope to be."

"We're both brave," I said. "And I'm very brave when I've had a drink."

"We're splendid people," Catherine said. She went over to the armoire and brought me the cognac and a glass. "Have a drink, darling," she said. "You've been awfully good."

"I don't really want one."

"Take one."

"All right." I poured the water glass a third full of cognac and drank it off.

"That was very big," she said. "I know brandy is for heroes. But you shouldn't exaggerate."

"Where will we live after the war?"

"In an old people's home probably," she said. "For three years I looked forward very childishly to the war ending at Christmas. But now I look forward till when our son will be a lieutenant commander."

"Maybe he'll be a general."

"If it's an hundred years' war he'll have time to try both of the services."

"Don't you want a drink?"

"No. It always makes you happy, darling, and it only makes me dizzy."

"Didn't you ever drink brandy?"

"No, darling. I'm a very old-fashioned wife."

I reached down to the floor for the bottle and poured another drink.

"I'd better go to have a look at your compatriots," Catherine said. "Perhaps you'll read the papers until I come back."

"Do you have to go?"

"Now or later."

"All right. Now."

"I'll come back later."

"I'll have finished the papers," I said.

22

IT turned cold that night and the next day it was raining. Coming home from the Ospedale Maggiore it rained very hard and I was wet when I came in. Up in my room the rain was coming down heavily outside on the balcony, and the wind blew it against the glass doors. I changed my clothing and drank some brandy but the brandy did not taste good. I felt sick in the night and in the morning after breakfast I was nauseated.

"There is no doubt about it," the house surgeon said. "Look at the whites of his eyes, Miss."

Miss Gage looked. They had me look in a glass. The whites of the eyes were yellow and it was the jaundice. I was sick for two weeks with it. For that reason we did not spend a convalescent leave together. We had planned to go to Pallanza on Lago Maggiore. It is nice there in the fall when the leaves turn. There are walks you can take and you can troll for trout in the lake. It would have been better than Stresa because there are fewer people at Pallanza. Stresa is so easy to get to from Milan that there are always people you know. There is a nice village at Pallanza and you can row out to the islands where the fishermen live and there is a restaurant on the biggest island. But we did not go.

One day while I was in bed with jaundice Miss Van Campen came in the room, opened the door into the armoire and saw the empty bottles there. I had sent a load of them down by the porter and I believe she must have seen them going out and come up to find some more. They were mostly vermouth bottles, marsala bottles, capri bottles, empty chianti flasks and a few cognac bottles. The porter had carried out the large bottles, those that had held vermouth, and the straw-covered chianti flasks, and left the brandy bottles for the last. It was the brandy bottles and a bottle shaped like a bear, which had held kümmel, that Miss Van Campen found. The bear-shaped bottle enraged her particularly. She held it up, the bear was sitting up on his haunches with his paws up, there was a cork in his glass head and a few sticky crystals at the bottom. I laughed.

"It is kümmel," I said. "The best kümmel comes in those bear-shaped bottles. It comes from Russia."

"Those are all brandy bottles, aren't they?" Miss Van Campen asked.

"I can't see them all," I said. "But they probably are."

"How long has this been going on?"

"I bought them and brought them in myself," I said. "I have had Italian officers visit me frequently and I have kept brandy to offer them."

"You haven't been drinking it yourself?" she said.

"I have also drunk it myself."

"Brandy," she said. "Eleven empty bottles of brandy and that bear liquid."

"Kümmel."

"I will send for some one to take them away. Those are all the empty bottles you have?"

"For the moment."

"And I was pitying you having jaundice. Pity is something that is wasted on you."

"Thank you."

"I suppose you can't be blamed for not wanting to go back to the front. But I should think you would try something more intelligent than producing jaundice with alcoholism."

"With what?"

"With alcoholism. You heard me say it." I did not say anything. "Unless you find something else I'm afraid you will have to go back to the front when you are through with your jaundice. I don't believe self-inflicted jaundice entitles you to a convalescent leave."

"You don't?"

"I do not."

"Have you ever had jaundice, Miss Van Campen?"

"No, but I have seen a great deal of it."

"You noticed how the patients enjoyed it?"

"I suppose it is better than the front."

"Miss Van Campen," I said, "did you ever know a man who tried to disable himself by kicking himself in the scrotum?"

Miss Van Campen ignored the actual question. She had to ignore it or leave the room. She was not ready to leave because she had disliked me for a long time and she was now cashing in.

"I have known many men to escape the front through self-inflicted wounds."

"That wasn't the question. I have seen self-inflicted wounds also. I asked you if you had ever known a man who had tried to disable himself by kicking himself in the scrotum. Because that is the nearest sensation to jaundice and it is a sensation that I believe few women have ever experienced. That was why I asked you if you had ever had the jaundice, Miss Van Campen, because—" Miss Van Campen left the room. Later Miss Gage came in.

"What did you say to Van Campen? She was furious."

"We were comparing sensations. I was going to suggest that she had never experienced childbirth——"

"You're a fool," Gage said. "She's after your scalp."

"She has my scalp," I said. "She's lost me my leave and she might try and get me court-martialled. She's mean enough."

"She never liked you," Gage said. "What's it about?"

"She says I've drunk myself into jaundice so as not to go back to the front."

"Pooh," said Gage. "I'll swear you've never taken a drink. Everybody will swear you've never taken a drink."

"She found the bottles."

"I've told you a hundred times to clear out those bottles. Where are they now?"

"In the armoire."

"Have you a suitcase?"

"No. Put them in that rucksack."

Miss Gage packed the bottles in the rucksack. "I'll give them to the porter," she said. She started for the door.

"Just a minute," Miss Van Campen said. "I'll take those bottles." She had the porter with her. "Carry them, please," she said. "I want to show them to the doctor when I make my report."

She went down the hall. The porter carried the sack. He knew what was in it.

Nothing happened except that I lost my leave.

23

THE night I was to return to the front I sent the porter down to hold a seat for me on the train when it came from Turin. The train was to leave at midnight. It was made up at Turin and reached Milan about half-past ten at night and lay in the station until time to leave. You had to be there when it came in, to get a seat. The porter took a friend with him, a machine-gunner on leave who worked in a tailor shop, and was sure that between them they could hold a place. I gave them money for platform tickets and had them take my baggage. There was a big rucksack and two musettes.

I said good-by at the hospital at about five o'clock and went out.

The porter had my baggage in his lodge and I told him I would be at the station a little before midnight. His wife called me "Signorino" and cried. She wiped her eyes and shook hands and then cried again. I patted her on the back and she cried once more. She had done my mending and was a very short dumpy, happy-faced woman with white hair. When she cried her whole face went to pieces. I went down to the corner where there was a wine shop and waited inside looking out the window. It was dark outside and cold and misty. I paid for my coffee and grappa and I watched the people going by in the light from the window. I saw Catherine and knocked on the window. She looked, saw me and smiled, and I went out to meet her. She was wearing a dark blue cape and a soft felt hat. We walked along together, along the sidewalk past the wine shops, then across the market square and up the street and through the archway to the cathedral square. There were streetcar tracks and beyond them was the cathedral. It was white and wet in the mist. We crossed the tram tracks. On our left were the shops, their windows lighted, and the entrance to the galleria. There was a fog in the square and when we came close to the front of the cathedral it was very big and the stone was wet.

"Would you like to go in?"

"No," Catherine said. We walked along. There was a soldier standing with his girl in the shadow of one of the stone buttresses ahead of us and we passed them. They were standing tight up against the stone and he had put his cape around her.

"They're like us," I said.

"Nobody is like us," Catherine said. She did not mean it happily.

"I wish they had some place to go."

"It mightn't do them any good."

"I don't know. Everybody ought to have some place to go."

"They have the cathedral," Catherine said. We were past it now. We crossed the far end of the square and looked back at the cathedral. It was fine in the mist. We were standing in front of the leather goods shop. There were riding boots, a rucksack and ski boots in the window. Each article was set apart as an exhibit; the rucksack in the centre, the riding boots on one side and the ski boots on the other. The leather was dark and oiled smooth as a used saddle. The electric light made high lights on the dull oiled leather.

"We'll ski some time."

"In two months there will be ski-ing at Mürren," Catherine said.

"Let's go there."

"All right," she said. We went on past other windows and turned down a side street.

"I've never been this way."

"This is the way I go to the hospital," I said. It was a narrow street and we kept on the right-hand side. There were many people passing in the fog. There were shops and all the windows were lighted. We looked in a window at a pile of cheese. I stopped in front of an armorer's shop.

"Come in a minute. I have to buy a gun."

"What sort of gun?"

"A pistol." We went in and I unbuttoned my belt and laid it with the empty holster on the counter. Two women were behind the counter. The women brought out several pistols.

"It must fit this," I said, opening the holster. It was a gray leather holster and I had bought it second-hand to wear in the town.

"Have they good pistols?" Catherine asked.

"They're all about the same. Can I try this one?" I asked the woman.

"I have no place now to shoot," she said. "But it is very good. You will not make a mistake with it."

I snapped it and pulled back the action. The spring was rather strong but it worked smoothly. I sighted it and snapped it again.

"It is used," the woman said. "It belonged to an officer who was an excellent shot."

"Did you sell it to him?"

"Yes."

"How did you get it back?"

"From his orderly."

"Maybe you have mine," I said. "How much is this?"

"Fifty lire. It is very cheap."

"All right. I want two extra clips and a box of cartridges."

She brought them from under the counter.

"Have you any need for a sword?" she asked. "I have some used swords very cheap."

"I'm going to the front," I said.

"Oh yes, then you won't need a sword," she said.

I paid for the cartridges and the pistol, filled the magazine and put it in place, put the pistol in my empty holster, filled the extra clips with cartridges and put them in the leather slots on the holster and then buckled on my belt. The pistol felt heavy on the belt. Still, I thought, it was better to have a regulation pistol. You could always get shells.

"Now we're fully armed," I said. "That was the one thing I had to remember to do. Some one got my other one going to the hospital."

"I hope it's a good pistol," Catherine said.

"Was there anything else?" the woman asked.

"I don't believe so."

"The pistol has a lanyard," she said.

"So I noticed." The woman wanted to sell something else.

"You don't need a whistle?"

"I don't believe so."

The woman said good-by and we went out onto the sidewalk. Catherine looked in the window. The woman looked out and bowed to us.

"What are those little mirrors set in wood for?"

"They're for attracting birds. They twirl them out in the field and larks see them and come out and the Italians shoot them."

"They are an ingenious people," Catherine said. "You don't shoot larks do you, darling, in America?"

"Not especially."

We crossed the street and started to walk up the other side.

"I feel better now," Catherine said. "I felt terrible when we started."

"We always feel good when we're together."

"We always will be together."

"Yes, except that I'm going away at midnight."

"Don't think about it, darling."

We walked on up the street. The fog made the lights yellow.

"Aren't you tired?" Catherine asked.

"How about you?"

"I'm all right. It's fun to walk."

"But let's not do it too long."

"No."

We turned down a side street where there were no lights and walked in the street. I stopped and kissed Catherine. While I kissed her I felt her hand on my shoulder. She had pulled my cape around her so it covered both of us. We were standing in the street against a high wall.

"Let's go some place," I said.

"Good," said Catherine. We walked on along the street until it came out onto a wider street that was beside a canal. On the other side was a brick wall and buildings. Ahead, down the street, I saw a streetcar cross a bridge.

"We can get a cab up at the bridge," I said. We stood on the bridge in the fog waiting for a carriage. Several streetcars passed, full of people going home. Then a carriage came along but there was some one in it. The fog was turning to rain.

"We could walk or take a tram," Catherine said.

"One will be along," I said. "They go by here."

"Here one comes," she said.

The driver stopped his horse and lowered the metal sign on his meter. The top of the carriage was up and there were drops of water on the driver's coat. His varnished hat was shining in the wet. We sat back in the seat together and the top of the carriage made it dark.

"Where did you tell him to go?"

"To the station. There's a hotel across from the station where we can go."

"We can go the way we are? Without luggage?"

"Yes," I said.

It was a long ride to the station up side streets in the rain.

"Won't we have dinner?" Catherine asked. "I'm afraid I'll be hungry."

"We'll have it in our room."

"I haven't anything to wear. I haven't even a night-gown."

"We'll get one," I said and called to the driver.

"Go to the Via Manzoni and up that." He nodded and turned off to the left at the next corner. On the big street Catherine watched for a shop.

"Here's a place," she said. I stopped the driver and Catherine got out, walked across the sidewalk and went inside. I sat back in the carriage and waited for her. It was raining and I could smell the wet street and the horse steaming in the rain. She came back with a package and got in and we drove on.

"I was very extravagant, darling," she said, "but it's a fine night-gown."

At the hotel I asked Catherine to wait in the carriage while I went in and spoke to the manager. There were plenty of rooms. Then I went out to the carriage, paid the driver, and Catherine and I walked in together. The small boy in buttons carried the package. The manager bowed us toward the elevator. There was much red plush and brass. The manager went up in the elevator with us.

"Monsieur and Madame wish dinner in their rooms?"

"Yes. Will you have the menu brought up?" I said.

"You wish something special for dinner. Some game or a souf-flé?"

The elevator passed three floors with a click each time, then clicked and stopped.

"What have you as game?"

"I could get a pheasant, or a woodcock."

"A woodcock," I said. We walked down the corridor. The carpet was worn. There were many doors. The manager stopped and un-locked a door and opened it.

"Here you are. A lovely room."

The small boy in buttons put the package on the table in the centre of the room. The manager opened the curtains.

"It is foggy outside," he said. The room was furnished in red plush. There were many mirrors, two chairs and a large bed with a satin coverlet. A door led to the bathroom.

"I will send up the menu," the manager said. He bowed and went out.

I went to the window and looked out, then pulled a cord that shut the thick plush curtains. Catherine was sitting on the bed, look-ing at the cut glass chandelier. She had taken her hat off and her hair shone under the light. She saw herself in one of the mirrors and put her hands to her hair. I saw her in three other mirrors. She did not look happy. She let her cape fall on the bed.

"What's the matter, darling?"

"I never felt like a whore before," she said. I went over to the window and pulled the curtain aside and looked out. I had not thought it would be like this.

"You're not a whore."

"I know it, darling. But it isn't nice to feel like one." Her voice was dry and flat.

"This was the best hotel we could get in," I said. I looked out the window. Across the square were the lights of the station. There were carriages going by on the street and I saw the trees in the park. The lights from the hotel shone on the wet pavement. Oh, hell, I thought, do we have to argue now?

"Come over here please," Catherine said. The flatness was all gone out of her voice. "Come over, please. I'm a good girl again." I looked over at the bed. She was smiling.

I went over and sat on the bed beside her and kissed her.

"You're my good girl."

"I'm certainly yours," she said.

After we had eaten we felt fine, and then after, we felt very happy and in a little time the room felt like our own home. My room at the hospital had been our own home and this room was our home too in the same way.

Catherine wore my tunic over her shoulders while we ate. We were very hungry and the meal was good and we drank a bottle of Capri and a bottle of St. Estephe. I drank most of it but Catherine drank some and it made her feel splendid. For dinner we had a woodcock and soufflé potatoes and purée de marron, a salad, and zabaione for dessert.

"It's a fine room," Catherine said. "It's a lovely room. We should have stayed here all the time we've been in Milan."

"It's a funny room. But it's nice."

"Vice is a wonderful thing," Catherine said. "The people who go in for it seem to have good taste about it. The red plush is really fine. It's just the thing. And the mirrors are very attractive."

"You're a lovely girl."

"I don't know how a room like this would be for waking up in the morning. But it's really a splendid room." I poured another glass of St. Estephe.

"I wish we could do something really sinful," Catherine said. "Everything we do seems so innocent and simple. I can't believe we do anything wrong."

"You're a grand girl."

"I only feel hungry. I get terribly hungry."

"You're a fine simple girl," I said.

"I am a simple girl. No one ever understood it except you."

"Once when I first met you I spent an afternoon thinking how we would go to the Hotel Cavour together and how it would be."

"That was awfully cheeky of you. This isn't the Cavour is it?"

"No. They wouldn't have taken us in there."

"They'll take us in some time. But that's how we differ, darling. I never thought about anything."

"Didn't you ever at all?"

"A little," she said.

"Oh you're a lovely girl."

I poured another glass of wine.

"I'm a very simple girl," Catherine said.

"I didn't think so at first. I thought you were a crazy girl."

"I was a little crazy. But I wasn't crazy in any complicated manner. I didn't confuse you did I, darling?"

"Wine is a grand thing," I said. "It makes you forget all the bad."

"It's lovely," said Catherine. "But it's given my father gout very badly."

"Have you a father?"

"Yes," said Catherine. "He has gout. You won't ever have to meet him. Haven't you a father?"

"No," I said. "A step-father."

"Will I like him?"

"You won't have to meet him."

"We have such a fine time," Catherine said. "I don't take any interest in anything else any more. I'm so very happy married to you."

The waiter came and took away the things. After a while we were very still and we could hear the rain. Down below on the street a motor car honked.

> " 'But at my back I always hear
>   Time's wingèd chariot hurrying near,' "

I said.

"I know that poem," Catherine said. "It's by Marvell. But it's about a girl who wouldn't live with a man."

My head felt very clear and cold and I wanted to talk facts.

"Where will you have the baby?"

"I don't know. The best place I can find."

"How will you arrange it?"

"The best way I can. Don't worry, darling. We may have several babies before the war is over."

"It's nearly time to go."

"I know. You can make it time if you want."

"No."

"Then don't worry, darling. You were fine until now and now you're worrying."

"I won't. How often will you write?"

"Every day. Do they read your letters?"

"They can't read English enough to hurt any."

"I'll make them very confusing," Catherine said.

"But not too confusing."

"I'll just make them a little confusing."

"I'm afraid we have to start to go."

"All right, darling."

"I hate to leave our fine house."

"So do I."

"But we have to go."

"All right. But we're never settled in our home very long."

"We will be."

"I'll have a fine home for you when you come back."

"Maybe I'll be back right away."

"Perhaps you'll be hurt just a little in the foot."

"Or the lobe of the ear."

"No I want your ears the way they are."

"And not my feet?"

"Your feet have been hit already."

"We have to go, darling. Really."

"All right. You go first."

24

WE walked down the stairs instead of taking the elevator. The carpet on the stairs was worn. I had paid for the dinner when it came up and the waiter, who had brought it, was sitting on a chair near the door. He jumped up and bowed and I went with him into the side room and paid the bill for the room. The manager had remembered me as a friend and refused payment in advance but when he retired he had remembered to have the waiter stationed at the door so that I should not get out without paying. I suppose that had happened; even with his friends. One had so many friends in a war.

I asked the waiter to get us a carriage and he took Catherine's package that I was carrying and went out with an umbrella. Outside through the window we saw him crossing the street in the rain. We stood in the side room and looked out the window.

"How do you feel, Cat?"

"Sleepy."

"I feel hollow and hungry."

"Have you anything to eat?"

"Yes, in my musette."

I saw the carriage coming. It stopped, the horse's head hanging in the rain, and the waiter stepped out, opened his umbrella, and came toward the hotel. We met him at the door and walked out under the umbrella down the wet walk to the carriage at the curb. Water was running in the gutter.

"There is your package on the seat," the waiter said. He stood with the umbrella until we were in and I had tipped him.

"Many thanks. Pleasant journey," he said. The coachman lifted the reins and the horse started. The waiter turned away under the umbrella and went toward the hotel. We drove down the street and turned to the left, then came around to the right in front of the station. There were two carabinieri standing under the light just out of the rain. The light shone on their hats. The rain was clear and transparent against the light from the station. A porter came out from under the shelter of the station, his shoulders up against the rain.

"No," I said. "Thanks. I don't need thee."

He went back under the shelter of the archway. I turned to Catherine. Her face was in the shadow from the hood of the carriage.

"We might as well say good-by."

"I can't go in?"

"No."

"Good-by, Cat."

"Will you tell him the hospital?"

"Yes."

I told the driver the address to drive to. He nodded.

"Good-by," I said. "Take good care of yourself and young Catherine."

"Good-by, darling."

"Good-by," I said. I stepped out into the rain and the carriage started. Catherine leaned out and I saw her face in the light. She smiled and waved. The carriage went up the street, Catherine pointed in toward the archway. I looked, there were only the two carabinieri and the archway. I realized she meant for me to get in out of the rain. I went in and stood and watched the carriage turn the corner. Then I started through the station and down the runway to the train.

The porter was on the platform looking for me. I followed him into the train, crowding past people and along the aisle and in through a door to where the machine-gunner sat in the corner of a full compartment. My rucksack and musettes were above his head on the luggage rack. There were many men standing in the corridor and the men in the compartment all looked at us when we came in. There were not enough places in the train and every one was hostile. The machine-gunner stood up for me to sit down. Some one tapped me on the shoulder. I looked around. It was a very tall gaunt captain of artillery with a red scar along his jaw. He had looked through the glass on the corridor and then come in.

"What do you say?" I asked. I had turned and faced him. He was taller than I and his face was very thin under the shadow of his cap-visor and the scar was new and shiny. Every one in the compartment was looking at me.

"You can't do that," he said. "You can't have a soldier save you a place."

"I have done it."

He swallowed and I saw his Adam's apple go up and then down. The machine-gunner stood in front of the place. Other men looked in through the glass. No one in the compartment said anything.

"You have no right to do that. I was here two hours before you came."

"What do you want?"

"The seat."

"So do I."

I watched his face and could feel the whole compartment against me. I did not blame them. He was in the right. But I wanted the seat. Still no one said anything.

Oh, hell, I thought.

"Sit down, Signor Capitano," I said. The machine-gunner moved out of the way and the tall captain sat down. He looked at me. His face seemed hurt. But he had the seat. "Get my things," I said to the machine-gunner. We went out in the corridor. The train was full and I knew there was no chance of a place. I gave the porter and the machine-gunner ten lire apiece. They went down the corridor and outside on the platform looking in the windows but there were no places.

"Maybe some will get off at Brescia," the porter said.

"More will get on at Brescia," said the machine-gunner. I said good-by to them and we shook hands and they left. They both felt badly. Inside the train we were all standing in the corridor when the train started. I watched the lights of the station and the yards as we went out. It was still raining and soon the windows were wet and you could not see out. Later I slept on the floor of the corridor; first putting my pocket-book with my money and papers in it inside my shirt and trousers so that it was inside the leg of my breeches. I slept all night, waking at Brescia and Verona when more men got on the train, but going back to sleep at once. I had my head on one of the musettes and my arms around the other and I could feel the pack and they could all walk over me if they wouldn't step on me. Men were sleeping on the floor all down the corridor. Others stood holding on to the window rods or leaning against the doors. That train was always crowded.

BOOK THREE

25

Now in the fall the trees were all bare and the roads were muddy. I rode to Gorizia from Udine on a camion. We passed other camions on the road and I looked at the country. The mulberry trees were bare and the fields were brown. There were wet dead leaves on the road from the rows of bare trees and men were working on the road, tamping stone in the ruts from piles of crushed stone along the side of the road between the trees. We saw the town with a mist over it that cut off the mountains. We crossed the river and I saw that it was running high. It had been raining in the mountains. We came into the town past the factories and then the houses and villas and I saw that many more houses had been hit. On a narrow street we passed a British Red Cross ambulance. The driver wore a cap and his face was thin and very tanned. I did not know him. I got down from the camion in the big square in front of the Town Major's house, the driver handed down my rucksack and I put it on and swung on the two musettes and walked to our villa. It did not feel like a homecoming.

I walked down the damp gravel driveway looking at the villa through the trees. The windows were all shut but the door was open. I went in and found the major sitting at a table in the bare room with maps and typed sheets of paper on the wall.

"Hello," he said. "How are you?" He looked older and drier.

"I'm good," I said. "How is everything?"

"It's all over," he said. "Take off your kit and sit down." I put my pack and the two musettes on the floor and my cap on the pack. I brought the other chair over from the wall and sat down by the desk.

"It's been a bad summer," the major said. "Are you strong now?"

"Yes."

"Did you ever get the decorations?"

"Yes. I got them fine. Thank you very much."

"Let's see them."

I opened my cape so he could see the two ribbons.

"Did you get the boxes with the medals?"

"No. Just the papers."

"The boxes will come later. That takes more time."

"What do you want me to do?"

"The cars are all away. There are six up north at Caporetto. You know Caporetto?"

"Yes," I said. I remembered it as a little white town with a campanile in a valley. It was a clean little town and there was a fine fountain in the square.

"They are working from there. There are many sick now. The fighting is over."

"Where are the others?"

"There are two up in the mountains and four still on the Bainsizza. The other two ambulance sections are in the Carso with the third army."

"What do you wish me to do?"

"You can go and take over the four cars on the Bainsizza if you like. Gino has been up there a long time. You haven't seen it up there, have you?"

"No."

"It was very bad. We lost three cars."

"I heard about it."

"Yes, Rinaldi wrote you."

"Where is Rinaldi?"

"He is here at the hospital. He has had a summer and fall of it."

"I believe it."

"It has been bad," the major said. "You couldn't believe how bad it's been. I've often thought you were lucky to be hit when you were."

"I know I was."

"Next year will be worse," the major said. "Perhaps they will attack now. They say they are to attack but I can't believe it. It is too late. You saw the river?"

"Yes. It's high already."

"I don't believe they will attack now that the rains have started. We will have the snow soon. What about your countrymen? Will there be other Americans besides yourself?"

"They are training an army of ten million."

"I hope we get some of them. But the French will hog them all. We'll never get any down here. All right. You stay here to-night and go out to-morrow with the little car and send Gino back. I'll send somebody with you that knows the road. Gino will tell you everything. They are shelling quite a little still but it is all over. You will want to see the Bainsizza."

"I'm glad to see it. I am glad to be back with you again, Signor Maggiore."

He smiled. "You are very good to say so. I am very tired of this war. If I was away I do not believe I would come back."

"Is it so bad?"

"Yes. It is so bad and worse. Go get cleaned up and find your friend Rinaldi."

I went out and carried my bags up the stairs. Rinaldi was not in the room but his things were there and I sat down on the bed and unwrapped my puttees and took the shoe off my right foot. Then I lay back on the bed. I was tired and my right foot hurt. It seemed silly to lie on the bed with one shoe off, so I sat up and unlaced the other shoe and dropped it on the floor, then lay back on the blanket again. The room was stuffy with the window closed but I was too tired to get up and open it. I saw my things were all in one corner of the room. Outside it was getting dark. I lay on the bed and thought about Catherine and waited for Rinaldi. I was going to try not to think about Catherine except at night before I went to sleep. But now I was tired and there was nothing to do, so I lay and thought about her. I was thinking about her when Rinaldi came in. He looked just the same. Perhaps he was a little thinner.

"Well, baby," he said. I sat up on the bed. He came over, sat down and put his arm around me. "Good old baby." He whacked me on the back and I held both his arms.

"Old baby," he said. "Let me see your knee."

"I'll have to take off my pants."

"Take off your pants, baby. We're all friends here. I want to see what kind of a job they did." I stood up, took off the breeches and pulled off the knee-brace. Rinaldi sat on the floor and bent the knee gently back and forth. He ran his finger along the scar; put his thumbs together over the kneecap and rocked the knee gently with his fingers.

"Is that all the articulation you have?"

"Yes."

"It's a crime to send you back. They ought to get complete articulation."

"It's a lot better than it was. It was stiff as a board."

Rinaldi bent it more. I watched his hands. He had fine surgeon's hands. I looked at the top of his head, his hair shiny and parted smoothly. He bent the knee too far.

"Ouch!" I said.

"You ought to have more treatment on it with the machines," Rinaldi said.

"It's better than it was."

"I see that, baby. This is something I know more about than you." He stood up and sat down on the bed. "The knee itself is a good job." He was through with the knee. "Tell me all about everything."

"There's nothing to tell," I said. "I've led a quiet life."

"You act like a married man," he said. "What's the matter with you?"

"Nothing," I said. "What's the matter with you?"

"This war is killing me," Rinaldi said, "I am very depressed by it." He folded his hands over his knee.

"Oh," I said.

"What's the matter? Can't I even have human impulses?"

"No. I can see you've been having a fine time. Tell me."

"All summer and all fall I've operated. I work all the time. I do everybody's work. All the hard ones they leave to me. By God, baby, I am becoming a lovely surgeon."

"That sounds better."

"I never think. No, by God, I don't think; I operate."

"That's right."

"But now, baby, it's all over. I don't operate now and I feel like hell. This is a terrible war, baby. You believe me when I say it. Now you cheer me up. Did you bring the phonograph records?"

"Yes."

They were wrapped in paper in a cardboard box in my rucksack. I was too tired to get them out.

"Don't you feel good yourself, baby?"

"I feel like hell."

"This war is terrible," Rinaldi said. "Come on. We'll both get drunk and be cheerful. Then we'll go get the ashes dragged. Then we'll feel fine."

"I've had the jaundice," I said, "and I can't get drunk."

"Oh, baby, how you've come back to me. You come back serious and with a liver. I tell you this war is a bad thing. Why did we make it anyway."

"We'll have a drink. I don't want to get drunk but we'll have a drink."

Rinaldi went across the room to the washstand and brought back two glasses and a bottle of cognac.

"It's Austrian cognac," he said. "Seven stars. It's all they captured on San Gabriele."

"Were you up there?"

"No. I haven't been anywhere. I've been here all the time operating. Look, baby, this is your old tooth-brushing glass. I kept it all the time to remind me of you."

"To remind you to brush your teeth."

"No. I have my own too. I kept this to remind me of you trying to brush away the Villa Rossa from your teeth in the morning, swearing and eating aspirin and cursing harlots. Every time I see that glass I think of you trying to clean your conscience with a toothbrush." He came over to the bed. "Kiss me once and tell me you're not serious."

"I never kiss you. You're an ape."

"I know, you are the fine good Anglo-Saxon boy. I know. You are the remorse boy, I know. I will wait till I see the Anglo-Saxon brushing away harlotry with a toothbrush."

"Put some cognac in the glass."

We touched glasses and drank. Rinaldi laughed at me.

"I will get you drunk and take out your liver and put you in a good Italian liver and make you a man again."

I held the glass for some more cognac. It was dark outside now. Holding the glass of cognac, I went over and opened the window. The rain had stopped falling. It was colder outside and there was a mist in the trees.

"Don't throw the cognac out the window," Rinaldi said. "If you can't drink it give it to me."

"Go something yourself," I said. I was glad to see Rinaldi again.

He had spent two years teasing me and I had always liked it. We understood each other very well.

"Are you married?" he asked from the bed. I was standing against the wall by the window.

"Not yet."

"Are you in love?"

"Yes."

"With that English girl?"

"Yes."

"Poor baby. Is she good to you?"

"Of course."

"I mean is she good to you practically speaking?"

"Shut up."

"I will. You will see I am a man of extreme delicacy. Does she——?"

"Rinin," I said. "Please shut up. If you want to be my friend, shut up."

"I don't *want* to be your friend, baby. I *am* your friend."

"Then shut up."

"All right."

I went over to the bed and sat down beside Rinaldi. He was holding his glass and looking at the floor.

"You see how it is, Rinin?"

"Oh, yes. All my life I encounter sacred subjects. But very few with you. I suppose you must have them too." He looked at the floor.

"You haven't any?"

"No."

"Not any?"

"No."

"I can say this about your mother and that about your sister?"

"And that about *your sister*," Rinaldi said swiftly. We both laughed.

"The old superman," I said.

"I am jealous maybe," Rinaldi said.

"No, you're not."

"I don't mean like that. I mean something else. Have you any married friends?"

"Yes," I said.

"I haven't," Rinaldi said. "Not if they love each other."

"Why not?"

"They don't like me."

"Why not?"

"I am the snake. I am the snake of reason."

"You're getting it mixed. The apple was reason."

"No, it was the snake." He was more cheerful.

"You are better when you don't think so deeply," I said.

"I love you, baby," he said. "You puncture me when I become a great Italian thinker. But I know many things I can't say. I know more than you."

"Yes. You do."

"But you will have a better time. Even with remorse you will have a better time."

"I don't think so."

"Oh, yes. That is true. Already I am only happy when I am working." He looked at the floor again.

"You'll get over that."

"No. I only like two other things; one is bad for my work and the other is over in half an hour or fifteen minutes. Sometimes less."

"Sometimes a good deal less."

"Perhaps I have improved, baby. You do not know. But there are only the two things and my work."

"You'll get other things."

"No. We never get anything. We are born with all we have and we never learn. We never get anything new. We all start complete. You should be glad not to be a Latin."

"There's no such thing as a Latin. That is 'Latin' thinking. You are so proud of your defects." Rinaldi looked up and laughed.

"We'll stop, baby. I am tired from thinking so much." He had looked tired when he came in. "It's nearly time to eat. I'm glad you're back. You are my best friend and my war brother."

"When do the war brothers eat?" I asked.

"Right away. We'll drink once more for your liver's sake."

"Like Saint Paul."

"You are inaccurate. That was wine and the stomach. Take a little wine for your stomach's sake."

"Whatever you have in the bottle," I said. "For any sake you mention."

"To your girl," Rinaldi said. He held out his glass.

"All right."

"I'll never say a dirty thing about her."

"Don't strain yourself."

He drank off the cognac. "I am pure," he said. "I am like you, baby. I will get an English girl too. As a matter of fact I knew your girl first but she was a little tall for me. A tall girl for a sister," he quoted.

"You have a lovely pure mind," I said.

"Haven't I? That's why they call me Rinaldo Purissimo."

"Rinaldo Sporchissimo."

"Come on, baby, we'll go down to eat while my mind is still pure."

I washed, combed my hair and we went down the stairs. Rinaldi was a little drunk. In the room where we ate, the meal was not quite ready.

"I'll go get the bottle," Rinaldi said. He went off up the stairs. I sat at the table and he came back with the bottle and poured us each a half tumbler of cognac.

"Too much," I said and held up the glass and sighted at the lamp on the table.

"Not for an empty stomach. It is a wonderful thing. It burns out the stomach completely. Nothing is worse for you."

"All right."

"Self-destruction day by day," Rinaldi said. "It ruins the stomach and makes the hand shake. Just the thing for a surgeon."

"You recommend it?"

"Heartily. I use no other. Drink it down, baby, and look forward to being sick."

I drank half the glass. In the hall I could hear the orderly calling. "Soup! Soup is ready!"

The major came in, nodded to us and sat down. He seemed very small at table.

"Is this all we are?" he asked. The orderly put the soup bowl down and he ladled out a plate full.

"We are all," Rinaldi said. "Unless the priest comes. If he knew Federico was here he would be here."

"Where is he?" I asked.

"He's at 307," the major said. He was busy with his soup. He wiped his mouth, wiping his upturned gray mustache carefully. "He will come I think. I called them and left word to tell him you were here."

"I miss the noise of the mess," I said.

"Yes, it's quiet," the major said.

"I will be noisy," said Rinaldi.

"Drink some wine, Enrico," said the major. He filled my glass. The spaghetti came in and we were all busy. We were finishing the spaghetti when the priest came in. He was the same as ever, small and brown and compact looking. I stood up and we shook hands. He put his hand on my shoulder.

"I came as soon as I heard," he said.

"Sit down," the major said. "You're late."

"Good-evening, priest," Rinaldi said, using the English word. They had taken that up from the priest-baiting captain, who spoke a little English. "Good-evening, Rinaldo," the priest said. The orderly brought him soup but he said he would start with the spaghetti.

"How are you?" he asked me.

"Fine," I said. "How have things been?"

"Drink some wine, priest," Rinaldi said. "Take a little wine for your stomach's sake. That's Saint Paul, you know."

"Yes I know," said the priest politely. Rinaldi filled his glass.

"That Saint Paul," said Rinaldi. "He's the one who makes all the trouble." The priest looked at me and smiled. I could see that the baiting did not touch him now.

"That Saint Paul," Rinaldi said. "He was a rounder and a chaser and then when he was no longer hot he said it was no good. When he was finished he made the rules for us who are still hot. Isn't it true, Federico?"

The major smiled. We were eating meat stew now.

"I never discuss a Saint after dark," I said. The priest looked up from the stew and smiled at me.

"There he is, gone over with the priest," Rinaldi said. "Where are all the good old priest-baiters? Where is Cavalcanti? Where is Brundi? Where is Cesare? Do I have to bait this priest alone without support?"

"He is a good priest," said the major.

"He is a good priest," said Rinaldi. "But still a priest. I try to make the mess like the old days. I want to make Federico happy. To hell with you, priest!"

I saw the major look at him and notice that he was drunk. His thin face was white. The line of his hair was very black against the white of his forehead.

"It's all right, Rinaldo," said the priest. "It's all right."

"To hell with you," said Rinaldi. "To hell with the whole damn business." He sat back in his chair.

"He's been under a strain and he's tired," the major said to me. He finished his meat and wiped up the gravy with a piece of bread.

"I don't give a damn," Rinaldi said to the table. "To hell with the whole business." He looked defiantly around the table, his eyes flat, his face pale.

"All right," I said. "To hell with the whole damn business."

"No, no," said Rinaldi. "You can't do it. You can't do it. I say you can't do it. You're dry and you're empty and there's nothing else. There's nothing else I tell you. Not a damned thing. I know, when I stop working."

The priest shook his head. The orderly took away the stew dish. "What are you eating meat for?" Rinaldi turned to the priest. "Don't you know it's Friday?"

"It's Thursday," the priest said.

"It's a lie. It's Friday. You're eating the body of our Lord. It's God-meat. I know. It's dead Austrian. That's what you're eating."

"The white meat is from officers," I said, completing the old joke.

Rinaldi laughed. He filled his glass.

"Don't mind me," he said. "I'm just a little crazy."

"You ought to have a leave," the priest said.

The major shook his head at him. Rinaldi looked at the priest. "You think I ought to have a leave?"

The major shook his head at the priest. Rinaldi was looking at the priest.

"Just as you like," the priest said. "Not if you don't want."

"To hell with you," Rinaldi said. "They try to get rid of me. Every night they try to get rid of me. I fight them off. What if I have it. Everybody has it. The whole world's got it. First," he went on, assuming the manner of a lecturer, "it's a little pimple. Then we notice a rash between the shoulders. Then we notice nothing at all. We put our faith in mercury."

"Or salvarsan," the major interrupted quietly.

"A mercurial product," Rinaldi said. He acted very elated now. "I know something worth two of that. Good old priest," he said. "You'll never get it. Baby will get it. It's an industrial accident. It's a simple industrial accident."

The orderly brought in the sweet and coffee. The dessert was a sort of black bread pudding with hard sauce. The lamp was smoking; the black smoke going close up inside the chimney.

"Bring two candles and take away the lamp," the major said. The orderly brought two lighted candles each in a saucer, and took out the lamp blowing it out. Rinaldi was quiet now. He seemed all right. We talked and after the coffee we all went out into the hall.

"You want to talk to the priest. I have to go in the town," Rinaldi said. "Good-night, priest."

"Good-night, Rinaldo," the priest said.

"I'll see you, Fredi," Rinaldi said.

"Yes," I said. "Come in early." He made a face and went out the door. The major was standing with us. "He's very tired and overworked," he said. "He thinks too he has syphilis. I don't believe it but he may have. He is treating himself for it. Good-night. You will leave before daylight, Enrico?"

"Yes."

"Good-by then," he said. "Good luck. Peduzzi will wake you and go with you."

"Good-by, Signor Maggiore."

"Good-by. They talk about an Austrian offensive but I don't believe it. I hope not. But anyway it won't be here. Gino will tell you everything. The telephone works well now."

"I'll call regularly."

"Please do. Good-night. Don't let Rinaldi drink so much brandy."

"I'll try not to."

"Good-night, priest."

"Good-night, Signor Maggiore."

He went off into his office.

26

I WENT to the door and looked out. It had stopped raining but there was a mist.

"Should we go upstairs?" I asked the priest.

"I can only stay a little while."

"Come on up."

We climbed the stairs and went into my room. I lay down on Rinaldi's bed. The priest sat on my cot that the orderly had set up. It was dark in the room.

"Well," he said, "how are you really?"

"I'm all right. I'm tired to-night."

"I'm tired too, but from no cause."

"What about the war?"

"I think it will be over soon. I don't know why, but I feel it."

"How do you feel it?"

"You know how your major is? Gentle? Many people are like that now."

"I feel that way myself," I said.

"It has been a terrible summer," said the priest. He was surer of himself now than when I had gone away. "You cannot believe how it has been. Except that you have been there and you know how it can be. Many people have realized the war this summer. Officers whom I thought could never realize it realize it now."

"What will happen?" I stroked the blanket with my hand.

"I do not know but I do not think it can go on much longer."

"What will happen?"

"They will stop fighting."

"Who?"

"Both sides."

"I hope so," I said.

"You don't believe it?"

"I don't believe both sides will stop fighting at once."

"I suppose not. It is too much to expect. But when I see the changes in men I do not think it can go on."

"Who won the fighting this summer?"

"No one."

"The Austrians won," I said. "They kept them from taking San Gabriele. They've won. They won't stop fighting."

"If they feel as we feel they may stop. They have gone through the same thing."

"No one ever stopped when they were winning."

"You discourage me."

"I can only say what I think."

"Then you think it will go on and on? Nothing will ever happen?"

"I don't know. I only think the Austrians will not stop when they have won a victory. It is in defeat that we become Christian."

"The Austrians are Christians—except for the Bosnians."

"I don't mean technically Christian. I mean like Our Lord."

He said nothing.

"We are all gentler now because we are beaten. How would Our Lord have been if Peter had rescued him in the Garden?"

"He would have been just the same."

"I don't think so," I said.

"You discourage me," he said. "I believe and I pray that something will happen. I have felt it very close."

"Something may happen," I said. "But it will happen only to us. If they felt the way we do, it would be all right. But they have beaten us. They feel another way."

"Many of the soldiers have always felt this way. It is not because they were beaten."

"They were beaten to start with. They were beaten when they took them from their farms and put them in the army. That is why the peasant has wisdom, because he is defeated from the start. Put him in power and see how wise he is."

He did not say anything. He was thinking.

"Now I am depressed myself," I said. "That's why I never think about these things. I never think and yet when I begin to talk I say the things I have found out in my mind without thinking."

"I had hoped for something."

"Defeat?"

"No. Something more."

"There isn't anything more. Except victory. It may be worse."

"I hoped for a long time for victory."

"Me too."

"Now I don't know."

"It has to be one or the other."

"I don't believe in victory any more."

"I don't. But I don't believe in defeat. Though it may be better."

"What do you believe in?"

"In sleep," I said. He stood up.

"I am very sorry to have stayed so long. But I like so to talk with you."

"It is very nice to talk again. I said that about sleeping, meaning nothing."

We stood up and shook hands in the dark.

"I sleep at 307 now," he said.

"I go out on post early to-morrow."

"I'll see you when you come back."

"We'll have a walk and talk together." I walked with him to the door.

"Don't go down," he said. "It is very nice that you are back. Though not so nice for you." He put his hand on my shoulder.

"It's all right for me," I said. "Good-night."

"Good-night. Ciaou!"

"Ciaou!" I said. I was deadly sleepy.

27

I WOKE when Rinaldi came in but he did not talk and I went back to sleep again. In the morning I was dressed and gone before it was light. Rinaldi did not wake when I left.

I had not seen the Bainsizza before and it was strange to go up the slope where the Austrians had been, beyond the place on the river where I had been wounded. There was a steep new road and many trucks. Beyond, the road flattened out and I saw woods and steep hills in the mist. There were woods that had been taken quickly and not smashed. Then beyond where the road was not protected by the hills it was screened by matting on the sides and over the top. The road ended in a wrecked village. The lines were up beyond. There was much artillery around. The houses were badly smashed but things were very well organized and there were signboards everywhere. We found Gino and he got us some coffee and later I went with him and met various people and saw the posts. Gino said the British cars were working further down the Bainsizza at Ravne. He had great admiration for the British. There was still a certain amount of shelling, he said, but not many wounded. There would be many sick now the rains had started. The Austrians were supposed to attack but he did not believe it. We were supposed to attack too, but they had not brought up any new troops so he thought that was off too. Food was scarce and he would be glad to get a full meal in Gorizia. What kind of supper had I had? I told him and he said that would be wonderful. He was especially impressed by the *dolce*. I did not describe it in detail, only said it was a *dolce,* and I think he believed it was something more elaborate than bread pudding.

Did I know where he was going to go? I said I didn't but that some of the other cars were at Caporetto. He hoped he would go up that way. It was a nice little place and he liked the high mountain hauling up beyond. He was a nice boy and every one seemed to like him. He said where it really had been hell was at San Gabriele and the attack beyond Lom that had gone bad. He said the Austrians had a great amount of artillery in the woods along Ternova ridge beyond and above us, and shelled the roads badly at night. There was a battery of naval guns that had gotten on his nerves. I would recognize them because of their flat trajectory. You heard the report and then the shriek commenced almost instantly. They usually fired two guns at once, one right after the other, and the fragments from the burst were enormous. He showed me one, a smoothly jagged piece of metal over a foot long. It looked like babbitting metal.

"I don't suppose they are so effective," Gino said. "But they scare me. They all sound as though they came directly for you. There is the boom, then instantly the shriek and burst. What's the use of not being wounded if they scare you to death?"

He said there were Croats in the lines opposite us now and some Magyars. Our troops were still in the attacking positions. There was no wire to speak of and no place to fall back to if there should be an Austrian attack. There were fine positions for defense along the low mountains that came up out of the plateau but nothing had been done about organizing them for defense. What did I think about the Bainsizza anyway?

I had expected it to be flatter, more like a plateau. I had not realized it was so broken up.

"Alto piano," Gino said, "but no piano."

We went back to the cellar of the house where he lived. I said I thought a ridge that flattened out on top and had a little depth would be easier and more practical to hold than a succession of small mountains. It was no harder to attack up a mountain than on the level, I argued. "That depends on the mountains," he said. "Look at San Gabriele."

"Yes," I said, "but where they had trouble was at the top where it was flat. They got up to the top easy enough."

"Not so easy," he said.

"Yes," I said, "but that was a special case because it was a fortress rather than a mountain, anyway. The Austrians had been fortifying it for years." I meant tactically speaking in a war where there was some movement a succession of mountains were nothing to hold as a line because it was too easy to turn them. You should have possible mobility and a mountain is not very mobile. Also, people always over-shoot downhill. If the flank were turned, the best men would be left on the highest mountains. I did not believe in a war in mountains. I had thought about it a lot, I said. You pinched off one mountain and they pinched off another but when something really started every one had to get down off the mountains.

What were you going to do if you had a mountain frontier? he asked.

I had not worked that out yet, I said, and we both laughed. "But," I said, "in the old days the Austrians were always whipped in the quadrilateral around Verona. They let them come down onto the plain and whipped them there."

"Yes," said Gino. "But those were Frenchmen and you can work out military problems clearly when you are fighting in somebody else's country."

"Yes," I agreed, "when it is your own country you cannot use it so scientifically."

"The Russians did, to trap Napoleon."

"Yes, but they had plenty of country. If you tried to retreat to trap Napoleon in Italy you would find yourself in Brindisi."

"A terrible place," said Gino. "Have you ever been there?"

"Not to stay."

"I am a patriot," Gino said. "But I cannot love Brindisi or Taranto."

"Do you love the Bainsizza?" I asked.

"The soil is sacred," he said. "But I wish it grew more potatoes. You know when we came here we found fields of potatoes the Austrians had planted."

"Has the food really been short?"

"I myself have never had enough to eat but I am a big eater and I have not starved. The mess is average. The regiments in the line get pretty good food but those in support don't get so much. Something is wrong somewhere. There should be plenty of food."

"The dogfish are selling it somewhere else."

"Yes, they give the battalions in the front line as much as they can but the ones in back are very short. They have eaten all the Austrians' potatoes and chestnuts from the woods. They ought to feed them better. We are big eaters. I am sure there is plenty of food. It is very bad for the soldiers to be short of food. Have you ever noticed the difference it makes in the way you think?"

"Yes," I said. "It can't win a war but it can lose one."

"We won't talk about losing. There is enough talk about losing. What has been done this summer cannot have been done in vain."

I did not say anything. I was always embarrassed by the words sacred, glorious, and sacrifice and the expression in vain. We had heard them, sometimes standing in the rain almost out of earshot, so that only the shouted words came through, and had read them, on proclamations that were slapped up by billposters over other proclamations, now for a long time, and I had seen nothing sacred, and the things that were glorious had no glory and the sacrifices were like the stockyards at Chicago if nothing was done with the meat except to bury it. There were many words that you could not stand to hear and finally only the names of places had dignity. Certain numbers were the same way and certain dates and these with the names of the places were all you could say and have them mean anything. Abstract words such as glory, honor, courage, or hallow were obscene beside the concrete names of villages, the numbers of roads, the names of rivers, the numbers of regiments and the dates. Gino was a patriot, so he said things that separated us sometimes, but he was also a fine boy and I understood his being a patriot. He was born one. He left with Peduzzi in the car to go back to Gorizia.

It stormed all that day. The wind drove down the rain and everywhere there was standing water and mud. The plaster of the broken houses was gray and wet. Late in the afternoon the rain stopped and from out number two post I saw the bare wet autumn country with clouds over the tops of the hills and the straw screening over the roads wet and dripping. The sun came out once before it went down and shone on the bare woods beyond the ridge. There were many Austrian guns in the woods on that ridge but only a few fired. I watched the sudden round puffs of shrapnel smoke in the sky above a broken farmhouse near where the line was; soft puffs with a yellow white flash in the centre. You saw the flash, then heard the crack, then saw the smoke ball distort and thin in the wind. There were many iron shrapnel balls in the rubble of the houses and on the road beside the broken house where the post was, but they did not shell near the post that afternoon. We loaded two cars and drove down the road that was screened with wet mats and the last of the sun came through in the breaks between the strips of mattings. Before we were out on the clear road behind the hill the sun was down. We went on down the clear road and as it turned a corner into the open and went into the square arched tunnel of matting the rain started again.

The wind rose in the night and at three o'clock in the morning with the rain coming in sheets there was a bombardment and the Croatians came over across the mountain meadows and through patches of woods and into the front line. They fought in the dark in the rain and a counter-attack of scared men from the second line drove them back. There was much shelling and many rockets in the rain and machine-gun and rifle fire all along the line. They did not come again and it was quieter and between the gusts of wind and rain we could hear the sound of a great bombardment far to the north.

The wounded were coming into the post, some were carried on stretchers, some walking and some were brought on the backs of men that came across the field. They were wet to the skin and all were scared. We filled two cars with stretcher cases as they came up from the cellar of the post and as I shut the door of the second car and fastened it I felt the rain on my face turn to snow. The flakes were coming heavy and fast in the rain.

When daylight came the storm was still blowing but the snow had stopped. It had melted as it fell on the wet ground and now it was raining again. There was another attack just after daylight but it was unsuccessful. We expected an attack all day but it did not come until the sun was going down. The bombardment started to the south below the long wooded ridge where the Austrian guns were concentrated. We expected a bombardment but it did not come. It was getting dark. Guns were firing from the field behind the village and the shells, going away, had a comfortable sound.

We heard that the attack to the south had been unsuccessful. They did not attack that night but we heard that they had broken through to the north. In the night word came that we were to prepare to retreat. The captain at the post told me this. He had it from the Brigade. A little while later he came from the telephone and said it was a lie. The Brigade had received orders that the line of the Bainsizza should be held no matter what happened. I asked about the break through and he said that he had heard at the Brigade that the Austrians had broken through the twenty-seventh army corps up toward Caporetto. There had been a great battle in the north all day.

"If those bastards let them through we are cooked," he said.

"It's Germans that are attacking," one of the medical officers said. The word Germans was something to be frightened of. We did not want to have anything to do with the Germans.

"There are fifteen divisions of Germans," the medical officer said. "They have broken through and we will be cut off."

"At the Brigade, they say this line is to be held. They say they have not broken through badly and that we will hold a line across the mountains from Monte Maggiore."

"Where do they hear this?"

"From the Division."

"The word that we were to retreat came from the Division."

"We work under the Army Corps," I said. "But here I work under you. Naturally when you tell me to go I will go. But get the orders straight."

"The orders are that we stay here. You clear the wounded from here to the clearing station."

"Sometimes we clear from the clearing station to the field hospitals too," I said. "Tell me, I have never seen a retreat—if there is a retreat how are all the wounded evacuated?"

"They are not. They take as many as they can and leave the rest."

"What will I take in the cars?"

"Hospital equipment."

"All right," I said.

The next night the retreat started. We heard that Germans and Austrians had broken through in the north and were coming down the mountain valleys toward Cividale and Udine. The retreat was orderly, wet and sullen. In the night, going slowly along the crowded roads we passed troops marching under the rain, guns, horses pulling wagons, mules, motor trucks, all moving away from the front. There was no more disorder than in an advance.

That night we helped empty the field hospitals that had been set up in the least ruined villages of the plateau, taking the wounded down to Plava on the river-bed: and the next day hauled all day in the rain to evacuate the hospitals and clearing station at Plava. It rained steadily and the army of the Bainsizza moved down off the plateau in the October rain and across the river where the great victories had commenced in the spring of that year. We came into Gorizia in the middle of the next day. The rain had stopped and the town was nearly empty. As we came up the street they were loading the girls from the soldiers' whorehouse into a truck. There were seven girls and they had on their hats and coats and carried small suitcases. Two of them were crying. Of the others one smiled at us and put out her tongue and fluttered it up and down. She had thick full lips and black eyes.

I stopped the car and went over and spoke to the matron. The girls from the officers' house had left early that morning, she said. Where were they going? To Conegliano, she said. The truck started. The girl with thick lips put out her tongue again at us. The matron waved. The two girls kept on crying. The others looked interestedly out at the town. I got back in the car.

"We ought to go with them," Bonello said. "That would be a good trip."

"We'll have a good trip," I said.

"We'll have a hell of a trip."

"That's what I mean," I said. We came up the drive to the villa.

"I'd like to be there when some of those tough babies climb in and try and hop them."

"You think they will?"

"Sure. Everybody in the Second Army knows that matron."

We were outside the villa.

"They call her the Mother Superior," Bonello said. "The girls are new but everybody knows her. They must have brought them up just before the retreat."

"They'll have a time."

"I'll say they'll have a time. I'd like to have a crack at them for nothing. They charge too much at that house anyway. The government gyps us."

"Take the car out and have the mechanics go over it," I said. "Change the oil and check the differential. Fill it up and then get some sleep."

"Yes, Signor Tenente."

The villa was empty. Rinaldi was gone with the hospital. The major was gone taking hospital personnel in the staff car. There was a note on the window for me to fill the cars with the material piled in the hall and to proceed to Pordenone. The mechanics were gone already. I went out back to the garage. The other two cars came in while I was there and their drivers got down. It was starting to rain again.

"I'm so —— sleepy I went to sleep three times coming here from Plava," Piani said. "What are we going to do, Tenente?"

"We'll change the oil, grease them, fill them up, then take them around in front and load up the junk they've left."

"Then do we start?"

"No, we'll sleep for three hours."

"Christ I'm glad to sleep," Bonello said. "I couldn't keep awake driving."

"How's your car, Aymo?" I asked.

"It's all right."

"Get me a monkey suit and I'll help you with the oil."

"Don't you do that, Tenente," Aymo said. "It's nothing to do. You go and pack your things."

"My things are all packed," I said. "I'll go and carry out the stuff that they left for us. Bring the cars around as soon as they're ready."

They brought the cars around to the front of the villa and we loaded them with the hospital equipment which was piled in the hallway. When it was all in, the three cars stood in line down the driveway under the trees in the rain. We went inside.

"Make a fire in the kitchen and dry your things," I said.

"I don't care about dry clothes," Piani said. "I want to sleep."

"I'm going to sleep on the major's bed," Bonello said. "I'm going to sleep where the old man corks off."

"I don't care where I sleep," Piani said.

"There are two beds in here." I opened the door.

"I never knew what was in that room," Bonello said.

"That was old fish-face's room," Piani said.

"You two sleep in there," I said. "I'll wake you."

"The Austrians will wake us if you sleep too long, Tenente," Bonello said.

"I won't oversleep," I said. "Where's Aymo?"

"He went out in the kitchen."

"Get to sleep," I said.

"I'll sleep," Piani said. "I've been asleep sitting up all day. The whole top of my head kept coming down over my eyes."

"Take your boots off," Bonello said. "That's old fish-face's bed."

"Fish-face is nothing to me." Piani lay on the bed, his muddy boots straight out, his head on his arm. I went out to the kitchen. Aymo had a fire in the stove and a kettle of water on.

"I thought I'd start some *pasta asciutta,*" he said. "We'll be hungry when we wake up."

"Aren't you sleepy, Bartolomeo?"

"Not so sleepy. When the water boils I'll leave it. The fire will go down."

"You'd better get some sleep," I said. "We can eat cheese and monkey meat."

"This is better," he said. "Something hot will be good for those two anarchists. You go to sleep, Tenente."

"There's a bed in the major's room."

"You sleep there."

"No, I'm going up to my old room. Do you want a drink, Bartolomeo?"

"When we go, Tenente. Now it wouldn't do me any good."

"If you wake in three hours and I haven't called you, wake me, will you?"

"I haven't any watch, Tenente."

"There's a clock on the wall in the major's room."

"All right."

I went out then through the dining-room and the hall and up the marble stairs to the room where I had lived with Rinaldi. It was raining outside. I went to the window and looked out. It was getting dark and I saw the three cars standing in line under the trees. The trees were dripping in the rain. It was cold and the drops hung to the branches. I went back to Rinaldi's bed and lay down and let sleep take me.

We ate in the kitchen before we started. Aymo had a basin of spaghetti with onions and tinned meat chopped up in it. We sat around the table and drank two bottles of the wine that had been left in the cellar of the villa. It was dark outside and still raining. Piani sat at the table very sleepy.

"I like a retreat better than an advance," Bonello said. "On a retreat we drink barbera."

"We drink it now. To-morrow maybe we drink rainwater," Aymo said.

"To-morrow we'll be in Udine. We'll drink champagne. That's where the slackers live. Wake up, Piani! We'll drink champagne to-morrow in Udine!"

"I'm awake," Piani said. He filled his plate with the spaghetti and meat. "Couldn't you find tomato sauce, Barto?"

"There wasn't any," Aymo said.

"We'll drink champagne in Udine," Bonello said. He filled his glass with the clear red barbera.

"We may drink —— before Udine," Piani said.

"Have you eaten enough, Tenente?" Aymo asked.

"I've got plenty. Give me the bottle, Bartolomeo."

"I have a bottle apiece to take in the cars," Aymo said.

"Did you sleep at all?"

"I don't need much sleep. I slept a little."

"To-morrow we'll sleep in the king's bed," Bonello said. He was feeling very good.

"To-morrow maybe we'll sleep in——," Piani said.

"I'll sleep with the queen," Bonello said. He looked to see how I took the joke.

"You'll sleep with ——," Piani said sleepily.

"That's treason, Tenente," Bonello said. "Isn't that treason?"

"Shut up," I said. "You get too funny with a little wine." Outside it was raining hard. I looked at my watch. It was half-past nine.

"It's time to roll," I said and stood up.

"Who are you going to ride with, Tenente?" Bonello asked.

"With Aymo. Then you come. Then Piani. We'll start out on the road for Cormons."

"I'm afraid I'll go to sleep," Piani said.

"All right. I'll ride with you. Then Bonello. Then Aymo."

"That's the best way," Piani said. "Because I'm so sleepy."

"I'll drive and you sleep awhile."

"No. I can drive just so long as I know somebody will wake me up if I go to sleep."

"I'll wake you up. Put out the lights, Barto."

"You might as well leave them," Bonello said. "We've got no more use for this place."

"I have a small locker trunk in my room," I said. "Will you help take it down, Piani?"

"We'll take it," Piani said. "Come on, Aldo." He went off into the hall with Bonello. I heard them going upstairs.

"This was a fine place," Bartolomeo Aymo said. He put two bottles of wine and half a cheese into his haversack. "There won't be a place like this again. Where will they retreat to, Tenente?"

"Beyond the Tagliamento, they say. The hospital and the sector are to be at Pordenone."

"This is a better town than Pordenone."

"I don't know Pordenone," I said. "I've just been through there."

"It's not much of a place," Aymo said.

28

As we moved out through the town it was empty in the rain and the dark except for columns of troops and guns that were going through the main street. There were many trucks too and some carts going through on other streets and converging on the main road. When we were out past the tanneries onto the main road the troops, the motor trucks, the horse-drawn carts and the guns were in one wide slow-moving column. We moved slowly but steadily in the rain, the radiator cap of our car almost against the tailboard of a truck that was loaded high, the load covered with wet canvas. Then the truck stopped. The whole column was stopped. It started again and we went a little farther, then stopped. I got out and walked ahead, going between the trucks and carts and under the wet necks of the horses. The block was farther ahead. I left the road, crossed the ditch on a footboard and walked along the field beyond the ditch. I could see the stalled column between the trees in the rain as I went forward across from it in the field. I went about a mile. The column did not move, although, on the other side beyond the stalled vehicles I could see the troops moving. I went back to the cars. This block might extend as far as Udine. Piani was asleep over the wheel. I climbed up beside him and went to sleep too. Several hours later I heard the truck ahead of us grinding into gear. I woke Piani and we started, moving a few yards, then stopping, then going on again. It was still raining.

The column stalled again in the night and did not start. I got down and went back to see Aymo and Bonello. Bonello had two sergeants of engineers on the seat of his car with him. They stiffened when I came up.

"They were left to do something to a bridge," Bonello said. "They can't find their unit so I gave them a ride."

"With the Sir Lieutenant's permission."

"With permission," I said.

"The lieutenant is an American," Bonello said. "He'll give anybody a ride."

One of the sergeants smiled. The other asked Bonello if I was an Italian from North or South America.

"He's not an Italian. He's North American English."

The sergeants were polite but did not believe it. I left them and went back to Aymo. He had two girls on the seat with him and was sitting back in the corner and smoking.

"Barto, Barto," I said. He laughed.

"Talk to them, Tenente," he said. "I can't understand them. Hey!" he put his hand on the girl's thigh and squeezed it in a friendly way. The girl drew her shawl tight around her and pushed his hand away. "Hey!" he said. "Tell the Tenente your name and what you're doing here."

The girl looked at me fiercely. The other girl kept her eyes down. The girl who looked at me said something in a dialect I could not understand a word of. She was plump and dark and looked about sixteen.

"Sorella?" I asked and pointed at the other girl.

She nodded her head and smiled.

"All right," I said and patted her knee. I felt her stiffen away when I touched her. The sister never looked up. She looked perhaps a year younger. Aymo put his hand on the elder girl's thigh and she pushed it away. He laughed at her.

"Good man," he pointed at himself. "Good man," he pointed at me. "Don't you worry." The girl looked at him fiercely. The pair of them were like two wild birds.

"What does she ride with me for if she doesn't like me?" Aymo asked. "They got right up in the car the minute I motioned to them." He turned to the girl. "Don't worry," he said. "No danger of ——," using the vulgar word. "No place for ——." I could see she understood the word and that was all. Her eyes looked at him very scared. She pulled the shawl tight. "Car all full," Aymo said. "No danger of ——. No place for ——." Every time he said the word the girl stiffened a little. Then sitting stiffly and looking at him she began to cry. I saw her lips working and then tears came down her plump cheeks. Her sister, not looking up, took her hand and they sat there together. The older one, who had been so fierce, began to sob.

"I guess I scared her," Aymo said. "I didn't mean to scare her."

Bartolomeo brought out his knapsack and cut off two pieces of cheese. "Here," he said. "Stop crying."

The older girl shook her head and still cried, but the younger girl took the cheese and commenced to eat. After a while the younger girl gave her sister the second piece of cheese and they both ate. The older sister still sobbed a little.

"She'll be all right after a while," Aymo said.

An idea came to him. "Virgin?" he asked the girl next to him. She nodded her head vigorously. "Virgin too?" he pointed to the sister. Both the girls nodded their heads and the elder said something in dialect.

"That's all right," Bartolomeo said. "That's all right."

Both the girls seemed cheered.

I left them sitting together with Aymo sitting back in the corner and went back to Piani's car. The column of vehicles did not move but the troops kept passing alongside. It was still raining hard and I thought some of the stops in the movement of the column might be from cars with wet wiring. More likely they were from horses or men going to sleep. Still, traffic could tie up in cities when every one was awake. It was the combination of horse and motor vehicles. They did not help each other any. The peasants' carts did not help much either. Those were a couple of fine girls with Barto. A retreat was no place for two virgins. Real virgins. Probably very religious. If there were no war we would probably all be in bed. In bed I lay me down my head. Bed and board. Stiff as a board in bed. Catherine was in bed now between two sheets, over her and under her. Which side did she sleep on? Maybe she wasn't asleep. Maybe she was lying thinking about me. Blow, blow, ye western wind. Well, it blew and it wasn't the small rain but the big rain down that rained. It rained all night. You knew it rained down that rained. Look at it. Christ, that my love were in my arms and I in my bed again. That my love Catherine. That my sweet love Catherine down might rain. Blow her again to me. Well, we were in it. Every one was caught in it and the small rain would not quiet it. "Good-night, Catherine," I said out loud. "I hope you sleep well. If it's too uncomfortable, darling, lie on the other side," I said. "I'll get you some cold water. In a little while it will be morning and then it won't be so bad. I'm sorry he makes you so uncomfortable. Try and go to sleep, sweet."

I was asleep all the time, she said. You've been talking in your sleep. Are you all right?

Are you really there?

Of course I'm here. I wouldn't go away. This doesn't make any difference between us.

You're so lovely and sweet. You wouldn't go away in the night, would you?

Of course I wouldn't go away. I'm always here. I come whenever you want me.

"——," Piani said. "They've started again."

"I was dopey," I said. I looked at my watch. It was three o'clock in the morning. I reached back behind the seat for a bottle of the barbera.

"You talked out loud," Piani said.

"I was having a dream in English," I said.

The rain was slacking and we were moving along. Before daylight we were stalled again and when it was light we were at a little rise in the ground and I saw the road of the retreat stretched out far ahead, everything stationary except for the infantry filtering through. We started to move again but seeing the rate of progress in the daylight, I knew we were going to have to get off that main road some way and go across country if we ever hoped to reach Udine.

In the night many peasants had joined the column from the roads of the country and in the column there were carts loaded with household goods; there were mirrors projecting up between mattresses, and chickens and ducks tied to carts. There was a sewing-machine on the cart ahead of us in the rain. They had saved the most valuable things. On some carts the women sat huddled from the rain and others walked beside the carts keeping as close to them as they could. There were dogs now in the column, keeping under the wagons as they moved along. The road was muddy, the ditches at the side were high with water and beyond the trees that lined the road the fields looked too wet and too soggy to try to cross. I got down from the car and worked up the road a way, looking for a place where I could see ahead to find a side-road we could take across country. I knew there were many side-roads but did not want one that would lead to nothing. I could not remember them because we had always passed them bowling along in the car on the main road and they all looked much alike. Now I knew we must find one if we hoped to get through. No one knew where the Austrians were nor how things were going but I was certain that if the rain should stop and planes come over and get to work on that column that it would be all over. All that was needed was for a few men to leave their trucks or a few horses be killed to tie up completely the movement on the road.

The rain was not falling so heavily now and I thought it might clear. I went ahead along the edge of the road and when there was a small road that led off to the north between two fields with a hedge of trees on both sides, I thought that we had better take it and hurried back to the cars. I told Piani to turn off and went back to tell Bonello and Aymo.

"If it leads nowhere we can turn around and cut back in," I said.

"What about these?" Bonello asked. His two sergeants were beside him on the seat. They were unshaven but still military looking in the early morning.

"They'll be good to push," I said. I went back to Aymo and told him we were going to try it across country.

"What about my virgin family?" Aymo asked. The two girls were asleep.

"They won't be very useful," I said. "You ought to have some one that could push."

"They could go back in the car," Aymo said. "There's room in the car."

"All right if you want them," I said. "Pick up somebody with a wide back to push."

"Bersaglieri," Aymo smiled. "They have the widest backs. They measure them. How do you feel, Tenente?"

"Fine. How are you?"

"Fine. But very hungry."

"There ought to be something up that road and we will stop and eat."

"How's your leg, Tenente?"

"Fine," I said. Standing on the step and looking up ahead I could see Piani's car pulling out onto the little side-road and starting up it, his car showing through the hedge of bare branches. Bonello turned off and followed him and then Piani worked his way out and we followed the two ambulances ahead along the narrow road between hedges. It led to a farmhouse. We found Piani and Bonello stopped in the farmyard. The house was low and long with a trellis with a grape-vine over the door. There was a well in the yard and Piani was getting up water to fill his radiator. So much going in low gear had boiled it out. The farmhouse was deserted. I looked back down the road, the farmhouse was on a slight elevation above the plain, and we could see over the country, and saw the road, the hedges, the fields and the line of trees along the main road where the retreat was passing. The two sergeants were looking through the house. The girls were awake and looking at the courtyard, the well and the two big ambulances in front of the farmhouse, with three drivers at the well. One of the sergeants came out with a clock in his hand.

"Put it back," I said. He looked at me, went in the house and came back without the clock.

"Where's your partner?" I asked.

"He's gone to the latrine." He got up on the seat of the ambulance. He was afraid we would leave him.

"What about breakfast, Tenente?" Bonello asked. "We could eat something. It wouldn't take very long."

"Do you think this road going down on the other side will lead to anything?"

"Sure."

"All right. Let's eat." Piani and Bonello went in the house.

"Come on," Aymo said to the girls. He held his hand to help them down. The older sister shook her head. They were not going into any deserted house. They looked after us.

"They are difficult," Aymo said. We went into the farmhouse together. It was large and dark, an abandoned feeling. Bonello and Piani were in the kitchen.

"There's not much to eat," Piani said. "They've cleaned it out."

Bonello sliced a big cheese on the heavy kitchen table.

"Where was the cheese?"

"In the cellar. Piani found wine too and apples."

"That's a good breakfast."

Piani was taking the wooden cork out of a big wicker-covered wine jug. He tipped it and poured a copper pan full.

"It smells all right," he said. "Find some beakers, Barto."

The two sergeants came in.

"Have some cheese, sergeants," Bonello said.

"We should go," one of the sergeants said, eating his cheese and drinking a cup of wine.

"We'll go. Don't worry," Bonello said.

"An army travels on its stomach," I said.

"What?" asked the sergeant.

"It's better to eat."

"Yes. But time is precious."

"I believe the bastards have eaten already," Piani said. The sergeants looked at him. They hated the lot of us.

"You know the road?" one of them asked me.

"No," I said. They looked at each other.

"We would do best to start," the first one said.

"We are starting," I said. I drank another cup of the red wine. It tasted very good after the cheese and apple.

"Bring the cheese," I said and went out. Bonello came out carrying the great jug of wine.

"That's too big," I said. He looked at it regretfully.

"I guess it is," he said. "Give me the canteens to fill." He filled the canteens and some of the wine ran out on the stone paving of the courtyard. Then he picked up the wine jug and put it just inside the door.

"The Austrians can find it without breaking the door down," he said.

"We'll roll," I said. "Piani and I will go ahead." The two engineers were already on the seat beside Bonello. The girls were eating cheese and apples. Aymo was smoking. We started off down the narrow road. I looked back at the two cars coming and the farmhouse. It was a fine, low, solid stone house and the ironwork of the well was very good. Ahead of us the road was narrow and muddy and there was a high hedge on either side. Behind, the cars were following closely.

29

AT noon we were stuck in a muddy road about, as nearly as we could figure, ten kilometres from Udine. The rain had stopped during the forenoon and three times we had heard planes coming, seen them pass overhead, watched them go far to the left and heard them bombing on the main highroad. We had worked through a network of secondary roads and had taken many roads that were blind, but had always, by backing up and finding another road, gotten closer to Udine. Now, Aymo's car, in backing so that we might get out of a blind road, had gotten into the soft earth at the side and the wheels, spinning, had dug deeper and deeper until the car rested on its differential. The thing to do now was to dig out in front of the wheels, put in brush so that the chains could grip, and then push until the car was on the road. We were all down on the road around the car. The two sergeants looked at the car and examined the wheels. Then they started off down the road without a word. I went after them.

"Come on," I said. "Cut some brush."

"We have to go," one said.

"Get busy," I said, "and cut brush."

"We have to go," one said. The other said nothing. They were in a hurry to start. They would not look at me.

"I order you to come back to the car and cut brush," I said. The one sergeant turned. "We have to go on. In a little while you will be cut off. You can't order us. You're not our officer."

"I order you to cut brush," I said. They turned and started down the road.

"Halt," I said. They kept on down the muddy road, the hedge on either side. "I order you to halt," I called. They went a little faster. I opened up my holster, took the pistol, aimed at the one who had talked the most, and fired. I missed and they both started to run. I shot three times and dropped one. The other went through the hedge and was out of sight. I fired at him through the hedge as he ran across the field. The pistol clicked empty and I put in another clip. I saw it was too far to shoot at the second sergeant. He was far across the field, running, his head held low. I commenced to reload the empty clip. Bonello came up.

"Let me go finish him," he said. I handed him the pistol and he walked down to where the sergeant of engineers lay face down across the road. Bonello leaned over, put the pistol against the man's head and pulled the trigger. The pistol did not fire.

"You have to cock it," I said. He cocked it and fired twice. He took hold of the sergeant's legs and pulled him to the side of the road so he lay beside the hedge. He came back and handed me the pistol.

"The son of a bitch," he said. He looked toward the sergeant. "You see me shoot him, Tenente?"

"We've got to get the brush quickly," I said. "Did I hit the other one at all?"

"I don't think so," Aymo said. "He was too far away to hit with a pistol."

"The dirty scum," Piani said. We were all cutting twigs and branches. Everything had been taken out of the car. Bonello was digging out in front of the wheels. When we were ready Aymo started the car and put it into gear. The wheels spun round throwing brush and mud. Bonello and I pushed until we could feel our joints crack. The car would not move.

"Rock her back and forth, Barto," I said.

He drove the engine in reverse, then forward. The wheels only dug in deeper. Then the car was resting on the differential again, and the wheels spun freely in the holes they had dug. I straightened up.

"We'll try her with a rope," I said.

"I don't think it's any use, Tenente. You can't get a straight pull."

"We have to try it," I said. "She won't come out any other way."

Piani's and Bonello's cars could only move straight ahead down the narrow road. We roped both cars together and pulled. The wheels only pulled sideways against the ruts.

"It's no good," I shouted. "Stop it."

Piani and Bonello got down from their cars and came back. Aymo got down. The girls were up the road about forty yards sitting on a stone wall.

"What do you say, Tenente?" Bonello asked.

"We'll dig out and try once more with the brush," I said. I looked down the road. It was my fault. I had led them up here. The sun was almost out from behind the clouds and the body of the sergeant lay beside the hedge.

"We'll put his coat and cape under," I said. Bonello went to get them. I cut brush and Aymo and Piani dug out in front and between the wheels. I cut the cape, then ripped it in two, and laid it under the wheel in the mud, then piled brush for the wheels to catch. We were ready to start and Aymo got up on the seat and started the car. The wheels spun and we pushed and pushed. But it wasn't any use.

"It's ——ed," I said. "Is there anything you want in the car, Barto?"

Aymo climbed up with Bonello, carrying the cheese and two bottles of wine and his cape. Bonello, sitting behind the wheel, was looking through the pockets of the sergeant's coat.

"Better throw the coat away," I said. "What about Barto's virgins?"

"They can get in the back," Piani said. "I don't think we are going far."

I opened the back door of the ambulance.

"Come on," I said. "Get in." The two girls climbed in and sat in the corner. They seemed to have taken no notice of the shooting. I looked back up the road. The sergeant lay in his dirty longsleeved underwear. I got up with Piani and we started. We were going to try to cross the field. When the road entered the field I got down and walked ahead. If we could get across, there was a road on the other side. We could not get across. It was too soft and muddy for the cars.

When they were finally and completely stalled, the wheels dug in to the hubs, we left them in the field and started on foot for Udine.

When we came to the road which led back toward the main highway I pointed down it to the two girls.

"Go down there," I said. "You'll meet people." They looked at me. I took out my pocket-book and gave them each a ten-lira note. "Go down there," I said, pointing. "Friends! Family!"

They did not understand but they held the money tightly and started down the road. They looked back as though they were afraid I might take the money back. I watched them go down the road, their shawls close around them, looking back apprehensively at us. The three drivers were laughing.

"How much will you give me to go in that direction, Tenente?" Bonello asked.

"They're better off in a bunch of people than alone if they catch them," I said.

"Give me two hundred lire and I'll walk straight back toward Austria," Bonello said.

"They'd take it away from you," Piani said.

"Maybe the war will be over," Aymo said. We were going up the road as fast as we could. The sun was trying to come through. Beside the road were mulberry trees. Through the trees I could see our two big moving-vans of cars stuck in the field. Piani looked back too.

"They'll have to build a road to get them out," he said.

"I wish to Christ we had bicycles," Bonello said.

"Do they ride bicycles in America?" Aymo asked.

"They used to."

"Here it is a great thing," Aymo said. "A bicycle is a splendid thing."

"I wish to Christ we had bicycles," Bonello said. "I'm no walker."

"Is that firing?" I asked. I thought I could hear firing a long way away.

"I don't know," Aymo said. He listened.

"I think so," I said.

"The first thing we will see will be the cavalry," Piani said.

"I don't think they've got any cavalry."

"I hope to Christ not," Bonello said. "I don't want to be stuck on a lance by any —— cavalry."

"You certainly shot that sergeant, Tenente," Piani said. We were walking fast.

"I killed him," Bonello said. "I never killed anybody in this war, and all my life I've wanted to kill a sergeant."

"You killed him on the sit all right," Piani said. "He wasn't flying very fast when you killed him."

"Never mind. That's one thing I can always remember. I killed that —— of a sergeant."

"What will you say in confession?" Aymo asked.

"I'll say, 'Bless me, father, I killed a sergeant.' " They all laughed.

"He's an anarchist," Piani said. "He doesn't go to church."

"Piani's an anarchist too," Bonello said.

"Are you really anarchists?" I asked.

"No, Tenente. We're socialists. We come from Imola."

"Haven't you ever been there?"

"No."

"By Christ it's a fine place, Tenente. You come there after the war and we'll show you something."

"Are you all socialists?"

"Everybody."

"Is it a fine town?"

"Wonderful. You never saw a town like that."

"How did you get to be socialists?"

"We're all socialists. Everybody is a socialist. We've always been socialists."

"You come, Tenente. We'll make you a socialist too."

Ahead the road turned off to the left and there was a little hill and, beyond a stone wall, an apple orchard. As the road went uphill they ceased talking. We walked along together all going fast against time.

30

LATER we were on a road that led to a river. There was a long line of abandoned trucks and carts on the road leading up to the bridge. No one was in sight. The river was high and the bridge had been blown up in the centre; the stone arch was fallen into the river and the brown water was going over it. We went on up the bank looking for a place to cross. Up ahead I knew there was a railway bridge and I thought we might be able to get across there. The path was wet and muddy. We did not see any troops; only abandoned trucks and stores. Along the river bank there was nothing and no one but the wet brush and muddy ground. We went up to the bank and finally we saw the railway bridge.

"What a beautiful bridge," Aymo said. It was a long plain iron bridge across what was usually a dry river-bed.

"We'd better hurry and get across before they blow it up," I said.

"There's nobody to blow it up," Piani said. "They're all gone."

"It's probably mined," Bonello said. "You cross first, Tenente."

"Listen to the anarchist," Aymo said. "Make him go first."

"I'll go," I said. "It won't be mined to blow up with one man."

"You see," Piani said. "That is brains. Why haven't you brains, anarchist?"

"If I had brains I wouldn't be here," Bonello said.

"That's pretty good, Tenente," Aymo said.

"That's pretty good," I said. We were close to the bridge now. The sky had clouded over again and it was raining a little. The bridge looked long and solid. We climbed up the embankment.

"Come one at a time," I said and started across the bridge. I watched the ties and the rails for any trip-wires or signs of explosive but I saw nothing. Down below the gaps in the ties the river ran muddy and fast. Ahead across the wet countryside I could see Udine in the rain. Across the bridge I looked back. Just up the river was another bridge. As I watched, a yellow mud-colored motor car crossed it. The sides of the bridge were high and the body of the car, once on, was out of sight. But I saw the heads of the driver, the man on the seat with him, and the two men on the rear seat. They all wore German helmets. Then the car was over the bridge and out of sight behind the trees and the abandoned vehicles on the road. I waved to Aymo who was crossing and to the others to come on. I climbed down and crouched beside the railway embankment. Aymo came down with me.

"Did you see the car?" I asked.

"No. We were watching you."

"A German staff car crossed on the upper bridge."

"A staff car?"

"Yes."

"Holy Mary."

The others came and we all crouched in the mud behind the embankment, looking across the rails at the bridge, the line of trees, the ditch and the road.

"Do you think we're cut off then, Tenente?"

"I don't know. All I know is a German staff car went along that road."

"You don't feel funny, Tenente? You haven't got strange feelings in the head?"

"Don't be funny, Bonello."

"What about a drink?" Piani asked. "If we're cut off we might as well have a drink." He unhooked his canteen and uncorked it.

"Look! Look!" Aymo said and pointed toward the road. Along the top of the stone bridge we could see German helmets moving. They were bent forward and moved smoothly, almost supernaturally, along. As they came off the bridge we saw them. They were bicycle troops. I saw the faces of the first two. They were ruddy and healthy-looking. Their helmets came low down over their foreheads and the side of their faces. Their carbines were clipped to the frame of the bicycles. Stick bombs hung handle down from their belts. Their helmets and their gray uniforms were wet and they rode easily, looking ahead and to both sides. There were two—then four in line, then two, then almost a dozen; then another dozen—then one alone. They did not talk but we could not have heard them because of the noise from the river. They were gone out of sight up the road.

"Holy Mary," Aymo said.

"They were Germans," Piani said. "Those weren't Austrians."

"Why isn't there somebody here to stop them?" I said. "Why haven't they blown the bridge up? Why aren't there machine-guns along this embankment?"

"You tell us, Tenente," Bonello said.

I was very angry.

"The whole bloody thing is crazy. Down below they blow up a little bridge. Here they leave a bridge on the main road. Where is everybody? Don't they try and stop them at all?"

"You tell us, Tenente," Bonello said. I shut up. It was none of my business; all I had to do was to get to Pordenone with three ambulances. I had failed at that. All I had to do now was get to

Pordenone. I probably could not even get to Udine. The hell I couldn't. The thing to do was to be calm and not get shot or captured.

"Didn't you have a canteen open?" I asked Piani. He handed it to me. I took a long drink. "We might as well start," I said. "There's no hurry though. Do you want to eat something?"

"This is no place to stay," Bonello said.

"All right. We'll start."

"Should we keep on this side—out of sight?"

"We'd be better off on top. They may come along this bridge too. We don't want them on top of us before we see them."

We walked along the railroad track. On both sides of us stretched the wet plain. Ahead across the plain was the hill of Udine. The roofs fell away from the castle on the hill. We could see the campanile and the clock-tower. There were many mulberry trees in the fields. Ahead I saw a place where the rails were torn up. The ties had been dug out too and thrown down the embankment.

"Down! down!" Aymo said. We dropped down beside the embankment. There was another group of bicyclists passing along the road. I looked over the edge and saw them go on.

"They saw us but they went on," Aymo said.

"We'll get killed up there, Tenente," Bonello said.

"They don't want us," I said. "They're after something else. We're in more danger if they should come on us suddenly."

"I'd rather walk here out of sight," Bonello said.

"All right. We'll walk along the tracks."

"Do you think we can get through?" Aymo asked.

"Sure. There aren't very many of them yet. We'll go through in the dark."

"What was that staff car doing?"

"Christ knows," I said. We kept on up the tracks. Bonello tired of walking in the mud of the embankment and came up with the rest of us. The railway moved south away from the highway now and we could not see what passed along the road. A short bridge over a canal was blown up but we climbed across on what was left of the span. We heard firing ahead of us.

We came up on the railway beyond the canal. It went on straight toward the town across the low fields. We could see the line of the other railway ahead of us. To the north was the main road where we had seen the cyclists; to the south there was a small branch-road across the fields with thick trees on each side. I thought we had better cut to the south and work around the town that way and across country toward Campoformio and the main road to the Tagliamento. We could avoid the main line of the retreat by keeping to the secondary roads beyond Udine. I knew there were plenty of side-roads across the plain. I started down the embankment.

"Come on," I said. We would make for the side-road and work to the south of the town. We all started down the embankment. A shot was fired at us from the side-road. The bullet went into the mud of the embankment.

"Go on back," I shouted. I started up the embankment, slipping in the mud. The drivers were ahead of me. I went up the embankment as fast as I could go. Two more shots came from the thick brush and Aymo, as he was crossing the tracks, lurched, tripped and fell face down. We pulled him down on the other side and turned him over. "His head ought to be uphill," I said. Piani moved him around. He lay in the mud on the side of the embankment, his feet pointing downhill, breathing blood irregularly. The three of us squatted over him in the rain. He was hit low in the back of the neck and the bullets had ranged upward and come out under the right eye. He died while I was stopping up the two holes. Piani laid his head down, wiped at his face, with a piece of the emergency dressing, then let it alone.

"The ——," he said.

"They weren't Germans," I said. "There can't be any Germans over there."

"Italians," Piani said, using the word as an epithet, "Italiani!" Bonello said nothing. He was sitting beside Aymo, not looking at him. Piani picked up Aymo's cap where it had rolled down the embankment and put it over his face. He took out his canteen.

"Do you want a drink?" Piani handed Bonello the canteen.

"No," Bonello said. He turned to me. "That might have happened to us any time on the railway tracks."

"No," I said. "It was because we started across the field."

Bonello shook his head. "Aymo's dead," he said. "Who's dead next, Tenente? Where do we go now?"

"Those were Italians that shot," I said. "They weren't Germans."

"I suppose if they were Germans they'd have killed all of us," Bonello said.

"We are in more danger from Italians than Germans," I said. "The rear guard are afraid of everything. The Germans know what they're after."

"You reason it out, Tenente," Bonello said.

"Where do we go now?" Piani asked.

"We better lie up some place till it's dark. If we could get south we'd be all right."

"They'd have to shoot us all to prove they were right the first time," Bonello said. "I'm not going to try them."

"We'll find a place to lie up as near to Udine as we can get and then go through when it's dark."

"Let's go then," Bonello said. We went down the north side of the embankment. I looked back. Aymo lay in the mud with the angle of the embankment. He was quite small and his arms were by his side, his puttee-wrapped legs and muddy boots together, his cap over his face. He looked very dead. It was raining. I had liked him as well as any one I ever knew. I had his papers in my pocket and would write to his family. Ahead across the fields was a farmhouse. There were trees around it and the farm buildings were built against the house. There was a balcony along the second floor held up by columns.

"We better keep a little way apart," I said. "I'll go ahead." I started toward the farmhouse. There was a path across the field.

Crossing the field, I did not know but that some one would fire on us from the trees near the farmhouse or from the farmhouse itself. I walked toward it, seeing it very clearly. The balcony of the second floor merged into the barn and there was hay coming out between the columns. The courtyard was of stone blocks and all the trees were dripping with the rain. There was a big empty two-wheeled cart, the shafts tipped high up in the rain. I came to the courtyard, crossed it, and stood under the shelter of the balcony. The door of the house was open and I went in. Bonello and Piani came in after me. It was dark inside. I went back to the kitchen. There were ashes of a fire on the big open hearth. The pots hung over the ashes, but they were empty. I looked around but I could not find anything to eat.

"We ought to lie up in the barn," I said. "Do you think you could find anything to eat, Piani, and bring it up there?"

"I'll look," Piani said.

"I'll look too," Bonello said.

"All right," I said. "I'll go up and look at the barn." I found a stone stairway that went up from the stable underneath. The stable smelt dry and pleasant in the rain. The cattle were all gone, probably driven off when they left. The barn was half full of hay. There were two windows in the roof, one was blocked with boards, the other was a narrow dormer window on the north side. There was a chute so that hay might be pitched down to the cattle. Beams crossed the opening down into the main floor where the hay-carts drove in when the hay was hauled in to be pitched up. I heard the rain on the roof and smelled the hay and, when I went down, the clean smell of dried dung in the stable. We could pry a board loose and see out of the south window down into the courtyard. The other window looked out on the field toward the north. We could get out of either window onto the roof and down, or go down the hay chute if the stairs were impractical. It was a big barn and we could hide in the hay if we heard any one. It seemed like a good place. I was sure we could have gotten through to the south if they had not fired on us. It was impossible that there were Germans there. They were coming from the north and down the road from Cividale. They could not have come through from the south. The Italians were even more dangerous. They were frightened and firing on anything they saw. Last night on the retreat we had heard that there had been many Germans in Italian uniforms mixing with the retreat in the north. I did not believe it. That was one of those things you always heard in the war. It was one of the things the enemy always did to you. You did not know any one who went over in German uniform to confuse them. Maybe they did but it sounded difficult. I did not believe the Germans did it. I did not believe they had to. There was no need to confuse our retreat. The size of the army and the fewness of the roads did that. Nobody gave any orders, let alone Germans. Still, they would shoot us for Germans. They shot Aymo. The hay smelled good and lying in a barn in the hay took away all the years in between. We had lain in hay and talked and shot sparrows with an air-rifle when they perched in the triangle cut high up in the wall of the barn. The barn was gone now and one year they had cut the hemlock woods and there were only stumps, dried tree-tops, branches and fireweed where the woods had been. You could not go back. If you did not go forward what happened? You never got back to Milan. And if you got back to Milan what happened? I listened to the firing to the north toward Udine. I could hear machine-gun firing. There was no shelling. That was something. They must have gotten some troops along the road. I looked down in the half-light of the hay-barn and saw Piani standing on the hauling floor. He had a long sausage, a jar of something and two bottles of wine under his arm.

"Come up," I said. "There is the ladder." Then I realized that I should help him with the things and went down. I was vague in the head from lying in the hay. I had been nearly asleep.

"Where's Bonello?" I asked.

"I'll tell you," Piani said. We went up the ladder. Up on the hay we set the things down. Piani took out his knife with the corkscrew and drew the cork on a wine bottle.

"They have sealing-wax on it," he said. "It must be good." He smiled.

"Where's Bonello?" I asked.

Piani looked at me.

"He went away, Tenente," he said. "He wanted to be a prisoner."

I did not say anything.

"He was afraid we would get killed."

I held the bottle of wine and did not say anything.

"You see we don't believe in the war anyway, Tenente."

"Why didn't you go?" I asked.

"I did not want to leave you."

"Where did he go?"

"I don't know, Tenente. He went away."

"All right," I said. "Will you cut the sausage?"

Piani looked at me in the half-light.

"I cut it while we were talking," he said. We sat in the hay and ate the sausage and drank the wine. It must have been wine they had saved for a wedding. It was so old that it was losing its color.

"You look out of this window, Luigi," I said. "I'll go look out the other window."

We had each been drinking out of one of the bottles and I took my bottle with me and went over and lay flat on the hay and looked out the narrow window at the wet country. I do not know what I expected to see but I did not see anything except the fields and the bare mulberry trees and the rain falling. I drank the wine and it did not make me feel good. They had kept it too long and it had gone to pieces and lost its quality and color. I watched it get dark outside; the darkness came very quickly. It would be a black night with the rain. When it was dark there was no use watching any more, so I went over to Piani. He was lying asleep and I did not wake him but sat down beside him for a while. He was a big man and he slept heavily. After a while I woke him and we started.

That was a very strange night. I do not know what I had expected, death perhaps and shooting in the dark and running, but nothing happened. We waited, lying flat beyond the ditch along the main road while a German battalion passed, then when they were gone we crossed the road and went on to the north. We were very close to Germans twice in the rain but they did not see us. We got past the town to the north without seeing any Italians, then after a while came on the main channels of the retreat and walked all night toward the Tagliamento. I had not realized how gigantic the retreat was. The whole country was moving, as well as the army. We walked all night, making better time than the vehicles. My leg ached and I was tired but we made good time. It seemed so silly for Bonello to have decided to be taken prisoner. There was no danger. We had walked through two armies without incident. If Aymo had not been killed there would never have seemed to be any danger. No one had bothered us when we were in plain sight along the railway. The killing came suddenly and unreasonably. I wondered where Bonello was.

"How do you feel, Tenente?" Piani asked. We were going along the side of a road crowded with vehicles and troops.

"Fine."

"I'm tired of this walking."

"Well, all we have to do is walk now. We don't have to worry."

"Bonello was a fool."

"He was a fool all right."

"What will you do about him, Tenente?"

"I don't know."

"Can't you just put him down as taken prisoner?"

"I don't know."

"You see if the war went on they would make bad trouble for his family."

"The war won't go on," a soldier said. "We're going home. The war is over."

"Everybody's going home."

"We're all going home."

"Come on, Tenente," Piani said. He wanted to get past them.

"Tenente? Who's a Tenente? *A basso gli ufficiali!* Down with the officers!"

Piani took me by the arm. "I better call you by your name," he said. "They might try and make trouble. They've shot some officers." We worked up past them.

"I won't make a report that will make trouble for his family." I went on with our conversation.

"If the war is over it makes no difference," Piani said. "But I don't believe it's over. It's too good that it should be over."

"We'll know pretty soon," I said.

"I don't believe it's over. They all think it's over but I don't believe it."

"*Viva la Pace!*" a soldier shouted out. "We're going home!"

"It would be fine if we all went home," Piani said. "Wouldn't you like to go home?"

"Yes."

"We'll never go. I don't think it's over."

"*Andiamo a casa!*" a soldier shouted.

"They throw away their rifles," Piani said. "They take them off and drop them down while they're marching. Then they shout."

"They ought to keep their rifles."

"They think if they throw away their rifles they can't make them fight."

In the dark and the rain, making our way along the side of the road I could see that many of the troops still had their rifles. They stuck up above the capes.

"What brigade are you?" an officer called out.

"*Brigata di Pace,*" some one shouted. "Peace Brigade!" The officer said nothing.

"What does he say? What does the officer say?"

"Down with the officer. *Viva la Pace!*"

"Come on," Piani said. We passed two British ambulances, abandoned in the block of vehicles.

"They're from Gorizia," Piani said. "I know the cars."

"They got further than we did."

"They started earlier."

"I wonder where the drivers are?"

"Up ahead probably."

"The Germans have stopped outside Udine," I said. "These people will all get across the river."

"Yes," Piani said. "That's why I think the war will go on."

"The Germans could come on," I said. "I wonder why they don't come on."

"I don't know. I don't know anything about this kind of war."

"They have to wait for their transport I suppose."

"I don't know," Piani said. Alone he was much gentler. When he was with the others he was a very rough talker.

"Are you married, Luigi?"

"You know I am married."

"Is that why you did not want to be a prisoner?"

"That is one reason. Are you married, Tenente?"

"No."

"Neither is Bonello."

"You can't tell anything by a man's being married. But I should think a married man would want to get back to his wife," I said. I would be glad to talk about wives.

"Yes."

"How are your feet?"

"They're sore enough."

Before daylight we reached the bank of the Tagliamento and followed down along the flooded river to the bridge where all the traffic was crossing.

"They ought to be able to hold at this river," Piani said. In the dark the flood looked high. The water swirled and it was wide. The wooden bridge was nearly three-quarters of a mile across, and the river, that usually ran in narrow channels in the wide stony bed far below the bridge, was close under the wooden planking. We went along the bank and then worked our way into the crowd that were crossing the bridge. Crossing slowly in the rain a few feet above the flood, pressed tight in the crowd, the box of an artillery caisson just ahead, I looked over the side and watched the river. Now that we could not go our own pace I felt very tired. There was no exhilaration

in crossing the bridge. I wondered what it would be like if a plane
bombed it in the daytime.

"Piani," I said.

"Here I am, Tenente." He was a little ahead in the jam. No one
was talking. They were all trying to get across as soon as they could:
thinking only of that. We were almost across. At the far end of the
bridge there were officers and carabinieri standing on both sides
flashing lights. I saw them silhouetted against the sky-line. As we
came close to them I saw one of the officers point to a man in the
column. A carabiniere went in after him and came out holding the
man by the arm. He took him away from the road. We came almost
opposite them. The officers were scrutinizing every one in the column,
sometimes speaking to each other, going forward to flash a light in
some one's face. They took some one else out just before we came
opposite. I saw the man. He was a lieutenant-colonel. I saw the stars
in the box on his sleeve as they flashed a light on him. His hair was
gray and he was short and fat. The carabiniere pulled him in behind
the line of officers. As we came opposite I saw one or two of them look
at me. Then one pointed at me and spoke to a carabiniere. I saw
the carabiniere start for me, come through the edge of the column
toward me, then felt him take me by the collar.

"What's the matter with you?" I said and hit him in the face.
I saw his face under the hat, upturned mustaches and blood coming
down his cheek. Another one dove in toward us.

"What's the matter with you?" I said. He did not answer. He was
watching a chance to grab me. I put my arm behind me to loosen my
pistol.

"Don't you know you can't touch an officer?"

The other one grabbed me from behind and pulled my arm up
so that it twisted in the socket. I turned with him and the other one
grabbed me around the neck. I kicked his shins and got my left knee
into his groin.

"Shoot him if he resists," I heard some one say.

"What's the meaning of this?" I tried to shout but my voice was
not very loud. They had me at the side of the road now.

"Shoot him if he resists," an officer said. "Take him over back."

"Who are you?"

"You'll find out."

"Who are you?"

"Battle police," another officer said.

"Why don't you ask me to step over instead of having one of these airplanes grab me?"

They did not answer. They did not have to answer. They were battle police.

"Take him back there with the others," the first officer said. "You see. He speaks Italian with an accent."

"So do you, you ——," I said.

"Take him back with the others," the first officer said. They took me down behind the line of officers below the road toward a group of people in a field by the river bank. As we walked toward them shots were fired. I saw flashes of the rifles and heard the reports. We came up to the group. There were four officers standing together, with a man in front of them with a carabiniere on each side of him. A group of men were standing guarded by carabinieri. Four other carabinieri stood near the questioning officers, leaning on their carbines. They were wide-hatted carabinieri. The two who had me shoved me in with the group waiting to be questioned. I looked at the man the officers were questioning. He was the fat gray-haired little lieutenant-colonel they had taken out of the column. The questioners had all the efficiency, coldness and command of themselves of Italians who are firing and are not being fired on.

"Your brigade?"

He told them.

"Regiment?"

He told them.

"Why are you not with your regiment?"

He told them.

"Do you not know that an officer should be with his troops?"

He did.

That was all. Another officer spoke.

"It is you and such as you that have let the barbarians onto the sacred soil of the fatherland."

"I beg your pardon," said the lieutenant-colonel.

"It is because of treachery such as yours that we have lost the fruits of victory."

"Have you ever been in a retreat?" the lieutenant-colonel asked.

"Italy should never retreat."

We stood there in the rain and listened to this. We were facing the officers and the prisoner stood in front and a little to one side of us.

"If you are going to shoot me," the lieutenant-colonel said, "please shoot me at once without further questioning. The questioning is stupid." He made the sign of the cross. The officers spoke together. One wrote something on a pad of paper.

"Abandoned his troops, ordered to be shot," he said.

Two carabinieri took the lieutenant-colonel to the river bank. He walked in the rain, an old man with his hat off, a carabinieri on either side. I did not watch them shoot him but I heard the shots. They were questioning some one else. This officer too was separated from his troops. He was not allowed to make an explanation. He cried when they read the sentence from the pad of paper, and they were questioning another when they shot him. They made a point of being intent on questioning the next man while the man who had been questioned before was being shot. In this way there was obviously nothing they could do about it. I did not know whether I should wait to be questioned or make a break now. I was obviously a German in Italian uniform. I saw how their minds worked; if they had minds and if they worked. They were all young men and they were saving their country. The second army was being re-formed beyond the Tagliamento. They were executing officers of the rank of major and above who were separated from their troops. They were also dealing summarily with German agitators in Italian uniform. They wore steel helmets. Only two of us had steel helmets. Some of the carabinieri had them. The other carabinieri wore the wide hat. Airplanes we called them. We stood in the rain and were taken out one at a time to be questioned and shot. So far they had shot every one they had questioned. The questioners had that beautiful detachment and devotion to stern justice of men dealing in death without being in any danger of it. They were questioning a full colonel of a line regiment. Three more officers had just been put in with us.

"Where was his regiment?"

I looked at the carabinieri. They were looking at the newcomers. The others were looking at the colonel. I ducked down, pushed between two men, and ran for the river, my head down. I tripped at the edge and went in with a splash. The water was very cold and I stayed under as long as I could. I could feel the current swirl me and I stayed under until I thought I could never come up. The minute I came up I took a breath and went down again. It was easy to stay under with so much clothing and my boots. When I came up the second time I saw a piece of timber ahead of me and reached it and held on with one hand. I kept my head behind it and did not even look over it. I did not want to see the bank. There were shots when I ran and shots when I came up the first time. I heard them when I was almost above water. There were no shots now. The piece of timber swung in the current and I held it with one hand. I looked at the bank. It seemed to be going by very fast. There was much wood in the stream. The water was very cold. We passed the brush of an island above the water. I held onto the timber with both hands and let it take me along. The shore was out of sight now.

31

You do not know how long you are in a river when the current moves swiftly. It seems a long time and it may be very short. The water was cold and in flood and many things passed that had been floated off the banks when the river rose. I was lucky to have a heavy timber to hold on to, and I lay in the icy water with my chin on the wood, holding as easily as I could with both hands. I was afraid of cramps and I hoped we would move toward the shore. We went down the river in a long curve. It was beginning to be light enough so I could see the bushes along the shore-line. There was a brush island ahead and the current moved toward the shore. I wondered if I should take off my boots and clothes and try to swim ashore, but decided not to. I had never thought of anything but that I would reach the shore some way, and I would be in a bad position if I landed barefoot. I had to get to Mestre some way.

I watched the shore come close, then swing away, then come closer again. We were floating more slowly. The shore was very close now. I could see twigs on the willow bush. The timber swung slowly so that the bank was behind me and I knew we were in an eddy. We went slowly around. As I saw the bank again, very close now, I tried holding with one arm and kicking and swimming the timber toward the bank with the other, but I did not bring it any closer. I was afraid we would move out of the eddy and, holding with one hand, I drew up my feet so they were against the side of the timber and shoved hard toward the bank. I could see the brush, but even with my momentum and swimming as hard as I could, the current was taking me away. I thought then I would drown because of my boots, but I thrashed and fought through the water, and when I looked up the bank was coming toward me, and I kept thrashing and swimming in a heavy-footed panic until I reached it. I hung to the willow branch and did not have strength to pull myself up but I knew I would not drown now. It had never occurred to me on the timber that I might drown. I felt hollow and sick in my stomach and chest from the effort, and I held to the branches and waited. When the sick feeling was gone I pulled into the willow bushes and rested again, my arms around some brush, holding tight with my hands to the branches. Then I crawled out, pushed on through the willows and onto the bank. It was half-daylight and I saw no one. I lay flat on the bank and heard the river and the rain.

After a while I got up and started along the bank. I knew there was no bridge across the river until Latisana. I thought I might be opposite San Vito. I began to think out what I should do. Ahead there was a ditch running into the river. I went toward it. So far I had seen no one and I sat down by some bushes along the bank of the ditch and took off my shoes and emptied them of water. I took off my coat, took my wallet with my papers and my money all wet in it out of the inside pocket and then wrung the coat out. I took off my trousers and wrung them too, then my shirt and under clothing. I slapped and rubbed myself and then dressed again. I had lost my cap.

Before I put on my coat I cut the cloth stars off my sleeves and put them in the inside pocket with my money. My money was wet but was all right. I counted it. There were three thousand and some lire. My clothes felt wet and clammy and I slapped my arms to keep the circulation going. I had woven underwear and I did not think I would catch cold if I kept moving. They had taken my pistol at the road and I put the holster under my coat. I had no cape and it was cold in the rain. I started up the bank of the canal. It was daylight and the country was wet, low and dismal looking. The fields were bare and wet; a long way away I could see a campanile rising out of the plain. I came up onto a road. Ahead I saw some troops coming down the road. I limped along the side of the road and they passed

me and paid no attention to me. They were a machine-gun detachment going up toward the river. I went on down the road.

That day I crossed the Venetian plain. It is a low level country
and under the rain it is even flatter. Toward the sea there are salt
marshes and very few roads. The roads all go along the river
mouths to the sea and to cross the country you must go along the
paths beside the canals. I was working across the country from the
north to the south and had crossed two railway lines and many
roads and finally I came out at the end of a path onto a railway line
where it ran beside a marsh. It was the main line from Venice to
Trieste, with a high solid embankment, a solid roadbed and double
track. Down the tracks a way was a flag-station and I could see soldiers
on guard. Up the line there was a bridge over a stream that flowed
into the marsh. I could see a guard too at the bridge. Crossing the
fields to the north I had seen a train pass on this railroad, visible a
long way across the flat plain, and I thought a train might come from
Portogruaro. I watched the guards and lay down on the embankment
so that I could see both ways along the track. The guard at the
bridge walked a way up the line toward where I lay, then turned and
went back toward the bridge. I lay, and was hungry, and waited for
the train. The one I had seen was so long that the engine moved it
very slowly and I was sure I could get aboard it. After I had almost
given up hoping for one I saw a train coming. The engine, coming
straight on, grew larger slowly. I looked at the guard at the bridge.
He was walking on the near side of the bridge but on the other side
of the tracks. That would put him out of sight when the train passed.
I watched the engine come nearer. It was working hard. I could see
there were many cars. I knew there would be guards on the train,
and I tried to see where they were, but, keeping out of sight, I could
not. The engine was almost to where I was lying. When it came
opposite, working and puffing even on the level, and I saw the
engineer pass, I stood up and stepped up close to the passing cars.
If the guards were watching I was a less suspicious object standing
beside the track. Several closed freight-cars passed. Then I saw a low
open car of the sort they call gondolas coming, covered with canvas. I
stood until it had almost passed, then jumped and caught the rear
hand-rods and pulled up. I crawled down between the gondola and
the shelter of the high freight-car behind. I did not think any one
had seen me. I was holding to the hand-rods and crouching low, my

feet on the coupling. We were almost opposite the bridge. I remembered the guard. As we passed him he looked at me. He was a boy and his helmet was too big for him. I stared at him contemptuously and he looked away. He thought I had something to do with the train.

We were past. I saw him still looking uncomfortable, watching the other cars pass and I stopped to see how the canvas was fastened. It had grummets and was laced down at the edge with cord. I took out my knife, cut the cord and put my arm under. There were hard bulges under the canvas that tightened in the rain. I looked up and ahead. There was a guard on the freight-car ahead but he was looking forward. I let go of the hand-rails and ducked under the canvas. My forehead hit something that gave me a violent bump and I felt blood on my face but I crawled on in and lay flat. Then I turned around and fastened down the canvas.

I was in under the canvas with guns. They smelled cleanly of oil and grease. I lay and listened to the rain on the canvas and the clicking of the car over the rails. There was a little light came through and I lay and looked at the guns. They had their canvas jackets on. I thought they must have been sent ahead from the third army. The bump on my forehead was swollen and I stopped the bleeding by lying still and letting it coagulate, then picked away the dried blood except over the cut. It was nothing. I had no handkerchief, but feeling with my fingers I washed away where the dried blood had been, with rainwater that dripped from the canvas, and wiped it clean with the sleeve of my coat. I did not want to look conspicuous. I knew I would have to get out before they got to Mestre because they would be taking care of these guns. They had no guns to lose or forget about. I was terrifically hungry.

32

LYING on the floor of the flat-car with the guns beside me under the canvas I was wet, cold and very hungry. Finally I rolled over and lay flat on my stomach with my head on my arms. My knee was stiff, but it had been very satisfactory. Valentini had done a fine job. I had done half the retreat on foot and swum part of the Tagliamento with his knee. It was his knee all right. The other knee was mine. Doctors did things to you and then it was not your body any more.

The head was mine, and the inside of the belly. It was very hungry in there. I could feel it turn over on itself. The head was mine, but not to use, not to think with, only to remember and not too much remember.

I could remember Catherine but I knew I would get crazy if I thought about her when I was not sure yet I would see her, so I would not think about her, only about her a little, only about her with the car going slowly and clickingly, and some light through the canvas and my lying with Catherine on the floor of the car. Hard as the floor of the car to lie not thinking only feeling, having been away too long, the clothes wet and the floor moving only a little each time and lonesome inside and alone with wet clothing and hard floor for a wife.

You did not love the floor of a flat-car nor guns with canvas jackets and the smell of vaselined metal or a canvas that rain leaked through, although it is very fine under a canvas and pleasant with guns; but you loved some one else whom now you knew was not even to be pretended there; you seeing now very clearly and coldly— not so coldly as clearly and emptily. You saw emptily, lying on your stomach, having been present when one army moved back and another came forward. You had lost your cars and your men as a floorwalker loses the stock of his department in a fire. There was, however, no insurance. You were out of it now. You had no more obligation. If they shot floorwalkers after a fire in the department store because they spoke with an accent they had always had, then certainly the floorwalkers would not be expected to return when the store opened again for business. They might seek other employment; if there was any other employment and the police did not get them.

Anger was washed away in the river along with any obligation. Although that ceased when the carabiniere put his hands on my collar. I would like to have had the uniform off although I did not care much about the outward forms. I had taken off the stars, but that was for convenience. It was no point of honor. I was not against them. I was through. I wished them all the luck. There were the good ones, and the brave ones, and the calm ones and the sensible ones, and they deserved it. But it was not my show any more and I wished this bloody train would get to Mestre and I would eat and stop thinking. I would have to stop.

Piani would tell them they had shot me. They went through the pockets and took the papers of the people they shot. They would not have my papers. They might call me drowned. I wondered what they would hear in the States. Dead from wounds and other causes. Good Christ I was hungry. I wondered what had become of the priest at the mess. And Rinaldi. He was probably at Pordenone. If they had not gone further back. Well, I would never see him now. I would never see any of them now. That life was over. I did not think he had syphilis. It was not a serious disease anyway if you took it in time, they said. But he would worry. I would worry too if I had it. Any one would worry.

I was not made to think. I was made to eat. My God, yes. Eat and drink and sleep with Catherine. To-night maybe. No that was impossible. But to-morrow night, and a good meal and sheets and never going away again except together. Probably have to go damned quickly. She would go. I knew she would go. When would we go? That was something to think about. It was getting dark. I lay and thought where we would go. There were many places.

BOOK FOUR

33

I DROPPED off the train in Milan as it slowed to come into the station early in the morning before it was light. I crossed the track and came out between some buildings and down onto the street. A wine shop was open and I went in for some coffee. It smelled of early morning, of swept dust, spoons in coffee-glasses and the wet circles left by wine-glasses. The proprietor was behind the bar. Two soldiers sat at a table. I stood at the bar and drank a glass of coffee and ate a piece of bread. The coffee was gray with milk, and I skimmed the milk scum off the top with a piece of bread. The proprietor looked at me.

"You want a glass of grappa?"

"No thanks."

"On me," he said and poured a small glass and pushed it toward me. "What's happening at the front?"

"I would not know."

"They are drunk," he said, moving his hand toward the two soldiers. I could believe him. They looked drunk.

"Tell me," he said, "what is happening at the front?"

"I would not know about the front."

"I saw you come down the wall. You came off the train."

"There is a big retreat."

"I read the papers. What happens? Is it over?"

"I don't think so."

He filled the glass with grappa from a short bottle. "If you are in trouble," he said, "I can keep you."

"I am not in trouble."

"If you are in trouble stay here with me."

"Where does one stay?"

"In the building. Many stay here. Any who are in trouble stay here."

"Are many in trouble?"

"It depends on the trouble. You are a South American?"

312

"No."

"Speak Spanish?"

"A little."

He wiped off the bar.

"It is hard now to leave the country but in no way impossible."

"I have no wish to leave."

"You can stay here as long as you want. You will see what sort of man I am."

"I have to go this morning but I will remember the address to return."

He shook his head. "You won't come back if you talk like that. I thought you were in real trouble."

"I am in no trouble. But I value the address of a friend."

I put a ten-lira note on the bar to pay for the coffee.

"Have a grappa with me," I said.

"It is not necessary."

"Have one."

He poured the two glasses.

"Remember," he said. "Come here. Do not let other people take you in. Here you are all right."

"I am sure."

"You are sure?"

"Yes."

He was serious. "Then let me tell you one thing. Do not go about with that coat."

"Why?"

"On the sleeves it shows very plainly where the stars have been cut away. The cloth is a different color."

I did not say anything.

"If you have no papers I can give you papers."

"What papers?"

"Leave-papers."

"I have no need for papers. I have papers."

"All right," he said. "But if you need papers I can get what you wish."

"How much are such papers?"

"It depends on what they are. The price is reasonable."

"I don't need any now."

He shrugged his shoulders.

"I'm all right," I said.

When I went out he said, "Don't forget that I am your friend."

"No."

"I will see you again," he said.

"Good," I said.

Outside I kept away from the station, where there were military police, and picked up a cab at the edge of the little park. I gave the driver the address of the hospital. At the hospital I went to the porter's lodge. His wife embraced me. He shook my hand.

"You are back. You are safe."

"Yes."

"Have you had breakfast?"

"Yes."

"How are you, Tenente? How are you?" the wife asked.

"Fine."

"Won't you have breakfast with us?"

"No, thank you. Tell me is Miss Barkley here at the hospital now?"

"Miss Barkley?"

"The English lady nurse."

"His girl," the wife said. She patted my arm and smiled.

"No," the porter said. "She is away."

My heart went down. "You are sure? I mean the tall blonde English young lady."

"I am sure. She is gone to Stresa."

"When did she go?"

"She went two days ago with the other lady English."

"Good," I said. "I wish you to do something for me. Do not tell any one you have seen me. It is very important."

"I won't tell any one," the porter said. I gave him a ten-lira note. He pushed it away.

"I promise you I will tell no one," he said. "I don't want any money."

"What can we do for you, Signor Tenente?" his wife asked.

"Only that," I said.

"We are dumb," the porter said. "You will let me know anything I can do?"

"Yes," I said. "Good-by. I will see you again."

They stood in the door, looking after me.

I got into the cab and gave the driver the address of Simmons, one of the men I knew who was studying singing.

Simmons lived a long way out in the town toward the Porta Magenta. He was still in bed and sleepy when I went to see him.

"You get up awfully early, Henry," he said.

"I came in on the early train."

"What's all this retreat? Were you at the front? Will you have a cigarette? They're in that box on the table." In was a big room with a bed beside the wall, a piano over on the far side and a dresser and table. I sat on a chair by the bed. Simmons sat propped up by the pillows and smoked.

"I'm in a jam, Sim," I said.

"So am I," he said. "I'm always in a jam. Won't you smoke?"

"No," I said. "What's the procedure in going to Switzerland?"

"For you? The Italians wouldn't let you out of the country."

"Yes. I know that. But the Swiss. What will they do?"

"They intern you."

"I know. But what's the mechanics of it?"

"Nothing. It's very simple. You can go anywhere. I think you just have to report or something. Why? Are you fleeing the police?"

"Nothing definite yet."

"Don't tell me if you don't want. But it would be interesting to hear. Nothing happens here. I was a great flop at Piacenza."

"I'm awfully sorry."

"Oh yes—I went very badly. I sung well too. I'm going to try it again at the Lyrico here."

"I'd like to be there."

"You're awfully polite. You aren't in a bad mess, are you?"

"I don't know."

"Don't tell me if you don't want. How do you happen to be away from the bloody front?"

"I think I'm through with it."

"Good boy. I always knew you had sense. Can I help you any way?"

"You're awfully busy."

"Not a bit of it, my dear Henry. Not a bit of it. I'd be happy to do anything."

"You're about my size. Would you go out and buy me an outfit of civilian clothes? I've clothes but they're all at Rome."

"You did live there, didn't you? It's a filthy place. How did you ever live there?"

"I wanted to be an architect."

"That's no place for that. Don't buy clothes. I'll give you all the clothes you want. I'll fit you out so you'll be a great success. Go in that dressing room. There's a closet. Take anything you want. My dear fellow, you don't want to buy clothes."

"I'd rather buy them, Sim."

"My dear fellow, it's easier for me to let you have them than go out and buy them. Have you got a passport? You won't get far without a passport."

"Yes. I've still got my passport."

"Then get dressed, my dear fellow, and off to old Helvetia."

"It's not that simple. I have to go up to Stresa first."

"Ideal, my dear fellow. You just row a boat across. If I wasn't trying to sing, I'd go with you. I'll go yet."

"You could take up yodelling."

"My dear fellow, I'll take up yodelling yet. I really can sing though. That's the strange part."

"I'll bet you can sing."

He lay back in bed smoking a cigarette.

"Don't bet too much. But I can sing though. It's damned funny, but I can. I like to sing. Listen." He roared into "Africana," his neck swelling, the veins standing out. "I can sing," he said. "Whether they like it or not." I looked out of the window. "I'll go down and let my cab go."

"Come back up, my dear fellow, and we'll have breakfast." He stepped out of bed, stood straight, took a deep breath and commenced doing bending exercises. I went downstairs and paid off the cab.

34

IN civilian clothes I felt a masquerader. I had been in uniform a long time and I missed the feeling of being held by your clothes. The trousers felt very floppy. I had bought a ticket at Milan for Stresa. I had also bought a new hat. I could not wear Sim's hat but his clothes were fine. They smelled of tobacco and as I sat in the compartment and looked out the window the new hat felt very new and the clothes very old. I myself felt as sad as the wet Lombard country that was outside through the window. There were some aviators in the compartment who did not think much of me. They avoided looking at me and were very scornful of a civilian my age. I did not feel insulted. In the old days I would have insulted them and picked a fight. They got off at Gallarate and I was glad to be alone. I had the paper but I did not read it because I did not want to read about the war. I was going to forget the war. I had made a separate peace. I felt damned lonely and was glad when the train got to Stresa.

At the station I had expected to see the porters from the hotels but there was no one. The season had been over a long time and no one met the train. I got down from the train with my bag, it was Sim's bag, and very light to carry, being empty except for two shirts, and stood under the roof of the station in the rain while the train went on. I found a man in the station and asked him if he knew what hotels were open. The Grand-Hôtel & des Isles Borromées was open and several small hotels that stayed open all the year. I started in the rain for the Isles Borromées carrying my bag. I saw a carriage coming down the street and signalled to the driver. It was better to arrive in a carriage. We drove up to the carriage entrance of the big hotel and the concierge came out with an umbrella and was very polite.

I took a good room. It was very big and light and looked out on the lake. The clouds were down over the lake but it would be beautiful with the sunlight. I was expecting my wife, I said. There was a big double bed, a *letto matrimoniale* with a satin coverlet. The hotel was very luxurious. I went down the long halls, down the wide stairs, through the rooms to the bar. I knew the barman and sat on a high stool and ate salted almonds and potato chips. The martini felt cool and clean.

"What are you doing here in *borghese*?" the barman asked after he had mixed a second martini.

"I am on leave. Convalescing-leave."

"There is no one here. I don't know why they keep the hotel open."

"Have you been fishing?"

"I've caught some beautiful pieces. Trolling this time of year you catch some beautiful pieces."

"Did you ever get the tobacco I sent?"

"Yes. Didn't you get my card?"

I laughed. I had not been able to get the tobacco. It was American pipe-tobacco that he wanted, but my relatives had stopped sending it or it was being held up. Anyway it never came.

"I'll get some somewhere," I said. "Tell me have you seen two English girls in the town? They came here day before yesterday."

"They are not at the hotel."

"They are nurses."

"I have seen two nurses. Wait a minute, I will find out where they are."

"One of them is my wife," I said. "I have come here to meet her."

"The other is my wife."

"I am not joking."

"Pardon my stupid joke," he said. "I did not understand." He went away and was gone quite a little while. I ate olives, salted almonds and potato chips and looked at myself in civilian clothes in the mirror behind the bar. The bartender came back. "They are at the little hotel near the station," he said.

"How about some sandwiches?"

"I'll ring for some. You understand there is nothing here, now there are no people."

"Isn't there really any one at all?"

"Yes. There are a few people."

The sandwiches came and I ate three and drank a couple more martinis. I had never tasted anything so cool and clean. They made me feel civilized. I had had too much red wine, bread, cheese, bad coffee and grappa. I sat on the high stool before the pleasant mahogany, the brass and the mirrors and did not think at all. The barman asked me some question.

"Don't talk about the war," I said. The war was a long way away. Maybe there wasn't any war. There was no war here. Then I realized it was over for me. But I did not have the feeling that it was really over. I had the feeling of a boy who thinks of what is happening at a certain hour at the schoolhouse from which he has played truant.

Catherine and Helen Ferguson were at supper when I came to their hotel. Standing in the hallway I saw them at table. Catherine's face was away from me and I saw the line of her hair and her cheek and her lovely neck and shoulders. Ferguson was talking. She stopped when I came in.

"My God," she said.

"Hello," I said.

"Why it's you!" Catherine said. Her face lighted up. She looked too happy to believe it. I kissed her. Catherine blushed and I sat down at the table.

"You're a fine mess," Ferguson said. "What are you doing here? Have you eaten?"

"No." The girl who was serving the meal came in and I told her to bring a plate for me. Catherine looked at me all the time, her eyes happy.

"What are you doing in mufti?" Ferguson asked.

"I'm in the cabinet."

"You're in some mess."

"Cheer up, Fergy. Cheer up just a little."

"I'm not cheered by seeing you. I know the mess you've gotten this girl into. You're no cheerful sight to me."

Catherine smiled at me and touched me with her foot under the table.

"No one got me in a mess, Fergy. I get in my own messes."

"I can't stand him," Ferguson said. "He's done nothing but ruin you with his sneaking Italian tricks. Americans are worse than Italians."

"The Scotch are such a moral people," Catherine said.

"I don't mean that. I mean his Italian sneakiness."

"Am I sneaky, Fergy?"

"You are. You're worse than sneaky. You're like a snake. A snake with an Italian uniform: with a cape around your neck."

"I haven't got an Italian uniform now."

"That's just another example of your sneakiness. You had a love affair all summer and got this girl with child and now I suppose you'll sneak off."

I smiled at Catherine and she smiled at me.

"We'll both sneak off," she said.

"You're two of the same thing," Ferguson said. "I'm ashamed of you, Catherine Barkley. You have no shame and no honor and you're as sneaky as he is."

"Don't, Fergy," Catherine said and patted her hand. "Don't denounce me. You know we like each other."

"Take your hand away," Ferguson said. Her face was red. "If you had any shame it would be different. But you're God knows how many months gone with child and you think it's a joke and are all smiles because your seducer's come back. You've no shame and no feelings." She began to cry. Catherine went over and put her arm around her. As she stood comforting Ferguson, I could see no change in her figure.

"I don't care," Ferguson sobbed. "I think it's dreadful."

"There, there, Fergy," Catherine comforted her. "I'll be ashamed. Don't cry, Fergy. Don't cry, old Fergy."

"I'm not crying," Ferguson sobbed. "I'm not crying. Except for the awful thing you've gotten into." She looked at me. "I hate you," she said. "She can't make me not hate you. You dirty sneaking American Italian." Her eyes and nose were red with crying.

Catherine smiled at me.

"Don't you smile at him with your arm around me."

"You're unreasonable, Fergy."

"I know it," Ferguson sobbed. "You mustn't mind me, either of you. I'm so upset. I'm not reasonable. I know it. I want you both to be happy."

"We're happy," Catherine said. "You're a sweet Fergy."

Ferguson cried again. "I don't want you happy the way you are. Why don't you get married? You haven't got another wife have you?"

"No," I said. Catherine laughed.

"It's nothing to laugh about," Ferguson said. "Plenty of them have other wives."

"We'll be married, Fergy," Catherine said, "if it will please you."

"Not to please me. You should want to be married."

"We've been very busy."

"Yes. I know. Busy making babies." I thought she was going to cry again but she went into bitterness instead. "I suppose you'll go off with him now to-night?"

"Yes," said Catherine. "If he wants me."

"What about me?"

"Are you afraid to stay here alone?"

"Yes, I am."

"Then I'll stay with you."

"No, go on with him. Go with him right away. I'm sick of seeing both of you."

"We'd better finish dinner."

"No. Go right away."

"Fergy, be reasonable."

"I say get out right away. Go away both of you."

"Let's go then," I said. I was sick of Fergy.

"You do want to go. You see you want to leave me even to eat dinner alone. I've always wanted to go to the Italian lakes and this is how it is. Oh, oh," she sobbed, then looked at Catherine and choked.

"We'll stay till after dinner," Catherine said. "And I'll not leave you alone if you want me to stay. I won't leave you alone, Fergy."

"No. No. I want you to go. I want you to go." She wiped her eyes. "I'm so unreasonable. Please don't mind me."

The girl who served the meal had been upset by all the crying. Now as she brought in the next course she seemed relieved that things were better.

That night at the hotel, in our room with the long empty hall outside and our shoes outside the door, a thick carpet on the floor of the room, outside the windows the rain falling and in the room light and pleasant and cheerful, then the light out and it exciting with smooth sheets and the bed comfortable, feeling that we had come home, feeling no longer alone, waking in the night to find the other one there, and not gone away; all other things were unreal. We slept when we were tired and if we woke the other one woke too so one was not alone. Often a man wishes to be alone and a girl wishes to be alone too and if they love each other they are jealous of that in each other, but I can truly say we never felt that. We could feel alone when we were together, alone against the others. It has only happened to me like that once. I have been alone while I was with many girls and that is the way that you can be most lonely. But we were never lonely and never afraid when we were together. I know that the night is not the same as the day: that all things are different, that the things of the night cannot be explained in the day, because they do not then exist, and the night can be a dreadful time for lonely people once their loneliness has started. But with Catherine there was almost no difference in the night except that it was an even better time. If people bring so much courage to this world the world has to kill them to break them, so of course it kills them. The world breaks every one and afterward many are strong at the broken places. But those that will not break it kills. It kills the very good and the very gentle and the very brave impartially. If you are none of these you can be sure it will kill you too but there will be no special hurry.

I remember waking in the morning. Catherine was asleep and the sunlight was coming in through the window. The rain had stopped and I stepped out of bed and across the floor to the window. Down below were the gardens, bare now but beautifully regular, the gravel paths, the trees, the stone wall by the lake and the lake in the sunlight with the mountains beyond. I stood at the window looking out and when I turned away I saw Catherine was awake and watching me.

"How are you, darling?" she said. "Isn't it a lovely day?"

"How do you feel?"

"I feel very well. We had a lovely night."

"Do you want breakfast?"

She wanted breakfast. So did I and we had it in bed, the November sunlight coming in the window, and the breakfast tray across my lap.

"Don't you want the paper? You always wanted the paper in the hospital?"

"No," I said. "I don't want the paper now."

"Was it so bad you don't want even to read about it?"

"I don't want to read about it."

"I wish I had been with you so I would know about it too."

"I'll tell you about it if I ever get it straight in my head."

"But won't they arrest you if they catch you out of uniform?"

"They'll probably shoot me."

"Then we'll not stay here. We'll get out of the country."

"I'd thought something of that."

"We'll get out. Darling, you shouldn't take silly chances. Tell me how did you come from Mestre to Milan?"

"I came on the train. I was in uniform then."

"Weren't you in danger then?"

"Not much. I had an old order of movement. I fixed the dates on it in Mestre."

"Darling, you're liable to be arrested here any time. I won't have it. It's silly to do something like that. Where would we be if they took you off?"

"Let's not think about it. I'm tired of thinking about it."

"What would you do if they came to arrest you?"

"Shoot them."

"You see how silly you are, I won't let you go out of the hotel until we leave here."

"Where are we going to go?"

"Please don't be that way, darling. We'll go wherever you say. But please find some place to go right away."

"Switzerland is down the lake, we can go there."

"That will be lovely."

It was clouding over outside and the lake was darkening.

"I wish we did not always have to live like criminals," I said.

"Darling, don't be that way. You haven't lived like a criminal very long. And we never live like criminals. We're going to have a fine time."

"I feel like a criminal. I've deserted from the army."

"Darling, *please* be sensible. It's not deserting from the army. It's only the Italian army."

I laughed. "You're a fine girl. Let's get back into bed. I feel fine in bed."

A little while later Catherine said, "You don't feel like a criminal do you?"

"No," I said. "Not when I'm with you."

"You're such a silly boy," she said. "But I'll look after you. Isn't it splendid, darling, that I don't have any morning-sickness?"

"It's grand."

"You don't appreciate what a fine wife you have. But I don't care. I'll get you some place where they can't arrest you and then we'll have a lovely time."

"Let's go there right away."

"We will, darling. I'll go any place any time you wish."

"Let's not think about anything."

"All right."

35

CATHERINE went along the lake to the little hotel to see Ferguson and I sat in the bar and read the papers. There were comfortable leather chairs in the bar and I sat in one of them and read until the barman came in. The army had not stood at the Tagliamento. They were falling back to the Piave. I remembered the Piave. The railroad crossed it near San Dona going up to the front. It was deep and slow there and quite narrow. Down below there were mosquito marshes and canals. There were some lovely villas. Once, before the war, going up to Cortina D'Ampezzo I had gone along it for several hours in the hills. Up there it looked like a trout stream, flowing swiftly with shallow stretches and pools under the shadow of the rocks. The road turned off from it at Cadore. I wondered how the army that was up there would come down. The barman came in.

"Count Greffi was asking for you," he said.

"Who?"

"Count Greffi. You remember the old man who was here when you were here before."

"Is he here?"

"Yes, he's here with his niece. I told him you were here. He wants you to play billiards."

"Where is he?"

"He's taking a walk."

"How is he?"

"He's younger than ever. He drank three champagne cocktails last night before dinner."

"How's his billiard game?"

"Good. He beat me. When I told him you were here he was very pleased. There's nobody here for him to play with."

Count Greffi was ninety-four years old. He had been a contemporary of Metternich and was an old man with white hair and mustache and beautiful manners. He had been in the diplomatic service of both Austria and Italy and his birthday parties were the great social event of Milan. He was living to be one hundred years old and played a smoothly fluent game of billiards that contrasted with his own ninety-four-year-old brittleness. I had met him when I had been at Stresa once before out of season and while we played billiards we drank champagne. I thought it was a splendid custom and he gave me fifteen points in a hundred and beat me.

"Why didn't you tell me he was here?"

"I forgot it."

"Who else is here?"

"No one you know. There are only six people altogether."

"What are you doing now?"

"Nothing."

"Come on out fishing."

"I could come for an hour."

"Come on. Bring the trolling line."

The barman put on a coat and we went out. We went down and got a boat and I rowed while the barman sat in the stern and let out the line with a spinner and a heavy sinker on the end to troll for lake trout. We rowed along the shore, the barman holding the line in his hand and giving it occasional jerks forward. Stresa looked very deserted from the lake. There were the long rows of bare trees, the big hotels and the closed villas. I rowed across to Isola Bella and went close to the walls, where the water deepened sharply, and you saw the rock wall slanting down in the clear water, and then up and along to the fisherman's island. The sun was under a cloud and the water was dark and smooth and very cold. We did not have a strike though we saw some circles on the water from rising fish.

I rowed up opposite the fisherman's island where there were boats drawn up and men were mending nets.

"Should we get a drink?"

"All right."

I brought the boat up to the stone pier and the barman pulled in the line, coiling it on the bottom of the boat and hooking the spinner on the edge of the gunwhale. I stepped out and tied the boat. We went into a little café, sat at a bare wooden table and ordered vermouth.

"Are you tired from rowing?"

"No."

"I'll row back," he said.

"I like to row."

"Maybe if you hold the line it will change the luck."

"All right."

"Tell me how goes the war."

"Rotten."

"I don't have to go. I'm too old, like Count Greffi."

"Maybe you'll have to go yet."

"Next year they'll call my class. But I won't go."

"What will you do?"

"Get out of the country. I wouldn't go to war. I was at the war once in Abyssinia. Nix. Why do you go?"

"I don't know. I was a fool."

"Have another vermouth?"

"All right."

The barman rowed back. We trolled up the lake beyond Stresa and then down not far from shore. I held the taut line and felt the faint pulsing of the spinner revolving while I looked at the dark November water of the lake and the deserted shore. The barman rowed with long strokes and on the forward thrust of the boat the line throbbed. Once I had a strike: the line hardened suddenly and jerked back. I pulled and felt the live weight of the trout and then the line throbbed again. I had missed him.

"Did he feel big?"

"Pretty big."

"Once when I was out trolling alone I had the line in my teeth and one struck and nearly took my mouth out."

"The best way is to have it over your leg," I said. "Then you feel it and don't lose your teeth."

I put my hand in the water. It was very cold. We were almost opposite the hotel now.

"I have to go in," the barman said, "to be there for eleven o'clock. *L'heure du cocktail.*"

"All right."

I pulled in the line and wrapped it on a stick notched at each end. The barman put the boat in a little slip in the stone wall and locked it with a chain and padlock.

"Any time you want it," he said, "I'll give you the key."

"Thanks."

We went up to the hotel and into the bar. I did not want another drink so early in the morning so I went up to our room. The maid had just finished doing the room and Catherine was not back yet. I lay down on the bed and tried to keep from thinking.

When Catherine came back it was all right again. Ferguson was downstairs, she said. She was coming to lunch.

"I knew you wouldn't mind," Catherine said.

"No," I said.

"What's the matter, darling?"

"I don't know."

"I know. You haven't anything to do. All you have is me and I go away."

"That's true."

"I'm sorry, darling. I know it must be a dreadful feeling to have nothing at all suddenly."

"My life used to be full of everything," I said. "Now if you aren't with me I haven't a thing in the world."

"But I'll be with you. I was only gone for two hours. Isn't there anything you can do?"

"I went fishing with the barman."

"Wasn't it fun?"

"Yes."

"Don't think about me when I'm not here."

"That's the way I worked it at the front. But there was something to do then."

"Othello with his occupation gone," she teased.

"Othello was a nigger," I said. "Besides, I'm not jealous. I'm just so in love with you that there isn't anything else."

"Will you be a good boy and be nice to Ferguson?"

"I'm always nice to Ferguson unless she curses me."

"Be nice to her. Think how much we have and she hasn't anything."

"I don't think she wants what we have."

"You don't know much, darling, for such a wise boy."

"I'll be nice to her."

"I know you will. You're so sweet."

"She won't stay afterward, will she?"

"No. I'll get rid of her."

"And then we'll come up here."

"Of course. What do you think I want to do?"

We went downstairs to have lunch with Ferguson. She was very impressed by the hotel and the splendor of the dining-room. We had a good lunch with a couple of bottles of white capri. Count Greffi came into the dining-room and bowed to us. His niece, who looked a little like my grandmother, was with him. I told Catherine and Ferguson about him and Ferguson was very impressed. The hotel was very big and grand and empty but the food was good, the wine was very pleasant and finally the wine made us all feel very well. Catherine had no need to feel any better. She was very happy. Ferguson became quite cheerful. I felt very well myself. After lunch Ferguson went back to her hotel. She was going to lie down for a while after lunch she said.

Along late in the afternoon some one knocked on our door.

"Who is it?"

"The Count Greffi wishes to know if you will play billiards with him."

I looked at my watch; I had taken it off and it was under the pillow.

"Do you have to go, darling?" Catherine whispered.

"I think I'd better." The watch was a quarter-past four o'clock. Out loud I said, "Tell the Count Greffi I will be in the billiard-room at five o'clock."

At a quarter to five I kissed Catherine good-by and went into the bathroom to dress. Knotting my tie and looking in the glass I looked strange to myself in the civilian clothes. I must remember to buy some more shirts and socks.

"Will you be away a long time?" Catherine asked. She looked lovely in the bed. "Would you hand me the brush?"

I watched her brushing her hair, holding her head so the weight of her hair all came on one side. It was dark outside and the light over the head of the bed shone on her hair and on her neck and shoulders. I went over and kissed her and held her hand with the brush and her head sunk back on the pillow. I kissed her neck and shoulders. I felt faint with loving her so much.

"I don't want to go away."

"I don't want you to go away."

"I won't go then."

"Yes. Go. It's only for a little while and then you'll come back."

"We'll have dinner up here."

"Hurry and come back."

I found the Count Greffi in the billiard-room. He was practising strokes, looking very fragile under the light that came down above the billiard table. On a card table a little way beyond the light was a silver icing-bucket with the necks and corks of two champagne bottles showing above the ice. The Count Greffi straightened up when I came toward the table and walked toward me. He put out his hand, "It is such a great pleasure that you are here. You were very kind to come to play with me."

"It was very nice of you to ask me."

"Are you quite well? They told me you were wounded on the Isonzo. I hope you are well again."

"I'm very well. Have you been well?"

"Oh, I am always well. But I am getting old. I detect signs of age now."

"I can't believe it."

"Yes. Do you want to know one? It is easier for me to talk Italian. I discipline myself but I find when I am tired that it is so much easier to talk Italian. So I know I must be getting old."

"We could talk Italian. I am a little tired, too."

"Oh, but when you are tired it will be easier for you to talk English."

"American."

"Yes. American. You will please talk American. It is a delightful language."

"I hardly ever see Americans."

"You must miss them. One misses one's countrymen and especially one's countrywomen. I know that experience. Should we play or are you too tired?"

"I'm not really tired. I said that for a joke. What handicap will you give me?"

"Have you been playing very much?"

"None at all."

"You play very well. Ten points in a hundred?"

"You flatter me."

"Fifteen?"

"That would be fine but you will beat me."

"Should we play for a stake? You always wished to play for a stake."

"I think we'd better."

"All right. I will give you eighteen points and we will play for a franc a point."

He played a lovely game of billiards and with the handicap I was only four ahead at fifty. Count Greffi pushed a button on the wall to ring for the barman.

"Open one bottle please," he said. Then to me, "We will take a little stimulant." The wine was icy cold and very dry and good.

"Should we talk Italian? Would you mind very much? It is my weakness now."

We went on playing, sipping the wine between shots, speaking in Italian, but talking little, concentrated on the game. Count Greffi made his one hundredth point and with the handicap I was only at ninety-four. He smiled and patted me on the shoulder.

"Now we will drink the other bottle and you will tell me about the war." He waited for me to sit down.

"About anything else," I said.

"You don't want to talk about it? Good. What have you been reading?"

"Nothing," I said. "I'm afraid I am very dull."

"No. But you should read."

"What is there written in war-time?"

"There is 'Le Feu' by a Frenchman, Barbusse. There is 'Mr. Britling Sees Through It.' "

"No, he doesn't."

"What?"

"He doesn't see through it. Those books were at the hospital."

"Then you have been reading?"

"Yes, but nothing any good."

"I thought 'Mr. Britling' a very good study of the English middle-class soul."

"I don't know about the soul."

"Poor boy. We none of us know about the soul. Are you *Croyant?*"

"At night."

Count Greffi smiled and turned the glass with his fingers. "I had expected to become more devout as I grow older but somehow I haven't," he said. "It is a great pity."

"Would you like to live after death?" I asked and instantly felt a fool to mention death. But he did not mind the word.

"It would depend on the life. This life is very pleasant. I would like to live forever," he smiled. "I very nearly have."

We were sitting in the deep leather chairs, the champagne in the ice-bucket and our glasses on the table between us.

"If you ever live to be as old as I am you will find many things strange."

"You never seem old."

"It is the body that is old. Sometimes I am afraid I will break off a finger as one breaks a stick of chalk. And the spirit is no older and not much wiser."

"You are wise."

"No, that is the great fallacy; the wisdom of old men. They do not grow wise. They grow careful."

"Perhaps that is wisdom."

"It is a very unattractive wisdom. What do you value most?"

"Some one I love."

"With me it is the same. That is not wisdom. Do you value life?"

"Yes."

"So do ⅼ. Because it is all I have. And to give birthday parties," he laughed. "You are probably wiser than I am. You do not give birthday parties."

We both drank the wine.

"What do you think of the war really?" I asked.

"I think it is stupid."

"Who will win it?"

"Italy."

"Why?"

"They are a younger nation."

"Do younger nations always win wars?"

"They are apt to for a time."

"Then what happens?"

"They become older nations."

"You said you were not wise."

"Dear boy, that is not wisdom. That is cynicism."

"It sounds very wise to me."

"It's not particularly. I could quote you the examples on the other side. But it is not bad. Have we finished the champagne?"

"Almost."

"Should we drink some more? Then I must dress."

"Perhaps we'd better not now."

"You are sure you don't want more?"

"Yes." He stood up.

"I hope you will be very fortunate and very happy and very, very healthy."

"Thank you. And I hope you will live forever."

"Thank you. I have. And if you ever become devout pray for me if I am dead. I am asking several of my friends to do that. I had expected to become devout myself but it has not come." I thought he smiled sadly but I could not tell. He was so old and his face was very wrinkled, so that a smile used so many lines that all gradations were lost.

"I might become very devout," I said. "Anyway, I will pray for you."

"I had always expected to become devout. All my family died very devout. But somehow it does not come."

"It's too early."

"Maybe it is too late. Perhaps I have outlived my religious feeling."

"My own comes only at night."

"Then too you are in love. Do not forget that is a religious feeling."

"You believe so?"

"Of course." He took a step toward the table. "You were very kind to play."

"It was a great pleasure."

"We will walk up stairs together."

36

THAT night there was a storm and I woke to hear the rain lashing the window-panes. It was coming in the open window. Some one had knocked on the door. I went to the door very softly, not to disturb Catherine, and opened it. The barman stood there. He wore his overcoat and carried his wet hat.

"Can I speak to you, Tenente?"

"What's the matter?"

"It's a very serious matter."

I looked around. The room was dark. I saw the water on the floor from the window. "Come in," I said. I took him by the arm into the bathroom; locked the door and put on the light. I sat down on the edge of the bathtub.

"What's the matter, Emilio? Are you in trouble?"

"No. You are, Tenente."

"Yes?"

"They are going to arrest you in the morning."

"Yes?"

"I came to tell you. I was out in the town and I heard them talking in a café."

"I see."

He stood there, his coat wet, holding his wet hat and said nothing.

"Why are they going to arrest me?"

"For something about the war."

"Do you know what?"

"No. But I know that they know you were here before as an officer and now you are here out of uniform. After this retreat they arrest everybody."

I thought a minute.

"What time do they come to arrest me?"

"In the morning. I don't know the time."

"What do you say to do?"

He put his hat in the washbowl. It was very wet and had been dripping on the floor.

"If you have nothing to fear an arrest is nothing. But it is always bad to be arrested—especially now."

"I don't want to be arrested."

"Then go to Switzerland."

"How?"

"In my boat."

"There is a storm," I said.

"The storm is over. It is rough but you will be all right."

"When should we go?"

"Right away. They might come to arrest you early in the morning."

"What about our bags?"

"Get them packed. Get your lady dressed. I will take care of them."

"Where will you be?"

"I will wait here. I don't want any one to see me outside in the hall."

I opened the door, closed it, and went into the bedroom. Catherine was awake.

"What is it, darling?"

"It's all right, Cat," I said. "Would you like to get dressed right away and go in a boat to Switzerland?"

"Would you?"

"No," I said. "I'd like to go back to bed."

"What is it about?"

"The barman says they are going to arrest me in the morning."

"Is the barman crazy?"

"No."

"Then please hurry, darling, and get dressed so we can start." She sat up on the side of the bed. She was still sleepy. "Is that the barman in the bathroom?"

"Yes."

"Then I won't wash. Please look the other way, darling, and I'll be dressed in just a minute."

I saw her white back as she took off her night-gown and then I looked away because she wanted me to. She was beginning to be a little big with the child and she did not want me to see her. I dressed hearing the rain on the windows. I did not have much to put in my bag.

"There's plenty of room in my bag, Cat, if you need any."

"I'm almost packed," she said. "Darling, I'm awfully stupid, but why is the barman in the bathroom?"

"Sh—he's waiting to take our bags down."

"He's awfully nice."

"He's an old friend," I said. "I nearly sent him some pipe-tobacco once."

I looked out the open window at the dark night. I could not see the lake, only the dark and the rain but the wind was quieter.

"I'm ready, darling," Catherine said.

"All right." I went to the bathroom door. "Here are the bags, Emilio," I said. The barman took the two bags.

"You're very good to help us," Catherine said.

"That's nothing, lady," the barman said. "I'm glad to help you just so I don't get in trouble myself. Listen," he said to me. "I'll take these out the servants' stairs and to the boat. You just go out as though you were going for a walk."

"It's a lovely night for a walk," Catherine said.

"It's a bad night all right."

"I'm glad I've an umbrella," Catherine said.

We walked down the hall and down the wide thickly carpeted stairs. At the foot of the stairs by the door the porter sat behind his desk.

He looked surprised at seeing us.

"You're not going out, sir?" he said.

"Yes," I said. "We're going to see the storm along the lake."

"Haven't you got an umbrella, sir?"

"No," I said. "This coat sheds water."

He looked at it doubtfully. "I'll get you an umbrella, sir," he said. He went away and came back with a big umbrella. "It is a little big, sir," he said. I gave him a ten-lira note. "Oh you are too good, sir. Thank you very much," he said. He held the door open and we went out into the rain. He smiled at Catherine and she smiled at him. "Don't stay out in the storm," he said. "You will get wet, sir and lady." He was only the second porter, and his English was still literally translated.

"We'll be back," I said. We walked down the path under the giant umbrella and out through the dark wet gardens to the road and across the road to the trellised pathway along the lake. The wind was blowing offshore now. It was a cold, wet November wind and I knew it was snowing in the mountains. We came along past the chained boats in the slips along the quay to where the barman's boat should be. The water was dark against the stone. The barman stepped out from beside the row of trees.

"The bags are in the boat," he said.

"I want to pay you for the boat," I said.

"How much money have you?"

"Not so much."

"You send me the money later. That will be all right."

"How much?"

"What you want."

"Tell me how much."

"If you get through send me five hundred francs. You won't mind that if you get through."

"All right."

"Here are sandwiches." He handed me a package. "Everything there was in the bar. It's all here. This is a bottle of brandy and a bottle of wine." I put them in my bag. "Let me pay you for those."

"All right, give me fifty lire."

I gave it to him. "The brandy is good," he said. "You don't need to be afraid to give it to your lady. She better get in the boat." He held the boat, it rising and falling against the stone wall and I helped Catherine in. She sat in the stern and pulled her cape around her.

"You know where to go?"

"Up the lake."

"You know how far?"

"Past Luino."

"Past Luino, Cannero, Cannobio, Tranzano. You aren't in Switzerland until you come to Brissago. You have to pass Monte Tamara."

"What time is it?" Catherine asked.

"It's only eleven o'clock," I said.

"If you row all the time you ought to be there by seven o'clock in the morning."

"Is it that far?"

"It's thirty-five kilometres."

"How should we go? In this rain we need a compass."

"No. Row to Isola Bella. Then on the other side of Isola Madre go with the wind. The wind will take you to Pallanza. You will see the lights. Then go up the shore."

"Maybe the wind will change."

"No," he said. "This wind will blow like this for three days. It comes straight down from the Mattarone. There is a can to bail with."

"Let me pay you something for the boat now."

"No, I'd rather take a chance. If you get through you pay me all you can."

"All right."

"I don't think you'll get drowned."

"That's good."

"Go with the wind up the lake."

"All right." I stepped in the boat.

"Did you leave the money for the hotel?"

"Yes. In an envelope in the room."

"All right. Good luck, Tenente."

"Good luck. We thank you many times."

"You won't thank me if you get drowned."

"What does he say?" Catherine asked.

"He says good luck."

"Good luck," Catherine said. "Thank you very much."

"Are you ready?"

"Yes."

He bent down and shoved us off. I dug at the water with the oars, then waved one hand. The barman waved back deprecatingly. I saw the lights of the hotel and rowed out, rowing straight out until they were out of sight. There was quite a sea running but we were going with the wind.

37

I ROWED in the dark keeping the wind in my face. The rain had stopped and only came occasionally in gusts. It was very dark, and the wind was cold. I could see Catherine in the stern but I could not see the water where the blades of the oars dipped. The oars were long and there were no leathers to keep them from slipping out. I pulled, raised, leaned forward, found the water, dipped and pulled, rowing as easily as I could. I did not feather the oars because the wind was with us. I knew my hands would blister and I wanted to delay it as long as I could. The boat was light and rowed easily. I pulled it along in the dark water. I could not see, and hoped we would soon come opposite Pallanza.

We never saw Pallanza. The wind was blowing up the lake and we passed the point that hides Pallanza in the dark and never saw the lights. When we finally saw some lights much further up the lake and close to the shore it was Intra. But for a long time we did not see any lights, nor did we see the shore but rowed steadily in the dark riding with the waves. Sometimes I missed the water with the oars in the dark as a wave lifted the boat. It was quite rough; but I kept on rowing, until suddenly we were close ashore against a point of rock that rose beside us; the waves striking against it, rushing high up, then falling back. I pulled hard on the right oar and backed water with the other and we went out into the lake again; the point was out of sight and we were going on up the lake.

"We're across the lake," I said to Catherine.

"Weren't we going to see Pallanza?"

"We've missed it."

"How are you, darling?"

"I'm fine."

"I could take the oars awhile."

"No, I'm fine."

"Poor Ferguson," Catherine said. "In the morning she'll come to the hotel and find we're gone."

"I'm not worrying so much about that," I said, "as about getting into the Swiss part of the lake before it's daylight and the custom guards see us."

"Is it a long way?"

"It's some thirty kilometres from here."

I rowed all night. Finally my hands were so sore I could hardly close them over the oars. We were nearly smashed up on the shore several times. I kept fairly close to the shore because I was afraid of getting lost on the lake and losing time. Sometimes we were so close we could see a row of trees and the road along the shore with the mountains behind. The rain stopped and the wind drove the clouds so that the moon shone through and looking back I could see the long dark point of Castagnola and the lake with white-caps and beyond, the moon on the high snow mountains. Then the clouds came over the moon again and the mountains and the lake were gone, but it was much lighter than it had been before and we could see the shore. I could see it too clearly and pulled out where they would not see the boat if there were custom guards along the Pallanza road. When the moon came out again we could see white villas on the shore on the slopes of the mountain and the white road where it showed through the trees. All the time I was rowing.

The lake widened and across it on the shore at the foot of the mountains on the other side we saw a few lights that should be

Luino. I saw a wedgelike gap between the mountains on the other shore and I thought that must be Luino. If it was we were making good time. I pulled in the oars and lay back on the seat. I was very, very tired of rowing. My arms and shoulders and back ached and my hands were sore.

"I could hold the umbrella," Catherine said. "We could sail with that with the wind."

"Can you steer?"

"I think so."

"You take this oar and hold it under your arm close to the side of the boat and steer and I'll hold the umbrella." I went back to the stern and showed her how to hold the oar. I took the big umbrella the porter had given me and sat facing the bow and opened it. It opened with a clap. I held it on both sides, sitting astride the handle hooked over the seat. The wind was full in it and I felt the boat suck forward while I held as hard as I could to the two edges. It pulled hard. The boat was moving fast.

"We're going beautifully," Catherine said. All I could see was umbrella ribs. The umbrella strained and pulled and I felt us driving along with it. I braced my feet and held back on it, then suddenly, it buckled; I felt a rib snap on my forehead, I tried to grab the top that was bending with the wind and the whole thing buckled and went inside out and I was astride the handle of an inside-out, ripped umbrella, where I had been holding a wind-filled pulling sail. I unhooked the handle from the seat, laid the umbrella in the bow and went back to Catherine for the oar. She was laughing. She took my hand and kept on laughing.

"What the matter?" I took the oar.

"You looked so funny holding that thing."

"I suppose so."

"Don't be cross, darling. It was awfully funny. You looked about twenty feet broad and very affectionate holding the umbrella by the edges—" she choked.

"I'll row."

"Take a rest and a drink. It's a grand night and we've come a long way."

"I have to keep the boat out of the trough of the waves."

"I'll get you a drink. Then rest a little while, darling."

I held the oars up and we sailed with them. Catherine was opening the bag. She handed me the brandy bottle. I pulled the cork with my pocket-knife and took a long drink. It was smooth and hot and the heat went all through me and I felt warmed and cheerful. "It's lovely brandy," I said. The moon was under again but I could see the shore. There seemed to be another point going out a long way ahead into the lake.

"Are you warm enough, Cat?"

"I'm splendid. I'm a little stiff."

"Bail out that water and you can put your feet down."

Then I rowed and listened to the oarlocks and the dip and scrape of the bailing tin under the stern seat.

"Would you give me the bailer?" I said. "I want a drink."

"It's awful dirty."

"That's all right. I'll rinse it."

I heard Catherine rinsing it over the side. Then she handed it to me dipped full of water. I was thirsty after the brandy and the water was icy cold, so cold it made my teeth ache. I looked toward the shore. We were closer to the long point. There were lights in the bay ahead.

"Thanks," I said and handed back the tin pail.

"You're ever so welcome," Catherine said. "There's much more if you want it."

"Don't you want to eat something?"

"No. I'll be hungry in a little while. We'll save it till then."

"All right."

What looked like a point ahead was a long high headland. I went further out in the lake to pass it. The lake was much narrower now. The moon was out again and the *guardia di finanza* could have seen our boat black on the water if they had been watching.

"How are you, Cat?" I asked.

"I'm all right. Where are we?"

"I don't think we have more than about eight miles more."

"That's a long way to row, you poor sweet. Aren't you dead?"

"No. I'm all right. My hands are sore is all."

We went on up the lake. There was a break in the mountains on the right bank, a flattening-out with a low shore line that I thought must be Cannobio. I stayed a long way out because it was from now on that we ran the most danger of meeting *guardia*. There was a high dome-capped mountain on the other shore a way ahead. I was tired.

It was no great distance to row but when you were out of condition it had been a long way. I knew I had to pass that mountain and go up the lake at least five miles further before we would be in Swiss water. The moon was almost down now but before it went down the sky clouded over again and it was very dark. I stayed well out in the lake, rowing awhile, then resting and holding the oars so that the wind struck the blades.

"Let me row awhile," Catherine said.

"I don't think you ought to."

"Nonsense. It would be good for me. It would keep me from being too stiff."

"I don't think you should, Cat."

"Nonsense. Rowing in moderation is very good for the pregnant lady."

"All right, you row a little moderately. I'll go back, then you come up. Hold on to both gunwales when you come up."

I sat in the stern with my coat on and the collar turned up and watched Catherine row. She rowed very well but the oars were too long and bothered her. I opened the bag and ate a couple of sandwiches and took a drink of the brandy. It made everything much better and I took another drink.

"Tell me when you're tired," I said. Then a little later, "Watch out the oar doesn't pop you in the tummy."

"If it did"—Catherine said between strokes—"life might be much simpler."

I took another drink of the brandy.

"How are you going?"

"All right."

"Tell me when you want to stop."

"All right."

I took another drink of the brandy, then took hold of the two gunwales of the boat and moved forward.

"No. I'm going beautifully."

"Go on back to the stern. I've had a grand rest."

For a while, with the brandy, I rowed easily and steadily. Then I began to catch crabs and soon I was just chopping along again with a thin brown taste of bile from having rowed too hard after the brandy.

"Give me a drink of water, will you?" I said.

"That's easy," Catherine said.

Before daylight it started to drizzle. The wind was down or we were protected by mountains that bounded the curve the lake had made. When I knew daylight was coming I settled down and rowed hard. I did not know where we were and I wanted to get into the Swiss part of the lake. When it was beginning to be daylight we were quite close to the shore. I could see the rocky shore and the trees.

"What's that?" Catherine said. I rested on the oars and listened. It was a motor boat chugging out on the lake. I pulled close up to the shore and lay quiet. The chugging came closer; then we saw the motor boat in the rain a little astern of us. There were four *guardia di finanza* in the stern, their *alpini* hats pulled down, their cape collars turned up and their carbines slung across their backs. They all looked sleepy so early in the morning. I could see the yellow on their hats and the yellow marks on their cape collars. The motor boat chugged on and out of sight in the rain.

I pulled out into the lake. If we were that close to the border I did not want to be hailed by a sentry along the road. I stayed out where I could just see the shore and rowed on for three quarters of an hour in the rain. We heard a motor boat once more but I kept quiet until the noise of the engine went away across the lake.

"I think we're in Switzerland, Cat," I said.

"Really?"

"There's no way to know until we see Swiss troops."

"Or the Swiss navy."

"The Swiss navy's no joke for us. That last motor boat we heard was probably the Swiss navy."

"If we're in Switzerland let's have a big breakfast. They have wonderful rolls and butter and jam in Switzerland."

It was clear daylight now and a fine rain was falling. The wind was still blowing outside up the lake and we could see the tops of the white-caps going away from us and up the lake. I was sure we were in Switzerland now. There were many houses back in the trees from the shore and up the shore a way was a village with stone houses, some villas on the hills and a church. I had been looking at the road that skirted the shore for guards but did not see any. The road came quite close to the lake now and I saw a soldier coming out of a café on the road. He wore a gray-green uniform and a helmet like the

Germans. He had a healthy-looking face and a little toothbrush mustache. He looked at us.

"Wave to him," I said to Catherine. She waved and the soldier smiled embarrassedly and gave a wave of his hand. I eased up rowing. We were passing the waterfront of the village.

"We must be well inside the border," I said.

"We want to be sure, darling. We don't want them to turn us back at the frontier."

"The frontier is a long way back. I think this is the customs town. I'm pretty sure it's Brissago."

"Won't there be Italians there? There are always both sides at a customs town."

"Not in war-time. I don't think they let the Italians cross the frontier."

It was a nice-looking little town. There were many fishing boats along the quay and nets were spread on racks. There was a fine November rain falling but it looked cheerful and clean even with the rain.

"Should we land then and have breakfast?"

"All right."

I pulled hard on the left oar and came in close, then straightened out when we were close to the quay and brought the boat alongside. I pulled in the oars, took hold of an iron ring, stepped up on the wet stone and was in Switzerland. I tied the boat and held my hand down to Catherine.

"Come on up, Cat. It's a grand feeling."

"What about the bags?"

"Leave them in the boat."

Catherine stepped up and we were in Switzerland together.

"What a lovely country," she said.

"Isn't it grand?"

"Let's go and have breakfast!"

"Isn't it a grand country? I love the way it feels under my shoes."

"I'm so stiff I can't feel it very well. But it feels like a splendid country. Darling, do you realize we're here and out of that bloody place?"

"I do. I really do. I've never realized anything before."

"Look at the houses. Isn't this a fine square? There's a place we can get breakfast."

"Isn't the rain fine? They never had rain like this in Italy. It's cheerful rain."

"And we're here, darling! Do you realize we're here?"

We went inside the café and sat down at a clean wooden table. We were cockeyed excited. A splendid clean-looking woman with an apron came and asked us what we wanted.

"Rolls and jam and coffee," Catherine said.

"I'm sorry, we haven't any rolls in war-time."

"Bread then."

"I can make you some toast."

"All right."

"I want some eggs fried too."

"How many eggs for the gentleman?"

"Three."

"Take four, darling."

"Four eggs."

The woman went away. I kissed Catherine and held her hand very tight. We looked at each other and at the café.

"Darling, darling, isn't it lovely?"

"It's grand," I said.

"I don't mind there not being rolls," Catherine said. "I thought about them all night. But I don't mind it. I don't mind it at all."

"I suppose pretty soon they will arrest us."

"Never mind, darling. We'll have breakfast first. You won't mind being arrested after breakfast. And then there's nothing they can do to us. We're British and American citizens in good standing."

"You have a passport, haven't you?"

"Of course. Oh let's not talk about it. Let's be happy."

"I couldn't be any happier," I said. A fat gray cat with a tail that lifted like a plume crossed the floor to our table and curved against my leg to purr each time she rubbed. I reached down and stroked her. Catherine smiled at me very happily. "Here comes the coffee," she said.

They arrested us after breakfast. We took a little walk through the village then went down to the quay to get our bags. A soldier was standing guard over the boat.

"Is this your boat?"

"Yes."

"Where do you come from?"

"Up the lake."

"Then I have to ask you to come with me."

"How about the bags?"

"You can carry the bags."

I carried the bags and Catherine walked beside me and the soldier walked along behind us to the old custom house. In the custom house a lieutenant, very thin and military, questioned us.

"What nationality are you?"

"American and British."

"Let me see your passports."

I gave him mine and Catherine got hers out of her handbag. He examined them for a long time.

"Why do you enter Switzerland this way in a boat?"

"I am a sportsman," I said. "Rowing is my great sport. I always row when I get a chance."

"Why do you come here?"

"For the winter sport. We are tourists and we want to do the winter sport."

"This is no place for winter sport."

"We know it. We want to go where they have the winter sport."

"What have you been doing in Italy?"

"I have been studying architecture. My cousin has been studying art."

"Why do you leave there?"

"We want to do the winter sport. With the war going on you cannot study architecture."

"You will please stay where you are," the lieutenant said. He went back into the building with our passports.

"You're splendid, darling," Catherine said. "Keep on the same track. You want to do the winter sport."

"Do you know anything about art?"

"Rubens," said Catherine.

"Large and fat," I said.

"Titian," Catherine said.

"Titian-haired," I said. "How about Mantegna?"

"Don't ask hard ones," Catherine said. "I know him though— very bitter."

"Very bitter," I said. "Lots of nail holes."

"You see I'll make you a fine wife," Catherine said. "I'll be able to talk art with your customers."

"Here he comes," I said. The thin lieutenant came down the length of the custom house, holding our passports.

"I will have to send you into Locarno," he said. "You can get a carriage and a soldier will go in with you."

"All right," I said. "What about the boat?"

"The boat is confiscated. What have you in those bags?"

He went all through the two bags and held up the quarter-bottle of brandy. "Would you join me in a drink?" I asked.

"No thank you." He straightened up. "How much money have you?"

"Twenty-five hundred lire."

He was favorably impressed. "How much has your cousin?"

Catherine had a little over twelve hundred lire. The lieutenant was pleased. His attitude toward us became less haughty.

"If you are going for winter sports," he said, "Wengen is the place. My father has a very fine hotel at Wengen. It is open all the time."

"That's splendid," I said. "Could you give me the name?"

"I will write it on a card." He handed me the card very politely.

"The soldier will take you into Locarno. He will keep your passports. I regret this but it is necessary. I have good hopes they will give you a visa or a police permit at Locarno."

He handed the two passports to the soldier and carrying the bags we started into the village to order a carriage. "Hi," the lieutenant called to the soldier. He said something in a German dialect to him. The soldier slung his rifle on his back and picked up the bags.

"It's a great country," I said to Catherine.

"It's so practical."

"Thank you very much," I said to the lieutenant. He waved his hand.

"*Service!*" he said. We followed our guard into the village.

We drove to Locarno in a carriage with the soldier sitting on the front seat with the driver. At Locarno we did not have a bad time. They questioned us but they were polite because we had passports and money. I do not think they believed a word of the story and I thought it was silly but it was like a law-court. You did not want something reasonable, you wanted something technical and then stuck to it without explanations. But we had passports and we would spend the money. So they gave us provisional visas. At any time this visa might be withdrawn. We were to report to the police wherever we went.

Could we go wherever we wanted? Yes. Where did we want to go?

"Where do you want to go, Cat?"

"Montreux."

"It is a very nice place," the official said. "I think you will like that place."

"Here at Locarno is a very nice place," another official said. "I am sure you would like it here very much at Locarno. Locarno is a very attractive place."

"We would like some place where there is winter sport."

"There is no winter sport at Montreux."

"I beg your pardon," the other official said. "I come from Montreux. There is very certainly winter sport on the Montreux Oberland Bernois railway. It would be false for you to deny that."

"I do not deny it. I simply said there is no winter sport at Montreux."

"I question that," the other official said. "I question that statement."

"I hold to that statement."

"I question that statement. I myself have *luge-ed* into the streets of Montreux. I have done it not once but several times. Luge-ing is certainly winter sport."

The other official turned to me.

"Is luge-ing your idea of winter sport, sir? I tell you you would be very comfortable here in Locarno. You would find the climate healthy, you would find the environs attractive. You would like it very much."

"The gentleman has expressed a wish to go to Montreux."

"What is luge-ing?" I asked.

"You see he has never even heard of luge-ing!"

That meant a great deal to the second official. He was pleased by that.

"Luge-ing," said the first official, "is tobogganing."

"I beg to differ," the other official shook his head. "I must differ again. The toboggan is very different from the luge. The toboggan is constructed in Canada of flat laths. The luge is a common sled with runners. Accuracy means something."

"Couldn't we toboggan?" I asked.

"Of course you could toboggan," the first official said. "You could toboggan very well. Excellent Canadian toboggans are sold in Montreux. Ochs Brothers sell toboggans. They import their own toboggans."

The second official turned away. "Tobogganing," he said, "requires a special *piste*. You could not toboggan into the streets of Montreux. Where are you stopping here?"

"We don't know," I said. "We just drove in from Brissago. The carriage is outside."

"You make no mistake in going to Montreux," the first official said. "You will find the climate delightful and beautiful. You will have no distance to go for winter sport."

"If you really want winter sport," the second official said, "you will go to the Engadine or to Mürren. I must protest against your being advised to go to Montreux for the winter sport."

"At Les Avants above Montreux there is excellent winter sport of every sort." The champion of Montreux glared at his colleague.

"Gentlemen," I said, "I am afraid we must go. My cousin is very tired. We will go tentatively to Montreux."

"I congratulate you," the first official shook my hand.

"I believe that you will regret leaving Locarno," the second official said. "At any rate you will report to the police at Montreux."

"There will be no unpleasantness with the police," the first official assured me. "You will find all the inhabitants extremely courteous and friendly."

"Thank you both very much," I said. "We appreciate your advice very much."

"Good-by," Catherine said. "Thank you both very much."

They bowed us to the door, the champion of Locarno a little coldly. We went down the steps and into the carriage.

"My God, darling," Catherine said. "Couldn't we have gotten away any sooner?" I gave the name of a hotel one of the officials had recommended to the driver. He picked up the reins.

"You've forgotten the army," Catherine said. The soldier was standing by the carriage. I gave him a ten-lira note. "I have no Swiss money yet," I said. He thanked me, saluted and went off. The carriage started and we drove to the hotel.

"How did you happen to pick out Montreux?" I asked Catherine. "Do you really want to go there?"

"It was the first place I could think of," she said. "It's not a bad place. We can find some place up in the mountains."

"Are you sleepy?"

"I'm asleep right now."

"We'll get a good sleep. Poor Cat, you had a long bad night."

"I had a lovely time," Catherine said. "Especially when you sailed with the umbrella."

"Can you realize we're in Switzerland?"

"No, I'm afraid I'll wake up and it won't be true."

"I am too."

"It is true, isn't it, darling? I'm not just driving down to the *stazione* in Milan to see you off."

"I hope not."

"Don't say that. It frightens me. Maybe that's where we're going."

"I'm so groggy I don't know," I said.

"Let me see your hands."

I put them out. They were both blistered raw.

"There's no hole in my side," I said.

"Don't be sacrilegious."

I felt very tired and vague in the head. The exhilaration was all gone. The carriage was going along the street.

"Poor hands," Catherine said.

"Don't touch them," I said. "By God I don't know where we are. Where are we going, driver?" The driver stopped his horse.

"To the Hotel Metropole. Don't you want to go there?"

"Yes," I said. "It's all right, Cat."

"It's all right, darling. Don't be upset. We'll get a good sleep and you won't feel groggy to-morrow."

"I get pretty groggy," I said. "It's like a comic opera to-day. Maybe I'm hungry."

"You're just tired, darling. You'll be fine." The carriage pulled up before the hotel. Some one came out to take our bags.

"I feel all right," I said. We were down on the pavement going into the hotel.

"I know you'll be all right. You're just tired. You've been up a long time."

"Anyhow we're here."

"Yes, we're really here."

We followed the boy with the bags into the hotel.

BOOK FIVE

38

THAT fall the snow came very late. We lived in a brown wooden house in the pine trees on the side of the mountain and at night there was frost so that there was thin ice over the water in the two pitchers on the dresser in the morning. Mrs. Guttingen came into the room early in the morning to shut the windows and started a fire in the tall porcelain stove. The pine wood crackled and sparked and then the fire roared in the stove and the second time Mrs. Guttingen came into the room she brought big chunks of wood for the fire and a pitcher of hot water. When the room was warm she brought in breakfast. Sitting up in bed eating breakfast we could see the lake and the mountains across the lake on the French side. There was snow on the tops of the mountains and the lake was a gray steel-blue.

Outside, in front of the chalet a road went up the mountain. The wheel ruts and ridges were iron hard with the frost, and the road climbed steadily through the forest and up and around the mountain to where there were meadows, and barns and cabins in the meadows at the edge of the woods looking across the valley. The valley was deep and there was a stream at the bottom that flowed down into the lake and when the wind blew across the valley you could hear the stream in the rocks.

Sometimes we went off the road and on a path through the pine forest. The floor of the forest was soft to walk on; the frost did not harden it as it did the road. But we did not mind the hardness of the road because we had nails in the soles and heels of our boots and the heel nails bit on the frozen ruts and with nailed boots it was good walking on the road and invigorating. But it was lovely walking in the woods.

In front of the house where we lived the mountain went down steeply to the little plain along the lake and we sat on the porch of the house in the sun and saw the winding of the road down the mountain-side and the terraced vineyards on the side of the lower mountain, the vines all dead now for the winter and the fields divided by stone walls, and below the vineyards the houses of the town on the narrow plain along the lake shore. There was an island with two trees on the lake and the trees looked like the double sails of a fishing-boat. The mountains were sharp and steep on the other side of the lake and down at the end of the lake was the plain of the Rhone Valley flat between the two ranges of mountains; and up the valley where the mountains cut it off was the Dent du Midi. It was a high snowy mountain and it dominated the valley but it was so far away that it did not make a shadow.

When the sun was bright we ate lunch on the porch but the rest of the time we ate upstairs in a small room with plain wooden walls and a big stove in the corner. We bought books and magazines in the town and a copy of "Hoyle" and learned many two-handed card games. The small room with the stove was our living-room. There were two comfortable chairs and a table for books and magazines and we played cards on the dining-table when it was cleared away. Mr. and Mrs. Guttingen lived downstairs and we would hear them talking sometimes in the evening and they were very happy together too. He had been a headwaiter and she had worked as maid in the same hotel and they had saved their money to buy this place. They had a son who was studying to be a headwaiter. He was at a hotel in Zurich. Downstairs there was a parlor where they sold wine and beer, and sometimes in the evening we would hear carts stop outside on the road and men come up the steps to go in the parlor to drink wine.

There was a box of wood in the hall outside the living-room and I kept up the fire from it. But we did not stay up very late. We went to bed in the dark in the big bedroom and when I was un-dressed I opened the windows and saw the night and the cold stars and the pine trees below the window and then got into bed as fast as I could. It was lovely in bed with the air so cold and clear and the night outside the window. We slept well and if I woke in the night I knew it was from only one cause and I would shift the feather bed over, very softly so that Catherine would not be wakened and then go back to sleep again, warm and with the new lightness of thin covers. The war seemed as far away as the football games of some one else's college. But I knew from the papers that they were still fighting in the mountains because the snow would not come.

Sometimes we walked down the mountain into Montreux. There was a path went down the mountain but it was steep and so usually we took the road and walked down on the wide hard road between fields and then below between the stone walls of the vineyards and on down between the houses of the villages along the way. There were three villages; Chernex, Fontanivent, and the other I forget. Then along the road we passed an old square-built stone château on a ledge on the side of the mountain-side with the terraced fields of vines, each vine tied to a stick to hold it up, the vines dry and brown and the earth ready for the snow and the lake down below flat and gray as steel. The road went down a long grade below the château and then turned to the right and went down very steeply and paved with cobbles, into Montreux.

We did not know any one in Montreux. We walked along beside the lake and saw the swans and the many gulls and terns that flew up when you came close and screamed while they looked down at the water. Out on the lake there were flocks of grebes, small and dark, and leaving trails in the water when they swam. In the town we walked along the main street and looked in the windows of the shops. There were many big hotels that were closed but most of the shops were open and the people were very glad to see us. There was a fine coiffeur's place where Catherine went to have her hair done. The woman who ran it was very cheerful and the only person we knew in Montreux. While Catherine was there I went up to a beer place and drank dark Munich beer and read the papers. I read the *Corriere della Sera* and the English and American papers from Paris. All the advertisements were blacked out, supposedly to prevent communication in that way with the enemy. The papers were bad reading. Everything was going very badly everywhere. I sat back in the corner with a heavy mug of dark beer and an opened glazed-paper package of pretzels and ate the pretzels for the salty flavor and the good way they made the beer taste and read about disaster. I thought Catherine would come by but she did not come, so I hung the papers back on the rack, paid for my beer and went up the street to look for her. The day was cold and dark and wintry and the stone of the houses looked cold. Catherine was still in the hairdresser's shop. The woman was waving her hair. I sat in the little booth and watched. It was exciting to watch and Catherine smiled and talked to me and my voice was a little thick from being excited. The tongs made a pleasant clicking sound and I could see Catherine in three mirrors and it was pleasant and warm in the booth. Then the woman put up Catherine's hair, and Catherine looked in the mirror and changed it a little, taking out and putting in pins; then stood up. "I'm sorry to have taken such a long time."

"Monsieur was very interested. Were you not, monsieur?" the woman smiled.

"Yes," I said.

We went out and up the street. It was cold and wintry and the wind was blowing. "Oh, darling, I love you so," I said.

"Don't we have a fine time?" Catherine said. "Look. Let's go some place and have beer instead of tea. It's very good for young Catherine. It keeps her small."

"Young Catherine," I said. "That loafer."

"She's been very good," Catherine said. "She makes very little trouble. The doctor says beer will be good for me and keep her small."

"If you keep her small enough and she's a boy, maybe he will be a jockey."

"I suppose if we really have this child we ought to get married," Catherine said. We were in the beer place at the corner table. It was getting dark outside. It was still early but the day was dark and the dusk was coming early.

"Let's get married now," I said.

"No," Catherine said. "It's too embarrassing now. I show too plainly. I won't go before any one and be married in this state."

"I wish we'd gotten married."

"I suppose it would have been better. But when could we, darling?"

"I don't know."

"I know one thing. I'm not going to be married in this splendid matronly state."

"You're not matronly."

"Oh yes, I am, darling. The hairdresser asked me if this was our first. I lied and said no, we had two boys and two girls."

"When will we be married?"

"Any time after I'm thin again. We want to have a splendid wedding with every one thinking what a handsome young couple."

"And you're not worried?"

"Darling, why should I be worried? The only time I ever felt badly was when I felt like a whore in Milan and that only lasted seven minutes and besides it was the room furnishings. Don't I make you a good wife?"

"You're a lovely wife."

"Then don't be too technical, darling. I'll marry you as soon as I'm thin again."

"All right."

"Do you think I ought to drink another beer? The doctor said I was rather narrow in the hips and it's all for the best if we keep young Catherine small."

"What else did he say?" I was worried.

"Nothing. I have a wonderful blood-pressure, darling. He admired my blood-pressure greatly."

"What did he say about you being too narrow in the hips?"

"Nothing. Nothing at all. He said I shouldn't ski."

"Quite right."

"He said it was too late to start if I'd never done it before. He said I could ski if I wouldn't fall down."

"He's just a big-hearted joker."

"Really he was very nice. We'll have him when the baby comes."

"Did you ask him if you ought to get married?"

"No. I told him we'd been married four years. You see, darling, if I marry you I'll be an American and any time we're married under American law the child is legitimate."

"Where did you find that out?"

"In the New York *World Almanac* in the library."

"You're a grand girl."

"I'll be very glad to be an American and we'll go to America won't we, darling? I want to see Niagara Falls."

"You're a fine girl."

"There's something else I want to see but I can't remember it."

"The stockyards?"

"No. I can't remember it."

"The Woolworth building?"

"No."

"The Grand Canyon?"

"No. But I'd like to see that."

"What was it?"

"The Golden Gate! That's what I want to see. Where is the Golden Gate?"

"San Francisco."

"Then let's go there. I want to see San Francisco anyway."

"All right. We'll go there."

"Now let's go up the mountain. Should we? Can we get the M. O. B.?"

"There's a train a little after five."

"Let's get that."

"All right. I'll drink one more beer first."

When we went out to go up the street and climb the stairs to the station it was very cold. A cold wind was coming down the Rhone Valley. There were lights in the shop windows and we climbed the steep stone stairway to the upper street, then up another stairs to the station. The electric train was there waiting, all the lights on. There was a dial that showed when it left. The clock hands pointed to ten minutes after five. I looked at the station clock. It was five minutes after. As we got on board I saw the motorman and conductor coming out of the station wine-shop. We sat down and opened the window. The train was electrically heated and stuffy but fresh cold air came in through the window.

"Are you tired, Cat?" I asked.

"No. I feel splendid."

"It isn't a long ride."

"I like the ride," she said. "Don't worry about me, darling. I feel fine."

Snow did not come until three days before Christmas. We woke one morning and it was snowing. We stayed in bed with the fire roaring in the stove and watched the snow fall. Mrs. Guttingen took away the breakfast trays and put more wood in the stove. It was a big snow storm. She said it had started about midnight. I went to the window and looked out but could not see across the road. It was blowing and snowing wildly. I went back to bed and we lay and talked.

"I wish I could ski," Catherine said. "It's rotten not to be able to ski."

"We'll get a bobsled and come down the road. That's no worse for you than riding in a car."

"Won't it be rough?"

"We can see."

"I hope it won't be too rough."

"After a while we'll take a walk in the snow."

"Before lunch," Catherine said, "so we'll have a good appetite."

"I'm always hungry."

"So am I."

We went out in the snow but it was drifted so that we could not walk fast. I went ahead and made a trail down to the station but when we reached there we had gone far enough. The snow was blowing so we could hardly see and we went into the little inn by the station and swept each other off with a broom and sat on a bench and had vermouths.

"It is a big storm," the barmaid said.

"Yes."

"The snow is very late this year."

"Yes."

"Could I eat a chocolate bar?" Catherine asked. "Or is it too close to lunch? I'm always hungry."

"Go on and eat one," I said.

"I'll take one with filberts," Catherine said.

"They are very good," the girl said, "I like them the best."

"I'll have another vermouth," I said.

When we came out to start back up the road our track was filled in by the snow. There were only faint indentations where the holes had been. The snow blew in our faces so we could hardly see. We brushed off and went in to have lunch. Mr. Guttingen served the lunch.

"To-morrow there will be ski-ing," he said. "Do you ski, Mr. Henry?"

"No. But I want to learn."

"You will learn very easily. My boy will be here for Christmas and he will teach you."

"That's fine. When does he come?"

"To-morrow night."

When we were sitting by the stove in the little room after lunch looking out the window at the snow coming down Catherine said,

"Wouldn't you like to go on a trip somewhere by yourself, darling, and be with men and ski?"

"No. Why should I?"

"I should think sometimes you would want to see other people besides me."

"Do you want to see other people?"

"No."

"Neither do I."

"I know. But you're different. I'm having a child and that makes me contented not to do anything. I know I'm awfully stupid now and I talk too much and I think you ought to get away so you won't be tired of me."

"Do you want me to go away?"

"No. I want you to stay."

"That's what I'm going to do."

"Come over here," she said. "I want to feel the bump on your head. It's a big bump." She ran her finger over it. "Darling, would you like to grow a beard?"

"Would you like me to?"

"It might be fun. I'd like to see you with a beard."

"All right. I'll grow one. I'll start now this minute. It's a good idea. It will give me something to do."

"Are you worried because you haven't anything to do?"

"No. I like it. I have a fine life. Don't you?"

"I have a lovely life. But I was afraid because I'm big now that maybe I was a bore to you."

"Oh, Cat. You don't know how crazy I am about you."

"This way?"

"Just the way you are. I have a fine time. Don't we have a good life?"

"I do, but I thought maybe you were restless."

"No. Sometimes I wonder about the front and about people I know but I don't worry. I don't think about anything much."

"Who do you wonder about?"

"About Rinaldi and the priest and lots of people I know. But I don't think about them much. I don't want to think about the war. I'm through with it."

"What are you thinking about now?"

"Nothing."

"Yes you were. Tell me."

"I was wondering whether Rinaldi had the syphilis."

"Was that all?"

"Yes."

"Has he the syphilis?"

"I don't know."

"I'm glad you haven't. Did you ever have anything like that?"

"I had gonorrhea."

"I don't want to hear about it. Was it very painful, darling?"

"Very."

"I wish I'd had it."

"No you don't."

"I do. I wish I'd had it to be like you. I wish I'd stayed with all your girls so I could make fun of them to you."

"That's a pretty picture."

"It's not a pretty picture you having gonorrhea."

"I know it. Look at it snow now."

"I'd rather look at you. Darling, why don't you let your hair grow?"

"How grow?"

"Just grow a little longer."

"It's long enough now."

"No, let it grow a little longer and I could cut mine and we'd be just alike only one of us blonde and one of us dark."

"I wouldn't let you cut yours."

"It would be fun. I'm tired of it. It's an awful nuisance in the bed at night."

"I like it."

"Wouldn't you like it short?"

"I might. I like it the way it is."

"It might be nice short. Then we'd both be alike. Oh, darling, I want you so much I want to be you too."

"You are. We're the same one."

"I know it. At night we are."

"The nights are grand."

"I want us to be all mixed up. I don't want you to go away. I just said that. You go if you want to. But hurry right back. Why, darling, I don't live at all when I'm not with you."

"I won't ever go away," I said. "I'm no good when you're not there. I haven't any life at all any more."

"I want you to have a life. I want you to have a fine life. But we'll have it together, won't we?"

"And now do you want me to stop growing my beard or let it go on?"

"Go on. Grow it. It will be exciting. Maybe it will be done for New Year's."

"Now do you want to play chess?"

"I'd rather play with you."

"No. Let's play chess."

"And afterward we'll play?"

"Yes."

"All right."

I got out the chess-board and arranged the pieces. It was still snowing hard outside.

One time in the night I woke up and knew that Catherine was awake too. The moon was shining in the window and made shadows on the bed from the bars on the window-panes.

"Are you awake, sweetheart?"

"Yes. Can't you sleep?"

"I just woke up thinking about how I was nearly crazy when I first met you. Do you remember?"

"You were just a little crazy."

"I'm never that way any more. I'm grand now. You say grand so sweetly. Say grand."

"Grand."

"Oh, you're sweet. And I'm not crazy now. I'm just very, very, very happy."

"Go on to sleep," I said.

"All right. Let's go to sleep at exactly the same moment."

"All right."

But we did not. I was awake for quite a long time thinking about things and watching Catherine sleeping, the moonlight on her face. Then I went to sleep, too.

39

BY the middle of January I had a beard and the winter had settled into bright cold days and hard cold nights. We could walk on the roads again. The snow was packed hard and smooth by the hay-sleds and wood-sledges and the logs that were hauled down the mountain. The snow lay over all the country, down almost to Montreux. The mountains on the other side of the lake were all white and the plain of the Rhone Valley was covered. We took long walks on the other side of the mountain to the Bains de l'Alliaz. Catherine wore hob-nailed boots and a cape and carried a stick with a sharp steel point. She did not look big with the cape and we would not walk too fast but stopped and sat on logs by the roadside to rest when she was tired.

There was an inn in the trees at the Bains de l'Alliaz where the woodcutters stopped to drink, and we sat inside warmed by the stove and drank hot red wine with spices and lemon in it. They called it *glühwein* and it was a good thing to warm you and to celebrate with. The inn was dark and smoky inside and afterward when you went out the cold air came sharply into your lungs and numbed the edge of your nose as you inhaled. We looked back at the inn with light coming from the windows and the workcutters' horses stamping and jerking their heads outside to keep warm. There was frost on the hairs of their muzzles and their breathing made plumes of frost in the air. Going up the road toward home the road was smooth and slippery for a while and the ice orange from the horses until the wood-hauling track turned off. Then the road was clean-packed snow and led through the woods, and twice coming home in the evening, we saw foxes.

It was a fine country and every time that we went out it was fun.

"You have a splendid beard now," Catherine said. "It looks just like the woodcutters'. Did you see the man with the tiny gold earrings?"

"He's a chamois hunter," I said. "They wear them because they say it makes them hear better."

"Really? I don't believe it. I think they wear them to show they are chamois hunters. Are there chamois near here?"

"Yes, beyond the Dent de Jaman."

"It was fun seeing the fox."

"When he sleeps he wraps that tail around him to keep warm."

"It must be a lovely feeling."

"I always wanted to have a tail like that. Wouldn't it be fun if we had brushes like a fox?"

"It might be very difficult dressing."

We'd have clothes made or live in a country where it wouldn't make any difference."

"We live in a country where nothing makes any difference. Isn't it grand how we never see any one? You don't want to see people do you, darling?"

"No."

"Should we sit here just a minute? I'm a little bit tired."

We sat close together on the logs. Ahead the road went down through the forest.

"She won't come between us, will she? The little brat."

"No. We won't let her."

"How are we for money?"

"We have plenty. They honored the last sight draft."

"Won't your family try and get hold of you now they know you're in Switzerland?"

"Probably. I'll write them something."

"Haven't you written them?"

"No. Only the sight draft."

"Thank God I'm not your family."

"I'll send them a cable."

"Don't you care anything about them?"

"I did, but we quarrelled so much it wore itself out."

"I think I'd like them. I'd probably like them very much."

"Let's not talk about them or I'll start to worry about them." After a while I said, "Let's go on if you're rested."

"I'm rested."

We went on down the road. It was dark now and the snow squeaked under our boots. The night was dry and cold and very clear.

"I love your beard," Catherine said. "It's a great success. It looks so stiff and fierce and it's very soft and a great pleasure."

"Do you like it better than without?"

"I think so. You know, darling, I'm not going to cut my hair now until after young Catherine's born. I look too big and matronly now. But after she's born and I'm thin again I'm going to cut it and then I'll be a fine new and different girl for you. We'll go together and get it cut, or I'll go alone and come and surprise you."

I did not say anything.

"You won't say I can't, will you?"

"No. I think it would be exciting."

"Oh, you're so sweet. And maybe I'd look lovely, darling, and be so thin and exciting to you and you'll fall in love with me all over again."

"Hell," I said, "I love you enough now. What do you want to do? Ruin me?"

"Yes. I want to ruin you."

"Good," I said, "that's what I want too."

40

WE had a fine life. We lived through the months of January and February and the winter was very fine and we were very happy. There had been short thaws when the wind blew warm and the snow softened and the air felt like spring, but always the clear hard cold had come again and the winter had returned. In March came the first break in the winter. In the night it started raining. It rained on all morning and turned the snow to slush and made the mountainside dismal. There were clouds over the lake and over the valley. It was raining high up the mountain. Catherine wore heavy overshoes and I wore Mr. Guttingen's rubber-boots and we walked to the station under an umbrella, through the slush and the running water that was washing the ice of the roads bare, to stop at the pub before lunch for a vermouth. Outside we could hear the rain.

"Do you think we ought to move into town?"

"What do you think?" Catherine asked.

"If the winter is over and the rain keeps up it won't be fun up here. How long is it before young Catherine?"

"About a month. Perhaps a little more."

"We might go down and stay in Montreux."

"Why don't we go to Lausanne? That's where the hospital is."

"All right. But I thought maybe that was too big a town."

"We can be as much alone in a bigger town and Lausanne might be nice."

"When should we go?"

"I don't care. Whenever you want, darling. I don't want to leave here if you don't want."

"Let's see how the weather turns out."

It rained for three days. The snow was all gone now on the mountain-side below the station. The road was a torrent of muddy snow-water. It was too wet and slushy to go out. On the morning of the third day of rain we decided to go down into town.

"That is all right, Mr. Henry," Guttingen said. "You do not have to give me any notice. I did not think you would want to stay now the bad weather is come."

"We have to be near the hospital anyway on account of Madame," I said.

"I understand," he said. "Will you come back some time and stay, with the little one?"

"Yes, if you would have room."

"In the spring when it is nice you could come and enjoy it. We could put the little one and the nurse in the big room that is closed now and you and Madame could have your same room looking out over the lake."

"I'll write about coming," I said. We packed and left on the train that went down after lunch. Mr. and Mrs. Guttingen came down to the station with us and he hauled our baggage down on a sled through the slush. They stood beside the station in the rain waving good-by.

"They were very sweet," Catherine said.

"They were fine to us."

We took the train to Lausanne from Montreux. Looking out the window toward where we had lived you could not see the mountains for the clouds. The train stopped in Vevey, then went on, passing the lake on one side and on the other the wet brown fields and the bare woods and the wet houses. We came into Lausanne and went into a medium-sized hotel to stay. It was still raining as we drove through the streets and into the carriage entrance of the hotel. The concierge with brass keys on his lapels, the elevator, the carpets on the floors, and the white washbowls with shining fixtures, the brass bed and the big comfortable bedroom all seemed very great luxury after the Guttingens. The windows of the room looked out on a wet garden with a wall topped by an iron fence. Across the street, which sloped steeply, was another hotel with a similar wall and garden. I looked out at the rain falling in the fountain of the garden.

Catherine turned on all the lights and commenced unpacking. I ordered a whiskey and soda and lay on the bed and read the papers I had bought at the station. It was March, 1918, and the German offensive had started in France. I drank the whiskey and soda and read while Catherine unpacked and moved around the room.

"You know what I have to get, darling," she said.

"What?"

"Baby clothes. There aren't many people reach my time without baby things."

"You can buy them."

"I know. That's what I'll do to-morrow. I'll find out what is necessary."

"You ought to know. You were a nurse."

"But so few of the soldiers had babies in the hospitals."

"I did."

She hit me with the pillow and spilled the whiskey and soda.

"I'll order you another," she said. "I'm sorry I spilled it."

"There wasn't much left. Come on over to the bed."

"No. I have to try and make this room look like something."

"Like what?"

"Like our home."

"Hang out the Allied flags."

"Oh shut up."

"Say it again."

"Shut up."

"You say it so cautiously," I said. "As though you didn't want to offend any one."

"I don't."

"Then come over to the bed."

"All right." She came and sat on the bed. "I know I'm no fun for you, darling. I'm like a big flour-barrel."

"No you're not. You're beautiful and you're sweet."

"I'm just something very ungainly that you've married."

"No you're not. You're more beautiful all the time."

"But I will be thin again, darling."

"You're thin now."

"You've been drinking."

"Just whiskey and soda."

"There's another one coming," she said. "And then should we order dinner up here?"

"That will be good."

"Then we won't go out, will we? We'll just stay in to-night."

"And play," I said.

"I'll drink some wine," Catherine said. "It won't hurt me. Maybe we can get some of our old white capri."

"I know we can," I said. "They'll have Italian wines at a hotel this size."

The waiter knocked at the door. He brought the whiskey in a glass with ice and beside the glass on a tray a small bottle of soda.

"Thank you," I said. "Put it down there. Will you please have dinner for two brought up here and two bottles of dry white capri in ice."

"Do you wish to commence your dinner with soup?"

"Do you want soup, Cat?"

"Please."

"Bring soup for one."

"Thank you, sir." He went out and shut the door. I went back to the papers and the war in the papers and poured the soda slowly over the ice into the whiskey. I would have to tell them not to put ice in the whiskey. Let them bring the ice separately. That way you could tell how much whiskey there was and it would not suddenly be too thin from the soda. I would get a bottle of whiskey and have them bring ice and soda. That was the sensible way. Good whiskey was very pleasant. It was one of the pleasant parts of life.

"What are you thinking, darling?"

"About whiskey."

"What about whiskey?"

"About how nice it is."

Catherine made a face. "All right," she said.

We stayed at that hotel three weeks. It was not bad; the dining-room was usually empty and very often we ate in our room at night. We walked in the town and took the cogwheel railway down to Ouchy and walked beside the lake. The weather became quite warm and it was like spring. We wished we were back in the mountains but the spring weather lasted only a few days and then the cold rawness of the breaking-up of winter came again.

Catherine bought the things she needed for the baby, up in the town. I went to a gymnasium in the arcade to box for exercise. I usually went up there in the morning while Catherine stayed late in bed. On the days of false spring it was very nice, after boxing and taking a shower, to walk along the streets smelling the spring in the air and stop at a café to sit and watch the people and read the paper and drink a vermouth; then go down to the hotel and have lunch with Catherine. The professor at the boxing gymnasium wore mustaches and was very precise and jerky and went all to pieces if you started after him. But it was pleasant in the gym. There was good air and light and I worked quite hard, skipping rope, shadow-boxing, doing abdominal exercises lying on the floor in a patch of sunlight that came through the open window, and occasionally scaring the professor when we boxed. I could not shadow-box in front of the narrow long mirror at first because it looked so strange to see a man with a beard boxing. But finally I just thought it was funny. I wanted to take off the beard as soon as I started boxing but Catherine did not want me to.

Sometimes Catherine and I went for rides out in the country in a carriage. It was nice to ride when the days were pleasant and we found two good places where we could ride out to eat. Catherine could not walk very far now and I loved to ride out along the country roads with her. When there was a good day we had a splendid time and we never had a bad time. We knew the baby was very close now and it gave us both a feeling as though something were hurrying us and we could not lose any time together.

41

ONE morning I awoke about three o'clock hearing Catherine stirring in the bed.

"Are you all right, Cat?"

"I've been having some pains, darling."

"Regularly?"

"No, not very."

"If you have them at all regularly we'll go to the hospital."

I was very sleepy and went back to sleep. A little while later I woke again.

"Maybe you'd better call up the doctor," Catherine said. "I think maybe this is it."

I went to the phone and called the doctor. "How often are the pains coming?" he asked.

"How often are they coming, Cat?"

"I should think every quarter of an hour."

"You should go to the hospital, then," the doctor said. "I will dress and go there right away myself."

I hung up and called the garage near the station to send up a taxi. No one answered the phone for a long time. Then I finally got a man who promised to send up a taxi at once. Catherine was dressing. Her bag was all packed with the things she would need at the hospital and the baby things. Outside in the hall I rang for the elevator. There was no answer. I went downstairs. There was no one downstairs except the night-watchman. I brought the elevator up myself, put Catherine's bag in it, she stepped in and we went down. The night-watchman opened the door for us and we sat outside on the stone slabs beside the stairs down to the driveway and waited for the taxi. The night was clear and the stars were out. Catherine was very excited.

"I'm so glad it's started," she said. "Now in a little while it will be all over."

"You're a good brave girl."

"I'm not afraid. I wish the taxi would come, though."

We heard it coming up the street and saw its headlights. It turned into the driveway and I helped Catherine in and the driver put the bag up in front.

"Drive to the hospital," I said.

We went out of the driveway and started up the hill.

At the hospital we went in and I carried the bag. There was a woman at the desk who wrote down Catherine's name, age, address, relatives and religion, in a book. She said she had no religion and the woman drew a line in the space after that word. She gave her name as Catherine Henry.

"I will take you up to your room," she said. We went up in an elevator. The woman stopped it and we stepped out and followed her down a hall. Catherine held tight to my arm.

"This is the room," the woman said. "Will you please undress and get into bed? Here is a night-gown for you to wear."

"I have a night-gown," Catherine said.

"It is better for you to wear this night-gown," the woman said.

I went outside and sat on a chair in the hallway.

"You can come in now," the woman said from the doorway. Catherine was lying in the narrow bed wearing a plain, square-cut night-gown that looked as though it were made of rough sheeting. She smiled at me.

"I'm having fine pains now," she said. The woman was holding her wrist and timing the pains with a watch.

"That was a big one," Catherine said. I saw it on her face.

"Where's the doctor?" I asked the woman.

"He's lying down sleeping. He will be here when he is needed."

"I must do something for Madame, now," the nurse said. "Would you please step out again?"

I went out into the hall. It was a bare hall with two windows and closed doors all down the corridor. It smelled of hospital. I sat on the chair and looked at the floor and prayed for Catherine.

"You can come in," the nurse said. I went in.

"Hello, darling," Catherine said.

"How is it?"

"They are coming quite often now." Her face drew up. Then she smiled.

"That was a real one. Do you want to put your hand on my back again, nurse?"

"If it helps you," the nurse said.

"You go away, darling," Catherine said. "Go out and get something to eat. I may do this for a long time the nurse says."

"The first labor is usually protracted," the nurse said.

"Please go out and get something to eat," Catherine said. "I'm fine, really."

"I'll stay awhile," I said.

The pains came quite regularly, then slackened off. Catherine was very excited. When the pains were bad she called them good ones. When they started to fall off she was disappointed and ashamed.

"You go out, darling," she said. "I think you are just making me self-conscious." Her face tied up. "There. That was better. I so want to be a good wife and have this child without any foolishness. Please go and get some breakfast, darling, and then come back. I won't miss you. Nurse is splendid to me."

"You have plenty of time for breakfast," the nurse said.

"I'll go then. Good-by, sweet."

"Good-by," Catherine said, "and have a fine breakfast for me too."

"Where can I get breakfast?" I asked the nurse.

"There's a café down the street at the square," she said. "It should be open now."

Outside it was getting light. I walked down the empty street to the café. There was a light in the window. I went in and stood at the zinc bar and an old man served me a glass of white wine and a brioche. The brioche was yesterday's. I dipped it in the wine and then drank a glass of coffee.

"What do you do at this hour?" the old man asked.

"My wife is in labor at the hospital."

"So. I wish you good luck."

"Give me another glass of wine."

He poured it from the bottle slopping it over a little so some ran down on the zinc. I drank this glass, paid and went out. Outside along the street were the refuse cans from the houses waiting for the collector. A dog was nosing at one of the cans.

"What do you want?" I asked and looked in the can to see if there was anything I could pull out for him; there was nothing on top but coffee-grounds, dust and some dead flowers.

"There isn't anything, dog," I said. The dog crossed the street. I went up the stairs in the hospital to the floor Catherine was on and down the hall to her room. I knocked on the door. There was no answer. I opened the door; the room was empty, except for Catherine's bag on a chair and her dressing-gown hanging on a hook on the wall. I went out and down the hall, looking for somebody. I found a nurse.

"Where is Madame Henry?"

"A lady has just gone to the delivery room."

"Where is it?"

"I will show you."

She took me down to the end of the hall. The door of the room
was partly open. I could see Catherine lying on a table, covered by
a sheet. The nurse was on one side and the doctor stood on the other
side of the table beside some cylinders. The doctor held a rubber
mask attached to a tube in one hand.

"I will give you a gown and you can go in," the nurse said.
"Come in here, please."

She put a white gown on me and pinned it at the neck in back
with a safety pin.

"Now you can go in," she said. I went into the room.

"Hello, darling," Catherine said in a strained voice. "I'm not
doing much."

"You are Mr. Henry?" the doctor asked.

"Yes. How is everything going, doctor?"

"Things are going very well," the doctor said. "We came in here
where it is easy to give gas for the pains."

"I want it now," Catherine said. The doctor placed the rubber
mask over her face and turned a dial and I watched Catherine breathing deeply and rapidly. Then she pushed the mask away. The doctor
shut off the petcock.

"That wasn't a very big one. I had a very big one a while ago.
The doctor made me go clear out, didn't you, doctor?" Her voice was
strange. It rose on the word doctor.

The doctor smiled.

"I want it again," Catherine said. She held the rubber tight to
her face and breathed fast. I heard her moaning a little. Then she
pulled the mask away and smiled.

"That was a big one," she said. "That was a very big one. Don't
you worry, darling. You go away. Go have another breakfast."

"I'll stay," I said.

We had gone to the hospital about three o'clock in the morning.
At noon Catherine was still in the delivery room. The pains had
slackened again. She looked very tired and worn now but she was still
cheerful.

"I'm not any good, darling," she said. "I'm so sorry. I thought I
would do it very easily. Now—there's one—" she reached out her
hand for the mask and held it over her face. The doctor moved the
dial and watched her. In a little while it was over.

"It wasn't much," Catherine said. She smiled. "I'm a fool about the gas. It's wonderful."

"We'll get some for the home," I said.

"*There one comes,*" Catherine said quickly. The doctor turned the dial and looked at his watch.

"What is the interval now?" I asked.

"About a minute."

"Don't you want lunch?"

"I will have something pretty soon," he said.

"You must have something to eat, doctor," Catherine said. "I'm so sorry I go on so long. Couldn't my husband give me the gas?"

"If you wish," the doctor said. "You turn it to the numeral two."

"I see," I said. There was a marker on a dial that turned with a handle.

"*I want it now,*" Catherine said. She held the mask tight to her face. I turned the dial to number two and when Catherine put down the mask I turned it off. It was very good of the doctor to let me do something.

"Did you do it, darling?" Catherine asked. She stroked my wrist.

"Sure."

"You're so lovely." She was a little drunk from the gas.

"I will eat from a tray in the next room," the doctor said. "You can call me any moment." While the time passed I watched him eat, then, after a while, I saw that he was lying down and smoking a cigarette. Catherine was getting very tired.

"Do you think I'll ever have this baby?" she asked.

"Yes, of course you will."

"I try as hard as I can. I push down but it goes away. *There it comes. Give it to me.*"

At two o'clock I went out and had lunch. There were a few men in the café sitting with coffee and glasses of kirsch or marc on the tables. I sat down at a table. "Can I eat?" I asked the waiter.

"It is past time for lunch."

"Isn't there anything for all hours?"

"You can have *choucroute.*"

"Give me *choucroute* and beer."

"A demi or a bock?"

"A light demi."

The waiter brought a dish of sauerkraut with a slice of ham over the top and a sausage buried in the hot wine-soaked cabbage. I ate it and drank the beer. I was very hungry. I watched the people at the tables in the café. At one table they were playing cards. Two men at the table next me were talking and smoking. The café was full of smoke. The zinc bar, where I had breakfasted, had three people behind it now; the old man, a plump woman in a black dress who sat behind a counter and kept track of everything served to the tables, and a boy in an apron. I wondered how many children the woman had and what it had been like.

When I was through with the *choucroute* I went back to the hospital. The street was all clean now. There were no refuse cans out. The day was cloudy but the sun was trying to come through. I rode upstairs in the elevator, stepped out and went down the hall to Catherine's room, where I had left my white gown. I put it on and pinned it in back at the neck. I looked in the glass and saw myself looking like a fake doctor with a beard. I went down the hall to the delivery room. The door was closed and I knocked. No one answered so I turned the handle and went in. The doctor sat by Catherine. The nurse was doing something at the other end of the room.

"Here is your husband," the doctor said.

"Oh, darling, I have the most wonderful doctor," Catherine said in a very strange voice. "He's been telling me the most wonderful story and when the pain came too badly he put me all the way out. He's wonderful. You're wonderful, doctor."

"You're drunk," I said.

"I know it," Catherine said. "But you shouldn't say it." Then *"Give it to me. Give it to me."* She clutched hold of the mask and breathed short and deep, pantingly, making the respirator click. Then she gave a long sigh and the doctor reached with his left hand and lifted away the mask.

"That was a very big one," Catherine said. Her voice was very strange. "I'm not going to die now, darling. I'm past where I was going to die. Aren't you glad?"

"Don't you get in that place again."

"I won't. I'm not afraid of it though. I won't die, darling."

"You will not do any such foolishness," the doctor said. "You would not die and leave your husband."

"Oh, no. I won't die. I wouldn't die. It's silly to die. There it comes. *Give it to me.*"

After a while the doctor said, "You will go out, Mr. Henry, for a few moments and I will make an examination."

"He wants to see how I am doing," Catherine said. "You can come back afterward, darling, can't he, doctor?"

"Yes," said the doctor. "I will send word when he can come back."

I went out the door and down the hall to the room where Catherine was to be after the baby came. I sat in a chair there and looked at the room. I had the paper in my coat that I had bought when I went out for lunch and I read it. It was beginning to be dark outside and I turned the light on to read. After a while I stopped reading and turned off the light and watched it get dark outside. I wondered why the doctor did not send for me. Maybe it was better I was away. He probably wanted me away for a while. I looked at my watch. If he did not send for me in ten minutes I would go down anyway.

Poor, poor dear Cat. And this was the price you paid for sleeping together. This was the end of the trap. That was what people got for loving each other. Thank God for gas, anyway. What must it have been like before there were anæsthetics? Once it started, they were in the mill-race. Catherine had a good time in the time of pregnancy. It wasn't bad. She was hardly ever sick. She was not awfully uncomfortable until toward the last. So now they got her in the end. You never got away with anything. Get away hell! It would have been the same if we had been married fifty times. And what if she should die? She won't die. People don't die in childbirth nowadays. That was what all husbands thought. Yes, but what if she should die? She won't die. She's just having a bad time. The initial labor is usually protracted. She's only having a bad time. Afterward we'd say what a bad time and Catherine would say it wasn't really so bad. But what if she should die? She can't die. Yes, but what if she should die? She can't, I tell you. Don't be a fool. It's just a bad time. It's just nature giving her hell. It's only the first labor, which is almost always protracted. Yes, but what if she should die? She can't die. Why would she die? What reason is there for her to die? There's just a child that has to be born, the by-product of good nights in Milan. It makes trouble and is born and then you look after it and get fond of it maybe. But what if she should die? She won't die. But what if she should die? She won't. She's all right. But what if she should die?

She can't die. But what if she should die? Hey, what about that? What if she should die?

The doctor came into the room.

"How does it go, doctor?"

"It doesn't go," he said.

"What do you mean?"

"Just that. I made an examination—" He detailed the result of the examination. "Since then I've waited to see. But it doesn't go."

"What do you advise?"

"There are two things. Either a high forceps delivery which can tear and be quite dangerous besides being possibly bad for the child, and a Cæsarean."

"What is the danger of a Cæsarean?" What if she should die!

"It should be no greater than the danger of an ordinary delivery."

"Would you do it yourself?"

"Yes. I would need possibly an hour to get things ready and to get the people I would need. Perhaps a little less."

"What do you think?"

"I would advise a Cæsarean operation. If it were my wife I would do a Cæsarean."

"What are the after effects?"

"There are none. There is only the scar."

"What about infection?"

"The danger is not so great as in a high forceps delivery."

"What if you just went on and did nothing?"

"You would have to do something eventually. Mrs. Henry is already losing much of her strength. The sooner we operate now the safer."

"Operate as soon as you can," I said.

"I will go and give the instructions."

I went into the delivery room. The nurse was with Catherine who lay on the table, big under the sheet, looking very pale and tired.

"Did you tell him he could do it?" she asked.

"Yes."

"Isn't that grand. Now it will be all over in an hour. I'm almost done, darling. I'm going all to pieces. *Please give me that.* It doesn't work. *Oh, it doesn't work!*"

"Breathe deeply."

"I am. Oh, it doesn't work any more. It doesn't work!"

"Get another cylinder," I said to the nurse.

"That is a new cylinder."

"I'm just a fool, darling," Catherine said. "But it doesn't work any more." She began to cry. "Oh, I wanted so to have this baby and not make trouble, and now I'm all done and all gone to pieces and it doesn't work. Oh, darling, it doesn't work at all. I don't care if I die if it will only stop. Oh, please, darling, please make it stop. *There it comes. Oh Oh Oh!*" She breathed sobbingly in the mask. "It doesn't work. It doesn't work. It doesn't work. Don't mind me, darling. Please don't cry. Don't mind me. I'm just gone all to pieces. You poor sweet. I love you so and I'll be good again. I'll be good this time. *Can't they give me something?* If they could only give me something."

"I'll make it work. I'll turn it all the way."

"Give it to me now."

I turned the dial all the way and as she breathed hard and deep her hand relaxed on the mask. I shut off the gas and lifted the mask. She came back from a long way away.

"That was lovely, darling. Oh, you're so good to me."

"You be brave, because I can't do that all the time. It might kill you."

"I'm not brave any more, darling. I'm all broken. They've broken me. I know it now."

"Everybody is that way."

"But it's awful. They just keep it up till they break you."

"In an hour it will be over."

"Isn't that lovely? Darling, I won't die, will I?"

"No. I promise you won't."

"Because I don't want to die and leave you, but I get so tired of it and I feel I'm going to die."

"Nonsense. Everybody feels that."

"Sometimes I know I'm going to die."

"You won't. You can't."

"But what if I should?"

"I won't let you."

"Give it to me quick. *Give it to me!*"

Then afterward, "I won't die. I won't let myself die."

"Of course you won't."

"You'll stay with me?"

"Not to watch it."

"No, just to be there."

"Sure. I'll be there all the time."

"You're so good to me. There, give it to me. Give me some more. *It's not working!*"

I turned the dial to three and then four. I wished the doctor would come back. I was afraid of the numbers above two.

Finally a new doctor came in with two nurses and they lifted Catherine onto a wheeled stretcher and we started down the hall. The stretcher went rapidly down the hall and into the elevator where every one had to crowd against the wall to make room; then up, then an open door and out of the elevator and down the hall on rubber wheels to the operating room. I did not recognize the doctor with his cap and mask on. There was another doctor and more nurses.

"*They've got to give me something,*" Catherine said. "*They've got to give me something.* Oh please, doctor, give me enough to do some good!"

One of the doctors put a mask over her face and I looked through the door and saw the bright small amphitheatre of the operating room.

"You can go in the other door and sit up there," a nurse said to me. There were benches behind a rail that looked down on the white table and the lights. I looked at Catherine. The mask was over her face and she was quiet now. They wheeled the stretcher forward. I turned away and walked down the hall. Two nurses were hurrying toward the entrance to the gallery.

"It's a Cæsarean," one said. "They're going to do a Cæsarean."

The other one laughed, "We're just in time. Aren't we lucky?" They went in the door that led to the gallery.

Another nurse came along. She was hurrying too.

"You go right in there. Go right in," she said.

"I'm staying outside."

She hurried in. I walked up and down the hall. I was afraid to go in. I looked out the window. It was dark but in the light from the window I could see it was raining. I went into a room at the far end of the hall and looked at the labels on bottles in a glass case.

Then I came out and stood in the empty hall and watched the door of the operating room.

A doctor came out followed by a nurse. He held something in his two hands that looked like a freshly skinned rabbit and hurried across the corridor with it and in through another door. I went down to the door he had gone into and found them in the room doing things to a new-born child. The doctor held him up for me to see. He held him by the heels and slapped him.

"Is he all right?"

"He's magnificent. He'll weigh five kilos."

I had no feeling for him. He did not seem to have anything to do with me. I felt no feeling of fatherhood.

"Aren't you proud of your son?" the nurse asked. They were washing him and wrapping him in something. I saw the little dark face and dark hand, but I did not see him move or hear him cry. The doctor was doing something to him again. He looked upset.

"No," I said. "He nearly killed his mother."

"It isn't the little darling's fault. Didn't you want a boy?"

"No," I said. The doctor was busy with him. He held him up by the feet and slapped him. I did not wait to see it. I went out in the hall. I could go in now and see. I went in the door and a little way down the gallery. The nurses who were sitting at the rail motioned for me to come down where they were. I shook my head. I could see enough where I was.

I thought Catherine was dead. She looked dead. Her face was gray, the part of it that I could see. Down below, under the light, the doctor was sewing up the great long, forcep-spread, thick-edged, wound. Another doctor in a mask gave the anæsthetic. Two nurses in masks handed things. It looked like a drawing of the Inquisition. I knew as I watched I could have watched it all, but I was glad I hadn't. I do not think I could have watched them cut, but I watched the wound closed into a high welted ridge with quick skilful-looking stitches like a cobbler's, and was glad. When the wound was closed I went out into the hall and walked up and down again. After a while the doctor came out.

"How is she?"

"She is all right. Did you watch?"

He looked tired.

"I saw you sew up. The incision looked very long."

"You thought so?"

"Yes. Will that scar flatten out?"

"Oh, yes."

After a while they brought out the wheeled stretcher and took it very rapidly down the hallway to the elevator. I went along beside it. Catherine was moaning. Downstairs they put her in the bed in her room. I sat in a chair at the foot of the bed. There was a nurse in the room. I got up and stood by the bed. It was dark in the room. Catherine put out her hand. "Hello, darling," she said. Her voice was very weak and tired.

"Hello, you sweet."

"What sort of baby was it?"

"Sh—don't talk," the nurse said.

"A boy. He's long and wide and dark."

"Is he all right?"

"Yes," I said. "He's fine."

I saw the nurse look at me strangely.

"I'm awfully tired," Catherine said. "And I hurt like hell. Are you all right, darling?"

"I'm fine. Don't talk."

"You were lovely to me. Oh, darling, I hurt dreadfully. What does he look like?"

"He looks like a skinned rabbit with a puckered-up old-man's face."

"You must go out," the nurse said. "Madame Henry must not talk."

"I'll be outside."

"Go and get something to eat."

"No. I'll be outside." I kissed Catherine. She was very gray and weak and tired.

"May I speak to you?" I said to the nurse. She came out in the hall with me. I walked a little way down the hall.

"What's the matter with the baby?" I asked.

"Didn't you know?"

"No."

"He wasn't alive."

"He was dead?"

"They couldn't start him breathing. The cord was caught around his neck or something."

"So he's dead."

"Yes. It's such a shame. He was such a fine big boy. I thought you knew."

"No," I said. "You better go back in with Madame."

I sat down on the chair in front of a table where there were nurses' reports hung on clips at the side and looked out of the window. I could see nothing but the dark and the rain falling across the light from the window. So that was it. The baby was dead. That was why the doctor looked so tired. But why had they acted the way they did in the room with him? They supposed he would come around and start breathing probably. I had no religion but I knew he ought to have been baptized. But what if he never breathed at all. He hadn't. He had never been alive. Except in Catherine. I'd felt him kick there often enough. But I hadn't for a week. Maybe he was choked all the time. Poor little kid. I wished the hell I'd been choked like that. No I didn't. Still there would not be all this dying to go through. Now Catherine would die. That was what you did. You died. You did not know what it was about. You never had time to learn. They threw you in and told you the rules and the first time they caught you off base they killed you. Or they killed you gratuitously like Aymo. Or gave you the syphilis like Rinaldi. But they killed you in the end. You could count on that. Stay around and they would kill you.

Once in camp I put a log on top of the fire and it was full of ants. As it commenced to burn, the ants swarmed out and went first toward the centre where the fire was; then turned back and ran toward the end. When there were enough on the end they fell off into the fire. Some got out, their bodies burnt and flattened, and went off not knowing where they were going. But most of them went toward the fire and then back toward the end and swarmed on the cool end and finally fell off into the fire. I remember thinking at the time that it was the end of the world and a splendid chance to be a messiah and lift the log off the fire and throw it out where the ants could get off onto the ground. But I did not do anything but throw a tin cup of water on the log, so that I would have the cup empty to put whiskey in before I added water to it. I think the cup of water on the burning log only steamed the ants.

So now I sat out in the hall and waited to hear how Catherine was. The nurse did not come out, so after a while I went to the door

and opened it very softly and looked in. I could not see at first because
there was a bright light in the hall and it was dark in the room.
Then I saw the nurse sitting by the bed and Catherine's head on a
pillow, and she was all flat under the sheet. The nurse put her finger
to her lips, then stood up and came to the door.

"How is she?" I asked.

"She's all right," the nurse said. "You should go and have your
supper and then come back if you wish."

I went down the hall and then down the stairs and out the door
of the hospital and down the dark street in the rain to the café. It
was brightly lighted inside and there were many people at the tables.
I did not see a place to sit, and a waiter came up to me and took my
wet coat and hat and showed me a place at a table across from an
elderly man who was drinking beer and reading the evening paper.
I sat down and asked the waiter what the *plat du jour* was.

"Veal stew—but it is finished."

"What can I have to eat?"

"Ham and eggs, eggs with cheese, or *choucroute*."

"I had *choucroute* this noon," I said.

"That's true," he said. "That's true. You ate *choucroute* this
noon." He was a middle-aged man with a bald top to his head and
his hair slicked over it. He had a kind face.

"What do you want? Ham and eggs or eggs with cheese?"

"Ham and eggs," I said, "and beer."

"A demi-blonde?"

"Yes," I said.

"I remembered," he said. "You took a demi-blonde this noon."

I ate the ham and eggs and drank the beer. The ham and eggs
were in a round dish—the ham underneath and the eggs on top. It
was very hot and at the first mouthful I had to take a drink of beer
to cool my mouth. I was hungry and I asked the waiter for another
order. I drank several glasses of beer. I was not thinking at all but
read the paper of the man opposite me. It was about the break
through on the British front. When he realized I was reading the
back of his paper he folded it over. I thought of asking the waiter for
a paper, but I could not concentrate. It was hot in the café and the
air was bad. Many of the people at the tables knew one another.
There were several card games going on. The waiters were busy
bringing drinks from the bar to the tables. Two men came in and

could find no place to sit. They stood opposite the table where I was. I ordered another beer. I was not ready to leave yet. It was too soon to go back to the hospital. I tried not to think and to be perfectly calm. The men stood around but no one was leaving, so they went out. I drank another beer. There was quite a pile of saucers now on the table in front of me. The man opposite me had taken off his spectacles, put them away in a case, folded his paper and put it in his pocket and now sat holding his liqueur glass and looking out at the room. Suddenly I knew I had to get back. I called the waiter, paid the reckoning, got into my coat, put on my hat and started out the door. I walked through the rain up to the hospital.

Upstairs I met the nurse coming down the hall.

"I just called you at the hotel," she said. Something dropped inside me.

"What is wrong?"

"Mrs. Henry has had a hemorrhage."

"Can I go in?"

"No, not yet. The doctor is with her."

"Is it dangerous?"

"It is very dangerous." The nurse went into the room and shut the door. I sat outside in the hall. Everything was gone inside of me. I did not think. I could not think. I knew she was going to die and I prayed that she would not. Don't let her die. Oh, God, please don't let her die. I'll do anything for you if you won't let her die. Please, please, please, dear God, don't let her die. Dear God, don't let her die. Please, please, please don't let her die. God please make her not die. I'll do anything you say if you don't let her die. You took the baby but don't let her die. That was all right but don't let her die. Please, please, dear God, don't let her die.

The nurse opened the door and motioned with her finger for me to come. I followed her into the room. Catherine did not look up when I came in. I went over to the side of the bed. The doctor was standing by the bed on the opposite side. Catherine looked at me and smiled. I bent down over the bed and started to cry.

"Poor darling," Catherine said very softly. She looked gray.

"You're all right, Cat," I said. "You're going to be all right."

"I'm going to die," she said; then waited and said, "I hate it."

I took her hand.

"Don't touch me," she said. I let go of her hand. She smiled. "Poor darling. You touch me all you want."

"You'll be all right, Cat. I know you'll be all right."

"I meant to write you a letter to have if anything happened, but I didn't do it."

"Do you want me to get a priest or any one to come and see you?"

"Just you," she said. Then a little later, "I'm not afraid. I just hate it."

"You must not talk so much," the doctor said.

"All right," Catherine said.

"Do you want me to do anything, Cat? Can I get you anything?"

Catherine smiled, "No." Then a little later, "You won't do our things with another girl, or say the same things, will you?"

"Never."

"I want you to have girls, though."

"I don't want them."

"You are talking too much," the doctor said. "Mr. Henry must go out. He can come back again later. You are not going to die. You must not be silly."

"All right," Catherine said. "I'll come and stay with you nights," she said. It was very hard for her to talk.

"Please go out of the room," the doctor said. "You cannot talk." Catherine winked at me, her face gray. "I'll be right outside," I said.

"Don't worry, darling," Catherine said. "I'm not a bit afraid. It's just a dirty trick."

"You dear, brave sweet."

I waited outside in the hall. I waited a long time. The nurse came to the door and came over to me. "I'm afraid Mrs. Henry is very ill," she said. "I'm afraid for her."

"Is she dead?"

"No, but she is unconscious."

It seems she had one hemorrhage after another. They couldn't stop it. I went into the room and stayed with Catherine until she died. She was unconscious all the time, and it did not take her very long to die.

Outside the room, in the hall, I spoke to the doctor, "Is there anything I can do to-night?"

"No. There is nothing to do. Can I take you to your hotel?"

"No, thank you. I am going to stay here a while."

"I know there is nothing to say. I cannot tell you——"

"No," I said. "There's nothing to say."

"Good-night," he said. "I cannot take you to your hotel?"

"No, thank you."

"It was the only thing to do," he said. "The operation proved——"

"I do not want to talk about it," I said.

"I would like to take you to your hotel."

"No, thank you."

He went down the hall. I went to the door of the room.

"You can't come in now," one of the nurses said.

"Yes I can," I said.

"You can't come in yet."

"You get out," I said. "The other one too."

But after I had got them out and shut the door and turned off the light it wasn't any good. It was like saying good-by to a statue. After a while I went out and left the hospital and walked back to the hotel in the rain.

THE END

In Another Country

In the fall the war was always there, but we did not go to it any more. It was cold in the fall in Milan and the dark came very early. Then the electric lights came on, and it was pleasant along the streets looking in the windows. There was much game hanging outside the shops, and the snow powdered in the fur of the foxes and the wind blew their tails. The deer hung stiff and heavy and empty, and small birds blew in the wind and the wind turned their feathers. It was a cold fall and the wind came down from the mountains.

We were all at the hospital every afternoon, and there were different ways of walking across the town through the dusk to the hospital. Two of the ways were alongside canals, but they were long. Always, though, you crossed a bridge across a canal to enter the hospital. There was a choice of three bridges. On one of them a woman sold roasted chestnuts. It was warm, standing in front of her charcoal fire, and the chestnuts were warm afterward in your pocket. The hospital was very old and very beautiful, and you entered through a gate and walked across a courtyard and out a gate on the other side. There were usually funerals starting from the courtyard. Beyond the old hospital were the new brick pavilions, and there we met every afternoon and were all very polite and interested in what was the matter, and sat in the machines that were to make so much difference.

The doctor came up to the machine where I was sitting and said: "What did you like best to do before the war? Did you practise a sport?"

I said: "Yes, football."

"Good," he said. "You will be able to play football again better than ever."

My knee did not bend and the leg dropped straight from the knee to the ankle without a calf, and the machine was to bend the knee and make it move as in riding a tricycle. But it did not bend yet, and instead the machine lurched when it came to the bending part. The doctor said: "That will all pass. You are a fortunate young man. You will play football again like a champion."

In the next machine was a major who had a little hand like a baby's. He winked at me when the doctor examined his hand, which was between two leather straps that bounced up and down and flapped the stiff fingers, and said: "And will I too play football, captain-doctor?" He had been a very great fencer, and before the war the greatest fencer in Italy.

The doctor went to his office in a back room and brought a photograph which showed a hand that had been withered almost as small as the major's, before it had taken a machine course, and after was a little larger. The major held the photograph with his good hand and looked at it very carefully. "A wound?" he asked.

"An industrial accident," the doctor said.

"Very interesting, very interesting," the major said, and handed it back to the doctor.

"You have confidence?"

"No," said the major.

There were three boys who came each day who were about the same age I was. They were all three from Milan, and one of them was to be a lawyer, and one was to be a painter, and one had intended to be a soldier, and after we were finished with the machines, sometimes we walked back together to the Café Cova, which was next door to the Scala. We walked the short way through the communist quarter because we were four together. The people hated us because we were officers, and from a wine-shop some one would call out, "A basso gli ufficiali!" as we passed. Another boy who walked with us sometimes and made us five wore a black silk handkerchief across his face because he had no nose then and his face was to be rebuilt. He had gone out to the front from the military academy and been wounded within an hour after he had gone into the front line for the first time. They rebuilt his face, but he came from a very old family and they could never get the nose exactly right. He went to South America and worked in a bank. But this was a long time ago, and then we did not any of us know how it was going to be afterward. We only knew then that there was always the war, but that we were not going to it any more.

We all had the same medals, except the boy with the black silk bandage across his face, and he had not been at the front long enough to get any medals. The tall boy with a very pale face who was to be a lawyer had been a lieutenant of Arditi and had three medals of the sort we each had only one of. He had lived a very long time with death and was a little detached. We were all a little detached, and there was nothing that held us together except that we met every afternoon at the hospital. Although, as we walked to the Cova through the tough part of town, walking in the dark, with light and singing coming out of the wine-shops, and sometimes having to walk into the street when the men and women would crowd together on the sidewalk so that we would have had to jostle them to get by, we felt held together by there being something that had happened that they, the people who disliked us, did not understand.

We ourselves all understood the Cova, where it was rich and warm and not too brightly lighted, and noisy and smoky at certain hours, and there were always girls at the tables and the illustrated papers on a rack on the wall. The girls at the Cova were very patriotic, and I found that the most patriotic people in Italy were the café girls—and I believe they are still patriotic.

The boys at first were very polite about my medals and asked me what I had done to get them. I showed them the papers, which were written in very beautiful language and full of *fratellanza* and *abnegazione,* but which really said, with the adjectives removed, that I had been given the medals because I was an American. After that their manner changed a little toward me, although I was their friend against outsiders. I was a friend, but I was never really one of them after they had read the citations, because it had been different with them and they had done very different things to get their medals. I had been wounded, it was true; but we all knew that being wounded, after all, was really an accident. I was never ashamed of the ribbons, though, and sometimes, after the cocktail hour, I would imagine myself having done all the things they had done to get their medals; but walking home at night through the empty streets with the cold wind and all the shops closed, trying to keep near the street lights, I knew that I would never have done such things, and I was very much afraid to die, and often lay in bed at night by myself, afraid to die and wondering how I would be when I went back to the front again.

The three with the medals were like hunting-hawks; and I was not a hawk, although I might seem a hawk to those who had never hunted; they, the three, knew better and so we drifted apart. But I stayed good friends with the boy who had been wounded his first day at the front, because he would never know now how he would have turned out; so he could never be accepted either, and I liked him because I thought perhaps he would not have turned out to be a hawk either.

The major, who had been the great fencer, did not believe in bravery, and spent much time while we sat in the machines correcting my grammar. He had complimented me on how I spoke Italian, and we talked together very easily. One day I had said that Italian seemed such an easy language to me that I could not take a great interest in it; everything was so easy to say. "Ah, yes," the major said. "Why, then, do you not take up the use of grammar?" So we took up the use of grammar, and soon Italian was such a difficult language that I was afraid to talk to him until I had the grammar straight in my mind.

The major came very regularly to the hospital. I do not think he ever missed a day, although I am sure he did not believe in the machines. There was a time when none of us believed in the machines, and one day the major said it was all nonsense. The machines were new then and it was we who were to prove them. It was an idiotic idea, he said, "a theory, like another." I had not learned my grammar, and he said I was a stupid impossible disgrace, and he was a fool to have bothered with me. He was a small man and he sat straight up in his chair with his right hand thrust into the machine and looked straight ahead at the wall while the straps thumped up and down with his fingers in them.

"What will you do when the war is over if it is over?" he asked me. "Speak grammatically!"

"I will go to the States."

"Are you married?"

"No, but I hope to be."

"The more of a fool you are," he said. He seemed very angry. "A man must not marry."

"Why, Signor Maggiore?"

"Don't call me 'Signor Maggiore.' "

"Why must not a man marry?"

"He cannot marry. He cannot marry," he said angrily. "If he is to lose everything, he should not place himself in a position to lose that. He should not place himself in a position to lose. He should find things he cannot lose."

He spoke very angrily and bitterly, and looked straight ahead while he talked.

"But why should he necessarily lose it?"

"He'll lose it," the major said. He was looking at the wall. Then he looked down at the machine and jerked his little hand out from between the straps and slapped it hard against his thigh. "He'll lose it," he almost shouted. "Don't argue with me!" Then he called to the attendant who ran the machines. "Come and turn this damned thing off."

He went back into the other room for the light treatment and the massage. Then I heard him ask the doctor if he might use his telephone and he shut the door. When he came back into the room, I was sitting in another machine. He was wearing his cape and had his cap on, and he came directly toward my machine and put his arm on my shoulder.

"I am so sorry," he said, and patted me on the shoulder with his good hand. "I would not be rude. My wife has just died. You must forgive me."

"Oh—" I said, feeling sick for him. "I am *so* sorry."

He stood there biting his lower lip. "It is very difficult," he said. "I cannot resign myself."

He looked straight past me and out through the window. Then he began to cry. "I am utterly unable to resign myself," he said and choked. And then crying, his head up looking at nothing, carrying himself straight and soldierly, with tears on both his cheeks and biting his lips, he walked past the machines and out the door.

The doctor told me that the major's wife, who was very young and whom he had not married until he was definitely invalided out of the war, had died of pneumonia. She had been sick only a few days. No one expected her to die. The major did not come to the hospital for three days. Then he came at the usual hour, wearing a black band on the sleeve of his uniform. When he came back, there were large framed photographs around the wall, of all sorts of wounds before and after they had been cured by the machines. In front of the machine the major used were three photographs of hands like his that were completely restored. I do not know where the doctor got them. I always understood we were the first to use the machines. The photographs did not make much difference to the major because he only looked out of the window.

❖ PART III ❖

TOROS Y TOREROS

From BY-LINE: ERNEST HEMINGWAY
Pamplona in July

THE SUN ALSO RISES (CHAPTERS 15–18)

From MEN WITHOUT WOMEN
The Undefeated

Pamplona in July

(*The Toronto Star Weekly*—OCTOBER 27, 1923)

IN Pamplona, a white-walled, sun-baked town high up in the hills of Navarre, is held in the first two weeks of July each year the World's Series of bull fighting.

Bull fight fans from all Spain jam into the little town. Hotels double their prices and fill every room. The cafés under the wide arcades that run around the Plaza de la Constitucion have every table crowded, the tall Pilgrim Father sombreros of Andalusia sitting over the same table with straw hats from Madrid and the flat blue Basque caps of Navarre and the Basque country.

Really beautiful girls, gorgeous, bright shawls over their shoulders, dark, dark-eyed, black-lace mantillas over their hair, walk with their escorts in the crowds that pass from morning until night along the narrow walk that runs between inner and outer belts of café tables under the shade of the arcade out of the white glare of the Plaza de la Constitucion. All day and all night there is dancing in the streets. Bands of blue-shirted peasants whirl and lift and swing behind a drum, fife and reed instruments in the ancient Basque Riau-Riau dances. And at night there is the throb of the big drums and the military band as the whole town dances in the great open square of the Plaza.

We landed at Pamplona at night. The streets were solid with people dancing. Music was pounding and throbbing. Fireworks were being set off from the big public square. All the carnivals I had ever seen paled down in comparison. A rocket exploded over our heads with a blinding burst and the stick came swirling and whishing down. Dancers, snapping their fingers and whirling in perfect time through the crowd, bumped into us before we could get our bags down from the top of the station bus. Finally I got the bags through the crowd to the hotel.

We had wired and written for rooms two weeks ahead. Nothing had been saved. We were offered a single room with a single bed opening on to the kitchen ventilator shaft for seven dollars a day apiece. There was a big row with the landlady, who stood in front of her desk with her hands on her hips, and her broad Indian face perfectly placid, and told us in a few words of French and much Basque Spanish that she had to make all her money for the whole year in the next ten days. That people would come and that people would have to pay what she asked. She could show us a better room for ten dollars apiece. We said it would be preferable to sleep in the streets with the pigs. The landlady agreed that might be possible. We said we preferred it to such a hotel. All perfectly amicable. The landlady considered. We stood our ground. Mrs. Hemingway sat down on our rucksacks.

"I can get you a room in a house in the town. You can eat here," said the landlady.

"How much?"

"Five dollars."

We started off through the dark, narrow, carnival-mad streets with a boy carrying our rucksacks. It was a lovely big room in an old Spanish house with walls thick as a fortress. A cool, pleasant room, with a red tile floor and two big, comfortable beds set back in an alcove. A window opened on to an iron grilled porch out over the street. We were very comfortable.

All night long the wild music kept up in the street below. Several times in the night there was a wild roll of drumming, and I got out of bed and across the tiled floor to the balcony. But it was always the same. Men, blue-shirted, bareheaded, whirling and floating in a wild fantastic dance down the street behind the rolling drums and shrill fifes.

Just at daylight there was a crash of music in the street below. Real military music. Herself was up, dressed, at the window.

"Come on," she said. "They're all going somewhere." Down below the street was full of people. It was five o'clock in the morning. They were all going in one direction. I dressed in a hurry and we started after them.

The crowd was all going toward the great public square. People were pouring into it from every street and moving out of it toward the open country we could see through the narrow gaps in the high walls.

"Let's get some coffee," said Herself.

"Do you think we've got time? Hey, what's going to happen?" I asked a newsboy.

"Encierro," he said scornfully. "The encierro commences at six o'clock."

"What's the encierro?" I asked him.

"Oh, ask me to-morrow," he said, and started to run. The entire crowd was running now.

"I've got to have my coffee. No matter what it is," Herself said.

The waiter poured two streams of coffee and milk into the glass out of his big kettles. The crowd was still running, coming from all the streets that fed into the Plaza.

"What is this encierro anyway?" Herself asked, gulping the coffee.

"All I know is that they let the bulls out into the streets."

We started out after the crowd. Out of a narrow gate into a great yellow open space of country with the new concrete bull ring standing high and white and black with people. The yellow and red Spanish flag blowing in the early morning breeze. Across the open and once inside the bull ring, we mounted to the top looking toward the town. It cost a peseta to go up to the top. All the other levels were free. There were easily twenty thousand people there. Everyone jammed on the outside of the big concrete amphitheatre, looking toward the yellow town with the bright red roofs, where a long wooden pen ran from the entrance of the city gate across the open, bare ground to the bull ring.

It was really a double wooden fence, making a long entryway from the main street of the town into the bull ring itself. It made a runway about two hundred and fifty yards long. People were jammed solid on each side of it. Looking up it toward the main street.

Then far away there was a dull report.

"They're off," everybody shouted.

"What is it?" I asked a man next to me who was leaning far out over the concrete rail.

"The bulls! They have released them from the corrals on the far side of the city. They are racing through the city."

"Whew," said Herself. "What do they do that for?"

Then down the narrow fenced-in runway came a crowd of men

and boys running. Running as hard as they could go. The gate feeding into the bull ring was opened and they all ran pell-mell under the entrance levels into the ring. Then there came another crowd. Running even harder. Straight up the long pen from the town.

"Where are the bulls?" asked Herself.

Then they came in sight. Eight bulls galloping along, full tilt, heavy set, black, glistening, sinister, their horns bare, tossing their heads. And running with them three steers with bells on their necks. They ran in a solid mass, and ahead of them sprinted, tore, ran and bolted the rear guard of the men and boys of Pamplona who had allowed themselves to be chased through the streets for a morning's pleasure.

A boy in his blue shirt, red sash, white canvas shoes with the inevitable leather wine bottle hung from his shoulders, stumbled as he sprinted down the straightaway. The first bull lowered his head and made a jerky, sideways toss. The boy crashed up against the fence and lay there limp, the herd running solidly together passed him up. The crowd roared.

Everybody made a dash for the inside of the ring, and we got into a box just in time to see the bulls come into the ring filled with men. The men ran in a panic to each side. The bulls, still bunched solidly together, ran straight with the trained steers across the ring and into the entrance that led to the pens.

That was the entry. Every morning during the bull fighting festival of San Fermin at Pamplona the bulls that are to fight in the afternoon are released from their corrals at six o'clock in the morning and race through the main street of the town for a mile and a half to the pen. The men who run ahead of them do it for the fun of the thing. It has been going on each year since a couple of hundred years before Columbus had his historic interview with Queen Isabella in the camp outside of Granada.

There are two things in favor of there being no accidents. First, that fighting bulls are not aroused and vicious when they are together. Second, that the steers are relied upon to keep them moving.

Sometimes things go wrong, a bull will be detached from the herd as they pile through into the pen and with his crest up, a ton of speed and viciousness, his needle-sharp horns lowered, will charge again and again into the packed mass of men and boys in the bull ring. There is no place for the men to get out of the ring. It is too jammed for them to climb over the barrera or red fence that rims the field. They have to stay in and take it. Eventually the steers get the bull out of the ring and into the pen. He may wound or kill thirty men before they can get him out. No armed men are allowed to oppose him. That is the chance the Pamplona bull fight fans take every morning during the Feria. It is the Pamplona tradition of giving the bulls a final shot at everyone in town before they enter the pens. They will not leave until they come out into the glare of the arena to die in the afternoon.

Consequently Pamplona is the toughest bull fight town in the world. The amateur fight that comes immediately after the bulls have entered the pens proves that. Every seat in the great amphitheatre is packed. About three hundred men, with capes, odd pieces of cloth, old shirts, anything that will imitate a bull fighter's cape, are singing and dancing in the arena. There is a shout, and the bull pen opens. Out comes a young bull just as fast as he can come. On his horns are leather knobs to prevent his goring anyone. He charges and hits a man. Tosses him high in the air, and the crowd roars. The man comes down on the ground, and the bull goes for him, bumping him with his head. Worrying him with his horns. Several amateur bull fighters are flopping their capes in his face to make the bull charge and leave the man on the ground. Then the bull charges and bags another man. The crowd roars with delight.

Then the bull will turn like a cat and get somebody who has been acting very brave about ten feet behind him. Then he will toss a man over the fence. Then he picks out one man and follows him in a wild twisting charge through the entire crowd until he bags him. The barrera is packed with men and boys sitting along the top, and the bull decides to clear them all off. He goes along, hooking carefully with his horn and dropping them off with a toss of his horns like a man pitching hay.

Each time the bull bags someone the crowd roars with joy. Most of it is home talent stuff. The braver the man has been or the more elegant pass he has attempted with his cape before the bull gets him the more the crowd roars. No one is armed. No one hurts or plagues the bull in any way. A man who grabbed the bull by the tail and tried to hang on was hissed and booed by the crowd and the next time he tried it was knocked down by another man in the bull ring. No one enjoys it all more than the bull.

As soon as he shows signs of tiring from his charges, the two old steers, one brown and the other looking like a big Holstein, come trotting in and alongside the young bull who falls in behind them like a dog and follows them meekly on a tour of the arena and then out.

Another comes right in, and the charging and tossing, the ineffectual cape waving, and wonderful music are repeated right over again. But always different. Some of the animals in this morning amateur fight are steers. Fighting bulls from the best strain who had some imperfection or other in build so they could never command the high prices paid for combat animals, $2,000 to $3,000 apiece. But there is nothing lacking in their fighting spirit.

The show comes off every morning. Everybody in town turns out at five-thirty when the military bands go through the streets. Many of them stay up all night for it. We didn't miss one, and it is quelque sporting event that will get us both up at five-thirty o'clock in the morning for six days running.

As far as I know we were the only English-speaking people in Pamplona during the Feria of last year [July].

There were three minor earthquakes while we were there. Terrific cloud bursts in the mountains and the Ebro River flooded out Zaragossa. For two days the bull ring was under water and the Corrida had to be suspended for the first time in over a hundred years. That was during the middle of the fair. Everyone was desperate. On the third day it looked gloomier than ever, poured rain all morning, and then at noon the clouds rolled away up across the valley, the sun came out bright and hot and baking and that afternoon there was the greatest bull fight I will perhaps ever see.

There were rockets going up into the air and the arena was nearly full when we got into our regular seats. The sun was hot and baking. Over on the other side we could see the bull fighters standing ready to come in. All wearing their oldest clothes because of the heavy, muddy going in the arena. We picked out the three matadors of the afternoon with our glasses. Only one of them was new. Olmos, a chubby faced, jolly looking man, something like Tris Speaker. The

others we had seen often before. Maera, dark, spare and deadly looking, one of the very greatest toreros of all time. The third, young
Algabeno, the son of a famous bull fighter, a slim young Andalusian
with a charming Indian looking face. All were wearing the suits they
had probably started bull fighting with, too tight, old fashioned, outmoded.

There was the procession of entrance, the wild bull fight music
played, the preliminaries were quickly over, the picadors retired
along the red fence with their horses, the heralds sounded their
trumpets and the door of the bull pen swung open. The bull came
out in a rush, saw a man standing near the barrera and charged him.
The man vaulted over the fence and the bull charged the barrera. He
crashed into the fence in full charge and ripped a two by eight plank
solidly out in a splintering smash. He broke his horn doing it and
the crowd called for a new bull. The trained steers trotted in, the
bull fell in meekly behind them, and the three of them trotted out
of the arena.

The next bull came in with the same rush. He was Maera's bull
and after perfect cape play Maera planted the banderillos. Maera is
Herself's favorite bull fighter. And if you want to keep any conception of yourself as a brave, hard, perfectly balanced, thoroughly com-
petent man in your wife's mind never take her to a real bull fight. I
used to go into the amateur fights in the morning to try and win back
a small amount of her esteem but the more I discovered that bull
fighting required a very great quantity of a certain type of courage
of which I had an almost complete lack the more it became apparent
that any admiration she might ever redevelop for me would have to
be simply an antidote to the real admiration for Maera and Villalta.
You cannot compete with bull fighters on their own ground. If anywhere. The only way most husbands are able to keep any drag with
their wives at all is that, first there are only a limited number of bull
fighters, second there are only a limited number of wives who have
ever seen bull fights.

Maera planted his first pair of banderillos sitting down on the
edge of the little step-up that runs around the barrera. He snarled at
the bull and as the animal charged leaned back tight against the
fence and as the horns struck on either side of him, swung forward over
the brute's head and planted the two darts in his hump. He planted

the next pair the same way, so near to us we could have leaned over and touched him. Then he went out to kill the bull and after he had made absolutely unbelievable passes with the little red cloth of the muleta drew up his sword and as the bull charged Maera thrust. The sword shot out of his hand and the bull caught him. He went up in the air on the horns of the bull and then came down. Young Algabeno flopped his cape in the bull's face. The bull charged him and Maera staggered to his feet. But his wrist was sprained.

With his wrist sprained, so that every time he raised it to sight for a thrust it brought beads of sweat out on his face, Maera tried again and again to make his death thrust. He lost his sword again and again, picked it up with his left hand from the mud floor of the arena and transferred it to the right for the thrust. Finally he made it and the bull went over. The bull nearly got him twenty times. As he came in to stand up under us at the barrera side his wrist was swollen to twice normal size. I thought of prize fighters I had seen quit because they had hurt their hands.

There was almost no pause while the mules galloped in and hitched on to the first bull and dragged him out and the second came in with a rush. The picadors took the first shock of him with their bull lances. There was the snort and charge, the shock and the mass against the sky, the wonderful defense by the picador with his lance that held off the bull, and then Rosario Olmos stepped out with his cape.

Once he flopped the cape at the bull and floated it around in an easy graceful swing. Then he tried the same swing, the classic "Veronica," and the bull caught him at the end of it. Instead of stopping at the finish the bull charged on in. He caught Olmos squarely with his horn, hoisted him high in the air. He fell heavily and the bull was on top of him, driving his horns again and again into him. Olmos lay on the sand, his head on his arms. One of his teammates was flopping his cape madly in the bull's face. The bull lifted his head for an instant and charged and got his man. Just one terrific toss. Then he whirled and chased a man just in back of him toward the barrera. The man was running full tilt and as he put his hand on the fence to vault it the bull had him and caught him with his horn, shooting him way up into the crowd. He rushed toward the fallen man he had tossed who was getting to his feet and all alone— Algabeno grabbed him by the tail. He hung on until I thought he or the bull would break. The wounded man got to his feet and started away.

The bull turned like a cat and charged Algabeno and Algabeno met him with the cape. Once, twice, three times he made the perfect, floating, slow swing with the cape, perfectly, graceful, debonair, back on his heels, baffling the bull. And he had command of the situation. There never was such a scene at any world's series game.

There are no substitute matadors allowed. Maera was finished. His wrist could not lift a sword for weeks. Olmos had been gored badly through the body. It was Algabeno's bull. This one and the next five.

He handled them all. Did it all. Cape play easy, graceful, confident. Beautiful work with the muleta. And serious, deadly killing. Five bulls he killed, one after the other, and each one was a separate problem to be worked out with death. At the end there was nothing debonair about him. It was only a question if he would last through or if the bulls would get him. They were all very wonderful bulls.

"He is a very great kid," said Herself. "He is only twenty."

"I wish we knew him," I said.

"Maybe we will some day," she said. Then considered a moment. "He will probably be spoiled by then."

They make twenty thousand a year.

That was just three months ago. It seems in a different century now, working in an office. It is a very long way from the sun baked town of Pamplona, where the men race through the streets in the mornings ahead of the bulls to the morning ride to work on a Bay-Caledonia car. But it is only fourteen days by water to Spain and there is no need for a castle. There is always that room at 5 Calle de Eslava, and a son, if he is to redeem the family reputation as a bull fighter, must start very early.

THE SUN ALSO RISES

(*CHAPTERS 15–18*)

15

AT noon of Sunday, the 6th of July, the fiesta exploded. There is no other way to describe it. People had been coming in all day from the country, but they were assimilated in the town and you did not notice them. The square was as quiet in the hot sun as on any other day. The peasants were in the outlying wine-shops. There they were drinking, getting ready for the fiesta. They had come in so recently from the plains and the hills that it was necessary that they make their shifting in values gradually. They could not start in paying café prices. They got their money's worth in the wine-shops. Money still had a definite value in hours worked and bushels of grain sold. Late in the fiesta it would not matter what they paid, nor where they bought.

Now on the day of the starting of the fiesta of San Fermin they had been in the wine-shops of the narrow streets of the town since early morning. Going down the streets in the morning on the way to mass in the cathedral, I heard them singing through the open doors of the shops. They were warming up. There were many people at the eleven o'clock mass. San Fermin is also a religious festival.

I walked down the hill from the cathedral and up the street to the café on the square. It was a little before noon. Robert Cohn and Bill were sitting at one of the tables. The marble-topped tables and the white wicker chairs were gone. They were replaced by cast-iron tables and severe folding chairs. The café was like a battleship stripped for action. To-day the waiters did not leave you alone all morning to read without asking if you wanted to order something. A waiter came up as soon as I sat down.

"What are you drinking?" I asked Bill and Robert.

"Sherry," Cohn said.

"Jerez," I said to the waiter.

Before the waiter brought the sherry the rocket that announced the fiesta went up in the square. It burst and there was a gray ball of smoke high up above the Theatre Gayarre, across on the other side of the plaza. The ball of smoke hung in the sky like a shrapnel burst, and as I watched, another rocket came up to it, trickling smoke in the bright sunlight. I saw the bright flash as it burst and another little cloud of smoke appeared. By the time the second rocket had burst there were so many people in the arcade, that had been empty a minute before, that the waiter, holding the bottle high up over his head, could hardly get through the crowd to our table. People were coming into the square from all sides, and down the street we heard the pipes and the fifes and the drums coming. They were playing the *riau-riau* music, the pipes shrill and the drums pounding, and behind them came the men and boys dancing. When the fifers stopped they all crouched down in the street, and when the reed-pipes and the fifes shrilled, and the flat, dry, hollow drums tapped it out again, they all went up in the air dancing. In the crowd you saw only the heads and shoulders of the dancers going up and down.

In the square a man, bent over, was playing on a reed-pipe, and a crowd of children were following him shouting, and pulling at his clothes. He came out of the square, the children following him, and piped them past the café and down a side street. We saw his blank pockmarked face as he went by, piping, the children close behind him shouting and pulling at him.

"He must be the village idiot," Bill said. "My God! look at that!"

Down the street came dancers. The street was solid with dancers, all men. They were all dancing in time behind their own fifers and drummers. They were a club of some sort, and all wore workmen's blue smocks, and red handkerchiefs around their necks, and carried a great banner on two poles. The banner danced up and down with them as they came down surrounded by the crowd.

"Hurray for Wine! Hurray for the Foreigners!" was painted on the banner.

"Where are the foreigners?" Robert Cohn asked.

"We're the foreigners," Bill said.

All the time rockets were going up. The café tables were all full now. The square was emptying of people and the crowd was filling the cafés.

"Where's Brett and Mike?" Bill asked.

"I'll go and get them," Cohn said.

"Bring them here."

The fiesta was really started. It kept up day and night for seven days. The dancing kept up, the drinking kept up, the noise went on. The things that happened could only have happened during a fiesta. Everything became quite unreal finally and it seemed as though nothing could have any consequences. It seemed out of place to think of consequences during the fiesta. All during the fiesta you had the feeling, even when it was quiet, that you had to shout any remark to make it heard. It was the same feeling about any action. It was a fiesta and it went on for seven days.

That afternoon was the big religious procession. San Fermin was translated from one church to another. In the procession were all the dignitaries, civil and religious. We could not see them because the crowd was too great. Ahead of the formal procession and behind it danced the *riau-riau* dancers. There was one mass of yellow shirts dancing up and down in the crowd. All we could see of the procession through the closely pressed people that crowded all the side streets and curbs were the great giants, cigar-store Indians, thirty feet high, Moors, a King and Queen, whirling and waltzing solemnly to the *riau-riau*.

They were all standing outside the chapel where San Fermin and the dignitaries had passed in, leaving a guard of soldiers, the giants, with the men who danced in them standing beside their resting frames, and the dwarfs moving with their whacking bladders through the crowd. We started inside and there was a smell of incense and people filing back into the church, but Brett was stopped just inside the door because she had no hat, so we went out again and along the street that ran back from the chapel into town. The street was lined on both sides with people keeping their place at the curb for the return of the procession. Some dancers formed a circle around Brett and started to dance. They wore big wreaths of white garlics around their necks. They took Bill and me by the arms and put us in the circle. Bill started to dance, too. They were all chanting. Brett wanted to dance but they did not want her to. They wanted her as an image to dance around. When the song ended with the sharp *riau-riau!* they rushed us into a wine-shop.

We stood at the counter. They had Brett seated on a wine-cask. It was dark in the wine-shop and full of men singing, hard-voiced singing. Back of the counter they drew the wine from casks. I put down money for the wine, but one of the men picked it up and put it back in my pocket.

"I want a leather wine-bottle," Bill said.

"There's a place down the street," I said. "I'll go get a couple."

The dancers did not want me to go out. Three of them were sitting on the high wine-cask beside Brett, teaching her to drink out of the wine-skins. They had hung a wreath of garlics around her neck. Some one insisted on giving her a glass. Somebody was teaching Bill a song. Singing it into his ear. Beating time on Bill's back.

I explained to them that I would be back. Outside in the street I went down the street looking for the shop that made leather wine-bottles. The crowd was packed on the sidewalks and many of the shops were shuttered, and I could not find it. I walked as far as the church, looking on both sides of the street. Then I asked a man and he took me by the arm and led me to it. The shutters were up but the door was open.

Inside it smelled of fresh tanned leather and hot tar. A man was stencilling completed wine-skins. They hung from the roof in bunches. He took one down, blew it up, screwed the nozzle tight, and then jumped on it.

"See! It doesn't leak."

"I want another one, too. A big one."

He took down a big one that would hold a gallon or more, from the roof. He blew it up, his cheeks puffing ahead of the wine-skin, and stood on the bota holding on to a chair.

"What are you going to do? Sell them in Bayonne?"

"No. Drink out of them."

He slapped me on the back.

"Good man. Eight pesetas for the two. The lowest price."

The man who was stencilling the new ones and tossing them into a pile stopped.

"It's true," he said. "Eight pesetas is cheap."

I paid and went out and along the street back to the wine-shop. It was darker than ever inside and very crowded. I did not see Brett and Bill, and some one said they were in the back room. At the counter the girl filled the two wine-skins for me. One held two litres. The other held five litres. Filling them both cost three pesetas sixty centimos. Some one at the counter, that I had never seen before, tried to pay for the wine, but I finally paid for it myself. The man who had wanted to pay then bought me a drink. He would not let me buy one in return, but said he would take a rinse of the mouth from the new wine-bag. He tipped the big five-litre bag up and squeezed it so the wine hissed against the back of his throat.

"All right," he said, and handed back the bag.

In the back room Brett and Bill were sitting on barrels surrounded by the dancers. Everybody had his arms on everybody else's shoulders, and they were all singing. Mike was sitting at a table with several men in their shirt-sleeves, eating from a bowl of tuna fish, chopped onions and vinegar. They were all drinking wine and mopping up the oil and vinegar with pieces of bread.

"Hello, Jake. Hello!" Mike called. "Come here. I want you to meet my friends. We're all having an hors-d'œuvre."

I was introduced to the people at the table. They supplied their names to Mike and sent for a fork for me.

"Stop eating their dinner, Michael," Brett shouted from the wine-barrels.

"I don't want to eat up your meal," I said when some one handed me a fork.

"Eat," he said. "What do you think it's here for?"

I unscrewed the nozzle of the big wine-bottle and handed it around. Every one took a drink, tipping the wine-skin at arm's length.

Outside, above the singing, we could hear the music of the procession going by.

"Isn't that the procession?" Mike asked.

"Nada," some one said. "It's nothing. Drink up. Lift the bottle."

"Where did they find you?" I asked Mike.

"Some one brought me here," Mike said. "They said you were here."

"Where's Cohn?"

"He's passed out," Brett called. "They've put him away somewhere."

"Where is he?"

"I don't know."

"How should we know," Bill said. "I think he's dead."

"He's not dead," Mike said. "I know he's not dead. He's just passed out on Anis del Mono."

As he said Anis del Mono one of the men at the table looked

up, brought out a bottle from inside his smock, and handed it to me.

"No," I said. "No, thanks!"

"Yes. Yes. Arriba! Up with the bottle!"

I took a drink. It tasted of licorice and warmed all the way. I could feel it warming in my stomach.

"Where the hell is Cohn?"

"I don't know," Mike said. "I'll ask. Where is the drunken comrade?" he asked in Spanish.

"You want to see him?"

"Yes," I said.

"Not me," said Mike. "This gent."

The Anis del Mono man wiped his mouth and stood up.

"Come on."

In a back room Robert Cohn was sleeping quietly on some wine-casks. It was almost too dark to see his face. They had covered him with a coat and another coat was folded under his head. Around his neck and on his chest was a big wreath of twisted garlics.

"Let him sleep," the man whispered. "He's all right."

Two hours later Cohn appeared. He came into the front room still with the wreath of garlics around his neck. The Spaniards shouted when he came in. Cohn wiped his eyes and grinned.

"I must have been sleeping," he said.

"Oh, not at all," Brett said.

"You were only dead," Bill said.

"Aren't we going to go and have some supper?" Cohn asked.

"Do you want to eat?"

"Yes. Why not? I'm hungry."

"Eat those garlics, Robert," Mike said. "I say. Do eat those garlics."

Cohn stood there. His sleep had made him quite all right.

"Do let's go and eat," Brett said. "I must get a bath."

"Come on," Bill said. "Let's translate Brett to the hotel."

We said good-bye to many people and shook hands with many people and went out. Outside it was dark.

"What time is it do you suppose?" Cohn asked.

"It's to-morrow," Mike said. "You've been asleep two days."

"No," said Cohn, "what time is it?"

"It's ten o'clock."

"What a lot we've drunk."

"You mean what a lot *we've* drunk. You went to sleep."

Going down the dark streets to the hotel we saw the sky-rockets going up in the square. Down the side streets that led to the square we saw the square solid with people, those in the centre all dancing.

It was a big meal at the hotel. It was the first meal of the prices being doubled for the fiesta, and there were several new courses. After the dinner we were out in the town. I remember resolving that I would stay up all night to watch the bulls go though the streets at six o'clock in the morning, and being so sleepy that I went to bed around four o'clock. The others stayed up.

My own room was locked and I could not find the key, so I went up-stairs and slept on one of the beds in Cohn's room. The fiesta was going on outside in the night, but I was too sleepy for it to keep me awake. When I woke it was the sound of the rocket exploding that announced the release of the bulls from the corrals at the edge of town. They would race through the streets and out to the bull-ring. I had been sleeping heavily and I woke feeling I was too late. I put on a coat of Cohn's and went out on the balcony. Down below the narrow street was empty. All the balconies were crowded with people. Suddenly a crowd came down the street. They were all running, packed close together. They passed along and up the street toward the bull-ring and behind them came more men running faster, and then some stragglers who were really running. Behind them was a little bare space, and then the bulls galloping, tossing their heads up and down. It all went out of sight around the corner. One man fell, rolled to the gutter, and lay quiet. But the bulls went right on and did not notice him. They were all running together.

After they went out of sight a great roar came from the bull-ring. It kept on. Then finally the pop of the rocket that meant the bulls had gotten through the people in the ring and into the corrals. I went back in the room and got into bed. I had been standing on the stone balcony in bare feet. I knew our crowd must have all been out at the bull-ring. Back in bed, I went to sleep.

Cohn woke me when he came in. He started to undress and went over and closed the window because the people on the balcony of the house just across the street were looking in.

"Did you see the show?" I asked.

"Yes. We were all there."

"Anybody get hurt?"

"One of the bulls got into the crowd in the ring and tossed six or eight people."

"How did Brett like it?"

"It was all so sudden there wasn't any time for it to bother anybody."

"I wish I'd been up."

"We didn't know where you were. We went to your room but it was locked."

"Where did you stay up?"

"We danced at some club."

"I got sleepy," I said.

"My gosh! I'm sleepy now," Cohn said. "Doesn't this thing ever stop?"

"Not for a week."

Bill opened the door and put his head in.

"Where were you, Jake?"

"I saw them go through from the balcony. How was it?"

"Grand."

"Where you going?"

"To sleep."

No one was up before noon. We ate at tables set out under the arcade. The town was full of people. We had to wait for a table. After lunch we went over to the Iruña. It had filled up, and as the time for the bull-fight came it got fuller, and the tables were crowded closer. There was a close, crowded hum that came every day before the bull-fight. The café did not make this same noise at any other time, no matter how crowded it was. This hum went on, and we were in it and a part of it.

I had taken six seats for all the fights. Three of them were barreras, the first row at the ring-side, and three were sobrepuertos, seats with wooden backs, half-way up the amphitheatre. Mike thought Brett had best sit high up for her first time, and Cohn wanted to sit with them. Bill and I were going to sit in the barreras, and I gave the extra ticket to a waiter to sell. Bill said something to Cohn about what to do and how to look so he would not mind the horses. Bill had seen one season of bull-fights.

"I'm not worried about how I'll stand it. I'm only afraid I may be bored," Cohn said.

"You think so?"

"Don't look at the horses, after the bull hits them," I said to Brett. "Watch the charge and see the picador try and keep the bull off, but then don't look again until the horse is dead if it's been hit."

"I'm a little nervy about it," Brett said. "I'm worried whether I'll be able to go through with it all right."

"You'll be all right. There's nothing but that horse part that will bother you, and they're only in for a few minutes with each bull. Just don't watch when it's bad."

"She'll be all right," Mike said. "I'll look after her."

"I don't think you'll be bored," Bill said.

"I'm going over to the hotel to get the glasses and the wine-skin," I said. "See you back here. Don't get cock-eyed."

"I'll come along," Bill said. Brett smiled at us.

We walked around through the arcade to avoid the heat of the square.

"That Cohn gets me," Bill said. "He's got this Jewish superiority so strong that he thinks the only emotion he'll get out of the fight will be being bored."

"We'll watch him with the glasses," I said.

"Oh, to hell with him!"

"He spends a lot of time there."

"I want him to stay there."

In the hotel on the stairs we met Montoya.

"Come on," said Montoya. "Do you want to meet Pedro Romero?"

"Fine," said Bill. "Let's go see him."

We followed Montoya up a flight and down the corridor.

"He's in room number eight," Montoya explained. "He's getting dressed for the bull-fight."

Montoya knocked on the door and opened it. It was a gloomy room with a little light coming in from the window on the narrow street. There were two beds separated by a monastic partition. The electric light was on. The boy stood very straight and unsmiling in his bull-fighting clothes. His jacket hung over the back of a chair. They were just finishing winding his sash. His black hair shone under the electric light. He wore a white linen shirt and the sword-handler finished his sash and stood up and stepped back. Pedro Romero nodded, seeming very far away and dignified when we shook hands.

Montoya said something about what great aficionados we were, and
that we wanted to wish him luck. Romero listened very seriously.
Then he turned to me. He was the best-looking boy I have ever seen.

"You go to the bull-fight," he said in English.

"You know English," I said, feeling like an idiot.

"No," he answered, and smiled.

One of three men who had been sitting on the beds came up and
asked us if we spoke French. "Would you like me to interpret for
you? Is there anything you would like to ask Pedro Romero?"

We thanked him. What was there that you would like to ask?
The boy was nineteen years old, alone except for his sword-handler,
and the three hangers-on, and the bull-fight was to commence in
twenty minutes. We wished him "Mucha suerte," shook hands, and
went out. He was standing, straight and handsome and altogether
by himself, alone in the room with the hangers-on as we shut the
door.

"He's a fine boy, don't you think so?" Montoya asked.

"He's a good-looking kid," I said.

"He looks like a torero," Montoya said. "He has the type."

"He's a fine boy."

"We'll see how he is in the ring," Montoya said.

We found the big leather wine-bottle leaning against the wall in
my room, took it and the field-glasses, locked the door, and went
down-stairs.

It was a good bull-fight. Bill and I were very excited about Pedro
Romero. Montoya was sitting about ten places away. After Romero
had killed his first bull Montoya caught my eye and nodded his head.
This was a real one. There had not been a real one for a long time.
Of the other two matadors, one was very fair and the other was
passable. But there was no comparison with Romero, although neither
of his bulls was much.

Several times during the bull-fight I looked up at Mike and
Brett and Cohn, with the glasses. They seemed to be all right. Brett
did not look upset. All three were leaning forward on the concrete
railing in front of them.

"Let me take the glasses," Bill said.

"Does Cohn look bored?" I asked.

"That kike!"

Outside the ring, after the bull-fight was over, you could not move in the crowd. We could not make our way through but had to be moved with the whole thing, slowly, as a glacier, back to town. We had that disturbed emotional feeling that always comes after a bull-fight, and the feeling of elation that comes after a good bull-fight. The fiesta was going on. The drums pounded and the pipe music was shrill, and everywhere the flow of the crowd was broken by patches of dancers. The dancers were in a crowd, so you did not see the intricate play of the feet. All you saw was the heads and shoulders going up and down, up and down. Finally, we got out of the crowd and made for the café. The waiter saved chairs for the others, and we each ordered an absinthe and watched the crowd in the square and the dancers.

"What do you suppose that dance is?" Bill asked.

"It's a sort of jota."

"They're not all the same," Bill said. "They dance differently to all the different tunes."

"It's swell dancing."

In front of us on a clear part of the street a company of boys were dancing. The steps were very intricate and their faces were intent and concentrated. They all looked down while they danced. Their rope-soled shoes tapped and spatted on the pavement. The toes touched. The heels touched. The balls of the feet touched. Then the music broke wildly and the step was finished and they were all dancing on up the street.

"Here come the gentry," Bill said.

They were crossing the street.

"Hello, men," I said.

"Hello, gents!" said Brett. "You saved us seats? How nice."

"I say," Mike said, "that Romero what'shisname is somebody. Am I wrong?"

"Oh, isn't he lovely," Brett said. "And those green trousers."

"Brett never took her eyes off them."

"I say, I must borrow your glasses to-morrow."

"How did it go?"

"Wonderfully! Simply perfect. I say, it is a spectacle!"

"How about the horses?"

"I couldn't help looking at them."

"She couldn't take her eyes off them," Mike said. "She's an extraordinary wench."

"They do have rather awful things happen to them," Brett said. "I couldn't look away, though."

"Did you feel all right?"

"I didn't feel badly at all."

"Robert Cohn did," Mike put in. "You were quite green, Robert."

"The first horse did bother me," Cohn said.

"You weren't bored, were you?" asked Bill.

Cohn laughed.

"No. I wasn't bored. I wish you'd forgive me that."

"It's all right," Bill said, "so long as you weren't bored."

"He didn't look bored," Mike said. "I thought he was going to be sick."

"I never felt that bad. It was just for a minute."

"*I* thought he was going to be sick. You weren't bored, were you, Robert?"

"Let up on that, Mike. I said I was sorry I said it."

"He was, you know. He was positively green."

"Oh, shove it along, Michael."

"You mustn't ever get bored at your first bull-fight, Robert," Mike said. "It might make such a mess."

"Oh, shove it along, Michael," Brett said.

"He said Brett was a sadist," Mike said. "Brett's not a sadist. She's just a lovely, healthy wench."

"Are you a sadist, Brett?" I asked.

"Hope not."

"He said Brett was a sadist just because she has a good, healthy stomach."

"Won't be healthy long."

Bill got Mike started on something else than Cohn. The waiter brought the absinthe glasses.

"Did you really like it?" Bill asked Cohn.

"No, I can't say I liked it. I think it's a wonderful show."

"Gad, yes! What a spectacle!" Brett said.

"I wish they didn't have the horse part," Cohn said.

"They're not important," Bill said. "After a while you never notice anything disgusting."

"It is a bit strong just at the start," Brett said. "There's a dreadful moment for me just when the bull starts for the horse."

"The bulls were fine," Cohn said.

"They were very good," Mike said.

"I want to sit down below, next time." Brett drank from her glass of absinthe.

"She wants to see the bull-fighters close by," Mike said.

"They are something," Brett said. "That Romero lad is just a child."

"He's a damned good-looking boy," I said. "When we were up in his room I never saw a better-looking kid."

"How old do you suppose he is?"

"Nineteen or twenty."

"Just imagine it."

The bull-fight on the second day was much better than on the first. Brett sat between Mike and me at the barrera, and Bill and Cohn went up above. Romero was the whole show. I do not think Brett saw any other bull-fighter. No one else did either, except the hard-shelled technicians. It was all Romero. There were two other matadors, but they did not count. I sat beside Brett and explained to Brett what it was all about. I told her about watching the bull, not the horse, when the bulls charged the picadors, and got her to watching the picador place the point of his pic so that she saw what it was all about, so that it became more something that was going on with a definite end, and less of a spectacle with unexplained horrors. I had her watch how Romero took the bull away from a fallen horse with his cape, and how he held him with the cape and turned him, smoothly and suavely, never wasting the bull. She saw how Romero avoided every brusque movement and saved his bulls for the last when he wanted them, not winded and discomposed but smoothly worn down. She saw how close Romero always worked to the bull, and I pointed out to her the tricks the other bull-fighters used to make it look as though they were working closely. She saw why she liked Romero's cape-work and why she did not like the others.

Romero never made any contortions, always it was straight and pure and natural in line. The others twisted themselves like corkscrews, their elbows raised, and leaned against the flanks of the bull after his horns had passed, to give a faked look of danger. Afterward, all that was faked turned bad and gave an unpleasant feeling. Romero's bull-fighting gave real emotion, because he kept the absolute purity of line in his movements and always quietly and calmly let the horns pass him close each time. He did not have to emphasize their closeness. Brett saw how something that was beautiful done close to the bull was ridiculous if it were done a little way off. I told her how since the death of Joselito all the bull-fighters had been developing a technic that simulated this appearance of danger in order to give a fake emotional feeling, while the bull-fighter was really safe. Romero had the old thing, the holding of his purity of line through the maximum of exposure, while he dominated the bull by making him realize he was unattainable, while he prepared him for the killing.

"I've never seen him do an awkward thing," Brett said.

"You won't until he gets frightened," I said.

"He'll never be frightened," Mike said. "He knows too damned much."

"He knew everything when he started. The others can't ever learn what he was born with."

"And God, what looks," Brett said.

"I believe, you know, that she's falling in love with this bull-fighter chap," Mike said.

"I wouldn't be surprised."

"Be a good chap, Jake. Don't tell her anything more about him. Tell her how they beat their old mothers."

"Tell me what drunks they are."

"Oh, frightful," Mike said. "Drunk all day and spend all their time beating their poor old mothers."

"He looks that way," Brett said.

"Doesn't he?" I said.

They had hitched the mules to the dead bull and then the whips cracked, the men ran, and the mules, straining forward, their legs pushing, broke into a gallop, and the bull, one horn up, his head on its side, swept a swath smoothly across the sand and out the red gate.

"This next is the last one."

"Not really," Brett said. She leaned forward on the barrera. Romero waved his picadors to their places, then stood, his cape against his chest, looking across the ring to where the bull would come out.

After it was over we went out and were pressed tight in the crowd.

"These bull-fights are hell on one," Brett said. "I'm limp as a rag."

"Oh, you'll get a drink," Mike said.

The next day Pedro Romero did not fight. It was Miura bulls, and a very bad bull-fight. The next day there was no bull-fight scheduled. But all day and all night the fiesta kept on.

16

IN the morning it was raining. A fog had come over the mountains from the sea. You could not see the tops of the mountains. The plateau was dull and gloomy, and the shapes of the trees and the houses were changed. I walked out beyond the town to look at the weather. The bad weather was coming over the mountains from the sea.

The flags in the square hung wet from the white poles and the banners were wet and hung damp against the front of the houses, and in between the steady drizzle the rain came down and drove every one under the arcades and made pools of water in the square, and the streets wet and dark and deserted; yet the fiesta kept up without any pause. It was only driven under cover.

The covered seats of the bull-ring had been crowded with people sitting out of the rain watching the concourse of Basque and Navarrais dancers and singers, and afterward the Val Carlos dancers in their costumes danced down the street in the rain, the drums sounding hollow and damp, and the chiefs of the bands riding ahead on their big, heavy-footed horses, their costumes wet, the horses' coats wet in the rain. The crowd was in the cafés and the dancers came in, too, and sat, their tight-wound white legs under the tables, shaking the water from their belled caps, and spreading their red and purple jackets over the chairs to dry. It was raining hard outside.

I left the crowd in the café and went over to the hotel to get shaved for dinner. I was shaving in my room when there was a knock on the door.

"Come in," I called.

Montoya walked in.

"How are you?" he said.

"Fine," I said.

"No bulls to-day."

"No," I said, "nothing but rain."

"Where are your friends?"

"Over at the Iruña."

Montoya smiled his embarrassed smile.

"Look," he said. "Do you know the American ambassador?"

"Yes," I said. "Everybody knows the American ambassador."

"He's here in town now."

"Yes," I said. "Everybody's seen them."

"I've seen them, too," Montoya said. He didn't say anything. I went on shaving.

"Sit down," I said. "Let me send for a drink."

"No, I have to go."

I finished shaving and put my face down into the bowl and washed it with cold water. Montoya was standing there looking more embarrassed.

"Look," he said. "I've just had a message from them at the Grand Hotel that they want Pedro Romero and Marcial Lalanda to come over for coffee to-night after dinner."

"Well," I said, "it can't hurt Marcial any."

"Marcial has been in San Sebastian all day. He drove over in a car this morning with Marquez. I don't think they'll be back to-night."

Montoya stood embarrassed. He wanted me to say something.

"Don't give Romero the message," I said.

"You think so?"

"Absolutely."

Montoya was very pleased.

"I wanted to ask you because you were an American," he said.

"That's what I'd do."

"Look," said Montoya. "People take a boy like that. They don't know what he's worth. They don't know what he means. Any foreigner can flatter him. They start this Grand Hotel business, and in one year they're through."

"Like Algabeno," I said.

"Yes, like Algabeno."

"They're a fine lot," I said. "There's one American woman down here now that collects bull-fighters."

"I know. They only want the young ones."

"Yes," I said. "The old ones get fat."

"Or crazy like Gallo."

"Well," I said, "it's easy. All you have to do is not give him the message."

"He's such a fine boy," said Montoya. "He ought to stay with his own people. He shouldn't mix in that stuff."

"Won't you have a drink?" I asked.

"No," said Montoya, "I have to go." He went out.

I went down-stairs and out the door and took a walk around through the arcades around the square. It was still raining. I looked in at the Iruña for the gang and they were not there, so I walked on around the square and back to the hotel. They were eating dinner in the down-stairs dining-room.

They were well ahead of me and it was no use trying to catch them. Bill was buying shoe-shines for Mike. Bootblacks opened the street door and each one Bill called over and started to work on Mike.

"This is the eleventh time my boots have been polished," Mike said. "I say, Bill is an ass."

The bootblacks had evidently spread the report. Another came in.

"Limpia botas?" he said to Bill.

"No," said Bill. "For this Señor."

The bootblack knelt down beside the one at work and started on Mike's free shoe that shone already in the electric light.

"Bill's a yell of laughter," Mike said.

I was drinking red wine, and so far behind them that I felt a little uncomfortable about all this shoe-shining. I looked around the room. At the next table was Pedro Romero. He stood up when I nodded, and asked me to come over and meet a friend. His table was beside ours, almost touching. I met the friend, a Madrid bull-fight critic, a little man with a drawn face. I told Romero how much I liked his work, and he was very pleased. We talked Spanish and the critic knew a little French. I reached to our table for my wine-bottle, but the critic took my arm. Romero laughed.

"Drink here," he said in English.

He was very bashful about his English, but he was really very pleased with it, and as we went on talking he brought out words he was not sure of, and asked me about them. He was anxious to know the English for *Corrida de toros*, the exact translation. Bull-fight he was suspicious of. I explained that bull-fight in Spanish was the *lidia* of a *toro*. The Spanish word *corrida* means in English the running of bulls—the French translation is *Course de taureaux*. The critic put that in. There is no Spanish word for bull-fight.

Pedro Romero said he had learned a little English in Gibraltar. He was born in Ronda. That is not far above Gibraltar. He started bull-fighting in Malaga in the bull-fighting school there. He had only been at it three years. The bull-fight critic joked him about the number of *Malagueño* expressions he used. He was nineteen years old, he said. His older brother was with him as a banderillero, but he did not live in this hotel. He lived in a smaller hotel with the other people who worked for Romero. He asked me how many times I had seen him in the ring. I told him only three. It was really only two, but I did not want to explain after I had made the mistake.

"Where did you see me the other time? In Madrid?"

"Yes," I lied. I had read the accounts of his two appearances in Madrid in the bull-fight papers, so I was all right.

"The first or the second time?"

"The first."

"I was very bad," he said. "The second time I was better. You remember?" He turned to the critic.

He was not at all embarrassed. He talked of his work as something altogether apart from himself. There was nothing conceited or braggartly about him.

"I like it very much that you like my work," he said. "But you haven't seen it yet. To-morrow, if I get a good bull, I will try and show it to you."

When he said this he smiled, anxious that neither the bull-fight critic nor I would think he was boasting.

"I am anxious to see it," the critic said. "I would like to be convinced."

"He doesn't like my work much." Romero turned to me. He was serious.

The critic explained that he liked it very much, but that so far it had been incomplete.

"Wait till to-morrow, if a good one comes out."

"Have you seen the bulls for to-morrow?" the critic asked me.

"Yes. I saw them unloaded."

Pedro Romero leaned forward.

"What did you think of them?"

"Very nice," I said. "About twenty-six arrobas. Very short horns. Haven't you seen them?"

"Oh, yes," said Romero.

"They won't weigh twenty-six arrobas," said the critic.

"No," said Romero.

"They've got bananas for horns," the critic said.

"You call them bananas?" asked Romero. He turned to me and smiled. "*You* wouldn't call them bananas?"

"No," I said. "They're horns all right."

"They're very short," said Pedro Romero. "Very, very short. Still, they aren't bananas."

"I say, Jake," Brett called from the next table, "you *have* deserted us."

"Just temporarily," I said. "We're talking bulls."

"You *are* superior."

"Tell him that bulls have no balls," Mike shouted. He was drunk.

Romero looked at me inquiringly.

"Drunk," I said. "Borracho! Muy borracho!"

"You might introduce your friends," Brett said. She had not stopped looking at Pedro Romero. I asked them if they would like to have coffee with us. They both stood up. Romero's face was very brown. He had very nice manners.

I introduced them all around and they started to sit down, but there was not enough room, so we all moved over to the big table by the wall to have coffee. Mike ordered a bottle of Fundador and glasses for everybody. There was a lot of drunken talking.

"Tell him I think writing is lousy," Bill said. "Go on, tell him. Tell him I'm ashamed of being a writer."

Pedro Romero was sitting beside Brett and listening to her.

"Go on. Tell him!" Bill said.

Romero looked up smiling.

"This gentleman," I said, "is a writer."

Romero was impressed. "This other one, too," I said, pointing at Cohn.

"He looks like Villalta," Romero said, looking at Bill. "Rafael, doesn't he look like Villalta?"

"I can't see it," the critic said.

"Really," Romero said in Spanish. "He looks a lot like Villalta. What does the drunken one do?"

"Nothing."

"Is that why he drinks?"

"No. He's waiting to marry this lady."

"Tell him bulls have no balls!" Mike shouted, very drunk, from the other end of the table.

"What does he say?"

"He's drunk."

"Jake," Mike called. "Tell him bulls have no balls!"

"You understand?" I said.

"Yes."

I was sure he didn't, so it was all right.

"Tell him Brett wants to see him put on those green pants."

"Pipe down, Mike."

"Tell him Brett is dying to know how he can get into those pants."

"Pipe down."

During this Romero was fingering his glass and talking with Brett. Brett was talking French and he was talking Spanish and a little English, and laughing.

Bill was filling the glasses.

"Tell him Brett wants to come into—"

"Oh, pipe down, Mike, for Christ's sake!"

Romero looked up smiling. "Pipe down! I know that," he said.

Just then Montoya came into the room. He started to smile at me, then he saw Pedro Romero with a big glass of cognac in his hand, sitting laughing between me and a woman with bare shoulders, at a table full of drunks. He did not even nod.

Montoya went out of the room. Mike was on his feet proposing a toast. "Let's all drink to—" he began. "Pedro Romero," I said. Everybody stood up. Romero took it very seriously, and we touched glasses and drank it down, I rushing it a little because Mike was trying to make it clear that that was not at all what he was going to drink to. But it went off all right, and Pedro Romero shook hands with every one and he and the critic went out together.

"My God! he's a lovely boy," Brett said. "And how I would love to see him get into those clothes. He must use a shoe-horn."

"I started to tell him," Mike began. "And Jake kept interrupting me. Why do you interrupt me? Do you think you talk Spanish better than I do?"

"Oh, shut up, Mike! Nobody interrupted you."

"No, I'd like to get this settled." He turned away from me. "Do you think you amount to something, Cohn? Do you think you belong here among us? People who are out to have a good time? For God's sake don't be so noisy, Cohn!"

"Oh, cut it out, Mike," Cohn said.

"Do you think Brett wants you here? Do you think you add to the party? Why don't you say something?"

"I said all I had to say the other night, Mike."

"I'm not one of you literary chaps." Mike stood shakily and leaned against the table. "I'm not clever. But I do know when I'm not wanted. Why don't you see when you're not wanted, Cohn? Go away. Go away, for God's sake. Take that sad Jewish face away. Don't you think I'm right?"

He looked at us.

"Sure," I said. "Let's all go over to the Iruña."

"No. Don't you think I'm right? I love that woman."

"Oh, don't start that again. Do shove it along, Michael," Brett said.

"Don't you think I'm right, Jake?"

Cohn still sat at the table. His face had the sallow, yellow look it got when he was insulted, but somehow he seemed to be enjoying it. The childish, drunken heroics of it. It was his affair with a lady of title.

"Jake," Mike said. He was almost crying. "You know I'm right. Listen, you!" He turned to Cohn: "Go away! Go away now!"

"But I won't go, Mike," said Cohn.

"Then I'll make you!" Mike started toward him around the table. Cohn stood up and took off his glasses. He stood waiting, his face sallow, his hands fairly low, proudly and firmly waiting for the assault, ready to do battle for his lady love.

I grabbed Mike. "Come on to the café," I said. "You can't hit him here in the hotel."

"Good!" said Mike. "Good idea!"

We started off. I looked back as Mike stumbled up the stairs and saw Cohn putting his glasses on again. Bill was sitting at the table pouring another glass of Fundador. Brett was sitting looking straight ahead at nothing.

Outside on the square it had stopped raining and the moon was trying to get through the clouds. There was a wind blowing. The military band was playing and the crowd was massed on the far side of the square where the fireworks specialist and his son were trying to send up fire balloons. A balloon would start up jerkily, on a great bias, and be torn by the wind or blown against the houses of the square. Some fell into the crowd. The magnesium flared and the fireworks exploded and chased about in the crowd. There was no one dancing in the square. The gravel was too wet.

Brett came out with Bill and joined us. We stood in the crowd and watched Don Manuel Orquito, the fireworks king, standing on a little platform, carefully starting the balloons with sticks, standing above the heads of the crowd to launch the balloons off into the wind. The wind brought them all down, and Don Manuel Orquito's face was sweaty in the light of his complicated fireworks that fell into the crowd and charged and chased, sputtering and cracking, between the legs of the people. The people shouted as each new luminous paper bubble careened, caught fire, and fell.

"They're razzing Don Manuel," Bill said.

"How do you know he's Don Manuel?" Brett said.

"His name's on the programme. Don Manuel Orquito, the pirotecnico of esta ciudad."

"Globos illuminados," Mike said. "A collection of globos illuminados. That's what the paper said."

The wind blew the band music away.

"I say, I wish one would go up," Brett said. "That Don Manuel chap is furious."

"He's probably worked for weeks fixing them to go off, spelling out 'Hail to San Fermin,' " Bill said.

"Globos illuminados," Mike said. "A bunch of bloody globos illuminados."

"Come on," said Brett. "We can't stand here."

"Her ladyship wants a drink," Mike said.

"How you know things," Brett said.

Inside, the café was crowded and very noisy. No one noticed us come in. We could not find a table. There was a great noise going on.

"Come on, let's get out of here," Bill said.

Outside the paseo was going in under the arcade. There were some English and Americans from Biarritz in sport clothes scattered at the tables. Some of the women stared at the people going by with lorgnons. We had acquired, at some time, a friend of Bill's from Biarritz. She was staying with another girl at the Grand Hotel. The other girl had a headache and had gone to bed.

"Here's the pub," Mike said. It was the Bar Milano, a small, tough bar where you could get food and where they danced in the back room. We all sat down at a table and ordered a bottle of Fundador. The bar was not full. There was nothing going on.

"This is a hell of a place," Bill said.

"It's too early."

"Let's take the bottle and come back later," Bill said. "I don't want to sit here on a night like this."

"Let's go and look at the English," Mike said. "I love to look at the English."

"They're awful," Bill said. "Where did they all come from?"

"They come from Biarritz," Mike said. "They come to see the last day of the quaint little Spanish fiesta."

"I'll festa them," Bill said.

"You're an extraordinarily beautiful girl." Mike turned to Bill's friend. "When did you come here?"

"Come off it, Michael."

"I say, she *is* a lovely girl. Where have I been? Where have I been looking all this while? You're a lovely thing. *Have* we met? Come along with me and Bill. We're going to festa the English."

"I'll festa them," Bill said. "What the hell are they doing at this fiesta?"

"Come on," Mike said. "Just us three. We're going to festa the bloody English. I hope you're not English? I'm Scotch. I hate the English. I'm going to festa them. Come on, Bill."

Through the window we saw them, all three arm in arm, going toward the café. Rockets were going up in the square.

"I'm going to sit here," Brett said.

"I'll stay with you," Cohn said.

"Oh, don't!" Brett said. "For God's sake, go off somewhere. Can't you see Jake and I want to talk?"

"I didn't," Cohn said. "I thought I'd sit here because I felt a little tight."

"What a hell of a reason for sitting with any one. If you're tight, go to bed. Go on to bed."

"Was I rude enough to him?" Brett asked. Cohn was gone. "My God! I'm so sick of him!"

"He doesn't add much to the gayety."

"He depresses me so."

"He's behaved very badly."

"Damned badly. He had a chance to behave so well."

"He's probably waiting just outside the door now."

"Yes. He would. You know I do know how he feels. He can't believe it didn't mean anything."

"I know."

"Nobody else would behave as badly. Oh, I'm so sick of the whole thing. And Michael. Michael's been lovely, too."

"It's been damned hard on Mike."

"Yes. But he didn't need to be a swine."

"Everybody behaves badly," I said. "Give them the proper chance."

"You wouldn't behave badly." Brett looked at me.

"I'd be as big an ass as Cohn," I said.

"Darling, don't let's talk a lot of rot."

"All right. Talk about anything you like."

"Don't be difficult. You're the only person I've got, and I feel rather awful to-night."

"You've got Mike."

"Yes, Mike. Hasn't he been pretty?"

"Well," I said, "it's been damned hard on Mike, having Cohn around and seeing him with you."

"Don't I know it, darling? Please don't make me feel any worse than I do."

Brett was nervous as I had never seen her before. She kept looking away from me and looking ahead at the wall.

"Want to go for a walk?"

"Yes. Come on."

I corked up the Fundador bottle and gave it to the bartender.

"Let's have one more drink of that," Brett said. "My nerves are rotten."

We each drank a glass of the smooth amontillado brandy.

"Come on," said Brett.

As we came out the door I saw Cohn walk out from under the arcade.

"He *was* there," Brett said.

"He can't be away from you."

"Poor devil!"

"I'm not sorry for him. I hate him, myself."

"I hate him, too," she shivered. "I hate his damned suffering."

We walked arm in arm down the side street away from the crowd and the lights of the square. The street was dark and wet, and we walked along it to the fortifications at the edge of town. We passed wine-shops with light coming out from their doors onto the black, wet street, and sudden bursts of music.

"Want to go in?"

"No."

We walked out across the wet grass and onto the stone wall of the fortifications. I spread a newspaper on the stone and Brett sat down. Across the plain it was dark, and we could see the mountains. The wind was high up and took the clouds across the moon. Below us were the dark pits of the fortifications. Behind were the trees and the shadow of the cathedral, and the town silhouetted against the moon.

"Don't feel bad," I said.

"I feel like hell," Brett said. "Don't let's talk."

We looked out at the plain. The long lines of trees were dark in the moonlight. There were the lights of a car on the road climbing the mountain. Up on the top of the mountain we saw the lights of the fort. Below to the left was the river. It was high from the rain, and black and smooth. Trees were dark along the banks. We sat and looked out. Brett stared straight ahead. Suddenly she shivered.

"It's cold."

"Want to walk back?"

"Through the park."

We climbed down. It was clouding over again. In the park it was dark under the trees.

"Do you still love me, Jake?"

"Yes," I said.

"Because I'm a goner," Brett said.

"How?"

"I'm a goner. I'm mad about the Romero boy. I'm in love with him, I think."

"I wouldn't be if I were you."

"I can't help it. I'm a goner. It's tearing me all up inside."

"Don't do it."

"I can't help it. I've never been able to help anything."

"You ought to stop it."

"How can I stop it? I can't stop things. Feel that?"

Her hand was trembling.

"I'm like that all through."

"You oughtn't to do it."

"I can't help it. I'm a goner now, anyway. Don't you see the difference?"

"No."

"I've got to do something. I've got to do something I really want to do. I've lost my self-respect."

"You don't have to do that."

"Oh, darling, don't be difficult. What do you think it's meant to have that damned Jew about, and Mike the way he's acted?"

"Sure."

"I can't just stay tight all the time."

"No."

"Oh, darling, please stay by me. Please stay by me and see me through this."

"Sure."

"I don't say it's right. It is right though for me. God knows, I've never felt such a bitch."

"What do you want me to do?"

"Come on," Brett said. "Let's go and find him."

Together we walked down the gravel path in the park in the dark, under the trees and then out from under the trees and past the gate into the street that led into town.

Pedro Romero was in the café. He was at a table with other bull-fighters and bull-fight critics. They were smoking cigars. When we came in they looked up. Romero smiled and bowed. We sat down at a table half-way down the room.

"Ask him to come over and have a drink."

"Not yet. He'll come over."

"I can't look at him."

"He's nice to look at," I said.

"I've always done just what I wanted."

"I know."

"I do feel such a bitch."

"Well," I said.

"My God!" said Brett, "the things a woman goes through."

"Yes?"

"Oh, I do feel such a bitch."

I looked across at the table. Pedro Romero smiled. He said something to the other people at his table, and stood up. He came over to our table. I stood up and we shook hands.

"Won't you have a drink?"

"You must have a drink with me," he said. He seated himself, asking Brett's permission without saying anything. He had very nice manners. But he kept on smoking his cigar. It went well with his face.

"You like cigars?" I asked.

"Oh, yes. I always smoke cigars."

It was part of his system of authority. It made him seem older. I noticed his skin. It was clear and smooth and very brown. There was a triangular scar on his cheek-bone. I saw he was watching Brett. He felt there was something between them. He must have felt it when Brett gave him her hand. He was being very careful. I think he was sure, but he did not want to make any mistake.

"You fight to-morrow?" I said.

"Yes," he said. "Algabeno was hurt to-day in Madrid. Did you hear?"

"No," I said. "Badly?"

He shook his head.

"Nothing. Here," he showed his hand. Brett reached out and spread the fingers apart.

"Oh!" he said in English, "you tell fortunes?"

"Sometimes. Do you mind?"

"No. I like it." He spread his hand flat on the table. "Tell me I live for always, and be a millionaire."

He was still very polite, but he was surer of himself. "Look," he said, "do you see any bulls in my hand?"

He laughed. His hand was very fine and the wrist was small.

"There are thousands of bulls," Brett said. She was not at all nervous now. She looked lovely.

"Good," Romero laughed. "At a thousand duros apiece," he said to me in Spanish. "Tell me some more."

"It's a good hand," Brett said. "I think he'll live a long time."

"Say it to me. Not to your friend."

"I said you'd live a long time."

"I know it," Romero said. "I'm never going to die."

I tapped with my finger-tips on the table. Romero saw it. He shook his head.

"No. Don't do that. The bulls are my best friends."

I translated to Brett.

"You kill your friends?" she asked.

"Always," he said in English, and laughed. "So they don't kill me." He looked at her across the table.

"You know English well."

"Yes," he said. "Pretty well, sometimes. But I must not let anybody know. It would be very bad, a torero who speaks English."

"Why?" asked Brett.

"It would be bad. The people would not like it. Not yet."

"Why not?"

"They would not like it. Bull-fighters are not like that."

"What are bull-fighters like?"

He laughed and tipped his hat down over his eyes and changed the angle of his cigar and the expression of his face.

"Like at the table," he said. I glanced over. He had mimicked exactly the expression of Nacional. He smiled, his face natural again. "No. I must forget English."

"Don't forget it, yet," Brett said.

"No?"

"No."

"All right."

He laughed again.

"I would like a hat like that," Brett said.

"Good. I'll get you one."

"Right. See that you do."

"I will. I'll get you one to-night."

I stood up. Romero rose, too.

"Sit down," I said. "I must go and find our friends and bring them here."

He looked at me. It was a final look to ask if it were understood. It was understood all right.

"Sit down," Brett said to him. "You must teach me Spanish."

He sat down and looked at her across the table. I went out. The hard-eyed people at the bull-fighter table watched me go. It was not pleasant. When I came back and looked in the café, twenty minutes later, Brett and Pedro Romero were gone. The coffee-glasses and our three empty cognac-glasses were on the table. A waiter came with a cloth and picked up the glasses and mopped off the table.

17

OUTSIDE the Bar Milano I found Bill and Mike and Edna. Edna was the girl's name.

"We've been thrown out," Edna said.

"By the police," said Mike. "There's some people in there that don't like me."

"I've kept them out of four fights," Edna said. "You've got to help me."

Bill's face was red.

"Come back in, Edna," he said. "Go on in there and dance with Mike."

"It's silly," Edna said. "There'll just be another row."

"Damned Biarritz swine," Bill said.

"Come on," Mike said. "After all, it's a pub. They can't occupy a whole pub."

"Good old Mike," Bill said. "Damned English swine come here and insult Mike and try and spoil the fiesta."

"They're so bloody," Mike said. "I hate the English."

"They can't insult Mike," Bill said. "Mike is a swell fellow. They can't insult Mike. I won't stand it. Who cares if he is a damn bankrupt?" His voice broke.

"Who cares?" Mike said. "I don't care. Jake doesn't care. Do *you* care?"

"No," Edna said. "Are you a bankrupt?"

"Of course I am. You don't care, do you, Bill?"

Bill put his arm around Mike's shoulder.

"I wish to hell I was a bankrupt. I'd show those bastards."

"They're just English," Mike said. "It never makes any difference what the English say."

"The dirty swine," Bill said. "I'm going to clean them out."

"Bill," Edna looked at me. "Please don't go in again, Bill. They're so stupid."

"That's it," said Mike. "They're stupid. I knew that was what it was."

"They can't say things like that about Mike," Bill said.

"Do you know them?" I asked Mike.

"No. I never saw them. They say they know me."

"I won't stand it," Bill said.

"Come on. Let's go over to the Suizo," I said.

"They're a bunch of Edna's friends from Biarritz," Bill said.

"They're simply stupid," Edna said.

"One of them's Charley Blackman, from Chicago," Bill said.

"I was never in Chicago," Mike said.

Edna started to laugh and could not stop.

"Take me away from here," she said, "you bankrupts."

"What kind of a row was it?" I asked Edna. We were walking across the square to the Suizo. Bill was gone.

"I don't know what happened, but some one had the police called to keep Mike out of the back room. There were some people that had known Mike at Cannes. What's the matter with Mike?"

"Probably he owes them money," I said. "That's what people usually get bitter about."

In front of the ticket-booths out in the square there were two lines of people waiting. They were sitting on chairs or crouched on the ground with blankets and newspapers around them. They were waiting for the wickets to open in the morning to buy tickets for the bull-fight. The night was clearing and the moon was out. Some of the people in the line were sleeping.

At the Café Suizo we had just sat down and ordered Fundador when Robert Cohn came up.

"Where's Brett?" he asked.

"I don't know."

"She was with you."

"She must have gone to bed."

"She's not."

"I don't know where she is."

His face was sallow under the light. He was standing up.

"Tell me where she is."

"Sit down," I said. "I don't know where she is."

"The hell you don't!"

"You can shut your face."

"Tell me where Brett is."

"I'll not tell you a damn thing."

"You know where she is."

"If I did I wouldn't tell you."

"Oh, go to hell, Cohn," Mike called from the table. "Brett's gone off with the bull-fighter chap. They're on their honeymoon."

"You shut up."

"Oh, go to hell!" Mike said languidly.

"Is that where she is?" Cohn turned to me.

"Go to hell!"

"She was with you. Is that where she is?"

"Go to hell!"

"I'll make you tell me"—he stepped forward—"you damned pimp."

I swung at him and he ducked. I saw his face duck sideways in the light. He hit me and I sat down on the pavement. As I started to get on my feet he hit me twice. I went down backward under a table. I tried to get up and felt I did not have any legs. I felt I must get on my feet and try and hit him. Mike helped me up. Some one poured a carafe of water on my head. Mike had an arm around me, and I found I was sitting on a chair. Mike was pulling at my ears.

"I say, you were cold," Mike said.

"Where the hell were you?"

"Oh, I was around."

"You didn't want to mix in it?"

"He knocked Mike down, too," Edna said.

"He didn't knock me out," Mike said. "I just lay there."

"Does this happen every night at your fiestas?" Edna asked. "Wasn't that Mr. Cohn?"

"I'm all right," I said. "My head's a little wobbly."

There were several waiters and a crowd of people standing around.

"Vaya!" said Mike. "Get away. Go on."

The waiters moved the people away.

"It was quite a thing to watch," Edna said. "He must be a boxer."

"He is."

"I wish Bill had been here," Edna said. "I'd like to have seen Bill knocked down, too. I've always wanted to see Bill knocked down. He's so big."

"I was hoping he would knock down a waiter," Mike said, "and get arrested. I'd like to see Mr. Robert Cohn in jail."

"No," I said.

"Oh, no," said Edna. "You don't mean that."

"I do, though," Mike said. "I'm not one of these chaps likes being knocked about. I never play games, even."

Mike took a drink.

"I never liked to hunt, you know. There was always the danger of having a horse fall on you. How do you feel, Jake?"

"All right."

"You're nice," Edna said to Mike. "Are you really a bankrupt?"

"I'm a tremendous bankrupt," Mike said. "I owe money to everybody. Don't you owe any money?"

"Tons."

"I owe everybody money," Mike said. "I borrowed a hundred pesetas from Montoya to-night."

"The hell you did," I said.

"I'll pay it back," Mike said. "I always pay everything back."

"That's why you're a bankrupt, isn't it?" Edna said.

I stood up. I had heard them talking from a long way away. It all seemed like some bad play.

"I'm going over to the hotel," I said. Then I heard them talking about me.

"Is he all right?" Edna asked.

"We'd better walk with him."

"I'm all right," I said. "Don't come. I'll see you all later."

I walked away from the café. They were sitting at the table. I looked back at them and at the empty tables. There was a waiter sitting at one of the tables with his head in his hands.

Walking across the square to the hotel everything looked new and changed. I had never seen the trees before. I had never seen the flagpoles before, nor the front of the theatre. It was all different. I felt as I felt once coming home from an out-of-town football game. I was carrying a suitcase with my football things in it, and I walked up the street from the station in the town I had lived in all my life and it was all new. They were raking the lawns and burning leaves in the road, and I stopped for a long time and watched. It was all strange. Then I went on, and my feet seemed to be a long way off, and everything seemed to come from a long way off, and I could hear my feet walking a great distance away. I had been kicked in the head early in the game. It was like that crossing the square. It was like that going up the stairs in the hotel. Going up the stairs took a long time, and I had the feeling that I was carrying my suitcase. There was a light in the room. Bill came out and met me in the hall.

"Say," he said, "go up and see Cohn. He's been in a jam, and he's asking for you."

"The hell with him."

"Go on. Go on up and see him."

I did not want to climb another flight of stairs.

"What are you looking at me that way for?"

"I'm not looking at you. Go on up and see Cohn. He's in bad shape."

"You were drunk a little while ago," I said.

"I'm drunk now," Bill said. "But you go up and see Cohn. He wants to see you."

"All right," I said. It was just a matter of climbing more stairs. I went on up the stairs carrying my phantom suitcase. I walked down the hall to Cohn's room. The room was shut and I knocked.

"Who is it?"

"Barnes."

"Come in, Jake."

I opened the door and went in, and set down my suitcase. There was no light in the room. Cohn was lying, face down, on the bed in the dark.

"Hello, Jake."

"Don't call me Jake."

I stood by the door. It was just like this that I had come home. Now it was a hot bath that I needed. A deep, hot bath, to lie back in.

"Where's the bathroom?" I asked.

Cohn was crying. There he was, face down on the bed, crying. He had on a white polo shirt, the kind he'd worn at Princeton.

"I'm sorry, Jake. Please forgive me."

"Forgive you, hell."

"Please forgive me, Jake."

I did not say anything. I stood there by the door.

"I was crazy. You must see how it was."

"Oh, that's all right."

"I couldn't stand it about Brett."

"You called me a pimp."

I did not care. I wanted a hot bath. I wanted a hot bath in deep water.

"I know. Please don't remember it. I was crazy."

"That's all right."

He was crying. His voice was funny. He lay there in his white shirt on the bed in the dark. His polo shirt.

"I'm going away in the morning."

He was crying without making any noise.

"I just couldn't stand it about Brett. I've been through hell, Jake. It's been simply hell. When I met her down here Brett treated me as though I were a perfect stranger. I just couldn't stand it. We lived together at San Sebastian. I suppose you know it. I can't stand it any more."

He lay there on the bed.

"Well," I said, "I'm going to take a bath."

"You were the only friend I had, and I loved Brett so."

"Well," I said, "so long."

"I guess it isn't any use," he said. "I guess it isn't any damn use."

"What?"

"Everything. Please say you forgive me, Jake."

"Sure," I said. "It's all right."

"I felt so terribly. I've been through such hell, Jake. Now everything's gone. Everything."

"Well," I said, "so long. I've got to go."

He rolled over, sat on the edge of the bed, and then stood up.

"So long, Jake," he said. "You'll shake hands, won't you?"

"Sure. Why not?"

We shook hands. In the dark I could not see his face very well.

"Well," I said, "see you in the morning."

"I'm going away in the morning."

"Oh, yes," I said.

I went out. Cohn was standing in the door of the room.

"Are you all right, Jake?" he asked.

"Oh, yes," I said. "I'm all right."

I could not find the bathroom. After a while I found it. There was a deep stone tub. I turned on the taps and the water would not run. I sat down on the edge of the bath-tub. When I got up to go I found I had taken off my shoes. I hunted for them and found them and carried them down-stairs. I found my room and went inside and undressed and got into bed.

I woke with a headache and the noise of the bands going by in the street. I remembered I had promised to take Bill's friend Edna to see the bulls go through the street and into the ring. I dressed and went down-stairs and out into the cold early morning. People were crossing the square, hurrying toward the bull-ring. Across the square were the two lines of men in front of the ticket-booths. They were still waiting for the tickets to go on sale at seven o'clock. I hurried across the street to the café. The waiter told me that my friends had been there and gone.

"How many were they?"

"Two gentlemen and a lady."

That was all right. Bill and Mike were with Edna. She had been afraid last night they would pass out. That was why I was to be sure to take her. I drank the coffee and hurried with the other people toward the bull-ring. I was not groggy now. There was only a bad headache. Everything looked sharp and clear, and the town smelt of the early morning.

The stretch of ground from the edge of the town to the bull-ring was muddy. There was a crowd all along the fence that led to the ring, and the outside balconies and the top of the bull-ring were solid with people. I heard the rocket and I knew I could not get into the ring in time to see the bulls come in, so I shoved through the crowd to the fence. I was pushed close against the planks of the fence. Between the two fences of the runway the police were clearing the crowd along. They walked or trotted on into the bull-ring. Then people commenced to come running. A drunk slipped and fell. Two policemen grabbed him and rushed him over to the fence. The crowd were running fast now. There was a great shout from the crowd, and putting my head through between the boards I saw the bulls just coming out of the street into the long running pen. They were going fast and gaining on the crowd. Just then another drunk started out from the fence with a blouse in his hands. He wanted to do capework with the bulls. The two policemen tore out, collared him, one hit him with a club, and they dragged him against the fence and stood flattened out against the fence as the last of the crowd and the bulls went by. There were so many people running ahead of the bulls that the mass thickened and slowed up going through the gate into the ring, and as the bulls passed, galloping together, heavy, muddy-sided, horns swinging, one shot ahead, caught a man in the running crowd in the back and lifted him in the air. Both the man's arms were by his sides, his head went back as the horn went in, and the bull lifted him and then dropped him. The bull picked another man running in front, but the man disappeared into the crowd, and the crowd was through the gate and into the ring with the bulls behind them. The red door of the ring went shut, the crowd on the outside balconies of the bull-ring were pressing through to the inside, there was a shout, then another shout.

The man who had been gored lay face down in the trampled mud. People climbed over the fence, and I could not see the man because the crowd was so thick around him. From inside the ring came the shouts. Each shout meant a charge by some bull into the crowd. You could tell by the degree of intensity in the shout how bad a thing it was that was happening. Then the rocket went up that meant the steers had gotten the bulls out of the ring and into the corrals. I left the fence and started back toward the town.

Back in the town I went to the café to have a second coffee and some buttered toast. The waiters were sweeping out the café and mopping off the tables. One came over and took my order.

"Anything happen at the encierro?"

"I didn't see it all. One man was badly cogido."

"Where?"

"Here." I put one hand on the small of my back and the other on my chest, where it looked as though the horn must have come through. The waiter nodded his head and swept the crumbs from the table with his cloth.

"Badly cogido," he said. "All for sport. All for pleasure."

He went away and came back with the long-handled coffee and milk pots. He poured the milk and coffee. It came out of the long spouts in two streams into the big cup. The waiter nodded his head.

"Badly cogido through the back," he said. He put the pots down on the table and sat down in the chair at the table. "A big horn wound. All for fun. Just for fun. What do you think of that?"

"I don't know."

"That's it. All for fun. Fun, you understand."

"You're not an aficionado?"

"Me? What are bulls? Animals. Brute animals." He stood up and put his hand on the small of his back. "Right through the back. A cornada right through the back. For fun—you understand."

He shook his head and walked away, carrying the coffee-pots. Two men were going by in the street. The waiter shouted to them. They were grave-looking. One shook his head. "Muerto!" he called.

The waiter nodded his head. The two men went on. They were on some errand. The waiter came over to my table.

"You hear? Muerto. Dead. He's dead. With a horn through him. All for morning fun. Es muy flamenco."

"It's bad."

"Not for me," the waiter said. "No fun in that for me."

Later in the day we learned that the man who was killed was named Vicente Girones, and came from near Tafalla. The next day in the paper we read that he was twenty-eight years old, and had a farm, a wife, and two children. He had continued to come to the fiesta each year after he was married. The next day his wife came in from Tafalla to be with the body, and the day after there was a service in the chapel of San Fermin, and the coffin was carried to the railway-station by members of the dancing and drinking society of Tafalla. The drums marched ahead, and there was music on the fifes, and behind the men who carried the coffin walked the wife and two children. . . . Behind them marched all the members of the dancing and drinking societies of Pamplona, Estella, Tafalla, and Sanguesa who could stay over for the funeral. The coffin was loaded into the baggage-car of the train, and the widow and the two children rode, sitting, all three together, in an open third-class railway-carriage. The train started with a jerk, and then ran smoothly, going down grade around the edge of the plateau and out into the fields of grain that blew in the wind on the plain on the way to Tafalla.

The bull who killed Vicente Girones was named Bocanegra, was Number 118 of the bull-breeding establishment of Sanchez Taberno, and was killed by Pedro Romero as the third bull of that same afternoon. His ear was cut by popular acclamation and given to Pedro Romero, who, in turn, gave it to Brett, who wrapped it in a handkerchief belonging to myself, and left both ear and handkerchief, along with a number of Muratti cigarette-stubs, shoved far back in the drawer of the bed-table that stood beside her bed in the Hotel Montoya, in Pamplona.

Back in the hotel, the night watchman was sitting on a bench inside the door. He had been there all night and was very sleepy. He stood up as I came in. Three of the waitresses came in at the same time. They had been to the morning show at the bull-ring. They went up-stairs laughing. I followed them up-stairs and went into my room. I took off my shoes and lay down on the bed. The window was open onto the balcony and the sunlight was bright in the room. I did not feel sleepy. It must have been half past three o'clock when I had gone to bed and the bands had waked me at six. My jaw was sore on both sides. I felt it with my thumb and fingers. That damn Cohn. He should have hit somebody the first time he was insulted, and then gone away. He was so sure that Brett loved him. He was going to stay, and true love would conquer all. Some one knocked on the door.

"Come in."

It was Bill and Mike. They sat down on the bed.

"Some encierro," Bill said. "Some encierro."

"I say, weren't you there?" Mike asked. "Ring for some beer, Bill."

"What a morning!" Bill said. He mopped off his face. "My God! what a morning! And here's old Jake. Old Jake, the human punching-bag."

"What happened inside?"

"Good God!" Bill said, "what happened, Mike?"

"There were these bulls coming in," Mike said. "Just ahead of them was the crowd, and some chap tripped and brought the whole lot of them down."

"And the bulls all came in right over them," Bill said.

"I heard them yell."

"That was Edna," Bill said.

"Chaps kept coming out and waving their shirts."

"One bull went along the barrera and hooked everybody over."

"They took about twenty chaps to the infirmary," Mike said.

"What a morning!" Bill said. "The damn police kept arresting chaps that wanted to go and commit suicide with the bulls."

"The steers took them in, in the end," Mike said.

"It took about an hour."

"It was really about a quarter of an hour," Mike objected.

"Oh, go to hell," Bill said. "You've been in the war. It was two hours and a half for me."

"Where's that beer?" Mike asked.

"What did you do with the lovely Edna?"

"We took her home just now. She's gone to bed."

"How did she like it?"

"Fine. We told her it was just like that every morning."

"She was impressed," Mike said.

"She wanted us to go down in the ring, too," Bill said. "She likes action."

"I said it wouldn't be fair to my creditors," Mike said.

"What a morning," Bill said. "And what a night!"

"How's your jaw, Jake?" Mike asked.

"Sore," I said.

Bill laughed.

"Why didn't you hit him with a chair?"

"You can talk," Mike said. "He'd have knocked you out, too. I never saw him hit me. I rather think I saw him just before, and then quite suddenly I was sitting down in the street, and Jake was lying under a table."

"Where did he go afterward?" I asked.

"Here she is," Mike said. "Here's the beautiful lady with the beer."

The chambermaid put the tray with the beer-bottles and glasses down on the table.

"Now bring up three more bottles," Mike said.

"Where did Cohn go after he hit me?" I asked Bill.

"Don't you know about that?" Mike was opening a beer-bottle. He poured the beer into one of the glasses, holding the glass close to the bottle.

"Really?" Bill asked.

"Why he went in and found Brett and the bull-fighter chap in the bull-fighter's room, and then he massacred the poor, bloody bull-fighter."

"No."

"Yes."

"What a night!" Bill said.

"He nearly killed the poor, bloody bull-fighter. Then Cohn wanted to take Brett away. Wanted to make an honest woman of her, I imagine. Damned touching scene."

He took a long drink of the beer.

"He is an ass."

"What happened?"

"Brett gave him what for. She told him off. I think she was rather good."

"I'll bet she was," Bill said.

"Then Cohn broke down and cried, and wanted to shake hands with the bull-fighter fellow. He wanted to shake hands with Brett, too."

"I know. He shook hands with me."

"Did he? Well, they weren't having any of it. The bull-fighter fellow was rather good. He didn't say much, but he kept getting up and getting knocked down again. Cohn couldn't knock him out. It must have been damned funny."

"Where did you hear all this?"

"Brett. I saw her this morning."

"What happened finally?"

"It seems the bull-fighter fellow was sitting on the bed. He'd been knocked down about fifteen times, and he wanted to fight some more. Brett held him and wouldn't let him get up. He was weak, but Brett couldn't hold him, and he got up. Then Cohn said he wouldn't hit him again. Said he couldn't do it. Said it would be wicked. So the bull-fighter chap sort of rather staggered over to him. Cohn went back against the wall.

" 'So you won't hit me?'

" 'No,' said Cohn. 'I'd be ashamed to.'

"So the bull-fighter fellow hit him just as hard as he could in the face, and then sat down on the floor. He couldn't get up, Brett said. Cohn wanted to pick him up and carry him to the bed. He said if Cohn helped him he'd kill him, and he'd kill him anyway this morning if Cohn wasn't out of town. Cohn was crying, and Brett had told him off, and he wanted to shake hands. I've told you that before."

"Tell the rest," Bill said.

"It seems the bull-fighter chap was sitting on the floor. He was waiting to get strength enough to get up and hit Cohn again. Brett wasn't having any shaking hands, and Cohn was crying and telling her how much he loved her, and she was telling him not to be a ruddy ass. Then Cohn leaned down to shake hands with the bull-fighter fellow. No hard feelings, you know. All for forgiveness. And the bull-fighter chap hit him in the face again."

"That's quite a kid," Bill said.

"He ruined Cohn," Mike said. "You know I don't think Cohn will ever want to knock people about again."

"When did you see Brett?"

"This morning. She came in to get some things. She's looking after this Romero lad."

He poured out another bottle of beer.

"Brett's rather cut up. But she loves looking after people. That's how we came to go off together. She was looking after me."

"I know," I said.

"I'm rather drunk," Mike said. "I think I'll *stay* rather drunk. This is all awfully amusing, but it's not too pleasant. It's not too pleasant for me."

He drank off the beer.

"I gave Brett what for, you know. I said if she would go about with Jews and bull-fighters and such people, she must expect trouble." He leaned forward. "I say, Jake, do you mind if I drink that bottle of yours? She'll bring you another one."

"Please," I said. "I wasn't drinking it, anyway."

Mike started to open the bottle. "Would you mind opening it?" I pressed up the wire fastener and poured it for him.

"You know," Mike went on, "Brett was rather good. She's always rather good. I gave her a fearful hiding about Jews and bull-fighters, and all those sort of people, and do you know what she said: 'Yes. I've had such a hell of a happy life with the British aristocracy!' "

He took a drink.

"That was rather good. Ashley, chap she got the title from, was a sailor, you know. Ninth baronet. When he came home he wouldn't sleep in a bed. Always made Brett sleep on the floor. Finally, when he got really bad, he used to tell her he'd kill her. Always slept with a loaded service revolver. Brett used to take the shells out when he'd gone to sleep. She hasn't had an absolutely happy life, Brett. Damned shame, too. She enjoys things so."

He stood up. His hand was shaky.

"I'm going in the room. Try and get a little sleep."

He smiled.

"We go too long without sleep in these fiestas. I'm going to start now and get plently of sleep. Damn bad thing not to get sleep. Makes you frightfully nervy."

"We'll see you at noon at the Iruña," Bill said.

Mike went out the door. We heard him in the next room.

He rang the bell and the chambermaid came and knocked at the door.

"Bring up half a dozen bottles of beer and a bottle of Fundador," Mike told her.

"Si, Señorito."

"I'm going to bed," Bill said. "Poor old Mike. I had a hell of a row about him last night."

"Where? At that Milano place?"

"Yes. There was a fellow there that had helped pay Brett and Mike out of Cannes, once. He was damned nasty."

"I know the story."

"I didn't. Nobody ought to have a right to say things about Mike."

"That's what makes it bad."

"They oughtn't to have any right. I wish to hell they didn't have any right. I'm going to bed."

"Was anybody killed in the ring?"

"I don't think so. Just badly hurt."

"A man was killed outside in the runway."

"Was there?" said Bill.

18

AT noon we were all at the café. It was crowded. We were eating shrimps and drinking beer. The town was crowded. Every street was full. Big motor-cars from Biarritz and San Sebastian kept driving up and parking around the square. They brought people for the bull-fight. Sight-seeing cars came up, too. There was one with twenty-five Englishwomen in it. They sat in the big, white car and looked through their glasses at the fiesta. The dancers were all quite drunk. It was the last day of the fiesta.

The fiesta was solid and unbroken, but the motor-cars and tourist-cars made little islands of onlookers. When the cars emptied, the onlookers were absorbed into the crowd. You did not see them again except as sport clothes, odd-looking at a table among the closely packed peasants in black smocks. The fiesta absorbed even the Biar-ritz English so that you did not see them unless you passed close to a table. All the time there was music in the street. The drums kept on pounding and the pipes were going. Inside the cafés men with their hands gripping the table, or on each other's shoulders, were singing the hard-voiced singing.

"Here comes Brett," Bill said.

I looked and saw her coming through the crowd in the square, walking, her head up, as though the fiesta were being staged in her honor, and she found it pleasant and amusing.

"Hello, you chaps!" she said. "I say, I *have* a thirst."

"Get another big beer," Bill said to the waiter.

"Shrimps?"

"Is Cohn gone?" Brett asked.

"Yes," Bill said. "He hired a car."

The beer came. Brett started to lift the glass mug and her hand shook. She saw it and smiled, and leaned forward and took a long sip.

"Good beer."

"Very good," I said. I was nervous about Mike. I did not think he had slept. He must have been drinking all the time, but he seemed to be under control.

"I heard Cohn had hurt you, Jake," Brett said.

"No. Knocked me out. That was all."

"I say, he did hurt Pedro Romero," Brett said. "He hurt him most badly."

"How is he?"

"He'll be all right. He won't go out of the room."

"Does he look badly?"

"Very. He was really hurt. I told him I wanted to pop out and see you chaps for a minute."

"Is he going to fight?"

"Rather. I'm going with you, if you don't mind."

"How's your boy friend?" Mike asked. He had not listened to anything that Brett had said.

"Brett's got a bull-fighter," he said. "She had a Jew named Cohn, but he turned out badly."

Brett stood up.

"I am not going to listen to that sort of rot from you, Michael."

"How's your boy friend?"

"Damned well," Brett said. "Watch him this afternoon."

"Brett's got a bull-fighter," Mike said. "A beautiful, bloody bull-fighter."

"Would you mind walking over with me? I want to talk to you, Jake."

"Tell him all about your bull-fighter," Mike said. "Oh, to hell with your bull-fighter!" He tipped the table so that all the beers and the dish of shrimps went over in a crash.

"Come on," Brett said. "Let's get out of this."

In the crowd crossing the square I said: "How is it?"

"I'm not going to see him after lunch until the fight. His people come in and dress him. They're very angry about me, he says."

Brett was radiant. She was happy. The sun was out and the day was bright.

"I feel altogether changed," Brett said. "You've no idea, Jake."

"Anything you want me to do?"

"No, just go to the fight with me."

"We'll see you at lunch?"

"No. I'm eating with him."

We were standing under the arcade at the door of the hotel. They were carrying tables out and setting them up under the arcade.

"Want to take a turn out to the park?" Brett asked. "I don't want to go up yet. I fancy he's sleeping."

We walked along past the theatre and out of the square and along through the barracks of the fair, moving with the crowd between the lines of booths. We came out on a cross-street that led to the Paseo de Sarasate. We could see the crowd walking there, all the fashionably dressed people. They were making the turn at the upper end of the park.

"Don't let's go there," Brett said. "I don't want staring at just now."

We stood in the sunlight. It was hot and good after the rain and the clouds from the sea.

"I hope the wind goes down," Brett said. "It's very bad for him."

"So do I."

"He says the bulls are all right."

"They're good."

"Is that San Fermin's?"

Brett looked at the yellow wall of the chapel.

"Yes. Where the show started on Sunday."

"Let's go in. Do you mind? I'd rather like to pray a little for him or something."

We went in through the heavy leather door that moved very lightly. It was dark inside. Many people were praying. You saw them as your eyes adjusted themselves to the half-light. We knelt at one of the long wooden benches. After a little I felt Brett stiffen beside me, and saw she was looking straight ahead.

"Come on," she whispered throatily. "Let's get out of here. Makes me damned nervous."

Outside in the hot brightness of the street Brett looked up at the tree-tops in the wind. The praying had not been much of a success.

"Don't know why I get so nervy in church," Brett said. "Never does me any good."

We walked along.

"I'm damned bad for a religious atmosphere," Brett said. "I've the wrong type of face."

"You know," Brett said, "I'm not worried about him at all. I just feel happy about him."

"Good."

"I wish the wind would drop, though."

"It's liable to go down by five o'clock."

"Let's hope."

"You might pray," I laughed.

"Never does me any good. I've never gotten anything I prayed for. Have you?"

"Oh, yes."

"Oh, rot," said Brett. "Maybe it works for some people, though. You don't look very religious, Jake."

"I'm pretty religious."

"Oh, rot," said Brett. "Don't start proselyting to-day. To-day's going to be bad enough as it is."

It was the first time I had seen her in the old happy, careless way since before she went off with Cohn. We were back again in front of the hotel. All the tables were set now, and already several were filled with people eating.

"Do look after Mike," Brett said. "Don't let him get too bad."

"Your frients haff gone up-stairs," the German maitre d'hôtel said in English. He was a continual eavesdropper. Brett turned to him:

"Thank you, so much. Have you anything else to say?"

"No, *ma'am.*"

"Good," said Brett.

"Save us a table for three," I said to the German. He smiled his dirty little pink-and-white smile.

"Iss madam eating here?"

"No," Brett said.

"Den I think a tabul for two will be enuff."

"Don't talk to him," Brett said. "Mike must have been in bad shape," she said on the stairs. We passed Montoya on the stairs. He bowed and did not smile.

"I'll see you at the café," Brett said. "Thank you, so much, Jake."

We had stopped at the floor our rooms were on. She went straight down the hall and into Romero's room. She did not knock. She simply opened the door, went in, and closed it behind her.

I stood in front of the door of Mike's room and knocked. There was no answer. I tried the knob and it opened. Inside the room was in great disorder. All the bags were opened and clothing was strewn around. There were empty bottles beside the bed. Mike lay on the bed looking like a death mask of himself. He opened his eyes and looked at me.

"Hello, Jake," he said very slowly. "I'm getting a lit tle sleep. I've want ed a lit tle sleep for a long time."

"Let me cover you over."

"No. I'm quite warm."

"Don't go. I have n't got ten to sleep yet."

"You'll sleep, Mike. Don't worry, boy."

"Brett's got a bull-fighter," Mike said. "But her Jew has gone away."

He turned his head and looked at me.

"Damned good thing, what?"

"Yes. Now go to sleep, Mike. You ought to get some sleep."

"I'm just start ing. I'm go ing to get a lit tle sleep."

He shut his eyes. I went out of the room and turned the door to quietly. Bill was in my room reading the paper.

"See Mike?"

"Yes."

"Let's go and eat."

"I won't eat down-stairs with that German head waiter. He was damned snotty when I was getting Mike up-stairs."

"He was snotty to us, too."

"Let's go out and eat in the town."

We went down the stairs. On the stairs we passed a girl coming up with a covered tray.

"There goes Brett's lunch," Bill said.

"And the kid's," I said.

Outside on the terrace under the arcade the German head waiter came up. His red cheeks were shiny. He was being polite.

"I haff a tabul for two for you gentlemen," he said.

"Go sit at it," Bill said. We went on out across the street.

We ate at a restaurant in a side street off the square. They were all men eating in the restaurant. It was full of smoke and drinking and singing. The food was good and so was the wine. We did not talk much. Afterward we went to the café and watched the fiesta come to the boiling-point. Brett came over soon after lunch. She said she had looked in the room and that Mike was asleep.

When the fiesta boiled over and toward the bull-ring we went with the crowd. Brett sat at the ringside between Bill and me. Directly below us was the callejon, the passageway between the stands and the red fence of the barrera. Behind us the concrete stands filled solidly. Out in front, beyond the red fence, the sand of the ring was smooth-rolled and yellow. It looked a little heavy from the rain, but it was dry in the sun and firm and smooth. The sword-handlers and bull-ring servants came down the callejon carrying on their shoulders the wicker baskets of fighting capes and muletas. They were blood-stained and compactly folded and packed in the baskets. The sword-handlers opened the heavy leather sword-cases so the red wrapped hilts of the sheaf of swords showed as the leather case leaned against the fence. They unfolded the dark-stained red flannel of the muletas and fixed batons in them to spread the stuff and give the matador something to hold. Brett watched it all. She was absorbed in the professional details.

"He's his name stencilled on all the capes and muletas," she said. "Why do they call them muletas?"

"I don't know."

"I wonder if they ever launder them."

"I don't think so. It might spoil the color."

"The blood must stiffen them," Bill said.

"Funny," Brett said. "How one doesn't mind the blood."

Below in the narrow passage of the callejon the sword-handlers arranged everything. All the seats were full. Above, all the boxes were full. There was not an empty seat except in the President's box. When he came in the fight would start. Across the smooth sand, in the high doorway that led into the corrals, the bull-fighters were standing, their arms furled in their capes, talking, waiting for the signal to march in across the arena. Brett was watching them with the glasses.

"Here, would you like to look?"

I looked through the glasses and saw the three matadors. Romero was in the centre, Belmonte on his left, Marcial on his right. Back of them were their people, and behind the banderilleros, back in the passageway and in the open space of the corral, I saw the picadors. Romero was wearing a black suit. His tricornered hat was low down over his eyes. I could not see his face clearly under the hat, but it looked badly marked. He was looking straight ahead. Marcial was smoking a cigarette guardedly, holding it in his hand. Belmonte looked ahead, his face wan and yellow, his long wolf jaw out. He was looking at nothing. Neither he nor Romero seemed to have anything

in common with the others. They were all alone. The President came
in; there was handclapping above us in the grand stand, and I handed
the glasses to Brett. There was applause. The music started. Brett
looked through the glasses.

"Here, take them," she said.

Through the glasses I saw Belmonte speak to Romero. Marcial
straightened up and dropped his cigarette, and, looking straight
ahead, their heads back, their free arms swinging, the three matadors
walked out. Behind them came all the procession, opening out, all
striding in step, all the capes furled, everybody with free arms swinging, and behind rode the picadors, their pics rising like lances. Behind all came the two trains of mules and the bull-ring servants. The
matadors bowed, holding their hats on, before the President's box,
and then came over to the barrera below us. Pedro Romero took off
his heavy gold-brocaded cape and handed it over the fence to his
sword-handler. He said something to the sword-handler. Close below
us we saw Romero's lips were puffed, both eyes were discolored. His
face was discolored and swollen. The sword-handler took the cape,
looked up at Brett, and came over to us and handed up the cape.

"Spread it out in front of you," I said.

Brett leaned forward. The cape was heavy and smoothly stiff with
gold. The sword-handler looked back, shook his head, and said something. A man beside me leaned over toward Brett.

"He doesn't want you to spread it," he said. "You should fold it
and keep it in your lap."

Brett folded the heavy cape.

Romero did not look up at us. He was speaking to Belmonte.
Belmonte had sent his formal cape over to some friends. He looked
across at them and smiled, his wolf smile that was only with the
mouth. Romero leaned over the barrera and asked for the water-jug.
The sword-handler brought it and Romero poured water over the
percale of his fighting-cape, and then scuffed the lower folds in the
sand with his slippered foot.

"What's that for?" Brett asked.

"To give it weight in the wind."

"His face looks bad," Bill said.

"He feels very badly," Brett said. "He should be in bed."

The first bull was Belmonte's. Belmonte was very good. But because he got thirty thousand pesetas and people had stayed in line all

night to buy tickets to see him, the crowd demanded that he should be more than very good. Belmonte's great attraction is working close to the bull. In bull-fighting they speak of the terrain of the bull and the terrain of the bull-fighter. As long as a bull-fighter stays in his own terrain he is comparatively safe. Each time he enters into the terrain of the bull he is in great danger. Belmonte, in his best days, worked always in the terrain of the bull. This way he gave the sensation of coming tragedy. People went to the corrida to see Belmonte, to be given tragic sensations, and perhaps to see the death of Belmonte. Fifteen years ago they said if you wanted to see Belmonte you should go quickly, while he was still alive. Since then he has killed more than a thousand bulls. When he retired the legend grew up about how his bull-fighting had been, and when he came out of retirement the public were disappointed because no real man could work as close to the bulls as Belmonte was supposed to have done, not, of course, even Belmonte.

Also Belmonte imposed conditions and insisted that his bulls should not be too large, nor too dangerously armed with horns, and so the element that was necessary to give the sensation of tragedy was not there, and the public, who wanted three times as much from Belmonte, who was sick with a fistula, as Belmonte had ever been able to give, felt defrauded and cheated, and Belmonte's jaw came further out in contempt, and his face turned yellower, and he moved with greater difficulty as his pain increased, and finally the crowd were actively against him, and he was utterly contemptuous and indifferent. He had meant to have a great afternoon, and instead it was an afternoon of sneers, shouted insults, and finally a volley of cushions and pieces of bread and vegetables, thrown down at him in the plaza where he had had his greatest triumphs. His jaw only went further out. Sometimes he turned to smile that toothed, long-jawed, lipless smile when he was called something particularly insulting, and always the pain that any movement produced grew stronger and stronger, until finally his yellow face was parchment color, and after his second bull was dead and the throwing of bread and cushions was over, after he had saluted the President with the same wolf-jawed smile and contemptuous eyes, and handed his sword over the barrera to be wiped, and put back in its case, he passed through into the callejón and leaned on the barrera below us, his head on his arms, not seeing, not hearing anything, only going through his pain. When he looked up, finally, he asked for a drink of water. He swallowed a little, rinsed his mouth, spat the water, took his cape, and went back into the ring.

Because they were against Belmonte the public were for Romero. From the moment he left the barrera and went toward the bull they applauded him. Belmonte watched Romero, too, watched him always without seeming to. He paid no attention to Marcial. Marcial was the sort of thing he knew all about. He had come out of retirement to compete with Marcial, knowing it was a competition gained in advance. He had expected to compete with Marcial and the other stars of the decadence of bull-fighting, and he knew that the sincerity of his own bull-fighting would be so set off by the false æsthetics of the bull-fighters of the decadent period that he would only have to be in the ring. His return from retirement had been spoiled by Romero. Romero did always, smoothly, calmly, and beautifully, what he, Belmonte, could only bring himself to do now sometimes. The crowd felt it, even the people from Biarritz, even the American ambassador saw it, finally. It was a competition that Belmonte would not enter because it would lead only to a bad horn wound or death. Belmonte was no longer well enough. He no longer had his greatest moments in the bull-ring. He was not sure that there were any great moments. Things were not the same and now life only came in flashes. He had flashes of the old greatness with his bulls, but they were not of value because he had discounted them in advance when he had picked the bulls out for their safety, getting out of a motor and leaning on a fence, looking over at the herd on the ranch of his friend the bull-breeder. So he had two small, manageable bulls without much horns, and when he felt the greatness again coming, just a little of it through the pain that was always with him, it had been discounted and sold in advance, and it did not give him a good feeling. It was the greatness, but it did not make bull-fighting wonderful to him any more.

Pedro Romero had the greatness. He loved bull-fighting, and I think he loved the bulls, and I think he loved Brett. Everything of which he could control the locality he did in front of her all that afternoon. Never once did he look up. He made it stronger that way, and did it for himself, too, as well as for her. Because he did not look

up to ask if it pleased he did it all for himself inside, and it strength-
ened him, and yet he did it for her, too. But he did not do it for her
at any loss to himself. He gained by it all through the afternoon.

His first "quite" was directly below us. The three matadors take
the bull in turn after each charge he makes at a picador. Belmonte
was the first. Marcial was the second. Then came Romero. The three
of them were standing at the left of the horse. The picador, his hat
down over his eyes, the shaft of his pic angling sharply toward the
bull, kicked in the spurs and held them and with the reins in his left
hand walked the horse forward toward the bull. The bull was watching. Seemingly he watched the white horse, but really he watched the
triangular steel point of the pic. Romero, watching, saw the bull start
to turn his head. He did not want to charge. Romero flicked his cape
so the color caught the bull's eye. The bull charged with the reflex,
charged, and found not the flash of color but a white horse, and a man
leaned far over the horse, shot the steel point of the long hickory
shaft into the hump of muscle on the bull's shoulder, and pulled his
horse sideways as he pivoted on the pic, making a wound, enforcing
the iron into the bull's shoulder, making him bleed for Belmonte.

The bull did not insist under the iron. He did not really want
to get at the horse. He turned and the group broke apart and Romero
was taking him out with his cape. He took him out softly and
smoothly, and then stopped and, standing squarely in front of the
bull, offered him the cape. The bull's tail went up and he charged,
and Romero moved his arms ahead of the bull, wheeling, his feet
firmed. The dampened, mud-weighted cape swung open and full as
a sail fills, and Romero pivoted with it just ahead of the bull. At
the end of the pass they were facing each other again. Romero smiled.
The bull wanted it again, and Romero's cape filled again, this time
on the other side. Each time he let the bull pass so close that the
man and the bull and the cape that filled and pivoted ahead of the
bull were all one sharply etched mass. It was all so slow and so controlled. It was as though he were rocking the bull to sleep. He made
four veronicas like that, and finished with a half-veronica that turned
his back on the bull and came away toward the applause, his hand
on his hip, his cape on his arm, and the bull watching his back going
away.

In his own bulls he was perfect. His first bull did not see well.
After the first two passes with the cape Romero knew exactly how

bad the vision was impaired. He worked accordingly. It was not brilliant bull-fighting. It was only perfect bull-fighting. The crowd wanted the bull changed. They made a great row. Nothing very fine could happen with a bull that could not see the lures, but the President would not order him replaced.

"Why don't they change him?" Brett asked.

"They've paid for him. They don't want to lose their money."

"It's hardly fair to Romero."

"Watch how he handles a bull that can't see the color."

"It's the sort of thing I don't like to see."

It was not nice to watch if you cared anything about the person who was doing it. With the bull who could not see the colors of the capes, or the scarlet flannel of the muleta, Romero had to make the bull consent with his body. He had to get so close that the bull saw his body, and would start for it, and then shift the bull's charge to the flannel and finish out the pass in the classic manner. The Biarritz crowd did not like it. They thought Romero was afraid, and that was why he gave that little sidestep each time as he transferred the bull's charge from his own body to the flannel. They preferred Belmonte's imitation of himself or Marcial's imitation of Belmonte. There were three of them in the row behind us.

"What's he afraid of the bull for? The bull's so dumb he only goes after the cloth."

"He's just a young bull-fighter. He hasn't learned it yet."

"But I thought he was fine with the cape before."

"Probably he's nervous now."

Out in the centre of the ring, all alone, Romero was going on with the same thing, getting so close that the bull could see him plainly, offering the body, offering it again a little closer, the bull watching dully, then so close that the bull thought he had him, offering again and finally drawing the charge and then, just before the horns came, giving the bull the red cloth to follow with that little, almost imperceptible, jerk that so offended the critical judgment of the Biarritz bull-fight experts.

"He's going to kill now," I said to Brett. "The bull's still strong. He wouldn't wear himself out."

Out in the centre of the ring Romero profiled in front of the bull, drew the sword out from the folds of the muleta, rose on his toes, and sighted along the blade. The bull charged as Romero charged. Romero's left hand dropped the muleta over the bull's muzzle to blind him, his left shoulder went forward between the horns as the sword went in, and for just an instant he and the bull were one, Romero way out over the bull, the right arm extended high up to where the hilt of the sword had gone in between the bull's shoulders. Then the figure was broken. There was a little jolt as Romero came clear, and then he was standing, one hand up, facing the bull, his shirt ripped out from under his sleeve, the white blowing in the wind, and the bull, the red sword hilt tight between his shoulders, his head going down and his legs settling.

"There he goes," Bill said.

Romero was close enough so the bull could see him. His hand still up, he spoke to the bull. The bull gathered himself, then his head went forward and he went over slowly, then all over, suddenly, four feet in the air.

They handed the sword to Romero, and carrying it blade down, the muleta in his other hand, he walked over to in front of the President's box, bowed, straightened, and came over to the barrera and handed over the sword and muleta.

"Bad one," said the sword-handler.

"He made me sweat," said Romero. He wiped off his face. The sword-handler handed him the water-jug. Romero wiped his lips. It hurt him to drink out of the jug. He did not look up at us.

Marcial had a big day. They were still applauding him when Romero's last bull came in. It was the bull that had sprinted out and killed the man in the morning running.

During Romero's first bull his face had been very noticeable. Everything he did showed it. All the concentration of the awkwardly delicate working with the bull that could not see well brought it out. The fight with Cohn had not touched his spirit but his face had been smashed and his body hurt. He was wiping all that out now. Each thing that he did with this bull wiped that out a little cleaner. It was a good bull, a big bull, and with horns, and it turned and recharged easily and surely. He was what Romero wanted in bulls.

When he had finished his work with the muleta and was ready to kill, the crowd made him go on. They did not want the bull killed yet, they did not want it to be over. Romero went on. It was like a course in bull-fighting. All the passes he linked up, all completed, all slow, templed and smooth. There were no tricks and no

mystifications. There was no brusqueness. And each pass as it reached
the summit gave you a sudden ache inside. The crowd did not want
it ever to be finished.

The bull was squared on all four feet to be killed, and Romero
killed directly below us. He killed not as he had been forced to by
the last bull, but as he wanted to. He profiled directly in front of the
bull, drew the sword out of the folds of the muleta and sighted along
the blade. The bull watched him. Romero spoke to the bull and
tapped one of his feet. The bull charged and Romero waited for the
charge, the muleta held low, sighting along the blade, his feet firm.
Then without taking a step forward, he became one with the bull,
the sword was in high between the shoulders, the bull had followed
the low-swung flannel, that disappeared as Romero lurched clear to
the left, and it was over. The bull tried to go forward, his legs commenced to settle, he swung from side to side, hesitated, then went
down on his knees, and Romero's older brother leaned forward behind him and drove a short knife into the bull's neck at the base of
the horns. The first time he missed. He drove the knife in again, and
the bull went over, twitching and rigid. Romero's brother, holding
the bull's horn in one hand, the knife in the other, looked up at the
President's box. Handkerchiefs were waving all over the bull-ring.
The President looked down from the box and waved his handkerchief. The brother cut the notched black ear from the dead bull and
trotted over with it to Romero. The bull lay heavy and black on the
sand, his tongue out. Boys were running toward him from all parts
of the arena, making a little circle around him. They were starting to
dance around the bull.

Romero took the ear from his brother and held it up toward the
President. The President bowed and Romero, running to get ahead
of the crowd, came toward us. He leaned up against the barrera and
gave the ear to Brett. He nodded his head and smiled. The crowd
were all about him. Brett held down the cape.

"You liked it?" Romero called.

Brett did not say anything. They looked at each other and smiled.
Brett had the ear in her hand.

"Don't get bloody," Romero said, and grinned. The crowd
wanted him. Several boys shouted at Brett. The crowd was the boys,
the dancers, and the drunks. Romero turned and tried to get through
the crowd. They were all around him trying to lift him and put him

on their shoulders. He fought and twisted away, and started running, in the midst of them, toward the exit. He did not want to be carried on people's shoulders. But they held him and lifted him. It was uncomfortable and his legs were spraddled and his body was very sore. They were lifting him and all running toward the gate. He had his hand on somebody's shoulder. He looked around at us apologetically. The crowd, running, went out the gate with him.

We all three went back to the hotel. Brett went upstairs. Bill and I sat in the down-stairs dining-room and ate some hard-boiled eggs and drank several bottles of beer. Belmonte came down in his street clothes with his manager and two other men. They sat at the next table and ate. Belmonte ate very little. They were leaving on the seven o'clock train for Barcelona. Belmonte wore a blue-striped shirt and a dark suit, and ate soft-boiled eggs. The others ate a big meal. Belmonte did not talk. He only answered questions.

Bill was tired after the bull-fight. So was I. We both took a bull-fight very hard. We sat and ate the eggs and I watched Belmonte and the people at his table. The men with him were tough-looking and businesslike.

"Come on over to the café," Bill said. "I want an absinthe."

It was the last day of the fiesta. Outside it was beginning to be cloudy again. The square was full of people and the fireworks experts were making up their set pieces for the night and covering them over with beech branches. Boys were watching. We passed stands of rockets with long bamboo stems. Outside the café there was a great crowd. The music and the dancing were going on. The giants and the dwarfs were passing.

"Where's Edna?" I asked Bill.

"I don't know."

We watched the beginning of the evening of the last night of the fiesta. The absinthe made everything seem better. I drank it without sugar in the dripping glass, and it was pleasantly bitter.

"I feel sorry about Cohn," Bill said. "He had an awful time."

"Oh, to hell with Cohn," I said.

"Where do you suppose he went?"

"Up to Paris."

"What do you suppose he'll do?"

"Oh, to hell with him."

"What do you suppose he'll do?"

"Pick up with his old girl, probably."

"Who was his old girl?"

"Somebody named Frances."

We had another absinthe.

"When do you go back?" I asked.

"To-morrow."

After a little while Bill said: "Well, it was a swell fiesta."

"Yes," I said; "something doing all the time."

"You wouldn't believe it. It's like a wonderful nightmare."

"Sure," I said. "I'd believe anything. Including nightmares."

"What's the matter? Feel low?"

"Low as hell."

"Have another absinthe. Here, waiter! Another absinthe for this
señor."

"I feel like hell," I said.

"Drink that," said Bill. "Drink it slow."

It was beginning to get dark. The fiesta was going on. I began to
feel drunk but I did not feel any better.

"How do you feel?"

"I feel like hell."

"Have another?"

"It won't do any good."

"Try it. You can't tell; maybe this is the one that gets it. Hey,
waiter! Another absinthe for this señor!"

I poured the water directly into it and stirred it instead of letting
it drip. Bill put in a lump of ice. I stirred the ice around with a spoon
in the brownish, cloudy mixture.

"How is it?"

"Fine."

"Don't drink it fast that way. It will make you sick."

I set down the glass. I had not meant to drink it fast.

"I feel tight."

"You ought to."

"That's what you wanted, wasn't it?"

"Sure. Get tight. Get over your damn depression."

"Well, I'm tight. Is that what you want?"

"Sit down."

"I won't sit down," I said. "I'm going over to the hotel."

I was very drunk. I was drunker than I ever remembered having been. At the hotel I went up-stairs. Brett's door was open. I put my head in the room. Mike was sitting on the bed. He waved a bottle.

"Jake," he said. "Come in, Jake."

I went in and sat down. The room was unstable unless I looked at some fixed point.

"Brett, you know. She's gone off with the bull-fighter chap."

"No."

"Yes. She looked for you to say good-bye. They went on the seven o'clock train."

"Did they?"

"Bad thing to do," Mike said. "She shouldn't have done it."

"No."

"Have a drink? Wait while I ring for some beer."

"I'm drunk," I said. "I'm going in and lie down."

"Are you blind? I was blind myself."

"Yes," I said, "I'm blind."

"Well, bung-o," Mike said. "Get some sleep, old Jake."

I went out the door and into my own room and lay on the bed. The bed went sailing off and I sat up in bed and looked at the wall to make it stop. Outside in the square the fiesta was going on. It did not mean anything. Later Bill and Mike came in to get me to go down and eat with them. I pretended to be asleep.

"He's asleep. Better let him alone."

"He's blind as a tick," Mike said. They went out.

I got up and went to the balcony and looked out at the dancing in the square. The world was not wheeling any more. It was just very clear and bright, and inclined to blur at the edges. I washed, brushed my hair. I looked strange to myself in the glass, and went down-stairs to the dining-room.

"Here he is!" said Bill. "Good old Jake! I knew you wouldn't pass out."

"Hello, you old drunk," Mike said.

"I got hungry and woke up."

"Eat some soup," Bill said.

The three of us sat at the table, and it seemed as though about six people were missing.

The Undefeated

Manuel Garcia climbed the stairs to Don Miguel Retana's office. He set down his suitcase and knocked on the door. There was no answer. Manuel, standing in the hallway, felt there was some one in the room. He felt it through the door.

"Retana," he said, listening.

There was no answer.

He's there, all right, Manuel thought.

"Retana," he said and banged the door.

"Who's there?" said some one in the office.

"Me, Manolo," Manuel said.

"What do you want?" asked the voice.

"I want to work," Manuel said.

Something in the door clicked several times and it swung open. Manuel went in, carrying his suitcase.

A little man sat behind a desk at the far side of the room. Over his head was a bull's head, stuffed by a Madrid taxidermist; on the walls were framed photographs and bull-fight posters.

The little man sat looking at Manuel.

"I thought they'd killed you," he said.

Manuel knocked with his knuckles on the desk. The little man sat looking at him across the desk.

"How many corridas you had this year?" Retana asked.

"One," he answered.

"Just that one?" the little man asked.

"That's all."

"I read about it in the papers," Retana said. He leaned back in the chair and looked at Manuel.

Manuel looked up at the stuffed bull. He had seen it often before. He felt a certain family interest in it. It had killed his brother, the promising one, about nine years ago. Manuel remembered the day. There was a brass plate on the oak shield the bull's head was

461

mounted on. Manuel could not read it, but he imagined it was in memory of his brother. Well, he had been a good kid.

The plate said: "The Bull 'Mariposa' of the Duke of Veragua, which accepted 9 varas for 7 caballos, and caused the death of Antonio Garcia, Novillero, April 27, 1909."

Retana saw him looking at the stuffed bull's head.

"The lot the Duke sent me for Sunday will make a scandal," he said. "They're all bad in the legs. What do they say about them at the Café?"

"I don't know," Manuel said. "I just got in."

"Yes," Retana said. "You still have your bag."

He looked at Manuel, leaning back behind the big desk.

"Sit down," he said. "Take off your cap."

Manuel sat down; his cap off, his face was changed. He looked pale, and his coleta pinned forward on his head, so that it would not show under the cap, gave him a strange look.

"You don't look well," Retana said.

"I just got out of the hospital," Manuel said.

"I heard they'd cut your leg off," Retana said.

"No," said Manuel. "It got all right."

Retana leaned forward across the desk and pushed a wooden box of cigarettes toward Manuel.

"Have a cigarette," he said.

"Thanks."

Manuel lit it.

"Smoke?" he said, offering the match to Retana.

"No," Retana waved his hand, "I never smoke."

Retana watched him smoking.

"Why don't you get a job and go to work?" he said.

"I don't want to work," Manuel said. "I am a bull-fighter."

"There aren't any bull-fighters any more," Retana said.

"I'm a bull-fighter," Manuel said.

"Yes, while you're in there," Retana said.

Manuel laughed.

Retana sat, saying nothing and looking at Manuel.

"I'll put you in a nocturnal if you want," Retana offered.

"When?" Manuel asked.

"To-morrow night."

"I don't like to substitute for anybody," Manuel said. That was the way they all got killed. That was the way Salvador got killed. He tapped with his knuckles on the table.

"It's all I've got," Retana said.

"Why don't you put me on next week?" Manuel suggested.

"You wouldn't draw," Retana said. "All they want is Litri and Rubito and La Torre. Those kids are good."

"They'd come to see me get it," Manuel said, hopefully.

"No, they wouldn't. They don't know who you are any more."

"I've got a lot of stuff," Manuel said.

"I'm offering to put you on to-morrow night," Retana said. "You can work with young Hernandez and kill two novillos after the Charlots."

"Whose novillos?" Manuel asked.

"I don't know. Whatever stuff they've got in the corrals. What the veterinaries won't pass in the daytime."

"I don't like to substitute," Manuel said.

"You can take it or leave it," Retana said. He leaned forward over the papers. He was no longer interested. The appeal that Manuel had made to him for a moment when he thought of the old days was gone. He would like to get him to substitute for Larita because he could get him cheaply. He could get others cheaply too. He would like to help him though. Still he had given him the chance. It was up to him.

"How much do I get?" Manuel asked. He was still playing with the idea of refusing. But he knew he could not refuse.

"Two hundred and fifty pesetas," Retana said. He had thought of five hundred, but when he opened his mouth it said two hundred and fifty.

"You pay Villalta seven thousand," Manuel said.

"You're not Villalta," Retana said.

"I know it," Manuel said.

"He draws it, Manolo," Retana said in explanation.

"Sure," said Manuel. He stood up. "Give me three hundred, Retana."

"All right," Retana agreed. He reached in the drawer for a paper.

"Can I have fifty now?" Manuel asked.

"Sure," said Retana. He took a fifty peseta note out of his pocketbook and laid it, spread out flat, on the table.

Manuel picked it up and put it in his pocket.

"What about a cuadrilla?" he asked.

"There's the boys that always work for me nights," Retana said. "They're all right."

"How about picadors?" Manuel asked.

"They're not much," Retana admitted.

"I've got to have one good pic," Manuel said.

"Get him then," Retana said. "Go and get him."

"Not out of this," Manuel said. "I'm not paying for any cuadrilla out of sixty duros."

Retana said nothing but looked at Manuel across the big desk.

"You know I've got to have one good pic," Manuel said.

Retana said nothing but looked at Manuel from a long way off.

"It isn't right," Manuel said.

Retana was still considering him, leaning back in his chair, considering him from a long way away.

"There're the regular pics," he offered.

"I know," Manuel said. "I know your regular pics."

Retana did not smile. Manuel knew it was over.

"All I want is an even break," Manuel said reasoningly. "When I go out there I want to be able to call my shots on the bull. It only takes one good picador."

He was talking to a man who was no longer listening.

"If you want something extra," Retana said, "go and get it. There will be a regular cuadrilla out there. Bring as many of your own pics as you want. The charlotada is over by 10.30."

"All right," Manuel said. "If that's the way you feel about it."

"That's the way," Retana said.

"I'll see you to-morrow night," Manuel said.

"I'll be out there," Retana said.

Manuel picked up his suitcase and went out.

"Shut the door," Retana called.

Manuel looked back. Retana was sitting forward looking at some papers. Manuel pulled the door tight until it clicked.

He went down the stairs and out of the door into the hot brightness of the street. It was very hot in the street and the light on the white buildings was sudden and hard on his eyes. He walked down the shady side of the steep street toward the Puerta del Sol. The shade felt solid and cool as running water. The heat came suddenly as he crossed the intersecting streets. Manuel saw no one he knew in all the people he passed.

Just before the Puerta del Sol he turned into a café.

It was quiet in the café. There were a few men sitting at tables against the wall. At one table four men played cards. Most of the men sat against the wall smoking, empty coffee-cups and liqueur-glasses before them on the tables. Manuel went through the long room to a small room in back. A man sat at a table in the corner asleep. Manuel sat down at one of the tables.

A waiter came in and stood beside Manuel's table.

"Have you seen Zurito?" Manuel asked him.

"He was in before lunch," the waiter answered. "He won't be back before five o'clock."

"Bring me some coffee and milk and a shot of the ordinary," Manuel said.

The waiter came back into the room carrying a tray with a big coffee-glass and a liqueur-glass on it. In his left hand he held a bottle of brandy. He swung these down to the table and a boy who had followed him poured coffee and milk into the glass from two shiny, spouted pots with long handles.

Manuel took off his cap and the waiter noticed his pigtail pinned forward on his head. He winked at the coffee-boy as he poured out the brandy into the little glass beside Manuel's coffee. The coffee-boy looked at Manuel's pale face curiously.

"You fighting here?" asked the waiter, corking up the bottle.

"Yes," Manuel said. "To-morrow."

The waiter stood there, holding the bottle on one hip.

"You in the Charlie Chaplins?" he asked.

The coffee-boy looked away, embarrassed.

"No. In the ordinary."

"I thought they were going to have Chaves and Hernandez," the waiter said.

"No. Me and another."

"Who? Chaves or Hernandez?"

"Hernandez, I think."

"What's the matter with Chaves?"

"He got hurt."

"Where did you hear that?"

"Retana."

"Hey, Looie," the waiter called to the next room, "Chaves got cogida."

Manuel had taken the wrapper off the lumps of sugar and dropped them into his coffee. He stirred it and drank it down, sweet, hot, and warming in his empty stomach. He drank off the brandy.

"Give me another shot of that," he said to the waiter.

The waiter uncorked the bottle and poured the glass full, slopping another drink into the saucer. Another waiter had come up in front of the table. The coffee-boy was gone.

"Is Chaves hurt bad?" the second waiter asked Manuel.

"I don't know," Manuel said, "Retana didn't say."

"A hell of a lot he cares," the tall waiter said. Manuel had not seen him before. He must have just come up.

"If you stand in with Retana in this town, you're a made man," the tall waiter said. "If you aren't in with him, you might just as well go out and shoot yourself."

"You said it," the other waiter who had come in said. "You said it then."

"You're right I said it," said the tall waiter. "I know what I'm talking about when I talk about that bird."

"Look what he's done for Villalta," the first waiter said.

"And that ain't all," the tall waiter said. "Look what he's done for Marcial Lalanda. Look what he's done for Nacional."

"You said it, kid," agreed the short waiter.

Manuel looked at them, standing talking in front of his table. He had drunk his second brandy. They had forgotten about him. They were not interested in him.

"Look at that bunch of camels," the tall waiter went on. "Did you ever see this Nacional II?"

"I seen him last Sunday didn't I?" the original waiter said.

"He's a giraffe," the short waiter said.

"What did I tell you?" the tall waiter said. "Those are Retana's boys."

"Say, give me another shot of that," Manuel said. He had poured the brandy the waiter had slopped over in the saucer into his glass and drank it while they were talking.

The original waiter poured his glass full mechanically, and the three of them went out of the room talking.

In the far corner the man was still asleep, snoring slightly on the intaking breath, his head back against the wall.

Manuel drank his brandy. He felt sleepy himself. It was too hot to go out into the town. Besides there was nothing to do. He wanted to see Zurito. He would go to sleep while he waited. He kicked his suitcase under the table to be sure it was there. Perhaps it would be better to put it back under the seat, against the wall. He leaned down and shoved it under. Then he leaned forward on the table and went to sleep.

When he woke there was some one sitting across the table from him. It was a big man with a heavy brown face like an Indian. He had been sitting there some time. He had waved the waiter away and sat reading the paper and occasionally looking down at Manuel, asleep, his head on the table. He read the paper laboriously, forming the words with his lips as he read. When it tired him he looked at Manuel. He sat heavily in the chair, his black Cordoba hat tipped forward.

Manuel sat up and looked at him.

"Hello, Zurito," he said.

"Hello, kid," the big man said.

"I've been asleep." Manuel rubbed his forehead with the back of his fist.

"I thought maybe you were."

"How's everything?"

"Good. How is everything with you?"

"Not so good."

They were both silent. Zurito, the picador, looked at Manuel's white face. Manuel looked down at the picador's enormous hands folding the paper to put away in his pocket.

"I got a favor to ask you, Manos," Manuel said.

Manosduros was Zurito's nickname. He never heard it without thinking of his huge hands. He put them forward on the table self-consciously.

"Let's have a drink," he said.

"Sure," said Manuel.

The waiter came and went and came again. He went out of the room looking back at the two men at the table.

"What the matter, Manolo?" Zurito set down his glass.

"Would you pic two bulls for me to-morrow night?" Manuel asked, looking up at Zurito across the table.

"No," said Zurito. "I'm not pic-ing."

Manuel looked down at his glass. He had expected that answer; now he had it. Well, he had it.

"I'm sorry, Manolo, but I'm not pic-ing." Zurito looked at his hands.

"That's all right," Manuel said.

"I'm too old," Zurito said.

"I just asked you," Manuel said.

"Is it the nocturnal to-morrow?"

"That's it. I figured if I had just one good pic, I could get away with it."

"How much are you getting?"

"Three hundred pesetas."

"I get more than that for pic-ing."

"I know," said Manuel. "I didn't have any right to ask you."

"What do you keep on doing it for?" Zurito asked. "Why don't you cut off your coleta, Manolo?"

"I don't know," Manuel said.

"You're pretty near as old as I am," Zurito said.

"I don't know," Manuel said. "I got to do it. If I can fix it so that I get an even break, that's all I want. I got to stick with it, Manos."

"No, you don't."

"Yes, I do. I've tried keeping away from it."

"I know how you feel. But it isn't right. You ought to get out and stay out."

"I can't do it. Besides, I've been going good lately."

Zurito looked at his face.

"You've been in the hospital."

"But I was going great when I got hurt."

Zurito said nothing. He tipped the cognac out of his saucer into his glass.

"The papers said they never saw a better faena," Manuel said.

Zurito looked at him.

"You know when I get going I'm good," Manuel said.

"You're too old," the picador said.

"No," said Manuel. "You're ten years older than I am."

"With me it's different."

"I'm not too old," Manuel said.

They sat silent, Manuel watching the picador's face.

"I was going great till I got hurt," Manuel offered.

"You ought to have seen me, Manos," Manuel said, reproach-fully.

"I don't want to see you," Zurito said. "It makes me nervous."

"You haven't seen me lately."

"I've seen you plenty."

Zurito looked at Manuel, avoiding his eyes.

"You ought to quit it, Manolo."

"I can't," Manuel said. "I'm going good now, I tell you."

Zurito leaned forward, his hands on the table.

"Listen. I'll pic for you and if you don't go big to-morrow night, you'll quit. See? Will you do that?"

"Sure."

Zurito leaned back, relieved.

"You got to quit," he said. "No monkey business. You got to cut the coleta."

"I won't have to quit," Manuel said. "You watch me. I've got the stuff."

Zurito stood up. He felt tired from arguing.

"You got to quit," he said. "I'll cut your coleta myself."

"No, you won't," Manuel said. "You won't have a chance."

Zurito called the waiter.

"Come on," said Zurito. "Come on up to the house."

Manuel reached under the seat for his suitcase. He was happy. He knew Zurito would pic for him. He was the best picador living. It was all simple now.

"Come on up to the house and we'll eat," Zurito said.

Manuel stood in the patio de caballos waiting for the Charlie Chaplins to be over. Zurito stood beside him. Where they stood it was dark. The high door that led into the bull-ring was shut. Above them they heard a shout, then another shout of laughter. Then there was silence. Manuel liked the smell of the stables about the patio de caballos. It smelt good in the dark. There was another roar from the arena and then applause, prolonged applause, going on and on.

"You ever seen these fellows?" Zurito asked, big and looming beside Manuel in the dark.

"No," Manuel said.

"They're pretty funny," Zurito said. He smiled to himself in the dark.

The high, double, tight-fitting door into the bull-ring swung open and Manuel saw the ring in the hard light of the arc-lights, the plaza, dark all the way around, rising high; around the edge of the ring were running and bowing two men dressed like tramps, followed by a third in the uniform of a hotel bell-boy who stooped and picked up the hats and canes thrown down onto the sand and tossed them back up into the darkness.

The electric light went on in the patio.

"I'll climb onto one of those ponies while you collect the kids," Zurito said.

Behind them came the jingle of the mules, coming out to go into the arena and be hitched onto the dead bull.

The members of the cuadrilla, who had been watching the burlesque from the runway between the barrera and the seats, came walking back and stood in a group talking, under the electric light in the patio. A good-looking lad in a silver-and-orange suit came up to Manuel and smiled.

"I'm Hernandez," he said and put out his hand.

Manuel shook it.

"They're regular elephants we've got to-night," the boy said cheerfully.

"They're big ones with horns," Manuel agreed.

"You drew the worst lot," the boy said.

"That's all right," Manuel said. "The bigger they are, the more meat for the poor."

"Where did you get that one?" Hernandez grinned.

"That's an old one," Manuel said. "You line up your cuadrilla, so I can see what I've got."

"You've got some good kids," Hernandez said. He was very cheerful. He had been on twice before in nocturnals and was beginning to get a following in Madrid. He was happy the fight would start in a few minutes.

"Where are the pics?" Manuel asked.

"They're back in the corrals fighting about who gets the beautiful horses," Hernandez grinned.

The mules came through the gate in a rush, the whips snapping, bells jangling and the young bull ploughing a furrow of sand.

They formed up for the paseo as soon as the bull had gone through.

Manuel and Hernandez stood in front. The youths of the cuadrillas were behind, their heavy capes furled over their arms. In back, the four picadors, mounted, holding their steel-tipped push-poles erect in the half-dark of the corral.

"It's a wonder Retana wouldn't give us enough light to see the horses by," one picador said.

"He knows we'll be happier if we don't get too good a look at these skins," another pic answered.

"This thing I'm on barely keeps me off the ground," the first picador said.

"Well, they're horses."

"Sure, they're horses."

They talked, sitting their gaunt horses in the dark.

Zurito said nothing. He had the only steady horse of the lot. He had tried him, wheeling him in the corrals and he responded to the bit and the spurs. He had taken the bandage off his right eye and cut the strings where they had tied his ears tight shut at the base. He was a good, solid horse, solid on his legs. That was all he needed. He intended to ride him all through the corrida. He had already, since he had mounted, sitting in the half-dark in the big, quilted saddle, waiting for the paseo, pic-ed through the whole corrida in his mind. The other picadors went on talking on both sides of him. He did not hear them.

The two matadors stood together in front of their three peones, their capes furled over their left arms in the same fashion. Manuel was thinking about the three lads in back of him. They were all three Madrilenos, like Hernandez, boys about nineteen. One of them, a gypsy, serious, aloof, and dark-faced, he liked the look of. He turned.

"What's your name, kid?" he asked the gypsy.

"Fuentes," the gypsy said.

"That's a good name," Manuel said.

The gypsy smiled, showing his teeth.

"You take the bull and give him a little run when he comes out," Manuel said.

"All right," the gypsy said. His face was serious. He began to think about just what he would do.

"Here she goes," Manuel said to Hernandez.

"All right. We'll go."

Heads up, swinging with the music, their right arms swinging free, they stepped out, crossing the sanded arena under the arc-lights, the cuadrillas opening out behind, the picadors riding after, behind came the bull-ring servants and the jingling mules. The crowd applauded Hernandez as they marched across the arena. Arrogant, swinging, they looked straight ahead as they marched.

They bowed before the president, and the procession broke up into its component parts. The bull-fighters went over to the barrera and changed their heavy mantles for the light fighting capes. The mules went out. The picadors galloped jerkily around the ring, and two rode out the gate they had come in by. The servants swept the sand smooth.

Manuel drank a glass of water poured for him by one of Retana's deputies, who was acting as his manager and sword-handler. Hernandez came over from speaking with his own manager.

"You got a good hand, kid," Manuel complimented him.

"They like me," Hernandez said happily.

"How did the paseo go?" Manuel asked Retana's man.

"Like a wedding," said the handler. "Fine. You came out like Joselito and Belmonte."

Zurito rode by, a bulky equestrian statue. He wheeled his horse and faced him toward the toril on the far side of the ring where the bull would come out. It was strange under the arc-light. He pic-ed in the hot afternoon sun for big money. He didn't like this arc-light business. He wished they would get started.

Manuel went up to him.

"Pic him, Manos," he said. "Cut him down to size for me."

"I'll pic him, kid," Zurito spat on the sand. "I'll make him jump out of the ring."

"Lean on him, Manos," Manuel said.

"I'll lean on him," Zurito said. "What's holding it up?"

"He's coming now," Manuel said.

Zurito sat there, his feet in the box-stirrups, his great legs in the buckskin-covered armor gripping the horse, the reins in his left hand, the long pic held in his right hand, his broad hat well down over his eyes to shade them from the lights, watching the distant door of the toril. His horse's ears quivered. Zurito patted him with his left hand.

The red door of the toril swung back and for a moment Zurito looked into the empty passageway far across the arena. Then the bull came out in a rush, skidding on his four legs as he came out under the lights, then charging in a gallop, moving softly in a fast gallop, silent except as he woofed through wide nostrils as he charged, glad to be free after the dark pen.

In the first row of seats, slightly bored, leaning forward to write on the cement wall in front of his knees, the substitute bull-fight critic of *El Heraldo* scribbled: "Campagnero, Negro, 42, came out at 90 miles an hour with plenty of gas——"

Manuel, leaning against the barrera, watching the bull, waved his hand and the gypsy ran out, trailing his cape. The bull, in full gallop, pivoted and charged the cape, his head down, his tail rising. The gypsy moved in a zigzag, and as he passed, the bull caught sight of him and abandoned the cape to charge the man. The gyp sprinted and vaulted the red fence of the barrera as the bull struck it with his horns. He tossed into it twice with his horns, banging into the wood blindly.

The critic of *El Heraldo* lit a cigarette and tossed the match at the bull, then wrote in his note-book, "large and with enough horns to satisfy the cash customers, Campagnero showed a tendency to cut into the terrane of the bull-fighters."

Manuel stepped out on the hard sand as the bull banged into the fence. Out of the corner of his eye he saw Zurito sitting the white horse close to the barrera, about a quarter of the way around the ring to the left. Manuel held the cape close in front of him, a fold in each hand, and shouted at the bull. "Huh! Huh!" The bull turned, seemed to brace against the fence as he charged in a scramble, driving into the cape as Manuel side-stepped, pivoted on his heels with the charge of the bull, and swung the cape just ahead of the horns. At the end of the swing he was facing the bull again and held the cape in the same position close in front of his body, and pivoted again as the bull recharged. Each time, as he swung, the crowd shouted.

Four times he swung with the bull, lifting the cape so it billowed full, and each time bringing the bull around to charge again. Then, at the end of the fifth swing, he held the cape against his hip and pivoted, so the cape swung out like a ballet dancer's skirt and wound the bull around himself like a belt, to step clear, leaving the bull facing Zurito on the white horse, come up and planted firm, the horse facing the bull, its ears forward, its lips nervous, Zurito, his hat over his eyes, leaning forward, the long pole sticking out before and behind in a sharp angle under his right arm, held half-way down, the triangular iron point facing the bull.

El Heraldo's second-string critic, drawing on his cigarette, his eyes on the bull, wrote: "the veteran Manolo designed a series of acceptable veronicas, ending in a very Belmontistic recorte that earned applause from the regulars, and we entered the tercio of the cavalry."

Zurito sat his horse, measuring the distance between the bull and the end of the pic. As he looked, the bull gathered himself together and charged, his eyes on the horse's chest. As he lowered his head to hook, Zurito sunk the point of the pic in the swelling hump of muscle above the bull's shoulder, leaned all his weight on the shaft, and with his left hand pulled the white horse into the air, front hoofs pawing, and swung him to the right as he pushed the bull under and through so the horns passed safely under the horse's belly and the horse came down, quivering, the bull's tail brushing his chest as he charged the cape Hernandez offered him.

Hernandez ran sideways, taking the bull out and away with the cape, toward the other picador. He fixed him with a swing of the cape, squarely facing the horse and rider, and stepped back. As the bull saw the horse he charged. The picador's lance slid along his back, and as the shock of the charge lifted the horse, the picador was already half-way out of the saddle, lifting his right leg clear as he missed with the lance and falling to the left side to keep the horse between him and the bull. The horse, lifted and gored, crashed over with the bull driving into him, the picador gave a shove with his boots against the horse and lay clear, waiting to be lifted and hauled away and put on his feet.

Manuel let the bull drive into the fallen horse; he was in no hurry, the picador was safe; besides, it did a picador like that good to worry. He'd stay on longer next time. Lousy pics! He looked across the sand at Zurito a little way out from the barrera, his horse rigid, waiting.

"Huh!" he called to the bull, "Tomar!" holding the cape in both hands so it would catch his eye. The bull detached himself from the horse and charged the cape, and Manuel, running sideways and holding the cape spread wide, stopped, swung on his heels, and brought the bull sharply around facing Zurito.

"Campagnero accepted a pair of varas for the death of one rosinante, with Hernandez and Manolo at the quites," El Heraldo's critic wrote. "He pressed on the iron and clearly showed he was no horse-lover. The veteran Zurito resurrected some of his old stuff with the pike-pole, notably the suerte——"

"Olé! Olé!" the man sitting beside him shouted. The shout was lost in the roar of the crowd, and he slapped the critic on the back. The critic looked up to see Zurito, directly below him, leaning far out over his horse, the length of the pic rising in a sharp angle under his armpit, holding the pic almost by the point, bearing down with all his weight, holding the bull off, the bull pushing and driving to get at the horse, and Zurito, far out, on top of him, holding him, holding him, and slowly pivoting the horse against the pressure, so that at last he was clear. Zurito felt the moment when the horse was clear and the bull could come past, and relaxed the absolute steel lock of his resistance, and the triangular steel point of the pic ripped in the bull's hump of shoulder muscle as he tore loose to find Hernandez's cape before his muzzle. He charged blindly into the cape and the boy took him out into the open arena.

Zurito sat patting his horse and looking at the bull charging the cape that Hernandez swung for him out under the bright light while the crowd shouted.

"You see that one?" he said to Manuel.

"It was a wonder," Manuel said.

"I got him that time," Zurito said. "Look at him now."

At the conclusion of a closely turned pass of the cape the bull slid to his knees. He was up at once, but far out across the sand Manuel and Zurito saw the shine of the pumping flow of blood, smooth against the black of the bull's shoulder.

"I got him that time," Zurito said.

"He's a good bull," Manuel said.

"If they gave me another shot at him, I'd kill him," Zurito said.

"They'll change the thirds on us," Manuel said.

"Look at him now," Zurito said.

"I got to go over there," Manuel said, and started on a run for the other side of the ring, where the monos were leading a horse out by the bridle toward the bull, whacking him on the legs with rods and all, in a procession, trying to get him toward the bull, who stood, dropping his head, pawing, unable to make up his mind to charge.

Zurito, sitting his horse, walking him toward the scene, not missing any detail, scowled.

Finally the bull charged, the horse leaders ran for the barrera, the picador hit too far back, and the bull got under the horse, lifted him, threw him onto his back.

Zurito watched. The monos, in their red shirts, running out to drag the picador clear. The picador, now on his feet, swearing and flopping his arms. Manuel and Hernandez standing ready with their capes. And the bull, the great, black bull, with a horse on his back, hooves dangling, the bridle caught in the horns. Black bull with a horse on his back, staggering short-legged, then arching his neck and lifting, thrusting, charging to slide the horse off, horse sliding down. Then the bull into a lunging charge at the cape Manuel spread for him.

The bull was slower now, Manuel felt. He was bleeding badly. There was a sheen of blood all down his flank.

Manuel offered him the cape again. There he came, eyes open, ugly, watching the cape. Manuel stepped to the side and raised his arms, tightening the cape ahead of the bull for the veronica.

Now he was facing the bull. Yes, his head was going down a little. He was carrying it lower. That was Zurito.

Manuel flopped the cape; there he comes; he side-stepped and swung in another veronica. He's shooting awfully accurately, he thought. He's had enough fight, so he's watching now. He's hunting now. Got his eye on me. But I always give him the cape.

He shook the cape at the bull; there he comes; he side-stepped. Awful close that time. I don't want to work that close to him.

The edge of the cape was wet with blood where it had swept along the bull's back as he went by.

All right, here's the last one.

Manuel, facing the bull, having turned with him each charge, offered the cape with his two hands. The bull looked at him. Eyes watching, horns straight forward, the bull looked at him, watching.

"Huh!" Manuel said, "Toro!" and leaning back, swung the cape forward. Here he comes. He side-stepped, swung the cape in back of him, and pivoted, so the bull followed a swirl of cape and then was left with nothing, fixed by the pass, dominated by the cape. Manuel swung the cape under his muzzle with one hand, to show the bull was fixed, and walked away.

There was no applause.

Manuel walked across the sand toward the barrera, while Zurito rode out of the ring. The trumpet had blown to change the act to the planting of the banderillos while Manuel had been working with the bull. He had not consciously noticed it. The monos were spreading canvas over the two dead horses and sprinkling sawdust around them.

Manuel came up to the barrera for a drink of water. Retana's man handed him the heavy porous jug.

Fuentes, the tall gypsy, was standing holding a pair of banderillos, holding them together, slim, red sticks, fish-hook points out. He looked at Manuel.

"Go on out there," Manuel said.

The gypsy trotted out. Manuel set down the jug and watched. He wiped his face with his handkerchief.

The critic of *El Heraldo* reached for the bottle of warm champagne that stood between his feet, took a drink, and finished his paragraph.

"—the aged Manolo rated no applause for a vulgar series of lances with the cape and we entered the third of the palings."

Alone in the centre of the ring the bull stood, still fixed. Fuentes, tall, flat-backed, walking toward him arrogantly, his arms spread out, the two slim, red sticks, one in each hand, held by the fingers, points straight forward. Fuentes walked forward. Back of him and to one side was a peon with a cape. The bull looked at him and was no longer fixed.

His eyes watched Fuentes, now standing still. Now he leaned back, calling to him. Fuentes twitched the two banderillos and the light on the steel points caught the bull's eye.

His tail went up and he charged.

He came straight, his eyes on the man. Fuentes stood still, leaning back, the banderillos pointing forward. As the bull lowered his head to hook, Fuentes leaned backward, his arms came together and rose, his two hands touching, the banderillos two descending red lines, and leaning forward drove the points into the bull's shoulder, leaning far in over the bull's horns and pivoting on the two upright sticks, his legs tight together, his body curving to one side to let the bull pass.

"Olé!" from the crowd.

The bull was hooking wildly, jumping like a trout, all four feet off the ground. The red shaft of the banderillos tossed as he jumped.

Manuel standing at the barrera, noticed that he hooked always to the right.

"Tell him to drop the next pair on the right," he said to the kid who started to run out to Fuentes with the new banderillos.

A heavy hand fell on his shoulder. It was Zurito.

"How do you feel, kid?" he asked.

Manuel was watching the bull.

Zurito leaned forward on the barrera, leaning the weight of his body on his arms. Manuel turned to him.

"You're going good," Zurito said.

Manuel shook his head. He had nothing to do until the next third. The gypsy was very good with the banderillos. The bull would come to him in the next third in good shape. He was a good bull. It had all been easy up to now. The final stuff with the sword was all he worried over. He did not really worry. He did not even think about it. But standing there he had a heavy sense of apprehension. He looked out at the bull, planning his faena, his work with the red cloth that was to reduce the bull, to make him manageable.

The gypsy was walking out toward the bull again, walking heel-and-toe, insultingly, like a ball-room dancer, the red shafts of the banderillos twitching with his walk. The bull watched him, not fixed now, hunting him, but waiting to get close enough so he could be sure of getting him, getting the horns into him.

As Fuentes walked forward the bull charged. Fuentes ran across the quarter of a circle as the bull charged and, as he passed running backward, stopped, swung forward, rose on his toes, arms straight out, and sunk the banderillos straight down into the tight of the big shoulder muscles as the bull missed him.

The crowd were wild about it.

"That kid won't stay in this night stuff long," Retana's man said to Zurito.

"He's good," Zurito said.

"Watch him now."

They watched.

Fuentes was standing with his back against the barrera. Two of the cuadrilla were back of him, with their capes ready to flop over the fence to distract the bull.

The bull, with his tongue out, his barrel heaving, was watching the gypsy. He thought he had him now. Back against the red planks. Only a short charge away. The bull watched him.

The gypsy bent back, drew back his arms, the banderillos pointing at the bull. He called to the bull, stamped one foot. The bull was suspicious. He wanted the man. No more barbs in the shoulder.

Fuentes walked a little closer to the bull. Bent back. Called again. Somebody in the crowd shouted a warning.

"He's too damn close," Zurito said.

"Watch him," Retana's man said.

Leaning back, inciting the bull with the banderillos, Fuentes jumped, both feet off the ground. As he jumped the bull's tail rose and he charged. Fuentes came down on his toes, arms straight out, whole body arching forward, and drove the shafts straight down as he swung his body clear of the right horn.

The bull crashed into the barrera where the flopping capes had attracted his eye as he lost the man.

The gypsy came running along the barrera toward Manuel, taking the applause of the crowd. His vest was ripped where he had not quite cleared the point of the horn. He was happy about it, showing it to the spectators. He made the tour of the ring. Zurito saw him go by, smiling, pointing at his vest. He smiled.

Somebody else was planting the last pair of banderillos. Nobody was paying any attention.

Retana's man tucked a baton inside the red cloth of a muleta, folded the cloth over it, and handed it over the barrera to Manuel. He reached in the leather sword-case, took out a sword, and holding it by its leather scabbard, reached it over the fence to Manuel. Manuel pulled the blade out by the red hilt and the scabbard fell limp.

He looked at Zurito. The big man saw he was sweating.

"Now you get him, kid," Zurito said.

Manuel nodded.

"He's in good shape," Zurito said.

"Just like you want him," Retana's man assured him.

Manuel nodded.

The trumpeter, up under the roof, blew for the final act, and Manuel walked across the arena toward where, up in the dark boxes, the president must be.

In the front row of seats the substitute bull-fight critic of *El Heraldo* took a long drink of the warm champagne. He had decided it was not worth while to write a running story and would write up the corrida back in the office. What the hell was it anyway? Only a nocturnal. If he missed anything he would get it out of the morning papers. He took another drink of the champagne. He had a date at Maxim's at twelve. Who were these bull-fighters anyway? Kids and bums. A bunch of bums. He put his pad of paper in his pocket and looked over toward Manuel, standing very much alone in the ring, gesturing with his hat in a salute toward a box he could not see high up in the dark plaza. Out in the ring the bull stood quiet, looking at nothing.

"I dedicate this bull to you, Mr. President, and to the public of Madrid, the most intelligent and generous of the world," was what Manuel was saying. It was a formula. He said it all. It was a little long for nocturnal use.

He bowed at the dark, straightened, tossed his hat over his shoulder, and, carrying the muleta in his left hand and the sword in his right, walked out toward the bull.

Manuel walked toward the bull. The bull looked at him; his eyes were quick. Manuel noticed the way the banderillos hung down on his left shoulder and the steady sheen of blood from Zurito's picing. He noticed the way the bull's feet were. As he walked forward, holding the muleta in his left hand and the sword in his right, he watched the bull's feet. The bull could not charge without gathering his feet together. Now he stood square on them, dully.

Manuel walked toward him, watching his feet. This was all right. He could do this. He must work to get the bull's head down, so he could go in past the horns and kill him. He did not think about the sword, not about killing the bull. He thought about one thing at a time. The coming things oppressed him, though. Walking forward, watching the bull's feet, he saw successively his eyes, his wet muzzle, and the wide, forward-pointing spread of his horns. The bull had light circles about his eyes. His eyes watched Manuel. He felt he was going to get this little one with the white face.

Standing still now and spreading the red cloth of the muleta with the sword, pricking the point into the cloth so that the sword, now held in his left hand, spread the red flannel like the jib of a boat, Manuel noticed the points of the bull's horns. One of them was splintered from banging against the barrera. The other was sharp as a porcupine quill. Manuel noticed while spreading the muleta that the white base of the horn was stained red. While he noticed these things he did not lose sight of the bull's feet. The bull watched Manuel steadily.

He's on the defensive now, Manuel thought. He's reserving himself. I've got to bring him out of that and get his head down. Always get his head down. Zurito had his head down once, but he's come back. He'll bleed when I start him going and that will bring it down.

Holding the muleta, with the sword in his left hand widening it in front of him, he called to the bull.

The bull looked at him.

He leaned back insultingly and shook the wide-spread flannel.

The bull saw the muleta. It was a bright scarlet under the arc-light. The bull's legs tightened.

Here he comes. Whoosh! Manuel turned as the bull came and raised the muleta so that it passed over the bull's horns and swept down his broad back from head to tail. The bull had gone clean up in the air with the charge. Manuel had not moved.

At the end of the pass the bull turned like a cat coming around a corner and faced Manuel.

He was on the offensive again. His heaviness was gone. Manuel noted the fresh blood shining down the black shoulder and dripping down the bull's leg. He drew the sword out of the muleta and held it in his right hand. The muleta held low down in his left hand, leaning toward the left, he called to the bull. The bull's legs tightened, his eyes on the muleta. Here he comes, Manuel thought. Yuh!

He swung with the charge, sweeping the muleta ahead of the bull, his feet firm, the sword following the curve, a point of light under the arcs.

The bull recharged as the pase natural finished and Manuel raised the muleta for a pase de pecho. Firmly planted, the bull came by his chest under the raised muleta. Manuel leaned his head back to avoid the clattering banderillo shafts. The hot, black bull body touched his chest as it passed.

Too damn close, Manuel thought. Zurito, leaning on the barrera, spoke rapidly to the gypsy, who trotted out toward Manuel with a cape. Zurito pulled his hat down low and looked out across the arena at Manuel.

Manuel was facing the bull again, the muleta held low and to the left. The bull's head was down as he watched the muleta.

"If it was Belmonte doing that stuff, they'd go crazy," Retana's man said.

Zurito said nothing. He was watching Manuel out in the centre of the arena.

"Where did the boss dig this fellow up?" Retana's man asked.

"Out of the hospital," Zurito said.

"That's where he's going damn quick," Retana's man said.

Zurito turned on him.

"Knock on that," he said, pointing to the barrera.

"I was just kidding, man," Retana's man said.

"Knock on the wood."

Retana's man leaned forward and knocked three times on the barrera.

"Watch the faena," Zurito said.

Out in the centre of the ring, under the lights, Manuel was kneeling, facing the bull, and as he raised the muleta in both hands the bull charged, tail up.

Manuel swung his body clear and, as the bull recharged, brought around the muleta in a half-circle that pulled the bull to his knees.

"Why, that one's a great bull-fighter," Retana's man said.

"No, he's not," said Zurito.

Manuel stood up and, the muleta in his left hand, the sword in his right, acknowledged the applause from the dark plaza.

The bull had humped himself up from his knees and stood waiting, his head hung low.

Zurito spoke to two of the other lads of the cuadrilla and they ran out to stand back of Manuel with their capes. There were four men back of him now. Hernandez had followed him since he first came out with the muleta. Fuentes stood watching, his cape held against his body, tall, in repose, watching lazy-eyed. Now the two came up. Hernandez motioned them to stand one at each side. Manuel stood alone, facing the bull.

Manuel waved back the men with the capes. Stepping back cautiously, they saw his face was white and sweating.

Didn't they know enough to keep back? Did they want to catch the bull's eye with the capes after he was fixed and ready? He had enough to worry about without that kind of thing.

The bull was standing, his four feet square, looking at the muleta. Manuel furled the muleta in his left hand. The bull's eyes watched it. His body was heavy on his feet. He carried his head low, but not too low.

Manuel lifted the muleta at him. The bull did not move. Only his eyes watched.

He's all lead, Manuel thought. He's all square. He's framed right. He'll take it.

He thought in bull-fight terms. Sometimes he had a thought and the particular piece of slang would not come into his mind and he could not realize the thought. His instincts and his knowledge worked automatically, and his brain worked slowly and in words. He knew all about bulls. He did not have to think about them. He just did the right thing. His eyes noted things and his body performed the necessary measures without thought. If he thought about it, he would be gone.

Now, facing the bull, he was conscious of many things at the same time. There were the horns, the one splintered, the other smoothly sharp, the need to profile himself toward the left horn, lance himself short and straight, lower the muleta so the bull would follow it, and, going in over the horns, put the sword all the way into a little spot about as big as a five-peseta piece straight in back of the neck, between the sharp pitch of the bull's shoulders. He must do all this and must then come out from between the horns. He was conscious he must do all this, but his only thought was in words: "Corto y derecho."

"Corto y derecho," he thought, furling the muleta. Short and straight. Corto y derecho, he drew the sword out of the muleta, profiled on the splintered left horn, dropped the muleta across his body, so his right hand with the sword on the level with his eye made the sign of the cross, and, rising on his toes, sighted along the dipping blade of the sword at the spot high up between the bull's shoulders.

Corto y derecho he lanced himself on the bull.

There was a shock, and he felt himself go up in the air. He pushed on the sword as he went up and over, and it flew out of his hand. He hit the ground and the bull was on him. Manuel, lying on the ground, kicked at the bull's muzzle with his slippered feet. Kicking, kicking, the bull after him, missing him in his excitement, bumping him with his head, driving the horns into the sand. Kicking like a man keeping a ball in the air, Manuel kept the bull from getting a clean thrust at him.

Manuel felt the wind on his back from the capes flopping at the bull, and then the bull was gone, gone over him in a rush. Dark, as his belly went over. Not even stepped on.

Manuel stood up and picked up the muleta. Fuentes handed him the sword. It was bent where it had struck the shoulder-blade. Manuel straightened it on his knee and ran toward the bull, standing now beside one of the dead horses. As he ran, his jacket flopped where it had been ripped under his armpit.

"Get him out of there," Manuel shouted to the gypsy. The bull had smelled the blood of the dead horse and ripped into the canvas-cover with his horns. He charged Fuentes's cape, with the canvas hanging from his splintered horn, and the crowd laughed. Out in the ring, he tossed his head to rid himself of the canvas. Hernandez, running up from behind him, grabbed the end of the canvas and neatly lifted it off the horn.

The bull followed it in a half-charge and stopped still. He was on the defensive again. Manuel was walking toward him with the sword and muleta. Manuel swung the muleta before him. The bull would not charge.

Manuel profiled toward the bull, sighting along the dipping blade of the sword. The bull was motionless, seemingly dead on his feet, incapable of another charge.

Manuel rose to his toes, sighting along the steel, and charged.

Again there was the shock and he felt himself being borne back in a rush, to strike hard on the sand. There was no chance of kicking this time. The bull was on top of him. Manuel lay as though dead, his head on his arms, and the bull bumped him. Bumped his back, bumped his face in the sand. He felt the horn go into the sand between his folded arms. The bull hit him in the small of the back. His face drove into the sand. The horn drove through one of his sleeves and the bull ripped it off. Manuel was tossed clear and the bull followed the capes.

Manuel got up, found the sword and muleta, tried the point of the sword with his thumb, and then ran toward the barrera for a new sword.

Retana's man handed him the sword over the edge of the barrera. "Wipe off your face," he said.

Manuel, running again toward the bull, wiped his bloody face with his handkerchief. He had not seen Zurito. Where was Zurito?

The cuadrilla had stepped away from the bull and waited with their capes. The bull stood, heavy and dull again after the action.

Manuel walked toward him with the muleta. He stopped and shook it. The bull did not respond. He passed it right and left, left and right before the bull's muzzle. The bull's eyes watched it and turned with the swing, but he would not charge. He was waiting for Manuel.

Manuel was worried. There was nothing to do but go in. Corto y derecho. He profiled close to the bull, crossed the muleta in front of his body and charged. As he pushed in the sword, he jerked his body to the left to clear the horn. The bull passed him and the sword shot up in the air, twinkling under the arc-lights, to fall red-hilted on the sand.

Manuel ran over and picked it up. It was bent and he straightened it over his knee.

As he came running toward the bull, fixed again now, he passed Hernandez standing with his cape.

"He's all bone," the boy said encouragingly.

Manuel nodded, wiping his face. He put the bloody handkerchief in his pocket.

There was the bull. He was close to the barrera now. Damn him. Maybe he was all bone. Maybe there was not any place for the sword to go in. The hell there wasn't! He'd show them.

He tried a pass with the muleta and the bull did not move. Manuel chopped the muleta back and forth in front of the bull. Nothing doing.

He furled the muleta, drew the sword out, profiled and drove in on the bull. He felt the sword buckle as he shoved it in, leaning his weight on it, and then it shot high in the air, end-over-ending into the crowd. Manuel had jerked clear as the sword jumped.

The first cushions thrown down out of the dark missed him. Then one hit him in the face, his bloody face looking toward the crowd. They were coming down fast. Spotting the sand. Somebody threw an empty champagne-bottle from close range. It hit Manuel on the foot. He stood there watching the dark, where the things were coming from. Then something whished through the air and struck by him. Manuel leaned over and picked it up. It was his sword. He straightened it over his knee and gestured with it to the crowd.

"Thank you," he said. "Thank you."

Oh, the dirty bastards! Dirty bastards! Oh, the lousy, dirty bastards! He kicked into a cushion as he ran.

There was the bull. The same as ever. All right, you dirty, lousy bastard!

Manuel passed the muleta in front of the bull's black muzzle.

Nothing doing.

You won't! All right. He stepped close and jammed the sharp peak of the muleta into the bull's damp muzzle.

The bull was on him as he jumped back and as he tripped on a cushion he felt the horn go into him, into his side. He grabbed the horn with his two hands and rode backward, holding tight onto the place. The bull tossed him and he was clear. He lay still. It was all right. The bull was gone.

He got up coughing and feeling broken and gone. The dirty bastards!

"Give me the sword," he shouted. "Give me the stuff."

Fuentes came up with the muleta and the sword.

Hernandez put his arm around him.

"Go on to the infirmary, man," he said. "Don't be a damn fool."

"Get away from me," Manuel said. "Get to hell away from me."

He twisted free. Hernandez shrugged his shoulders. Manuel ran toward the bull.

There was the bull standing, heavy, firmly planted.

All right, you bastard! Manuel drew the sword out of the muleta, sighted with the same movement, and flung himself onto the bull. He felt the sword go in all the way. Right up to the guard. Four fingers and his thumb into the bull. The blood was hot on his knuckles, and he was on top of the bull.

The bull lurched with him as he lay on, and seemed to sink; then he was standing clear. He looked at the bull going down slowly over on his side, then suddenly four feet in the air.

Then he gestured at the crowd, his hand warm from the bull blood.

All right, you bastards! He wanted to say something, but he started to cough. It was hot and choking. He looked down for the muleta. He must go over and salute the president. President hell! He was sitting down looking at something. It was the bull. His four feet up. Thick tongue out. Things crawling around on his belly and under his legs. Crawling where the hair was thin. Dead bull. To hell with the bull! To hell with them all! He started to get to his feet and commenced to cough. He sat down again, coughing. Somebody came and pushed him up.

They carried him across the ring to the infirmary, running with him across the sand, standing blocked at the gate as the mules came in, then around under the dark passageway, men grunting as they took him up the stairway, and then laid him down.

The doctor and two men in white were waiting for him. They laid him out on the table. They were cutting away his shirt. Manuel felt tired. His whole chest felt scalding inside. He started to cough and they held something to his mouth. Everybody was very busy.

There was an electric light in his eyes. He shut his eyes.

He heard some one coming very heavily up the stairs. Then he did not hear it. Then he heard a noise far off. That was the crowd. Well, somebody would have to kill his other bull. They had cut away all his shirt. The doctor smiled at him. There was Retana.

"Hello, Retana!" Manuel said. He could not hear his voice.

Retana smiled at him and said something. Manuel could not hear it.

Zurito stood beside the table, bending over where the doctor was working. He was in his picador clothes, without his hat.

Zurito said something to him. Manuel could not hear it.

Zurito was speaking to Retana. One of the men in white smiled and handed Retana a pair of scissors. Retana gave them to Zurito. Zurito said something to Manuel. He could not hear it.

To hell with this operating-table! He'd been on plenty of operating-tables before. He was not going to die. There would be a priest if he was going to die.

Zurito was saying something to him. Holding up the scissors.

That was it. They were going to cut off his coleta. They were going to cut off his pigtail.

Manuel sat up on the operating-table. The doctor stepped back, angry. Some one grabbed him and held him.

"You couldn't do a thing like that, Manos," he said.

He heard suddenly, clearly, Zurito's voice.

"That's all right," Zurito said. "I won't do it. I was joking."

"I was going good," Manuel said. "I didn't have any luck. That was all."

Manuel lay back. They had put something over his face. It was all familiar. He inhaled deeply. He felt very tired. He was very, very tired. They took the thing away from his face.

"I was going good," Manuel said weakly. "I was going great."

Retana looked at Zurito and started for the door.

"I'll stay here with him," Zurito said.

Retana shrugged his shoulders.

Manuel opened his eyes and looked at Zurito.

"Wasn't I going good, Manos?" he asked, for confirmation.

"Sure," said Zurito. "You were going great."

The doctor's assistant put the cone over Manuel's face and he inhaled deeply. Zurito stood awkwardly, watching.

❂ PART IV ❂

DANGEROUS GAME

GREEN HILLS OF AFRICA (CHAPTERS 1–4)

From THE SHORT STORIES
OF ERNEST HEMINGWAY

The Short Happy Life of Francis Macomber

From THE AFRICAN JOURNAL

Miss Mary's Lion

GREEN HILLS OF AFRICA

(*CHAPTERS 1-4*)

PART I

PURSUIT AND CONVERSATION

1

WE were sitting in the blind that Wanderobo hunters had built of twigs and branches at the edge of the salt-lick when we heard the truck coming. At first it was far away and no one could tell what the noise was. Then it was stopped and we hoped it had been nothing or perhaps only the wind. Then it moved slowly nearer, unmistakable now, louder and louder until, agonizing in a clank of loud irregular explosions, it passed close behind us to go on up the road. The theatrical one of the two trackers stood up.

"It is finished," he said.

I put my hand to my mouth and motioned him down.

"It is finished," he said again and spread his arms wide. I had never liked him and I liked him less now.

"After," I whispered. M'Cola shook his head. I looked at his bald black skull and he turned his face a little so that I saw the thin Chinese hairs at the corners of his mouth.

"No good," he said. *"Hapana m'uzuri."*

"Wait a little," I told him. He bent his head down again so that it would not show above the dead branches and we sat there in the dust of the hole until it was too dark to see the front sight on my rifle; but nothing more came. The theatrical tracker was impatient and restless. A little before the last of the light was gone he whispered to M'Cola that it was now too dark to shoot.

"Shut up, you," M'Cola told him. "The Bwana can shoot after you cannot see."

The other tracker, the educated one, gave another demonstration of his education by scratching his name, Abdullah, on the black skin of his leg with a sharp twig. I watched without admiration and

M'Cola looked at the word without a shadow of expression on his face. After a while the tracker scratched it out.

Finally I made a last sight against what was left of the light and saw it was no use, even with the large aperture.

M'Cola was watching.

"No good," I said.

"Yes," he agreed, in Swahili. "Go to camp?"

"Yes."

We stood up and made our way out of the blind and out through the trees, walking on the sandy loam, feeling our way between trees and under branches, back to the road. A mile along the road was the car. As we came alongside, Kamau, the driver, put the lights on.

The truck had spoiled it. That afternoon we had left the car up the road and approached the salt-lick very carefully. There had been a little rain, the day before, though not enough to flood the lick, which was simply an opening in the trees with a patch of earth worn into deep circles and grooved at the edges with hollows where the animals had licked the dirt for salt, and we had seen long, heart-shaped, fresh tracks of four greater kudu bulls that had been on the salt the night before, as well as many newly pressed tracks of lesser kudu. There was also a rhino who, from the tracks and the kicked-up mound of strawy dung, came there each night. The blind had been built at close arrow-shot of the lick and sitting, leaning back, knees high, heads low, in a hollow half full of ashes and dust, watching through the dried leaves and thin branches I had seen a lesser kudu bull come out of the brush to the edge of the opening where the salt was and stand there, heavy-necked, gray, and handsome, the horns spiralled against the sun while I sighted on his chest and then refused the shot, wanting not to frighten the greater kudu that should surely come at dusk. But before we ever heard the truck the bull had heard it and run off into the trees and everything else that had been moving, in the bush on the flats, or coming down from the small hills through the trees, coming toward the salt, had halted at that exploding, clanking sound. They would come, later, in the dark; but then it would be too late.

So now, going along the sandy track of the road in the car, the lights picking out the eyes of night birds that squatted close on the sand until the bulk of the car was on them and they rose in soft panic;

passing the fires of the travellers that all moved to the westward by day along this road, abandoning the famine country that was ahead of us; me sitting, the butt of my rifle on my foot, the barrel in the crook of my left arm, a flask of whiskey between my knees, pouring the whiskey into a tin cup and passing it over my shoulder in the dark for M'Cola to pour water into it from the canteen, drinking this, the first one of the day, the finest one there is, and looking at the thick bush we passed in the dark, feeling the cool wind of the night and smelling the good smell of Africa, I was altogether happy.

Then ahead we saw a big fire and as we came up and passed, I made out a truck beside the road. I told Kamau to stop and go back and as we backed into the firelight there was a short, bandy-legged man with a Tyroler hat, leather shorts, and an open shirt standing before an un-hooded engine in a crowd of natives.

"Can we help?" I asked him.

"No," he said. "Unless you are a mechanic. It has taken a dislike to me. All engines dislike me."

"Do you think it could be the timer? It sounded as though it might be a timing knock when you went past us."

"I think it is much worse than that. It sounds to be something very bad."

"If you can get to our camp we have a mechanic."

"How far is it?"

"About twenty miles."

"In the morning I will try it. Now I am afraid to make it go farther with that noise of death inside. It is trying to die because it dislikes me. Well, I dislike it too. But if I die it would not annoy it."

"Will you have a drink?" I held out the flask. "Hemingway is my name."

"Kandisky," he said and bowed. "Hemingway is a name I have heard. Where? Where have I heard it? Oh, yes. The *Dichter*. You know Hemingway the poet?"

"Where did you read him?"

"In the *Querschnitt*."

"That is me," I said, very pleased. The *Querschnitt* was a German magazine I had written some rather obscene poems for, and published a long story in, years before I could sell anything in America.

"This is very strange," the man in the Tyroler hat said. "Tell me, what do you think of Ringelnatz?"

"He is splendid."

"So. You like Ringelnatz. Good. What do you think of Heinrich Mann?"

"He is no good."

"You believe it?"

"All I know is that I cannot read him."

"He is no good at all. I see we have things in common. What are you doing here?"

"Shooting."

"Not ivory, I hope."

"No. For kudu."

"Why should any man shoot a kudu? You, an intelligent man, a poet, to shoot kudu."

"I haven't shot any yet," I said. "But we've been hunting them hard now for ten days. We would have got one tonight if it hadn't been for your lorry."

"That poor lorry. But you should hunt for a year. At the end of that time you have shot everything and you are sorry for it. To hunt for one special animal is nonsense. Why do you do it?"

"I like to do it."

"Of course, if you *like* to do it. Tell me, what do you really think of Rilke?"

"I have read only the one thing."

"Which?"

"The Cornet."

"You liked it?"

"Yes."

"I have no patience with it. It is snobbery. Valéry, yes. I see the point of Valéry; although there is much snobbery too. Well at least you do not kill elephants."

"I'd kill a big enough one."

"How big?"

"A seventy pounder. Maybe smaller."

"I see there are things we do not agree on. But it is a pleasure to meet one of the great old *Querschnitt* group. Tell me what is Joyce like? I have not the money to buy it. Sinclair Lewis is nothing. I bought it. No. No. Tell me tomorrow. You do not mind if I am camped near? You are with friends? You have a white hunter?"

"With my wife. We would be delighted. Yes, a white hunter."

"Why is he not out with you?"

"He believes you should hunt kudu alone."

"It is better not to hunt them at all. What is he? English?"

"Yes."

"Bloody English?"

"No. Very nice. You will like him."

"You must go. I must not keep you. Perhaps I will see you to-morrow. It was very strange that we should meet."

"Yes," I said. "Have them look at the truck tomorrow. Anything we can do."

"Good night," he said. "Good trip."

"Good night," I said. We started off and I saw him walking toward the fire waving an arm at the natives. I had not asked him why he had twenty up-country natives with him, nor where he was going. Looking back, I had asked him nothing. I do not like to ask questions, and where I was brought up it was not polite. But here we had not seen a white man for two weeks, not since we had left Babati to go south, and then to run into one on this road where you met only an occasional Indian trader and the steady migration of the natives out of the famine country, to have him look like a caricature of Benchley in Tyrolean costume, to have him know your name, to call you a poet, to have read the *Querschnitt,* to be an admirer of Joachim Ringelnatz and to want to talk about Rilke, was too fantastic to deal with. So, just then, to crown this fantasy, the lights of the car showed three tall, conical, mounds of something smoking in the road ahead. I motioned to Kamau to stop, and putting on the brakes we skidded just short of them. They were from two to three feet high and when I touched one it was quite warm.

"*Tembo,*" M'Cola said.

It was dung from elephants that had just crossed the road, and in the cold of the evening you could see it steaming. In a little while we were in camp.

Next morning I was up and gone to another salt-lick before day-light. There was a kudu bull on the lick when we approached through the trees and he gave a loud bark, like a dog's but higher in pitch and sharply throaty, and was gone, making no noise at first, then crashing in the brush when he was well away; and we never saw him. This lick had an impossible approach. Trees grew around its open area so that it was as though the game were in the blind and you had to come to them across the open. The only way to make it would have been for one man to go alone and crawl and then it would be impossible to get any sort of a close shot through the interlacing trees until you were within twenty yards. Of course once you were inside the protecting trees, and in the blind, you were wonderfully placed, for anything that came to the salt had to come out in the open twenty-five yards from any cover. But though we stayed until eleven o'clock nothing came. We smoothed the dust of the lick carefully with our feet so that any new tracks would show when we came back again and walked the two miles to the road. Being hunted, the game had learned to come only at night and leave before daylight. One bull had stayed and our spooking him that morning would make it even more difficult now.

This was the tenth day we had been hunting greater kudu and I had not seen a mature bull yet. We had only three days more because the rains were moving north each day from Rhodesia and unless we were prepared to stay where we were through the rains we must be out as far as Handeni before they came. We had set the seventeenth of February as the last safe date to leave. Every morning now it took the heavy, wooled sky an hour or so longer to clear and you could feel the rains coming, as they moved steadily north, as surely as though you watched them on a chart.

Now it is pleasant to hunt something that you want very much over a long period of time, being outwitted, out-manœuvred, and failing at the end of each day, but having the hunt and knowing every time you are out that, sooner or later, your luck will change and that you will get the chance that you are seeking. But it is not pleasant to have a time limit by which you must get your kudu or perhaps never get it, nor even see one. It is not the way hunting should be. It is too much like those boys who used to be sent to Paris with two years in which to make good as writers or painters after which, if they had not made good, they could go home and into their fathers' business. The way to hunt is for as long as you live against as long as there is such and such an animal; just as the way to paint is as long as there is you and colors and canvas, and to write as long as you can live and there is pencil and paper or ink or any machine to do it with, or anything you care to write about, and you feel a fool, and you are a fool, to do it any other way. But here we were, now, caught by time, by the season, and by the running out of our money, so that what should have been as much fun to do each day whether you killed or not was being forced into that most exciting perversion of life; the necessity of accomplishing something in less time than should truly be allowed for its doing. So, coming in at noon, up since two hours before daylight, with only three days left, I was starting to be nervous about it, and there, at the table under the dining tent fly, talking away, was Kandisky of the Tyroler pants. I had forgotten all about him.

"Hello. Hello," he said. "No success? Nothing doing? Where is the kudu?"

"He coughed once and went away," I said. "Hello, girl."

She smiled. She was worried too. The two of them had been listening since daylight for a shot. Listening all the time, even when our guest had arrived; listening while writing letters, listening while reading, listening when Kandisky came back and talked.

"You did not shoot him?"

"No. Nor see him." I saw that Pop was worried too, and a little nervous. There had evidently been considerable talking going on.

"Have a beer, Colonel," he said to me.

"We spooked one," I reported. "No chance of a shot. There were plenty of tracks. Nothing more came. The wind was blowing around. Ask the boys about it."

"As I was telling Colonel Phillips," Kandisky began, shifting his leather-breeched behind and crossing one heavy-calved, well-haired, bare leg over the other, "you must not stay here too long. You must realize the rains are coming. There is one stretch of twelve miles beyond here you can never get through if it rains. It is impossible."

"So he's been telling me," Pop said. "I'm a Mister, by the way. We use these military titles as nicknames. No offense if you're a Colonel yourself." Then to me, "Damn these salt-licks. If you'd leave them alone you'd get one."

"They ball it all up," I agreed. "You're so sure of a shot sooner or later on the lick."

"Hunt the hills too."

"I'll hunt them, Pop."

"What is killing a kudu, anyway?" Kandisky asked. "You should not take it so seriously. It is nothing. In a year you kill twenty."

"Best not say anything about that to the game department, though," Pop said.

"You misunderstand," Kandisky said. "I mean in a year a man could. Of course no man would wish to."

"Absolutely," Pop said. "If he lived in kudu country, he could. They're the commonest big antelope in this bush country. It's just that when you want to see them you don't."

"I kill nothing, you understand," Kandisky told us. "Why are you not more interested in the natives?"

"We are," my wife assured him.

"They are really interesting. Listen—" Kandisky said, and he spoke on to her.

"The hell of it is," I said to Pop, "when I'm in the hills I'm sure the bastards are down there on the salt. The cows are in the hills but I don't believe the bulls are with them now. Then you get there in the evening and there are the tracks. They *have* been on the lousy salt. I think they come any time."

"Probably they do."

"I'm sure we get different bulls there. They probably only come to the salt every couple of days. Some are certainly spooked because Karl shot that one. If he'd only killed it clean instead of following it through the whole damn countryside. Christ, if he'd only kill any damn thing clean. Other new ones will come in. All we have to do is to wait them out, though. Of course they can't all know about it. But he's spooked this country to hell."

"He gets so very excited," Pop said. "But he's a good lad. He made a beautiful shot on that leopard, you know. You don't want them killed any cleaner than that. Let it quiet down again."

"Sure. I don't mean anything when I curse him."

"What about staying in the blind all day?"

"The damned wind started to go round in a circle. It blew our scent every bloody direction. No bloody use to sit there broadcasting it. If the damn wind would hold. Abdullah took an ash can today."

"I saw him starting off with it."

"There wasn't a bit of wind when we stalked the salt and there was just light to shoot. He tried the wind with the ashes all the way. I went alone with Abdullah and left the others behind and we went quietly. I had on these crêpe-soled boots and it's soft cotton dirt. The bastard spooked at fifty yards."

"Did you ever see their ears?"

"Did I ever see their ears? If I can see the bastard's ears, the skinner can work on him."

"They're bastards," Pop said. "I hate this salt-lick business. They're not as smart as we think. The trouble is you're working on them where they are smart. They've been shot at there ever since there's been salt."

"That's what makes it fun," I said. "I'd be glad to do it for a month. I like to hunt sitting on my tail. No sweat. No nothing. Sit there and catch flies and feed them to the ant lions in the dust. I like it. But what about the time?"

"That's it. The bloody time."

"So," Kandisky was saying to my wife. "That is what you should see. The big ngomas. The big native dance festivals. The real ones."

"Listen," I said to Pop. "The other lick, the one I was at last night, is fool-proof except for being near that *bloody* road."

"The trackers say it is really the property of the lesser kudu. It's a long way too. It's eighty miles there and back."

"I know. But there were four *big* bull tracks. It's certain. If it wasn't for that truck last night. What about staying there tonight? Then I'd get the night and the early morning and give this lick a rest. There's a big rhino there too. Big track, anyway."

"Good," Pop said. "Shoot the damn rhino too." He hated to have anything killed except what we were after, no killing on the side, no ornamental killing, no killing to kill, only when you wanted it more than you wanted not to kill it, only when getting it was necessary to his being first in his trade, and I saw he was offering up the rhino to please me.

"I won't kill him unless he's good," I promised.

"Shoot the bastard," Pop said, making a gift of him.

"Ah, Pop," I said.

"Shoot him," said Pop. "You'll enjoy it, being by yourself. You can sell the horn if you don't want it. You've still one on your license."

"So," said Kandisky. "You have arrested a plan of campaign? You have decided on how to outwit the poor animals?"

"Yes," I said. "How is the truck?"

"That lorry is finished," the Austrian said. "In a way I am glad. It was too much of a symbol. It was all that remained of my shamba. Now everything is gone and it is much simpler."

"What is a shamba?" asked P. O. M., my wife. "I've been hearing about them for months. I'm afraid to ask about those words every one uses."

"A plantation," he said. "It is all gone except that lorry. With the lorry I carry laborers to the shamba of an Indian. It is a very rich Indian who raises sisal. I am a manager for this Indian. An Indian can make a profit from a sisal shamba."

"From anything," Pop said.

"Yes. Where we fail, where we would starve, he makes money. This Indian is very intelligent, however. He values me. I represent European organization. I come now from organizing recruitment of the natives. This takes time. It is impressive. I have been away from my family for three months. The organization is organized. You do it in a week as easily, but it is not so impressive."

"And your wife?" asked mine.

"She waits at my house, the house of the manager, with my daughter."

"Does she love you very much?" my wife asked.

"She must, or she would be gone long ago."

"How old is the daughter?"

"She is thirteen now."

"It must be very nice to have a daughter."

"You cannot know how nice it is. It is like a second wife. My wife knows now all I think, all I say, all I believe, all I can do, all that I cannot do and cannot be. I know also about my wife—completely. But now there is always someone you do not know, who does not know you, who loves you in ignorance and is strange to you both. Some one very attractive that is yours and not yours and that makes the conversation more—how shall I say? Yes, it is like—what do you call—having here with you—with the two of you—yes there— It is the Heinz Tomato Ketchup on the daily food."

"That's very good," I said.

"We have books," he said. "I cannot buy new books now but we can always talk. Ideas and conversation are very interesting. We discuss all things. Everything. We have a very interesting mental life. Formerly, with the shamba, we had the *Querschnitt*. That gave you a feeling of belonging, of being made a part of, to a very brilliant group of people. The people one would see if one saw whom one wished to see. You know all of those people? You must know them."

"Some of them," I said. "Some in Paris. Some in Berlin."

I did not wish to destroy anything this man had, and so I did not go into those brilliant people in detail.

"They're marvellous," I said, lying.

"I envy you to know them," he said. "And tell me, who is the greatest writer in America?"

"My husband," said my wife.

"No. I do not mean for you to speak from family pride. I mean who really? Certainly not Upton Sinclair. Certainly not Sinclair Lewis. Who is your Thomas Mann? Who is your Valéry?"

"We do not have great writers," I said. "Something happens to our good writers at a certain age. I can explain but it is quite long and may bore you."

"Please explain," he said. "This is what I enjoy. This is the best part of life. The life of the mind. This is not killing kudu."

"You haven't heard it yet," I said.

"Ah, but I can see it coming. You must take more beer to loosen your tongue."

"It's loose," I told him. "It's always too bloody loose. But _you_ don't drink anything."

"No, I never drink. It is not good for the mind. It is unnecessary. But tell me. Please tell me."

"Well," I said, "we have had, in America, skillful writers. Poe is a skillful writer. It is skillful, marvellously constructed, and it is dead. We have had writers of rhetoric who had the good fortune to find a little, in a chronicle of another man and from voyaging, of how things, actual things, can be, whales for instance, and this knowledge is wrapped in the rhetoric like plums in a pudding. Occasionally it is there, alone, unwrapped in pudding, and it is good. This is Melville. But the people who praise it, praise it for the rhetoric which is not important. They put a mystery in which is not there."

"Yes," he said. "I see. But it is the mind working, its ability to work, which makes the rhetoric. Rhetoric is the blue sparks from the dynamo."

"Sometimes. And sometimes it is only blue sparks and what is the dynamo driving?"

"So. Go on."

"I've forgotten."

"No. Go on. Do not pretend to be stupid."

"Did you ever get up before daylight——"

"Every morning," he said. "Go on."

"All right. There were others who wrote like exiled English colonials from an England of which they were never a part to a newer England that they were making. Very good men with the small, dried, and excellent wisdom of Unitarians; men of letters; Quakers with a sense of humor."

"Who were these?"

"Emerson, Hawthorne, Whittier, and Company. All our early classics who did not know that a new classic does not bear any resemblance to the classics that have preceded it. It can steal from anything that it is better than, anything that is not a classic, all classics do that. Some writers are only born to help another writer to write one sentence. But it cannot derive from or resemble a previous classic. Also all these men were gentlemen, or wished to be. They were all very respectable. They did not use the words that people always have used in speech, the words that survive in language. Nor would you gather that they had bodies. They had minds, yes. Nice, dry, clean minds. This is all very dull, I would not state it except that you ask for it."

"Go on."

"There is one at that time that is supposed to be really good, Thoreau. I cannot tell you about it because I have not yet been able to read it. But that means nothing because I cannot read other naturalists unless they are being extremely accurate and not literary. Naturalists should all work alone and some one else should correlate their findings for them. Writers should work alone. They should see each other only after their work is done, and not too often then. Otherwise they become like writers in New York. All angleworms in a bottle, trying to derive knowledge and nourishment from their own contact and from the bottle. Sometimes the bottle is shaped art, sometimes economics, sometimes economic-religion. But once they are in the bottle they stay there. They are lonesome outside of the bottle. They do not want to be lonesome. They are afraid to be alone in their beliefs and no woman would love any of them enough so that they could kill their lonesomeness in that woman, or pool it with hers, or make something with her that makes the rest unimportant."

"But what about Thoreau?"

"You'll have to read him. Maybe I'll be able to later. I can do nearly everything later."

"Better have some more beer, Papa."

"All right."

"What about the good writers?"

"The good writers are Henry James, Stephen Crane, and Mark Twain. That's not the order they're good in. There is no order for good writers."

"Mark Twain is a humorist. The others I do not know."

"All modern American literature comes from one book by Mark Twain called *Huckleberry Finn.* If you read it you must stop where the Nigger Jim is stolen from the boys. That is the real end. The rest is just cheating. But it's the best book we've had. All American writing comes from that. There was nothing before. There has been nothing as good since."

"What about the others?"

"Crane wrote two fine stories. *The Open Boat* and *The Blue Hotel.* The last one is the best."

"And what happened to him?"

"He died. That's simple. He was dying from the start."

"But the other two?"

"They both lived to be old men but they did not get any wiser as they got older. I don't know what they really wanted. You see we make our writers into something very strange."

"I do not understand."

"We destroy them in many ways. First, economically. They make money. It is only by hazard that a writer makes money although good books always make money eventually. Then our writers when they have made some money increase their standard of living and they are caught. They have to write to keep up their establishments, their wives, and so on, and they write slop. It is slop not on purpose but because it is hurried. Because they write when there is nothing to say or no water in the well. Because they are ambitious. Then, once they have betrayed themselves, they justify it and you get more slop. Or else they read the critics. If they believe the critics when they say they are great then they must believe them when they say they are rotten and they lose confidence. At present we have two good writers who cannot write because they have lost confidence through reading critics. If they wrote, sometimes it would be good and sometimes not so good and sometimes it would be quite bad, but the good would get out. But they have read the critics and they must write masterpieces. The masterpieces the critics said they wrote. They weren't masterpieces, of course. They were just quite good books. So now they cannot write at all. The critics have made them impotent."

"Who are these writers?"

"Their names would mean nothing to you and by now they may have written, become frightened, and be impotent again."

"But what is it that happens to American writers? Be definite."

"I was not here in the old days so I cannot tell you about them, but now there are various things. At a certain age the men writers change into Old Mother Hubbard. The women writers become Joan of Arc without the fighting. They become leaders. It doesn't matter who they lead. If they do not have followers they invent them. It is useless for those selected as followers to protest. They are accused of disloyalty. Oh, hell. There are too many things happen to them. That is one thing. The others try to save their souls with what they write. That is an easy way out. Others are ruined by the first money, the first praise, the first attack, the first time they find they cannot write, or the first time they cannot do anything else, or else they get frightened and join organizations that do their thinking for them. Or they do not know what they want. Henry James wanted to make money. He never did, of course."

"And you?"

"I am interested in other things. I have a good life but I must write because if I do not write a certain amount I do not enjoy the rest of my life."

"And what do you want?"

"To write as well as I can and learn as I go along. At the same time I have my life which I enjoy and which is a damned good life."

"Hunting kudu?"

"Yes. Hunting kudu and many other things."

"What other things?"

"Plenty of other things."

"And you know what you want?"

"Yes."

"You really like to do this, what you do now, this silliness of kudu?"

"Just as much as I like to be in the Prado."

"One is not better than the other?"

"One is as necessary as the other. There are other things, too."

"Naturally. There must be. But this sort of thing means something to you, really?"

"Truly."

"And you know what you want?"

"Absolutely, and I get it all the time."

"But it takes money."

"I could always make money and besides I have been very lucky."

"Then you are happy?"

"Except when I think of other people."

"Then you think of other people?"

"Oh, yes."

"But you do nothing for them?"

"No."

"Nothing?"

"Maybe a little."

"Do you think your writing is worth doing—as an end in itself?"

"Oh, yes."

"You are sure?"

"Very sure."

"That must be very pleasant."

"It is," I said. "It is the one altogether pleasant thing about it."

"This is getting awfully serious," my wife said.

"It's a damned serious subject."

"You see, he is really serious about something," Kandisky said. "I knew he must be serious on something besides kudu."

"The reason every one now tries to avoid it, to deny that it is important, to make it seem vain to try to do it, is because it is so difficult. Too many factors must combine to make it possible."

"What is this now?"

"The kind of writing that can be done. How far prose can be carried if any one is serious enough and has luck. There is a fourth and fifth dimension that can be gotten."

"You believe it?"

"I know it."

"And if a writer can get this?"

"Then nothing else matters. It is more important than anything he can do. The chances are, of course, that he will fail. But there is a chance that he succeeds."

"But that is poetry you are talking about."

"No. It is much more difficult than poetry. It is a prose that has never been written. But it can be written, without tricks and without cheating. With nothing that will go bad afterwards."

"And why has it not been written?"

"Because there are too many factors. First, there must be talent, much talent. Talent such as Kipling had. Then there must be discipline. The discipline of Flaubert. Then there must be the conception of what it can be and an absolute conscience as unchanging as the standard meter in Paris, to prevent faking. Then the writer must be intelligent and disinterested and above all he must survive. Try to get all these in one person and have him come through all the influences that press on a writer. The hardest thing, because time is so short, is for him to survive and get his work done. But I would like us to have such a writer and to read what he would write. What do you say? Should we talk about something else?"

"It is interesting what you say. Naturally I do not agree with everything."

"Naturally."

"What about a gimlet?" Pop asked. "Don't you think a gimlet might help?"

"Tell me first what are the things, the actual, concrete things that harm a writer?"

I was tired of the conversation which was becoming an interview. So I would make it an interview and finish it. The necessity to put a thousand intangibles into a sentence, now, before lunch, was too bloody.

"Politics, women, drink, money, ambition. And the lack of politics, women, drink, money and ambition," I said profoundly.

"He's getting much too easy now," Pop said.

"But drink. I do not understand about that. That has always seemed silly to me. I understand it as a weakness."

"It is a way of ending a day. It has great benefits. Don't you ever want to change your ideas?"

"Let's have one," Pop said. "M'Wendi!"

Pop never drank before lunch except as a mistake and I knew he was trying to help me out.

"Let's all have a gimlet," I said.

"I never drink," Kandisky said. "I will go to the lorry and fetch some fresh butter for lunch. It is fresh from Kandoa, un-salted. Very good. Tonight we will have a special dish of Viennese dessert. My cook has learned to make it very well."

He went off and my wife said: "You were getting awfully profound. What was that about all these women?"

"What women?"

"When you were talking about women."

"The hell with them," I said. "Those are the ones you get involved with when you're drunk."

"So that's what you do."

"No."

"I don't get involved with people when I'm drunk."

"Come, come," said Pop. "We're none of us ever drunk. My God, that man can talk."

"He didn't have a chance to talk after B'wana M'Kumba started."

"I did have verbal dysentery," I said.

"What about his lorry? Can we tow it in without ruining ours?"

"I think so," Pop said. "When ours comes back from Handeni."

At lunch under the green fly of the dining tent, in the shade of a big tree, the wind blowing, the fresh butter much admired, Grant's gazelle chops, mashed potatoes, green corn, and then mixed fruit for dessert, Kandisky told us why the East Indians were taking the country over.

"You see, during the war they sent the Indian troops to fight here. To keep them out of India because they feared another mutiny. They promised the Aga Khan that because they fought in Africa, Indians could come freely to settle and for business afterwards. They cannot break that promise and now the Indians have taken the country over from the Europeans. They live on nothing and they send all the money back to India. When they have made enough to go home they leave, bringing out their poor relations to take over from them and continue to exploit the country."

Pop said nothing. He would not argue with a guest at table.

"It is the Aga Khan," Kandisky said. "You are an American. You know nothing of these combinations."

"Were you with Von Lettöw?" Pop asked him.

"From the start," Kandisky said. "Until the end."

"He was a great fighter," Pop said. "I have great admiration for him."

"You fought?" Kandisky asked.

"Yes."

"I do not care for Lettöw," Kandisky said. "He fought, yes. No one ever better. When we wanted quinine he would order it captured. All supplies the same. But afterwards he cared nothing for his men. After the war I am in Germany. I go to see about indemnification for my property. 'You are an Austrian,' they say. 'You must go through Austrian channels.' So I go to Austria. 'But why did you fight?' they ask me. 'You cannot hold us responsible. Suppose you go to fight in China. That is your own affair. We cannot do anything for you.'

" 'But I went as a patriot,' I say, very foolishly. 'I fight where I can because I am an Austrian and I know my duty.' 'Yes,' they say. 'That is very beautiful. But you cannot hold us responsible for your noble sentiments.' So they passed me from one to the other and nothing. Still I love the country very much. I have lost everything here but I have more than anyone has in Europe. To me it is always interesting. The natives and the language. I have many books of notes on them. Then too, in reality, I am a king here. It is very pleasant. Waking in the morning I extend one foot and the boy places the sock on it. When I am ready I extend the other foot and he adjusts the other sock. I step from under the mosquito bar into my drawers which are held for me. Don't you think that is very marvellous?"

"It's marvellous."

"When you come back another time we must take a safari to study the natives. And shoot nothing, or only to eat. Look, I will show you a dance and sing a song."

Crouched, elbows lifting and falling, knees humping, he shuffled around the table, singing. Undoubtedly it was very fine.

"That is only one of a thousand," he said. "Now I must go for a time. You will be sleeping."

"There's no hurry. Stay around."

"No. Surely you will be sleeping. I also. I will take the butter to keep it cool."

"We'll see you at supper," Pop said.

"Now you must sleep. Good-bye."

After he was gone, Pop said: "I wouldn't believe all that about the Aga Khan, you know."

"It sounded pretty good."

"Of course he feels badly," Pop said. "Who wouldn't. Von Lettöw was a hell of a man."

"He's very intelligent," my wife said. "He talks wonderfully about the natives. But he's bitter about American women."

"So am I," said Pop. "He's a good man. You better get some shut-eye. You'll need to start about three-thirty."

"Have them call me."

Molo raised the back of the tent, propping it with sticks, so the wind blew through and I went to sleep reading, the wind coming in cool and fresh under the heated canvas.

When I woke it was time to go. There were rain clouds in the sky and it was very hot. They had packed some tinned fruit, a five-pound piece of roast meat, bread, tea, a tea pot, and some tinned milk in a whiskey box with four bottles of beer. There was a canvas water bag and a ground cloth to use as a tent. M'Cola was taking the big gun out to the car.

"There's no hurry about getting back," Pop said. "We'll look for you when we see you."

"All right."

"We'll send the truck to haul that sportsman into Handeni. He's sending his men ahead walking."

"You're sure the truck can stand it? Don't do it because he's a friend of mine."

"Have to get him out. The truck will be in tonight."

"The Memsahib's still asleep," I said. "Maybe she can get out for a walk and shoot some guineas."

"I'm here," she said. "Don't worry about us. *Oh,* I hope you get them."

"Don't send out to look for us along the road until day after tomorrow," I said. "If there's a good chance we'll stay."

"Good luck."

"Good luck, sweet. Good-bye, Mr. J. P."

2

WE were out from under the shade of camp and along the sandy river of a road, driving into the western sun, the bush thick to the edge of the sand, solid as a thicket, the little hills rising above it, and all along the road we passed groups of people making their way to the westward. Some were naked except for a greasy cloth knotted over one shoulder, and carried bows and sealed quivers of arrows. Others carried spears. The wealthy carried umbrellas and wore draped white cloth and their women walked behind them, with their pots and pans. Bundles and loads of skins were scattered along ahead on the heads of other natives. All were travelling away from the famine. And in the heat, my feet out over the side of the car to keep them away from the heat of the engine, hat low over the eyes against the sun, watching the road, the people, and all clearings in the bush for game, we drove to the westward.

Once we saw three lesser kudu cows in an open place of broken bush. Gray, big bellied, long necked, small headed, and with big ears, they moved quickly into the woods and were gone. We left the car and tracked them but there was no bull track.

A little beyond there a flock of guineas quick-legged across the road running steady-headed with the motion of trotters. As I jumped from the car and sprinted after them they rocketed up, their legs tucked close beneath them, heavy-bodied, short wings drumming, cackling, to go over the trees ahead. I dropped two that thumped hard when they fell and as they lay, wings beating, Abdullah cut their heads off so they would be legal eating. He put them in the car where M'Cola sat laughing; his old man's healthy laugh, his making-fun-of-me laugh, his bird-shooting laugh that dated from a streak of raging misses one time that had delighted him. Now when I killed, it was a joke as when we shot a hyena; the funniest joke of all. He laughed always to see the birds tumble and when I missed he roared and shook his head again and again.

"Ask him what the hell he's laughing about?" I asked Pop once.

"At B'wana," M'Cola said, and shook his head, "at the little birds."

"He thinks you're funny," Pop said.

"Goddam it. I am funny. But the hell with him."

"He thinks you're very funny," Pop said. "Now the Memsahib and I would never laugh."

"Shoot them yourself."

"No, you're the bird shot. The self-confessed bird shot," she said.

So bird shooting became this marvellous joke. If I killed, the joke was on the birds and M'Cola would shake his head and laugh and make his hands go round and round to show how the bird turned over in the air. And if I missed, I was the clown of the piece and he would look at me and shake with laughing. Only the hyenas were funnier.

Highly humorous was the hyena obscenely loping, full belly dragging, at daylight on the plain, who, shot from the stern, skittered on into speed to tumble end over end. Mirth provoking was the hyena that stopped out of range by an alkali lake to look back and, hit in the chest, went over on his back, his four feet and his full belly in the air. Nothing could be more jolly than the hyena coming suddenly wedge-headed and stinking out of high grass by a *donga,* hit at ten yards, who raced his tail in three narrowing, scampering circles until he died.

It was funny to M'Cola to see a hyena shot at close range. There was that comic slap of the bullet and the hyena's agitated surprise to find death inside of him. It was funnier to see a hyena shot at a great distance, in the heat shimmer of the plain, to see him go over backwards, to see him start that frantic circle, to see that electric speed that meant that he was racing the little nickelled death inside him. But the great joke of all, the thing M'Cola waved his hands across his face about, and turned away and shook his head and laughed, ashamed even of the hyena; the pinnacle of hyenic humor, was the hyena, the classic hyena, that hit too far back while running, would circle madly, snapping and tearing at himself until he pulled his own intestines out, and then stood there, jerking them out and eating them with relish.

"Fisi," M'Cola would say and shake his head in delighted sorrow at there being such an awful beast. Fisi, the hyena, hermaphroditic, self-eating devourer of the dead, trailer of calving cows, ham-stringer, potential biter-off of your face at night while you slept, sad yowler, camp-follower, stinking, foul, with jaws that crack the bones the lion leaves, belly dragging, loping away on the brown plain, looking back, mongrel dog-smart in the face; whack from the little Mann-

licher and then the horrid circle starting. *"Fisi,"* M'Cola laughed, ashamed of him, shaking his bald black head. *"Fisi.* Eats himself. *Fisi."*

The hyena was a dirty joke but bird shooting was a clean joke. My whiskey was a clean joke. There were many variations of that joke. Some we come to later. The Mohammedans and all religions were a joke. A joke on all the people who had them. Charo, the other gun bearer, was short, very serious and highly religious. All Ramadan he never swallowed his saliva until sunset and when the sun was almost down I'd see him watching nervously. He had a bottle with him of some sort of tea and he would finger it and watch the sun and I would see M'Cola watching him and pretending not to see. This was not outrightly funny to him. This was something that he could not laugh about openly but that he felt superior to and wondered at the silliness of it. The Mohammedan religion was very fashionable and all the higher social grades among the boys were Mohammedans. It was something that gave caste, something to believe in, something fashionable and god-giving to suffer a little for each year, something that made you superior to other people, something that gave you more complicated habits of eating, something that I understood and M'Cola did not understand, nor care about, and he watched Charo watch for the sun to set with that blank look on his face that it put on about all things that he was not a part of. Charo was deadly thirsty and truly devout and the sun set very slowly. I looked at it, red over the trees, nudged him and he grinned. M'Cola offered me the water bottle solemnly. I shook my head and Charo grinned again. M'Cola looked blank. Then the sun was down and Charo had the bottle tilted up, his Adam's apple rising and falling greedily and M'Cola looking at him and then looking away.

In the early days, before we became good friends, he did not trust me at all. When anything came up he went into this blankness. I liked Charo much better then. We understood each other on the question of religion and Charo admired my shooting and always shook hands and smiled when we had killed anything particularly good. This was flattering and pleasing. M'Cola looked on all this early shooting as a series of lucky accidents. We were supposed to shoot. We had not yet shot anything that amounted to anything and he was not really my gun bearer. He was Mr. Jackson Phillip's gun bearer and he had been loaned to me. I meant nothing to him. He did not like me nor dislike me. He was politely contemptuous of Karl. Who he liked was Mama.

The evening we killed the first lion it was dark when we came in sight of camp. The killing of the lion had been confused and unsatisfactory. It was agreed beforehand that P. O. M. should have the first shot but since it was the first lion any of us had ever shot at, and it was very late in the day, really too late to take the lion on, once he was hit we were to make a dogfight of it and any one was free to get him. This was a good plan as it was nearly sundown and if the lion got into cover, wounded, it would be too dark to do anything about it without a mess. I remember seeing the lion looking yellow and heavy-headed and enormous against a scrubby-looking tree in a patch of orchard bush and P. O. M. kneeling to shoot and wanting to tell her to sit down and make sure of him. Then there was the short-barrelled explosion of the Mannlicher and the lion was going to the left on a run, a strange, heavy-shouldered, foot-swinging, cat run. I hit him with the Springfield and he went down and spun over and I shot again, too quickly, and threw a cloud of dirt over him. But there he was, stretched out, on his belly, and, with the sun just over the top of the trees, and the grass very green, we walked up on him like a posse, or a gang of Black and Tans, guns ready and cocked, not knowing whether he was stunned or dead. When we were close M'Cola threw a stone at him. It hit him in the flank and from the way it hit you could tell he was a dead animal. I was sure P. O. M. had hit him but there was only one bullet hole, well back, just below the spine and ranging forward to come to the surface under the skin of the chest. You could feel the bullet under the skin and M'Cola made a slit and cut it out. It was a 220-grain solid bullet from the Springfield and it had raked him, going through lungs and heart.

I was so surprised by the way he had rolled over dead from the shot after we had been prepared for a charge, for heroics, and for drama, that I felt more let down than pleased. It was our first lion and we were very ignorant and this was not what we had paid to see. Charo and M'Cola both shook P. O. M.'s hand and then Charo came over and shook hands with me.

"Good shot, B'wana," he said in Swahili. *"Piga m'uzuri."*

"Did you shoot, Karl?" I asked.

"No. I was just going to when you shot."

"You didn't shoot him, Pop?"

"No. You'd have heard it." He opened the breech and took out the two big .450 No. 2's.

"I'm sure I missed him," P. O. M. said.

"I was sure you hit him. I still think you hit him," I said.

"Mama hit," M'Cola said.

"Where?" Charo asked.

"Hit," said M'Cola. "Hit."

"You rolled him over," Pop said to me. "God, he went over like a rabbit."

"I couldn't believe it."

"Mama *piga*," M'Cola said. *"Piga Simba."*

As we saw the camp fire in the dark ahead of us, coming in that night, M'Cola suddenly commenced to shout a stream of high-pitched, rapid, singing words in Wakamba ending in the word *"Simba."* Some one at the camp shouted back one word.

"Mama!" M'Cola shouted. Then another long stream. Then "Mama! Mama!"

Through the dark came all the porters, the cook, the skinner, the boys, and the headman.

"Mama!" M'Cola shouted. "Mama *piga Simba."*

The boys came dancing, crowding, and beating time and chanting something from down in their chests that started like a cough and sounded like *"Hey la Mama! Hay la Mama! Hey la Mama!"*

The rolling-eyed skinner picked P. O. M. up, the big cook and the boys held her, and the others pressing forward to lift, and if not to lift to touch and hold, they danced and sang through the dark, around the fire and to our tent.

"Hey la Mama! huh! huh! huh! Hay la Mama! huh! huh! huh!" they sang the lion dance with that deep, lion asthmatic cough in it. Then at the tent they put her down and every one, very shyly, shook hands, the boys saying *"m'uzuri, Memsahib,"* and M'Cola and the porters all saying *"m'uzuri,* Mama" with much feeling in the accenting of the word "Mama."

Afterwards in the chairs in front of the fire, sitting with the drinks, Pop said, "You shot it. M'Cola would kill any one who said you didn't."

"You know, I feel as though I did shoot it," P. O. M. said. "I don't believe I'd be able to stand it if I really had shot it. I'd be too proud. Isn't triumph marvellous?"

"Good old Mama," Karl said.

"I believe you did shoot him," I said.

"Oh, let's not go into that," P. O. M. said. "I feel so wonderful about just being supposed to have killed him. You know people never used to carry me on their shoulders much at home."

"No one knows how to behave in America," Pop said. "Most uncivilized."

"We'll carry you in Key West," Karl said. "Poor old Mama."

"Let's not talk about it," P. O. M. said. "I like it too much. Shouldn't I maybe distribute largess?"

"They didn't do it for that," Pop said. "But it is all right to give something to celebrate."

"Oh, I want to give them all a great deal of money," P. O. M. said. "Isn't triumph simply marvellous?"

"Good old Mama," I said. "You killed him."

"No I didn't. Don't lie to me. Just let me enjoy my triumph."

Anyway M'Cola did not trust me for a long time. Until P. O. M.'s license ran out, she was his favorite and we were simply a lot of people who interfered and kept Mama from shooting things. Once her license was out and she was no longer shooting, she dropped back into non-combatant status with him and as we began to hunt kudu and Pop stayed in camp and sent us out alone with the trackers, Karl with Charo and M'Cola and I together, M'Cola dropped Pop visibly in his estimation. It was only temporary of course. He was Pop's man and I believe his working estimations were only from day to day and required an unbroken series of events to have any meaning. But something had happened between us.

PURSUIT REMEMBERED

3

It dated back to the time of Droopy, after I had come back from
being ill in Nairobi and we had gone on a foot safari to hunt rhino
in the forest. Droopy was a real savage with lids to his eyes that nearly
covered them, handsome, with a great deal of style, a fine hunter
and a beautiful tracker. He was about thirty-five, I should think,
and wore only a piece of cloth, knotted over one shoulder, and a
fez that some hunter had given him. He always carried a spear.
M'Cola wore an old U. S. Army khaki tunic, complete with buttons,
that had originally been brought out for Droopy who had been
away somewhere and had missed getting it. Twice Pop had brought
it out for Droopy and finally M'Cola had said, "Give it to me."

Pop had let him have it and M'Cola had worn it ever since. It, a
pair of shorts, his fuzzy wool curler's cap, and a knitted army sweater
he wore when washing the tunic, were the only garments I ever saw
on the old man until he took my bird-shooting coat. For shoes he
used sandals cut from old motor-car tires. He had slim, handsome
legs with well-turned ankles on the style of Babe Ruth's and I remember how surprised I was the first time I saw him with the tunic
off and noticed how old his upper body was. It had that aged look
you see in photographs of Jeffries and Sharkey posing thirty years
after, the ugly, old-man biceps and the fallen pectoral muscles.

"How old is M'Cola?" I asked Pop.

"He must be over fifty," Pop said. "He's got a grown-up family in
the native reserve."

"How are his kids?"

"No good, worthless. He can't handle them. We tried one as a
porter. But he was no good."

M'Cola was not jealous of Droopy. He simply knew that Droop
was a better man than he was. More of a hunter, a faster and a
cleaner tracker, and a great stylist in everything he did. He admired

Droopy in the same way we did and being out with him, it made him realize that he was wearing Droopy's tunic and that he had been a porter before he became a gun bearer and suddenly he ceased being an old timer and we were hunting together; he and I hunting together and Droopy in command of the show.

That had been a fine hunt. The afternoon of the day we came into the country we walked about four miles from camp along a deep rhino trail that graded through the grassy hills with their abandoned orchard-looking trees, as smoothly and evenly as though an engineer had planned it. The trail was a foot deep in the ground and smoothly worn and we left it where it slanted down through a divide in the hills like a dry irrigation ditch and climbed, sweating, the small, steep hill on the right to sit there with our backs against the hilltop and glass the country. It was a green, pleasant country, with hills below the forest that grew thick on the side of a mountain, and it was cut by the valleys of several watercourses that came down out of the thick timber on the mountain. Fingers of the forest came down onto the heads of some of the slopes and it was there, at the forest edge, that we watched for rhino to come out. If you looked away from the forest and the mountain side you could follow the watercourses and the hilly slope of the land down until the land flattened and the grass was brown and burned and, away, across a long sweep of country, was the brown Rift Valley and the shine of Lake Manyara.

We all lay there on the hillside and watched the country carefully for rhino. Droopy was on the other side of the hilltop, squatted on his heels, looking, and M'Cola sat below us. There was a cool breeze from the east and it blew the grass in waves on the hillsides. There were many large white clouds and the tall trees of the forest on the mountain side grew so closely and were so foliaged that it looked as though you could walk on their tops. Behind this mountain there was a gap and then another mountain and the far mountain was dark blue with forest in the distance.

Until five o'clock we did not see anything. Then, without the glasses, I saw something moving over the shoulder of one of the valleys toward a strip of the timber. In the glasses it was a rhino, showing very clear and minute at the distance, red-colored in the sun, moving with a quick waterbug-like motion across the hill. Then there were three more of them that came out of the forest, dark in the shadow, and two that fought, tinily, in the glasses, pushing head-on, fighting in front of a clump of bushes while we watched them and the light failed. It was too dark to get down the hill, across the valley and up the narrow slope of mountain side to them in time for a shot. So we went back to the camp, down the hill in the dark, edging down on our shoes and then feeling the trail smooth under foot, walking along that deep trail, that wound through the dark hills, until we saw the firelight in the trees.

We were excited that night because we had seen the three rhino and early the next morning while we were eating breakfast before starting out, Droopy came in to report a herd of buffalo he had found feeding at the edge of the forest not two miles from camp. We went there, still tasting coffee and kippers in the early morning heart-pounding of excitement, and the native Droopy had left watching them pointed where they had crossed a deep gulch and gone into an open patch of forest. He said there were two big bulls in a herd of a dozen or more. We followed them in, moving very quietly on the game trails, pushing the vines aside and seeing the tracks and the quantities of fresh dung, but though we went on into the forest where it was too thick to shoot and made a wide circle, we did not see or hear them. Once we heard the tick birds and saw them flying, but that was all. There were numbers of rhino trails there in the woods and many strawy piles of dung, but we saw nothing but the green wood-pigeons and some monkeys, and when we came out we were wet to our waists from the dew and the sun was quite high. The day was very hot, now before the wind had gotten up, and we knew whatever rhino and buffalo had been out would have gone back deep into the forest to rest out of the heat.

The others started back to camp with Pop and M'Cola. There was no meat in camp and I wanted to hunt back in a circle with Droopy to see if we could kill a piece. I was beginning to feel strong again after the dysentery and it was a pleasure to walk in the easy rolling country, simply to walk, and to be able to hunt, not knowing what we might see and free to shoot for the meat we needed. Then, too, I liked Droopy and liked to watch him walk. He strode very loosely and with a slight lift, and I liked to watch him and to feel the grass under my soft-soled shoes and the pleasant weight of the rifle, held just back of the muzzle, the barrel resting on my shoulder, and the sun hot enough to sweat you well as it burned the dew from

the grass; with the breeze starting and the country like an abandoned
New England orchard to walk through. I knew that I was shooting
well again and I wanted to make a shot to impress Droopy.

From the top of one rise we saw two kongoni showing yellow
on a hillside about a mile away and I motioned to Droop that we
would go after them. We started down and in a ravine jumped a
waterbuck bull and two cows. Waterbuck was the one animal we
might get that I knew was worthless as meat and I had shot a better
head than this one carried. I had the sights on the buck as he tore
away, remembered about the worthless meat, and having the head,
and did not shoot.

"No shoot kuro?" Droopy asked in Swahili. *"Doumi sana.* A good
bull."

I tried to tell him that I had a better one and that it was no
good to eat.

He grinned.

"Piga kongoni m'uzuri."

"Piga" was a fine word. It sounded exactly as the command
to fire should sound or the announcement of a hit. "M'uzuri," meaning good, well, better, had sounded too much like the name of a
state for a long time and walking I used to make up sentences in
Swahili with Arkansas and M'uzuri in them, but now it seemed
natural, no longer to be italicized, just as all the words came to
seem the proper and natural words and there was nothing odd or
unseemly in the stretching of the ears, in the tribal scars, or in a
man carrying a spear. The tribal marks and the tattooed places
seemed natural and handsome adornments and I regretted not having any of my own. My own scars were all informal, some irregular
and sprawling, others simply puffy welts. I had one on my forehead
that people still commented on, asking if I had bumped my head;
but Droop had handsome ones beside his cheekbones and others,
symmetrical and decorative, on his chest and belly. I was thinking
that I had one good one, a sort of embossed Christmas tree, on the
bottom of my right foot that only served to wear out socks, when
we jumped two reedbuck. They went off through the trees and then
stood at sixty yards, the thin, graceful buck looking back, and I
shot him high and a touch behind the shoulder. He gave a jump
and went off very fast.

"Piga." Droopy smiled. We had both heard the whunk of the bullet.

"Kufa," I told him. "Dead."

But when we came up to him, lying on his side, his heart was still beating strongly, although to all appearances he was dead. Droopy had no skinning knife and I had only a penknife to stick him with. I felt for the heart behind the foreleg with my fingers and feeling it beating under the hide slipped the knife in but it was short and pushed the heart away. I could feel it, hot and rubbery against my fingers, and feel the knife push it, but I felt around and cut the big artery and the blood came hot against my fingers. Once bled, I started to open him, with the little knife, still showing off to Droopy, and emptying him neatly took out the liver, cut away the gall, and laying the liver on a hummock of grass, put the kidneys beside it.

Droopy asked for the knife. Now he was going to show me something. Skilfully he slit open the stomach and turned it inside, tripe side, out, emptying the grass in it on the ground, shook it, then put the liver and kidneys inside it and with the knife cut a switch from the tree the buck lay under and sewed the stomach together with the withe so that the tripe made a bag to carry the other delicacies in. Then he cut a pole and put the bag on the end of it, running it through the flaps, and put it over his shoulder in the way tramps carried their property in a handkerchief on the end of a stick in Blue Jay corn plaster advertisements when we were children. It was a good trick and I thought how I would show it to John Staib in Wyoming some time and he would smile his deaf man's smile (you had to throw pebbles at him to make him stop when you heard a bull bugle), and I knew what John would say. He would say, "By Godd, Urnust, dot's smardt."

Droop handed me the stick, then took off his single garment, made a sling and got the buck up on his back. I tried to help him and suggested by signs that we cut a pole and sling him, carrying him between us, but he wanted to carry him alone. So we started for camp, me with the tripe bag on the end of a stick over my shoulder, my rifle slung, and Droopy staggering steadily ahead, sweating heavily, under the buck. I tried to get him to hang him in a tree and leave him until we could send out a couple of porters,

and to that end we put him in the crotch of a tree. But when Droop
saw that I meant to go off and leave him there rather than simply
allow him to drain he got him down onto his shoulders again and
we went on into camp, the boys, around the cooking fire, all laughing at the tripe bag over my shoulder as we came in.

This was the kind of hunting that I liked. No riding in cars,
the country broken up instead of the plains, and I was completely
happy. I had been quite ill and had that pleasant feeling of getting
stronger each day. I was underweight, had a great appetite for meat,
and could eat all I wanted without feeling stuffy. Each day I sweated
out whatever we drank sitting at the fire at night, and in the heat of
the day, now, I lay in the shade with a breeze in the trees and read
with no obligation and no compulsion to write, happy in knowing
that at four o'clock we would be starting out to hunt again. I
would not even write a letter. The only person I really cared about,
except the children, was with me and I had no wish to share this
life with any one who was not there, only to live it, being completely happy and quite tired. I knew that I was shooting well and
I had that feeling of well being and confidence that is so much
more pleasant to have than to hear about.

As it turned out, we started soon after three to be on the hill
by four. But it was nearly five before we saw the first rhino come
bustling short-leggedly across the ridge of hill in almost the same
place we had seen the rhino the night before. We saw where he
went into the edge of the forest near where we had seen the two
fighting and then took a course that would lead us down the hill,
across the grown-over gully at the bottom, and up the steep slope
to where there was a thorn tree with yellow blossoms that marked
the place where we had seen the rhino go in.

Coming straight up the slope in sight of the thorn tree, the
wind blowing across the hill, I tried to walk as slowly as I could
and put a handkerchief inside the sweatband of my hat to keep
the perspiration out of my glasses. I expected to shoot at any minute
and I wanted to slow up enough so my heart would not be pounding. In shooting large animals there is no reason ever to miss if you
have a clear shot and can shoot and know where to shoot, unless
you are unsteady from a run or a climb or fog your glasses, break
them or run out of cloth or paper to wipe them clean. The glasses

were the biggest hazard and I used to carry four handkerchiefs and change them from the left to the right pocket when they were wet.

We came up to the yellow blossomed tree very carefully, like people walking up to a covey of quail the dogs have pointed, and the rhino was not in sight. We went all through the edge of the forest and it was full of tracks and fresh rhino sign, but there was no rhino. The sun was setting and it was getting too dark to shoot, but we followed the forest around the side of the mountain, hoping to see a rhino in the open glades. When it was almost too dark to shoot, I saw Droopy stop and crouch. With his head down he motioned us forward. Crawling up, we saw a large rhino and a small one standing chest deep in brush, facing us across a little valley.

"Cow and calf," Pop said softly. "Can't shoot her. Let me look at her horn." He took the glasses from M'Cola.

"Can she see us?" P. O. M. asked.

"No."

"How far are they?"

"Must be nearly five hundred yards."

"My God, she looks big," I whispered.

"She's a big cow," Pop said. "Wonder what became of the bull?" He was pleased and excited by the sight of game. "Too dark to shoot unless we're right on him."

The rhinos had turned and were feeding. They never seemed to move slowly. They either bustled or stood still.

"What makes them so red?" P. O. M. asked.

"Rolling in the mud," Pop answered. "We better get along while there's light."

The sun was down when we came out of the forest and looked down the slope and across to the hill where we had watched from with our glasses. We should have back-tracked and gone down, crossed the gulch, and climbed back up the trail the way we had come but we decided, like fools, to grade straight across the mountain side below the edge of the forest. So in the dark, following this ideal line, we descended into steep ravines that showed only as wooded patches until you were in them, slid down, clung to vines, stumbled and climbed and slid again, down and down, then steeply, impossibly, up, hearing the rustle of night things and the cough of a leopard hunting baboons; me scared of snakes and touching each root and branch with snake fear in the dark.

To go down and up two hands-and-knee-climbing ravines and then out into the moonlight and the long, too-steep shoulder of mountain that you climbed one foot up to the other, one foot after the other, one stride at a time, leaning forward against the grade and the altitude, dead tired and gun weary, single file in the moonlight across the slope, on up and to the top where it was easy, the country spread in the moonlight, then up and down and on, through the small hills, tired but now in sight of the fires and on into camp.

So then you sit, bundled against the evening chill, at the fire, with a whiskey and soda, waiting for the announcement that the canvas bath had been a quarter filled with hot water.

"*Bathi,* B'wana."

"God damn it, I could never hunt sheep again," you say.

"I never could," says P. O. M. "You all made me."

"You climbed a damn sight better than any of us."

"Do you suppose we could hunt sheep again, Pop?"

"I wonder," Pop said. "I suppose it's merely condition."

"It's riding in the damned cars that ruins us."

"If we did that walk every night we could come back in three nights from now and never feel it."

"Yes. But I'd be as scared of snakes if we did it every night for a year."

"You'd get over it."

"No," I said. "They scare me stiff. Do you remember that time we touched hands behind the tree?"

"Rather," said Pop. "You jumped two yards. Are you really afraid of them, or only talking?"

"They scare me sick," I said. "They always have."

"What's the matter with you men?" P. O. M. said. "Why haven't I heard anything about the war tonight?"

"We're too bloody tired. Were you in the war, Pop?"

"Not me," said Pop. "Where is that boy with the whiskey?" Then calling in that feeble, clowning falsetto, "Kayti—Katy-ay!"

"*Bathi,*" said Molo again softly, but insistently.

"Too tired."

"Memsahib *bathi,*" Molo said hopefully.

"I'll go," said P. O. M. "But you two hurry up with your drinking. I'm hungry."

"*Bathi,*" said Kayti severely to Pop.

"*Bathi* yourself," said Pop. "Don't bully me."

Kayti turned away in fire-lit slanting smile.

"All right. All right," said Pop. "Going to have one?" he asked.

"We'll have just one," I said, "and then we'll *bathi.*"

"*Bathi,* B'wana M'Kumba," Molo said. P. O. M. came toward the fire wearing her blue dressing gown and mosquito boots.

"Go on," she said. "You can have another when you come out. There's nice, warm, muddy water."

"They bully us," Pop said.

"Do you remember the time we were sheep hunting and your hat blew off and nearly fell onto the ram?" I asked her, the whiskey racing my mind back to Wyoming.

"Go take your bath," P. O. M. said. "I'm going to have a gimlet."

In the morning we were dressed before daylight, ate breakfast, and were hunting the forest edge and the sunken valleys where Droop had seen the buffalo before the sun was up. But they were not there. It was a long hunt and we came back to camp and decided to send the trucks for porters and move with a foot safari to where there was supposed to be water in a stream that came down out of the mountain beyond where we had seen the rhinos the night before. Being camped there we could hunt a new country along the forest edge and we would be much closer to the mountain.

The trucks were to bring in Karl from his kudu camp where he seemed to be getting disgusted, or discouraged, or both, and he could go down to the Rift Valley the next day and kill some meat and try for an oryx. If we found good rhino we would send for him. We did not want to fire any shots where we were going except at rhino in order not to scare them, and we needed meat. The rhino seemed very shy and I knew from Wyoming how the shy game will all shift out of a small country, a country being an area, a valley or range of hills, a man can hunt in, after a shot or two. We planned this all out, Pop consulting with Droopy, and then sent the trucks off with Dan to recruit porters.

Late in the afternoon they were back with Karl, his outfit, and forty M'Bulus, good looking savages with a pompous headman who wore the only pair of shorts among them. Karl was thin now, his skin sallow, his eyes very tired looking and he seemed a little desperate. He had been eight days in the kudu camp in the hills, hunting hard, with no one with him who spoke any English, and they had only seen two cows and jumped a bull out of range. The guides claimed they had seen another bull but Karl had thought it was a kongoni, or that they said it was a kongoni, and had not shot. He was bitter about this and it was not a happy outfit.

"I never saw his horns. I don't believe it was a bull," he said. Kudu hunting was a touchy subject with him now and we let it alone.

"He'll get an oryx down there and he'll feel better," Pop said. "It's gotten on his nerves a little."

Karl agreed to the plan for us to move ahead into the new country and for him to go down for meat.

"Whatever you say," he said. "Absolutely whatever you say."

"It will give him some shooting," Pop said. "Then he'll feel better."

"We'll get one. Then you get one. Whoever gets his first can go on down after oryx. You'll probably get an oryx tomorrow anyway when you're hunting meat."

"Whatever you say," Karl said. His mind was bitterly revolving eight blank days of hill climbing in the heat, out before daylight, back at dark, hunting an animal whose Swahili name he could not then remember, with trackers in whom he had no confidence, coming back to eat alone, no one to whom he could talk, his wife nine thousand miles and three months away, and how was his dog and how was his job, and god-damn it where were they and what if he missed one when he got a shot, he wouldn't, you never missed when it was really important, he was sure of that, that was one of the tenets of his faith, but what if he got excited and missed, and why didn't he get any letters, what did the guide say kongoni for that time, they did, he knew they did, but he said nothing of all that, only, "Whatever you say," a little desperately.

"Come on, cheer up, you bastard," I said.

"I'm cheerful. What's the matter with you?"

"Have a drink."

"I don't want a drink. I want a god-damned kudu."

Later Pop said, "I thought he'd do well off by himself with

no one to hurry him or rattle him. He'll be all right. He's a good lad."

"He wants some one to tell him exactly what to do and still leave him alone and not rattle him," I said. "It's hell for him to shoot in front of everybody. He's not a damned show-off like me."

"He made a damned fine shot at that leopard," Pop said.

"Two of them," I said. "The second was as good as the first. Hell, he can shoot. On the range he'll shoot the pants off of any of us. But he worries about it and I rattle him trying to get him to speed up."

"You're a little hard on him sometimes," Pop said.

"Hell, he knows me. He knows what I think of him. He doesn't mind."

"I still think he'll find himself off by himself," Pop said. "It's just a question of confidence. He's really a good shot."

"Hell, he's got the best buff, the best waterbuck, and the best lion, now," I said. "He's got nothing to worry about."

"The Memsahib has the best lion, brother. Don't make any mistake about that."

"I'm glad of that. But he's got a damned fine lion and a big leopard. Everything he has is good. We've got plenty of time. He's got nothing to worry about. What the hell is he so gloomy about?"

"We'll get an early start in the morning so we can finish it off before it gets too hot for the little Memsahib."

"She's in the best shape of any one."

"She's marvellous. She's like a little terrier."

We went out that afternoon and glassed the country from the hills and never saw a thing. That night after supper we were in the tent. P. O. M. disliked intensely being compared to a little terrier. If she must be like any dog, and she did not wish to be, she would prefer a wolfhound, something lean, racy, long-legged and ornamental. Her courage was so automatic and so much a simple state of being that she never thought of danger; then, too, danger was in the hands of Pop and for Pop she had a complete, clear-seeing, absolutely trusting adoration. Pop was her ideal of how a man should be, brave, gentle, comic, never losing his temper, never bragging, never complaining except in a joke, tolerant, understanding, intelligent, drinking a little too much as a good man should, and, to her eyes, very handsome.

"Don't you think Pop's handsome?"

"No," I said. "Droopy's handsome."

"Droopy's *beautiful*. But don't you *really* think Pop's hand-some?"

"Hell, no. I like him as well as any man I've ever known, but I'm damned if he's handsome."

"I think he's lovely looking. But you understand about how I feel about him, don't you?"

"Sure. I'm as fond of the bastard myself."

"But *don't* you think he's handsome, really?"

"Nope."

Then, a little later:

"Well, who's handsome to you?"

"Belmonte and Pop. And you."

"Don't be patriotic," I said. "Who's a beautiful woman?"

"Garbo."

"Not any more. Josie is. Margot is."

"Yes, they are. I know I'm not."

"You're lovely."

"Let's talk about Mr. J. P. I don't like you to call him Pop. It's not dignified."

"He and I aren't dignified together."

"Yes, but I'm dignified with him. Don't you think he's won-derful?"

"Yes, and he doesn't have to read books written by some female he's tried to help get published saying how he's yellow."

"She's just jealous and malicious. You never should have helped her. Some people never forgive that."

"It's a damned shame, though, with all that talent gone to malice and nonsense and self-praise. It's a god-damned shame, really. It's a shame you never knew her before she went to pot. You know a funny thing; she never could write dialogue. It was terrible. She learned how to do it from my stuff and used it in that book. She had never written like that before. She never could forgive learning that and she was afraid people would notice it, where she'd learned it, so she had to attack me. It's a funny racket, really. But I swear she was damned nice before she got ambitious. You would have liked her then, really."

"Maybe, but I don't think so," said P. O. M. "We have fun though, don't we? Without all those people."

"God damn it if we don't. I've had a better time every year since I can remember."

"But isn't Mr. J. P. wonderful? Really?"

"Yes. He's wonderful."

"Oh, you're nice to say it. Poor Karl."

"Why?"

"Without his wife."

"Yes," I said. "Poor Karl."

4

So in the morning, again, we started ahead of the porters and went down and across the hills and through a deeply forested valley and then up and across a long rise of country with high grass that made the walking difficult and on and up and across, resting sometimes in the shade of a tree, and then on and up and down and across, all in high grass, now, that you had to break a trail in, and the sun was very hot. The five of us in single file, Droop and M'Cola with a big gun apiece, hung with musettes and water bottles and the cameras, we all sweating in the sun, Pop and I with guns and the Memsahib trying to walk like Droopy, her Stetson tilted on one side, happy to be on a trip, pleased about how comfortable her boots were, we came finally to a thicket of thorn trees over a ravine that ran down from the side of a ridge to the water and we leaned the guns against the trees and went in under the close shade and lay on the ground. P. O. M. got the books out of one of the musettes and she and Pop read while I followed the ravine down to the little stream that came out of the mountain side, and found a fresh lion track and many rhino tunnels in the tall grass that came higher than your head. It was very hot climbing back up the sandy ravine and I was glad to lean my back against the tree trunk and read in Tolstoi's *Sevastopol*. It was a very young book and had one fine description of fighting in it, where the French take the redoubt and I thought about Tolstoi and about what a great advantage an experience of war was to a writer. It was one of the major subjects and certainly one of the hardest to write truly of and those writers who had not seen it were always very jealous and tried to make it seem unimportant, or abnormal, or a disease as a subject, while, really, it was just something quite irreplaceable that they had missed. Then Sevastopol made me think of the Boulevard Sevastopol in Paris, about riding a bicycle down it in the rain on the way home from Strassburg and the slipperiness of the rails of the tram cars and the feeling of riding on greasy, slippery asphalt and cobble stones in traffic in the rain, and how we had nearly lived on the Boulevard du Temple that time, and I remembered the look of that apartment, how it was arranged, and the wall paper, and instead we had taken the upstairs of the pavilion in Notre Dame des Champs in the courtyard with the sawmill (*and the sudden whine of the saw, the smell of sawdust and the chestnut tree over the roof with a mad woman downstairs*) and the year worrying about money (*all of the stories back in the mail that came in through a slit in the saw-mill door, with notes of rejection that would never call them stories, but always anecdotes, sketches, contes, etc. They did not want them, and we lived on poireaux and drank cahors and water*) and how fine the fountains were at the Place de L'Observatoire (*water sheen rippling on the bronze of horses' manes, bronze breasts and shoulders, green under thin-flowing water*) and when they put up the bust of Flaubert in the Luxembourg on the short cut through the gardens on the way to the rue Soufflot (*one that we believed in, loved without criticism, heavy now in stone as an idol should be*). He had not seen war but he had seen a revolution and the Commune and a revolution is much the best if you do not become bigoted because every one speaks the same language. Just as civil war is the best war for a writer, the most complete. Stendhal had seen a war and Napoleon taught him to write. He was teaching everybody then; but no one else learned. Dostoevsky was made by being sent to Siberia. Writers are forged in injustice as a sword is forged. I wondered if it would make a writer of him, give him the necessary shock to cut the over-flow of words and give him a sense of propor- tion, if they sent Tom Wolfe to Siberia or to the Dry Tortugas. Maybe it would and maybe it wouldn't. He seemed sad, really, like Carnera. Tolstoi was a small man. Joyce was of medium height and he wore his eyes out. And that last night, drunk, with Joyce and the thing he kept quoting from Edgar Quinet, "Fraîche et rose comme au jour de la bataille." I didn't have it right I knew. And when you saw him he would take up a conversation interrupted three years before. It was nice to see a great writer in our time.

What I had to do was work. I did not care, particularly, how it all came out. I did not take my own life seriously any more, any one else's life, yes, but not mine. They all wanted something that I did not want and I would get it without wanting it, if I worked. To work was the only thing, it was the one thing that always made you feel good, and in the meantime it was my own damned life and I would lead it where and how I pleased. And where I had led it now pleased me very much. This was a better sky than Italy. The hell it was. The best sky was in Italy and Spain and Northern Michigan in the fall and in the fall in the Gulf off Cuba. You could beat this sky; but not the country.

All I wanted to do now was get back to Africa. We had not left it, yet, but when I would wake in the night I would lie, listening, homesick for it already.

Now, looking out the tunnel of trees over the ravine at the sky with white clouds moving across in the wind, I loved the country so that I was happy as you are after you have been with a woman that you really love, when, empty, you feel it welling up again and there it is and you can never have it all and yet what there is, now, you can have, and you want more and more, to have, and be, and live in, to possess now again for always, for that long, sudden-ended always; making time stand still, sometimes so very still that afterwards you wait to hear it move, and it is slow in starting. But you are not alone, because if you have ever really loved her happy and untragic, she loves you always; no matter whom she loves nor where she goes she loves you more. So if you have loved some woman and some country you are very fortunate and, if you die afterwards it makes no difference. Now, being in Africa, I was hungry for more of it, the changes of the seasons, the rains with no need to travel, the discomforts that you paid to make it real, the names of the trees, of the small animals, and all the birds, to know the language and have time to be in it and to move slowly. I had loved country all my life; the country was always better than the people. I could only care about people a very few at a time.

P. O. M. was sleeping. She was always lovely to look at asleep, sleeping quietly, close curled like an animal, with nothing of the being dead look that Karl had asleep. Pop slept quietly too, you could see his soul was close in his body. His body no longer housed him fittingly. It had gone on and changed, thickening here, losing its lines, bloating a little there, but inside he was young and lean and tall and hard as when he galloped lion on the plain below Wami, and the pouches under his eyes were all outside, so that now I saw him asleep the way P. O. M. saw him always. M'Cola was an old man asleep, without history and without mystery. Droopy did not sleep. He sat on his heels and watched for the safari.

We saw them coming a long way off. At first the boxes just showed above the high grass, then a line of heads, then they were in a hollow, and there was only the point of a spear in the sun, then they came up a rise of ground and I could see the strung out line coming toward us. They had gone a little too far to the left and Droopy waved to signal them toward us. They made camp, Pop warning them to be quiet, and we sat under the dining tent and were comfortable in the chairs and talked. That night we hunted and saw nothing. The next morning we hunted and saw nothing and the next evening the same. It was very interesting but there were no results. The wind blew hard from the east and the ground was broken in short ridges of hills coming down close from the forest so you could not get above it without sending your scent on ahead of you on the wind to warn everything. You could not see into the sun in the evening, nor on the heavy shadowed hill- sides to the west, beyond which the sun was setting at the time the rhino would be coming out of the forest; so all the country to the westward was a loss in the evening and in the country we could hunt we found nothing. Meat came in from Karl's camp by some porters we sent back. They came in carrying quarters of tommy, Grant, and wildebeeste, dusty, the meat seared dry by the sun, and the porters were happy, crouched around their fires roasting the meat on sticks. Pop was puzzled why the rhino were all gone. Each day we had seen less and we discussed whether it could be the full moon, that they fed out at night and were back in the forest in the morning before it was light, or that they winded us, or heard the men, and were simply shy and kept in the forest, or what was it? Me putting out the theories, Pop pricking them with his wit, some- times considering them from politeness, sometimes with interest, like the one about the moon.

We went to bed early and in the night it rained a little, not a real rain but a shower from the mountains, and in the morning we were up before daylight and had climbed up to the top of the steep grassy ridge that looked down onto the camp, onto the ravine of the river bed, and across to the steep opposite bank of the stream, and from where we could see all the hilly slopes and the edge of the forest. It was not yet light when some geese flew overhead and the light was still too gray to be able to see the edge of the forest clearly in the glasses. We had scouts out on three different hill tops and we were waiting for it to be light enough for us to see them if they signalled.

Then Pop said, "Look at that son of a bitch," and shouted at M'Cola to bring the rifles. M'Cola went jumping down the hill, and across the stream, directly opposite us, a rhino was running with a quick trot along the top of the bank. As we watched he speeded up and came, fast trotting, angling down across the face of the bank. He was a muddy red, his horn showed clearly, and there was nothing ponderous in his quick, purposeful movement. I was very excited at seeing him.

"He'll cross the stream," Pop said. "He's shootable."

M'Cola put the Springfield in my hand and I opened it to make sure I had solids. The rhino was out of sight now but I could see the shaking of the high grass.

"How far would you call it?"

"All of three hundred."

"I'll bust the son of a bitch."

I was watching, freezing myself deliberately inside, stopping the excitement as you close a valve, going into that impersonal state you shoot from.

He showed, trotting into the shallow, boulder filled stream. Thinking of one thing, that the shot was perfectly possible, but that I must lead him enough, must get ahead, I got on him, then well ahead of him, and squeezed off. I heard the *whonk* of the bullet and, from his trot, he seemed to explode forward. With a whooshing snort he smashed ahead, splashing water and snorting. I shot again and raised a little column of water behind him, and shot again as he went into the grass; behind him again.

"Piga," M'Cola said. "Piga!"

Droopy agreed.

"Did you hit him?" Pop said.

"Absolutely," I said. "I think I've got him."

Droopy was running and I re-loaded and ran off after him. Half the camp was strung out across the hills waving and yelling. The rhino had come in right below where they were and gone on up the valley toward where the forest came close down into the head of the valley.

Pop and P. O. M. came up. Pop with his big gun and M'Cola carrying mine.

"Droopy will get the tracks," Pop said. "M'Cola swears you hit him."

"Piga!" M'Cola said.

"He snorted like a steam engine," P. O. M. said. "Didn't he look wonderful going along there?"

"He was late getting home with the milk," Pop said. "Are you *sure* you hit him? It was a godawful long shot."

"I *know* I hit him. I'm *pretty* sure I've killed him."

"Don't tell any one if you did," Pop said. "They'll never believe you. Look! Droopy's got blood."

Below, in the high grass Droop was holding up a grass blade toward us. Then, stooped, he went on trailing fast by the blood spoor.

"Piga," M'Cola said. "M'uzuri!"

"We'll keep up above where we can see if he makes a break," Pop said. "Look at Droopy."

Droop had removed his fez and held it in his hand.

"That's all the precautions he needs," Pop said. "We bring up a couple of heavy guns and Droopy goes in after him with one article less of clothing."

Below us Droopy and his partner who was trailing with him had stopped. Droopy held up his hand.

"They hear him," Pop said. "Come on."

We started toward them. Droopy came toward us and spoke to Pop.

"He's in there," Pop whispered. "They can hear the tick birds. One of the boys says he heard the faro, too. We'll go in against the wind. You go ahead with Droopy. Let the Memsahib stay behind me. Take the big gun. All right."

The rhino was in high grass, somewhere in there behind some bushes. As we went forward we heard a deep, moaning sort of groan.

Droopy looked around at me and grinned. The noise came again, ending this time like a blood-choked sigh. Droopy was laughing. "Faro," he whispered and put his hand palm open on the side of his head in the gesture that means to go to sleep. Then in a jerky-flighted, sharp-beaked little flock we saw the tick birds rise and fly away. We knew where he was and, as we went slowly forward, parting the high grass, we saw him. He was on his side, dead.

"Better shoot him once to make sure," Pop said. M'Cola handed me the Springfield he had been carrying. I noticed it was cocked, looked at M'Cola, furious with him, kneeled down and shot the rhino in the sticking place. He never moved. Droopy shook my hand and so did M'Cola.

"He had that damned Springfield cocked," I said to Pop. The cocked gun, behind my back, made me black angry.

That meant nothing to M'Cola. He was very happy, stroking the rhino's horn, measuring it with his fingers spread, looking for the bullet hole.

"It's on the side he's lying on," I said.

"You should have seen him when he was protecting Mama," Pop said. "That's why he had the gun cocked."

"Can he shoot?"

"No," Pop said. "But he would."

"Shoot me in the pants," I said. "Romantic bastard." When the whole outfit came up, we rolled the rhino into a sort of kneeling position and cut away the grass to take some pictures. The bullet hole was fairly high in the back, a little behind the lungs.

"That was a hell of a shot," Pop said. "A hell of a shot. Don't ever tell any one you made that one."

"You'll have to give me a certificate."

"That would just make us both liars. They're a strange beast, aren't they?"

There he was, long-hulked, heavy-sided, prehistoric looking, the hide like vulcanized rubber and faintly transparent looking, scarred with a badly healed horn wound that the birds had pecked at, his tail thick, round, and pointed, flat many-legged ticks crawling on him, his ears fringed with hair, tiny pig eyes, moss growing on the base of his horn that grew out forward from his nose. M'Cola looked at him and shook his head. I agreed with him. This was the hell of an animal.

"How is his horn?"

"It isn't bad," Pop said. "It's nothing extra. That was a hell of a shot you made on him though, brother."

"M'Cola's pleased with it," I said.

"You're pretty pleased with it yourself," P. O. M. said.

"I'm crazy about it," I said. "But don't let me start on it. Don't worry about how I feel about it. I can wake up and think about that any night."

"And you're a good tracker, and a hell of a fine bird shot, too," Pop said. "Tell us the rest of that."

"Lay off me. I only said that once when I was drunk."

"Once," said P. O. M. "Doesn't he tell us that every night?"

"By God, I *am* a good bird shot."

"Amazing," said Pop. "I never would have thought it. What else is it you do?"

"Oh, go to hell."

"Mustn't ever let him realize what a shot that was or he'll get unbearable," Pop said to P. O. M.

"M'Cola and I know," I said.

M'Cola came up. "M'uzuri, B'wana," he said. "M'uzuri sana."

"He thinks you did it on purpose," Pop said.

"Don't you ever tell him different."

"Piga m'uzuri," M'Cola said. "M'uzuri."

"I believe he feels just the way you do about it," Pop said.

"He's my pal."

"I believe he is, you know," Pop said.

On our way back across country to our main camp I made a fancy shot on a reedbuck at about two hundred yards, offhand, breaking his neck at the base of the skull. M'Cola was very pleased and Droopy was delighted.

"We've got to put a stop to him," Pop said to P. O. M. "Where did you shoot for, really?"

"In the neck," I lied. I had held full on the center of the shoulder.

"It was awfully pretty," P. O. M. said. The bullet had made a crack when it hit like a baseball bat swung against a fast ball and the buck had collapsed without a move.

"I think he's a damned liar," Pop said.

"None of us great shots is appreciated. Wait till we're gone."

"His idea of being appreciated is for us to carry him on our shoulders," Pop said. "That rhino shot has ruined him."

"All right. You watch from now on. Hell, I've shot well the whole time."

"I seem to remember a Grant of some sort," Pop was teasing. So did I remember him. I'd followed a fine one out of the country missing shot after shot all morning after a series of stalks in the heat, then crawled up to an ant hill to shoot one that was not nearly as good, taken a rest on the ant hill, missed the buck at fifty yards, seen him stand facing me, absolutely still, his nose up, and shot him in the chest. He went over backwards and as I went up to him he jumped up and went off, staggering. I sat down and waited for him to stop and when he did, obviously anchored, I sat there, using the sling, and shot for his neck, slowly and carefully, missing him eight times straight in a mounting, stubborn rage, not making a correction but shooting exactly for the same place in the same way each time, the gun bearers all laughing, the truck that had come up with the outfit holding more amused niggers, P. O. M. and Pop saying nothing, me sitting there cold, crazy-stubborn-furious, determined to break his neck rather than walk up and perhaps start him off over that heat-hazy, baking, noontime plain. Nobody said anything. I reached up my hand to M'Cola for more cartridges, shot again, carefully, and missed, and on the tenth shot broke his damned neck. I turned away without looking toward him.

"Poor Papa," P. O. M. said.

"It's the light and the wind," Pop said. We had not known each other very well then. "They were all hitting the same place. I could see them throw the dust."

"I was a damned bloody stubborn fool," I said.

Anyway, I could shoot now. So far, and aided by flukes, my luck was running now.

We came on into sight of camp and shouted. No one came out. Finally Karl came out of his tent. He went back in as soon as he saw us, then came out again.

"Hey, Karl," I yelled. He waved and went back in the tent again. Then came toward us. He was shaky with excitement and I saw he had been washing blood off his hands.

"What is it?"

"Rhino," he said.

"Did you get in trouble with him?"

"No. We killed him."

"Fine. Where is he?"

"Over there behind that tree."

We went over. There was the newly servered head of a rhino that was a rhino. He was twice the size of the one I had killed. The little eyes were shut and a fresh drop of blood stood in the corner of one like a tear. The head bulked enormous and the horn swept up and back in a fine curve. The hide was an inch thick where it hung in a cape behind the head and was as white where it was cut as freshly sliced coconut.

"What is he? About thirty inches?"

"Hell, no," said Pop. "No thirty inches."

"But he iss a very fine one, Mr. Jackson," Dan said.

"Yes. He's a fine one," Pop said.

"Where did you get him?"

"Just outside of camp."

"He wass standing in some bush. We heard him grunt."

"We thought he was a buffalo," Karl said.

"He iss a very fine one," Dan repeated.

"I'm damned glad you got him," I said.

There we were, the three of us, wanting to congratulate, waiting to be good sports about this rhino whose smaller horn was longer than our big one, this huge, tear-eyed marvel of a rhino, this dead, head-severed dream rhino, and instead we all spoke like people who were about to become seasick on a boat, or people who had suffered some heavy financial loss. We were ashamed and could do nothing about it. I wanted to say something pleasant and hearty, instead, "How many times did you shoot him?" I asked.

"I don't know. We didn't count. Five or six, I guess."

"Five, I think," said Dan.

Poor Karl, faced by these three sad-faced congratulators, was beginning to feel his pleasure in the rhino drained away from him.

"We got one too," said P. O. M.

"That's fine," said Karl. "Is he bigger than this one?"

"Hell, no. He's a lousy runt."

"I'm sorry," Karl said. He meant it, simply and truly.

"What the hell have you got to be sorry about with a rhino like that? Goddamn it, he's a beauty. Let me get the camera and take some pictures of him."

I went after the camera. P. O. M. took me by the arm and walked close beside me.

"Papa, please try to act like a human being," she said. "Poor Karl. You're making him feel dreadfully."

"I know it," I said. "I'm trying not to act that way."

There was Pop. He shook his head. "I never felt more of a four-letter man," he said. "But it was like a kick in the stomach. I'm really delighted, of course."

"Me too," I said. "I'd rather have him beat me. You know that. Truly. But why couldn't he just get a good one, two or three inches longer? Why did he have to get one that makes mine ridiculous? It just makes ours silly."

"You can always remember that shot."

"The hell with that shot. That bloody fluke. God, what a beautiful rhino."

"Come on, let's pull ourselves together and try to act like white people with him."

"We were *awful*," P. O. M. said.

"I know it," I said. "And all the time I was trying to be jolly. You *know* I'm delighted he has it."

"You were certainly jolly. Both of you," P. O. M. said.

"But did you see M'Cola?" Pop asked. M'Cola had looked at the rhino dismally, shaken his head and walked away.

"He's a wonderful rhino," P. O. M. said. "We must act decently and make Karl feel good."

But it was too late. We could not make Karl feel good and for a long time we could not feel good ourselves. The porters came into camp with the loads and we could see them all, and all of our outfit, go over to where the rhino head lay in the shade. They were all very quiet. Only the skinner was delighted to see such a rhino head in camp.

"M'uzuri sana," he said to me. And measured the horn with shiftings of his widespread hand. "Kubwa sana!"

"N'Dio. M'uzuri sana," I agreed.

"B'wana Kabor shoot him?"

"Yes."

"M'uzuri sana."

"Yes," I agreed. "M'uzuri sana."

The skinner was the only gent in the outfit. We had tried, in all the shoot, never to be competitive. Karl and I had each tried to give the other the better chance on everything that came up. I was, truly, very fond of him and he was entirely unselfish and altogether self-sacrificing. I knew I could outshoot him and I could always outwalk him and, steadily, he got trophies that made mine dwarfs in comparison. He had done some of the worst shooting at game I had ever seen and I had shot badly twice on the trip, at that Grant, and at a bustard once on the plain, still he beat me on all the tangible things we had to show. For a while we had joked about it and I knew everything would even up. But it didn't even up. Now, on this rhino hunt, I had taken the first crack at the country. We had sent him after meat while we had gone into a new country. We had not treated him badly, but we had not treated him too well, and still he had beaten me. Not only beaten, beaten was all right. He had made my rhino look so small that I could never keep him in the same small town where we lived. He had wiped him out. I had the shot I had made on him to remember and nothing could take that away except that it was so bloody marvellous I knew I would wonder, sooner or later, if it was not really a fluke in spite of my unholy self-confidence. Old Karl had put it on us all right with that rhino. He was in his tent now, writing a letter.

Under the dining tent fly Pop and I talked over what we had better do.

"He's got his rhino anyway," Pop said. "That saves us time. Now you can't stand on that one."

"No."

"But this country is washed out. Something wrong with it. Droopy claims to know a good country about three hours from here in the trucks and another hour or so in with the porters. We can head for there this afternoon with a light outfit, send the trucks back, and Karl and Dan can move on down to M'uto Umbu and he can get his oryx."

"Fine."

"He has a chance to get a leopard on that rhino carcass this evening, too, or in the morning. Dan said they heard one. We'll try to get a rhino out of this country of Droopy's and then you join up with them and go on for kudu. We want to leave plenty of time for them."

"Fine."

"Even if you don't get an oryx. You'll pick one up somewhere."

"Even if I don't get one at all, it's all right. We'll get one another time. I want a kudu, though."

"You'll get one. You're sure to."

"I'd rather get one, a good one, than all the rest. I don't give a damn about these rhino outside of the fun of hunting them. But I'd like to get one that wouldn't look silly beside that dream rhino of his."

"Absolutely."

So we told Karl and he said: "Whatever you say. Sure. I hope you get one twice as big." He really meant it. He was feeling better now and so were we all.

The Short Happy Life of
Francis Macomber

It was now lunch time and they were all sitting under the double green fly of the dining tent pretending that nothing had happened.

"Will you have lime juice or lemon squash?" Macomber asked.

"I'll have a gimlet," Robert Wilson told him.

"I'll have a gimlet too. I need something," Macomber's wife said.

"I suppose it's the thing to do," Macomber agreed. "Tell him to make three gimlets."

The mess boy had started them already, lifting the bottles out of the canvas cooling bags that sweated wet in the wind that blew through the trees that shaded the tents.

"What had I ought to give them?" Macomber asked.

"A quid would be plenty," Wilson told him. "You don't want to spoil them."

"Will the headman distribute it?"

"Absolutely."

Francis Macomber had, half an hour before, been carried to his tent from the edge of the camp in triumph on the arms and shoulders of the cook, the personal boys, the skinner and the porters. The gun-bearers had taken no part in the demonstration. When the native boys put him down at the door of his tent, he had shaken all their hands, received their congratulations, and then gone into the tent and sat on the bed until his wife came in. She did not speak to him when she came in and he left the tent at once to wash his face and hands in the portable wash basin outside and go over to the dining tent to sit in a comfortable canvas chair in the breeze and the shade.

"You've got your lion," Robert Wilson said to him, "and a damned fine one too."

Mrs. Macomber looked at Wilson quickly. She was an extremely handsome and well-kept woman of the beauty and social position which had, five years before, commanded five thousand dollars as the price of endorsing, with photographs, a beauty product which she had never used. She had been married to Francis Macomber for eleven years.

"He is a good lion, isn't he?" Macomber said. His wife looked at him now. She looked at both these men as though she had never seen them before.

One, Wilson, the white hunter, she knew she had never truly seen before. He was about middle height with sandy hair, a stubby mustache, a very red face and extremely cold blue eyes with faint white wrinkles at the corners that grooved merrily when he smiled. He smiled at her now and she looked away from his face at the way his shoulders sloped in the loose tunic he wore with the four big cartridges held in loops where the left breast pocket should have been, at his big brown hands, his old slacks, his very dirty boots and back to his red face again. She noticed where the baked red of his face stopped in a white line that marked the circle left by his Stetson hat that hung now from one of the pegs of the tent pole.

"Well, here's to the lion," Robert Wilson said. He smiled at her again and, not smiling, she looked curiously at her husband.

Francis Macomber was very tall, very well built if you did not mind that length of bone, dark, his hair cropped like an oarsman, rather thin-lipped, and was considered handsome. He was dressed in the same sort of safari clothes that Wilson wore except that his were new, he was thirty-five years old, kept himself very fit, was good at court games, had a number of big-game fishing records, and had just shown himself, very publicly, to be a coward.

"Here's to the lion," he said. "I can't ever thank you for what you did."

Margaret, his wife, looked away from him and back to Wilson.

"Let's not talk about the lion," she said.

Wilson looked over at her without smiling and now she smiled at him.

"It's been a very strange day," she said. "Hadn't you ought to put your hat on even under the canvas at noon? You told me that, you know."

"Might put it on," said Wilson.

"You know you have a very red face, Mr. Wilson," she told him and smiled again.

"Drink," said Wilson.

"I don't think so," she said. "Francis drinks a great deal, but his face is never red."

"It's red today," Macomber tried a joke.

"No," said Margaret. "It's mine that's red today. But Mr. Wilson's is always red."

"Must be racial," said Wilson. "I say, you wouldn't like to drop my beauty as a topic, would you?"

"I've just started on it."

"Let's check it," said Wilson.

"Conversation is going to be so difficult," Margaret said.

"Don't be silly, Margot," her husband said.

"No difficulty," Wilson said. "Got a damn fine lion."

Margot looked at them both and they both saw that she was going to cry. Wilson had seen it coming for a long time and he dreaded it. Macomber was past dreading it.

"I wish it hadn't happened. Oh, I wish it hadn't happened," she said and started for her tent. She made no noise of crying but they could see that her shoulders were shaking under the rose-colored, sun-proofed shirt she wore.

"Women upset," said Wilson to the tall man. "Amounts to nothing. Strain on the nerves and one thing'n another."

"No," said Macomber. "I suppose that I rate that for the rest of my life now."

"Nonsense. Let's have a spot of the giant killer," said Wilson. "Forget the whole thing. Nothing to it anyway."

"We might try," said Macomber. "I won't forget what you did for me though."

"Nothing," said Wilson. "All nonsense."

So they sat there in the shade where the camp was pitched under some wide-topped acacia trees with a boulder-strewn cliff behind them, and a stretch of grass that ran to the bank of a boulder-filled stream in front with forest beyond it, and drank their just-cool lime drinks and avoided one another's eyes while the boys set the table for lunch. Wilson could tell that the boys all knew about it now and when he saw Macomber's personal boy looking curiously at his master while he was putting dishes on the table he snapped at him in Swahili. The boy turned away with his face blank.

"What were you telling him?" Macomber asked.

"Nothing. Told him to look alive or I'd see he got about fifteen of the best."

"What's that? Lashes?"

"It's quite illegal," Wilson said. "You're supposed to fine them."

"Do you still have them whipped?"

"Oh, yes. They could raise a row if they chose to complain. But they don't. They prefer it to the fines."

"How strange!" said Macomber.

"Not strange, really," Wilson said. "Which would you rather do? Take a good birching or lose your pay?"

Then he felt embarrassed at asking it and before Macomber could answer he went on, "We all take a beating every day, you know, one way or another."

This was no better. "Good God," he thought. "I am a diplomat, aren't I?"

"Yes, we take a beating," said Macomber, still not looking at him. "I'm awfully sorry about that lion business. It doesn't have to go any further, does it? I mean no one will hear about it, will they?"

"You mean will I tell it at the Mathaiga Club?" Wilson looked at him now coldly. He had not expected this. So he's a bloody four-letter man as well as a bloody coward, he thought. I rather liked him too until today. But how is one to know about an American?

"No," said Wilson. "I'm a professional hunter. We never talk about our clients. You can be quite easy on that. It's supposed to be bad form to ask us not to talk though."

He had decided now that to break would be much easier. He would eat, then, by himself and could read a book with his meals. They would eat by themselves. He would see them through the safari on a very formal basis—what was it the French called it? Distinguished consideration—and it would be a damn sight easier than having to go through this emotional trash. He'd insult him and make a good clean break. Then he could read a book with his meals and he'd still be drinking their whisky. That was the phrase for it when a safari went bad. You ran into another white hunter and you asked, "How is everything going?" and he answered, "Oh, I'm still drinking their whisky," and you knew everything had gone to pot.

"I'm sorry," Macomber said and looked at him with his American face that would stay adolescent until it became middle-aged, and Wilson noted his crew-cropped hair, fine eyes only faintly shifty, good nose, thin lips and handsome jaw. "I'm sorry I didn't realize that. There are lots of things I don't know."

So what could he do, Wilson thought. He was all ready to break it off quickly and neatly and here the beggar was apologizing after he had just insulted him. He made one more attempt. "Don't worry about me talking," he said. "I have a living to make. You know in Africa no woman ever misses her lion and no white man ever bolts."

"I bolted like a rabbit," Macomber said.

Now what in hell were you going to do about a man who talked like that, Wilson wondered.

Wilson looked at Macomber with his flat, blue, machine-gunner's eyes and the other smiled back at him. He had a pleasant smile if you did not notice how his eyes showed when he was hurt.

"Maybe I can fix it up on buffalo," he said. "We're after them next, aren't we?"

"In the morning if you like," Wilson told him. Perhaps he had been wrong. This was certainly the way to take it. You most certainly could not tell a damned thing about an American. He was all for Macomber again. If you could forget the morning. But, of course, you couldn't. The morning had been about as bad as they come.

"Here comes the Memsahib," he said. She was walking over from her tent looking refreshed and cheerful and quite lovely. She had a very perfect oval face, so perfect that you expected her to be stupid. But she wasn't stupid, Wilson thought, no, not stupid.

"How is the beautiful red-faced Mr. Wilson? Are you feeling better, Francis, my pearl?"

"Oh, much," said Macomber.

"I've dropped the whole thing," she said, sitting down at the table. "What importance is there to whether Francis is any good at killing lions? That's not his trade. That's Mr. Wilson's trade. Mr. Wilson is really very impressive killing anything. You do kill anything, don't you?"

"Oh, anything," said Wilson. "Simply anything." They are, he thought, the hardest in the world; the hardest, the cruelest, the most predatory and the most attractive and their men have softened or gone to pieces nervously as they have hardened. Or is it that they pick men they can handle? They can't know that much at the age they marry, he thought. He was grateful that he had gone through his education on American women before now because this was a very attractive one.

"We're going after buff in the morning," he told her.

"I'm coming," she said.

"No, you're not."

"Oh, yes, I am. Mayn't I, Francis?"

"Why not stay in camp?"

"Not for anything," she said. "I wouldn't miss something like today for anything."

When she left, Wilson was thinking, when she went off to cry, she seemed a hell of a fine woman. She seemed to understand, to realize, to be hurt for him and for herself and to know how things really stood. She is away for twenty minutes and now she is back, simply enamelled in that American female cruelty. They are the damnedest women. Really the damnedest.

"We'll put on another show for you tomorrow," Francis Macomber said.

"You're not coming," Wilson said.

"You're very mistaken," she told him. "And I want *so* to see you perform again. You were lovely this morning. That is if blowing things' heads off is lovely."

"Here's the lunch," said Wilson. "You're very merry, aren't you?"

"Why not? I didn't come out here to be dull."

"Well, it hasn't been dull," Wilson said. He could see the boulders in the river and the high bank beyond with the trees and he remembered the morning.

"Oh, no," she said. "It's been charming. And tomorrow. You don't know how I look forward to tomorrow."

"That's eland he's offering you," Wilson said.

"They're the big cowy things that jump like hares, aren't they?"

"I suppose that describes them," Wilson said.

"It's very good meat," Macomber said.

"Did you shoot it, Francis?" she asked.

"Yes."

"They're not dangerous, are they?"

"Only if they fall on you," Wilson told her.

"I'm so glad."

"Why not let up on the bitchery just a little, Margot," Macomber said, cutting the eland steak and putting some mashed potato, gravy and carrot on the down-turned fork that tined through the piece of meat.

"I suppose I could," she said, "since you put it so prettily."

"Tonight we'll have champagne for the lion," Wilson said. "It's a bit too hot at noon."

"Oh, the lion," Margot said. "I'd forgotten the lion!"

So, Robert Wilson thought to himself, she *is* giving him a ride, isn't she? Or do you suppose that's her idea of putting up a good show? How should a woman act when she discovers her husband is a bloody coward? She's damn cruel but they're all cruel. They govern, of course, and to govern one has to be cruel sometimes. Still, I've seen enough of their damn terrorism.

"Have some more eland," he said to her politely.

That afternoon, late, Wilson and Macomber went out in the motor car with the native driver and the two gun-bearers. Mrs. Macomber stayed in the camp. It was too hot to go out, she said, and she was going with them in the early morning. As they drove off Wilson saw her standing under the big tree, looking pretty rather than beautiful in her faintly rosy khaki, her dark hair drawn back off her forehead and gathered in a knot low on her neck, her face as fresh, he thought, as though she were in England. She waved to them as the car went off through the swale of high grass and curved around through the trees into the small hills of orchard bush.

In the orchard bush they found a herd of impala, and leaving the car they stalked one old ram with long, wide-spread horns and Macomber killed it with a very creditable shot that knocked the buck down at a good two hundred yards and sent the herd off bounding wildly and leaping over one another's backs in long, leg-drawn-up leaps as unbelievable and as floating as those one makes sometimes in dreams.

"That was a good shot," Wilson said. "They're a small target."

"Is it a worth-while head?" Macomber asked.

"It's excellent," Wilson told him. "You shoot like that and you'll have no trouble."

"Do you think we'll find buffalo tomorrow?"

"There's a good chance of it. They feed out early in the morning and with luck we may catch them in the open."

"I'd like to clear away that lion business," Macomber said. "It's not very pleasant to have your wife see you do something like that."

I should think it would be even more unpleasant to do it, Wilson thought, wife or no wife, or to talk about it having done it. But he said, "I wouldn't think about that any more. Any one could be upset by his first lion. That's all over."

But that night after dinner and a whisky and soda by the fire before going to bed, as Francis Macomber lay on his cot with the mosquito bar over him and listened to the night noises it was not all over. It was neither all over nor was it beginning. It was there exactly as it happened with some parts of it indelibly emphasized and he was miserably ashamed at it. But more than shame he felt cold, hollow fear in him. The fear was still there like a cold slimy hollow in all the emptiness where once his confidence had been and it made him feel sick. It was still there with him now.

It had started the night before when he had wakened and heard the lion roaring somewhere up along the river. It was a deep sound and at the end there were sort of coughing grunts that made him seem just outside the tent, and when Francis Macomber woke in the night to hear it he was afraid. He could hear his wife breathing quietly, asleep. There was no one to tell he was afraid, nor to be afraid with him, and, lying alone, he did not know the Somali proverb that says a brave man is always frightened three times by a lion; when he first sees his track, when he first hears him roar and when he first confronts him. Then while they were eating breakfast by lantern light out in the dining tent, before the sun was up, the lion roared again and Francis thought he was just at the edge of camp.

"Sounds like an old-timer," Robert Wilson said, looking up from his kippers and coffee. "Listen to him cough."

"Is he very close?"

"A mile or so up the stream."

"Will we see him?"

"We'll have a look."

"Does his roaring carry that far? It sounds as though he were right in camp."

"Carries a hell of a long way," said Robert Wilson. "It's strange the way it carries. Hope he's a shootable cat. The boys said there was a very big one about here."

"If I get a shot, where should I hit him," Macomber asked, "to stop him?"

"In the shoulders," Wilson said. "In the neck if you can make it. Shoot for bone. Break him down."

"I hope I can place it properly," Macomber said.

"You shoot very well," Wilson told him. "Take your time. Make sure of him. The first one in is the one that counts."

"What range will it be?"

"Can't tell. Lion has something to say about that. Won't shoot unless it's close enough so you can make sure."

"At under a hundred yards?" Macomber asked.

Wilson looked at him quickly.

"Hundred's about right. Might have to take him a bit under. Shouldn't chance a shot at much over that. A hundred's a decent range. You can hit him wherever you want at that. Here comes the Memsahib."

"Good morning," she said. "Are we going after that lion?"

"As soon as you deal with your breakfast," Wilson said. "How are you feeling?"

"Marvellous," she said. "I'm very excited."

"I'll just go and see that everything is ready." Wilson went off. As he left the lion roared again.

"Noisy beggar," Wilson said. "We'll put a stop to that."

"What's the matter, Francis?" his wife asked him.

"Nothing," Macomber said.

"Yes, there is," she said. "What are you upset about?"

"Nothing," he said.

"Tell me," she looked at him. "Don't you feel well?"

"It's that damned roaring," he said. "It's been going on all night, you know."

"Why didn't you wake me," she said. "I'd love to have heard it."

"I've got to kill the damned thing," Macomber said, miserably.

"Well, that's what you're out here for, isn't it?"

"Yes. But I'm nervous. Hearing the thing roar gets on my nerves."

"Well then, as Wilson said, kill him and stop his roaring."

"Yes, darling," said Francis Macomber. "It sounds easy, doesn't it?"

"You're not afraid, are you?"

"Of course not. But I'm nervous from hearing him roar all night."

"You'll kill him marvellously," she said. "I know you will. I'm awfully anxious to see it."

"Finish your breakfast and we'll be starting."

"It's not light yet," she said. "This is a ridiculous hour."

Just then the lion roared in a deep-chested moaning, suddenly guttural, ascending vibration that seemed to shake the air and ended in a sigh and a heavy, deep-chested grunt.

"He sounds almost here," Macomber's wife said.

"My God," said Macomber. "I hate that damned noise."

"It's very impressive."

"Impressive. It's frightful."

Robert Wilson came up then carrying his short, ugly, shockingly big-bored .505 Gibbs and grinning.

"Come on," he said. "Your gun-bearer has your Springfield and the big gun. Everything's in the car. Have you solids?"

"Yes."

"I'm ready," Mrs. Macomber said.

"Must make him stop that racket," Wilson said. "You get in front. The Memsahib can sit back here with me."

They climbed into the motor car and, in the gray first daylight, moved off up the river through the trees. Macomber opened the breech of his rifle and saw he had metal-cased bullets, shut the bolt and put the rifle on safety. He saw his hand was trembling. He felt in his pocket for more cartridges and moved his fingers over the cartridges in the loops of his tunic front. He turned back to where Wilson sat in the rear seat of the doorless, box-bodied motor car beside his wife, then both grinning with excitement, and Wilson leaned forward and whispered,

"See the birds dropping. Means the old boy has left his kill."

On the far bank of the stream Macomber could see, above the trees, vultures circling and plummeting down.

"Chances are he'll come to drink along here," Wilson whispered. "Before he goes to lay up. Keep an eye out."

They were driving slowly along the high bank of the stream which here cut deeply to its boulder-filled bed, and they wound in and out through big trees as they drove. Macomber was watching the opposite bank when he felt Wilson take hold of his arm. The car stopped.

"There he is," he heard the whisper. "Ahead and to the right. Get out and take him. He's a marvellous lion."

Macomber saw the lion now. He was standing almost broadside, his great head up and turned toward them. The early morning breeze that blew toward them was just stirring his dark mane, and the lion looked huge, silhouetted on the rise of bank in the gray morning light, his shoulders heavy, his barrel of a body bulking smoothly.

"How far is he?" asked Macomber, raising his rifle.

"About seventy-five. Get out and take him."

"Why not shoot from where I am?"

"You don't shoot them from cars," he heard Wilson saying in his ear. "Get out. He's not going to stay there all day."

Macomber stepped out of the curved opening at the side of the front seat, onto the step and down onto the ground. The lion still stood looking majestically and coolly toward this object that his eyes only showed in silhouette, bulking like some super-rhino. There was no man smell carried toward him and he watched the object, moving his great head a little from side to side. Then watching the object, not afraid, but hesitating before going down the bank to drink with such a thing opposite him, he saw a man figure detach itself from it and he turned his heavy head and swung away toward the cover of the trees as he heard a cracking crash and felt the slam of a .30-06 220-grain solid bullet that bit his flank and ripped in sudden hot scalding nausea through his stomach. He trotted, heavy, big-footed, swinging wounded full-bellied, through the trees toward the tall grass and cover, and the crash came again to go past him ripping the air apart. Then it crashed again and he felt the blow as it hit his lower ribs and ripped on through, blood sudden hot and frothy in his mouth, and he galloped toward the high grass where he could crouch and not be seen and make them bring the crashing thing close enough so he could make a rush and get the man that held it.

Macomber had not thought how the lion felt as he got out of the car. He only knew his hands were shaking and as he walked away from the car it was almost impossible for him to make his legs move. They were stiff in the thighs, but he could feel the muscles fluttering. He raised the rifle, sighted on the junction of the lion's head and shoulders and pulled the trigger. Nothing happened though he pulled until he thought his finger would break. Then he knew he had the safety on and as he lowered the rifle to move the safety over he moved another frozen pace forward, and the lion seeing his silhouette now clear of the silhouette of the car, turned and started off at a trot, and, as Macomber fired, he heard a whunk that meant that the bullet was home; but the lion kept on going. Macomber shot again and every one saw the bullet throw a spout of dirt beyond the trotting lion. He shot again, remembering to lower his aim, and they all heard the bullet hit, and the lion went into a gallop and was in the tall grass before he had the bolt pushed forward.

Macomber stood there feeling sick at his stomach, his hands that held the Springfield still cocked, shaking, and his wife and Robert Wilson were standing by him. Beside him too were the two gun-bearers chattering in Wakamba.

"I hit him," Macomber said. "I hit him twice."

"You gut-shot him and you hit him somewhere forward," Wilson said without enthusiasm. The gun-bearers looked very grave. They were silent now.

"You may have killed him," Wilson went on. "We'll have to wait a while before we go in to find out."

"What do you mean?"

"Let him get sick before we follow him up."

"Oh," said Macomber.

"He's a hell of a fine lion," Wilson said cheerfully. "He's gotten into a bad place though."

"Why is it bad?"

"Can't see him until you're on him."

"Oh," said Macomber.

"Come on," said Wilson. "The Memsahib can stay here in the car. We'll go to have a look at the blood spoor."

"Stay here, Margot," Macomber said to his wife. His mouth was very dry and it was hard for him to talk.

"Why?" she asked.

"Wilson says to."

"We're going to have a look," Wilson said. "You stay here. You can see even better from here."

"All right."

Wilson spoke in Swahili to the driver. He nodded and said, "Yes, Bwana."

Then they went down the steep bank and across the stream, climbing over and around the boulders and up the other bank, pulling up by some projecting roots, and along it until they found where the lion had been trotting when Macomber first shot. There was dark blood on the short grass that the gun-bearers pointed out with grass stems, and that ran away behind the river bank trees.

"What do we do?" asked Macomber.

"Not much choice," said Wilson. "We can't bring the car over. Bank's too steep. We'll let him stiffen up a bit and then you and I'll go in and have a look for him."

"Can't we set the grass on fire?" Macomber asked.

"Too green."

"Can't we send beaters?"

Wilson looked at him appraisingly. "Of course we can," he said. "But it's just a touch murderous. You see we know the lion's wounded. You can drive an unwounded lion—he'll move on ahead of a noise—but a wounded lion's going to charge. You can't see him until you're right on him. He'll make himself perfectly flat in cover you wouldn't think would hide a hare. You can't very well send boys in there to that sort of a show. Somebody bound to get mauled."

"What about the gun-bearers?"

"Oh, they'll go with us. It's their *shauri*. You see, they signed on for it. They don't look too happy though, do they?"

"I don't want to go in there," said Macomber. It was out before he knew he'd said it.

"Neither do I," said Wilson very cheerily. "Really no choice though." Then, as an afterthought, he glanced at Macomber and saw suddenly how he was trembling and the pitiful look on his face.

"You don't have to go in, of course," he said. "That's what I'm hired for, you know. That's why I'm so expensive."

"You mean you'd go in by yourself? Why not leave him there?"

Robert Wilson, whose entire occupation had been with the lion and the problem he presented, and who had not been thinking about

Macomber except to note that he was rather windy, suddenly felt as though he had opened the wrong door in a hotel and seen something shameful.

"What do you mean?"

"Why not just leave him?"

"You mean pretend to ourselves he hasn't been hit?"

"No. Just drop it."

"It isn't done."

"Why not?"

"For one thing, he's certain to be suffering. For another, some one else might run onto him."

"I see."

"But you don't have to have anything to do with it."

"I'd like to," Macomber said. "I'm just scared, you know."

"I'll go ahead when we go in," Wilson said, "with Kongoni tracking. You keep behind me and a little to one side. Chances are we'll hear him growl. If we see him we'll both shoot. Don't worry about anything. I'll keep you backed up. As a matter of fact, you know, perhaps you'd better not go. It might be much better. Why don't you go over and join the Memsahib while I just get it over with?"

"No, I want to go."

"All right," said Wilson. "But don't go in if you don't want to. This is my *shauri* now, you know."

"I want to go," said Macomber.

They sat under a tree and smoked.

"Want to go back and speak to the Memsahib while we're waiting?" Wilson asked.

"No."

"I'll just step back and tell her to be patient."

"Good," said Macomber. He sat there, sweating under his arms, his mouth dry, his stomach hollow feeling, wanting to find courage to tell Wilson to go on and finish off the lion without him. He could not know that Wilson was furious because he had not noticed the state he was in earlier and sent him back to his wife. While he sat there Wilson came up. "I have your big gun," he said. "Take it. We've given him time, I think. Come on."

Macomber took the big gun and Wilson said:

"Keep behind me and about five yards to the right and do exactly as I tell you." Then he spoke in Swahili to the two gun-bearers who looked the picture of gloom.

"Let's go," he said.

"Could I have a drink of water?" Macomber asked. Wilson spoke to the older gun-bearer, who wore a canteen on his belt, and the man unbuckled it, unscrewed the top and handed it to Macomber, who took it noticing how heavy it seemed and how hairy and shoddy the felt covering was in his hand. He raised it to drink and looked ahead at the high grass with the flat-topped trees behind it. A breeze was blowing toward them and the grass rippled gently in the wind. He looked at the gun-bearer and he could see the gun-bearer was suffering too with fear.

Thirty-five yards into the grass the big lion lay flattened out along the ground. His ears were back and his only movement was a slight twitching up and down of his long, black-tufted tail. He had turned at bay as soon as he had reached this cover and he was sick with the wound through his full belly, and weakening with the wound through his lungs that brought a thin foamy red to his mouth each time he breathed. His flanks were wet and hot and flies were on the little openings the solid bullets had made in his tawny hide, and his big yellow eyes, narrowed with hate, looked straight ahead, only blinking when the pain came as he breathed, and his claws dug in the soft baked earth. All of him, pain, sickness, hatred and all of his remaining strength, was tightening into an absolute concentration for a rush. He could hear the men talking and he waited, gathering all of himself into this preparation for a charge as soon as the men would come into the grass. As he heard their voices his tail stiffened to twitch up and down, and, as they came into the edge of the grass, he made a coughing grunt and charged.

Kongoni, the old gun-bearer, in the lead watching the blood spoor, Wilson watching the grass for any movement, his big gun ready, the second gun-bearer looking ahead and listening, Macomber close to Wilson, his rifle cocked, they had just moved into the grass when Macomber heard the blood-choked coughing grunt, and saw the swishing rush in the grass. The next thing he knew he was running; running wildly, in panic in the open, running toward the stream.

He heard the *ca-ra-wong!* of Wilson's big rifle, and again in a second crashing *carawong!* and turning saw the lion, horrible-looking now, with half his head seeming to be gone, crawling toward Wilson in the edge of the tall grass while the red-faced man worked the bolt on the short ugly rifle and aimed carefully as another blasting *carawong!* came from the muzzle, and the crawling, heavy, yellow bulk of the lion stiffened and the huge, mutilated head slid forward and Macomber, standing by himself in the clearing where he had run, holding a loaded rifle, while two black men and a white man looked back at him in contempt, knew the lion was dead. He came toward Wilson, his tallness all seeming a naked reproach, and Wilson looked at him and said:

"Want to take pictures?"

"No," he said.

That was all any one had said until they reached the motor car. Then Wilson had said:

"Hell of a fine lion. Boys will skin him out. We might as well stay here in the shade."

Macomber's wife had not looked at him nor he at her and he had sat by her in the back seat with Wilson sitting in the front seat. Once he had reached over and taken his wife's hand without looking at her and she had removed her hand from his. Looking across the stream to where the gun-bearers were skinning out the lion he could see that she had been able to see the whole thing. While they sat there his wife had reached forward and put her hand on Wilson's shoulder. He turned and she had leaned forward over the low seat and kissed him on the mouth.

"Oh, I say," said Wilson, going redder than his natural baked color.

"Mr. Robert Wilson," she said. "The beautiful red-faced Mr. Robert Wilson."

Then she sat down beside Macomber again and looked away across the stream to where the lion lay, with uplifted, white-muscled, tendon-marked naked forearms, and white bloating belly, as the black men fleshed away the skin. Finally the gun-bearers brought the skin over, wet and heavy, and climbed in behind with it, rolling it up before they got in, and the motor car started. No one had said anything more until they were back in camp.

That was the story of the lion. Macomber did not know how the lion had felt before he started his rush, nor during it when the unbelievable smash of the .505 with a muzzle velocity of two tons had hit him in the mouth, nor what kept him coming after that, when the second ripping crash had smashed his hind quarters and he had come crawling on toward the crashing, blasting thing that had destroyed him. Wilson knew something about it and only expressed it by saying, "Damned fine lion," but Macomber did not know how Wilson felt about things either. He did not know how his wife felt except that she was through with him.

His wife had been through with him before but it never lasted. He was very wealthy, and would be much wealthier, and he knew she would not leave him ever now. That was one of the few things that he really knew. He knew about that, about motor cycles—that was earliest—about motor cars, about duck-shooting, about fishing, trout, salmon and big-sea, about sex in books, many books, too many books, about all court games, about dogs, not much about horses, about hanging on to his money, about most of the other things his world dealt in, and about his wife not leaving him. His wife had been a great beauty and she was still a great beauty in Africa, but she was not a great enough beauty any more at home to be able to leave him and better herself and she knew it and he knew it. She had missed the chance to leave him and he knew it. If he had been better with women she would probably have started to worry about him getting another new, beautiful wife; but she knew too much about him to worry about him either. Also, he had always had a great tolerance which seemed the nicest thing about him if it were not the most sinister.

All in all they were known as a comparatively happily married couple, one of those whose disruption is often rumored but never occurs, and as the society columnist put it, they were adding more than a spice of *adventure* to their much envied and ever-enduring *Romance* by a *Safari* in what was known as *Darkest Africa* until the Martin Johnsons lighted it on so many silver screens where they were pursuing *Old Simba* the lion, the buffalo, *Tembo* the elephant and as well collecting specimens for the Museum of Natural History. This same columnist had reported them *on the verge* at least three times in the past and they had been. But they always made it up. They had a sound basis of union. Margot was too beautiful for Macomber to divorce her and Macomber had too much money for Margot ever to leave him.

It was now about three o'clock in the morning and Francis Macomber, who had been asleep a little while after he had stopped thinking about the lion, wakened and then slept again, woke suddenly, frightened in a dream of the bloody-headed lion standing over him, and listening while his heart pounded, he realized that his wife was not in the other cot in the tent. He lay awake with that knowledge for two hours.

At the end of that time his wife came into the tent, lifted her mosquito bar and crawled cozily into bed.

"Where have you been?" Macomber asked in the darkness.

"Hello," she said. "Are you awake?"

"Where have you been?"

"I just went out to get a breath of air."

"You did, like hell."

"What do you want me to say, darling?"

"Where have you been?"

"Out to get a breath of air."

"That's a new name for it. You *are* a bitch."

"Well, you're a coward."

"All right," he said. "What of it?"

"Nothing as far as I'm concerned. But please let's not talk, darling, because I'm very sleepy."

"You think that I'll take anything."

"I know you will, sweet."

"Well, I won't."

"Please, darling, let's not talk. I'm so very sleepy."

"There wasn't going to be any of that. You promised there wouldn't be."

"Well, there is now," she said sweetly.

"You said if we made this trip that there would be none of that. You promised."

"Yes, darling. That's the way I meant it to be. But the trip was spoiled yesterday. We don't have to talk about it, do we?"

"You don't wait long when you have an advantage, do you?"

"Please let's not talk. I'm so sleepy, darling."

"I'm going to talk."

"Don't mind me then, because I'm going to sleep." And she did.

At breakfast they were all three at the table before daylight and

Francis Macomber found that, of all the many men that he had hated, he hated Robert Wilson the most.

"Sleep well?" Wilson asked in his throaty voice, filling a pipe.

"Did you?"

"Topping," the white hunter told him.

You bastard, thought Macomber, you insolent bastard.

So she woke him when she came in, Wilson thought, looking at them both with his flat, cold eyes. Well, why doesn't he keep his wife where she belongs? What does he think I am, a bloody plaster saint? Let him keep her where she belongs. It's his own fault.

"Do you think we'll find buffalo?" Margot asked, pushing away a dish of apricots.

"Chance of it," Wilson said and smiled at her. "Why don't you stay in camp?"

"Not for anything," she told him.

"Why not order her to stay in camp?" Wilson said to Macomber.

"You order her," said Macomber coldly.

"Let's not have any ordering, nor," turning to Macomber, "any silliness, Francis," Margot said quite pleasantly.

"Are you ready to start?" Macomber asked.

"Any time," Wilson told him. "Do you want the Memsahib to go?"

"Does it make any difference whether I do or not?"

The hell with it, thought Robert Wilson. The utter complete hell with it. So this is what it's going to be like. Well, this is what it's going to be like, then.

"Makes no difference," he said.

"You're sure you wouldn't like to stay in camp with her yourself and let me go out and hunt the buffalo?" Macomber asked.

"Can't do that," said Wilson. "Wouldn't talk rot if I were you."

"I'm not talking rot. I'm disgusted."

"Bad word, disgusted."

"Francis, will you please try to speak sensibly!" his wife said.

"I speak too damned sensibly," Macomber said. "Did you ever eat such filthy food?"

"Something wrong with the food?" asked Wilson quietly.

"No more than with everything else."

"I'd pull yourself together, laddybuck," Wilson said very quietly. "There's a boy waits at table that understands a little English."

"The hell with him."

Wilson stood up and puffing on his pipe strolled away, speaking a few words in Swahili to one of the gun-bearers who was standing waiting for him. Macomber and his wife sat on at the table. He was staring at his coffee cup.

"If you make a scene I'll leave you, darling," Margot said quietly.

"No, you won't."

"You can try it and see."

"You won't leave me."

"No," she said. "I won't leave you and you'll behave yourself."

"Behave myself? That's a way to talk. Behave myself."

"Yes. Behave yourself."

"Why don't *you* try behaving?"

"I've tried it so long. So very long."

"I hate that red-faced swine," Macomber said. "I loathe the sight of him."

"He's really *very* nice."

"Oh, *shut up*," Macomber almost shouted. Just then the car came up and stopped in front of the dining tent and the driver and the two gun-bearers got out. Wilson walked over and looked at the husband and wife sitting there at the table.

"Going shooting?" he asked.

"Yes," said Macomber, standing up. "Yes."

"Better bring a woolly. It will be cool in the car," Wilson said.

"I'll get my leather jacket," Margot said.

"The boy has it," Wilson told her. He climbed into the front with the driver and Francis Macomber and his wife sat, not speaking, in the back seat.

Hope the silly beggar doesn't take a notion to blow the back of my head off, Wilson thought to himself. Women *are* a nuisance on safari.

The car was grinding down to cross the river at a pebbly ford in the gray daylight and then climbed, angling up the steep bank, where Wilson had ordered a way shovelled out the day before so they could reach the parklike wooded rolling country on the far side.

It was a good morning, Wilson thought. There was a heavy dew and as the wheels went through the grass and low bushes he could smell the odor of the crushed fronds. It was an odor like verbena and he liked this early morning smell of the dew, the crushed bracken

and the look of the tree trunks showing black through the early morning mist, as the car made its way through the untracked, parklike
country. He had put the two in the back seat out of his mind now
and was thinking about buffalo. The buffalo that he was after stayed
in the daytime in a thick swamp where it was impossible to get a shot,
but in the night they fed out into an open stretch of country and
if he could come between them and their swamp with the car,
Macomber would have a good chance at them in the open. He did not
want to hunt buff with Macomber in thick cover. He did not want to
hunt buff or anything else with Macomber at all, but he was a professional hunter and he had hunted with some rare ones in his time.
If they got buff today there would only be rhino to come and the
poor man would have gone through his dangerous game and things
might pick up. He'd have nothing more to do with the woman and
Macomber would get over that too. He must have gone through
plenty of that before by the look of things. Poor beggar. He must
have a way of getting over it. Well, it was the poor sod's own bloody
fault.

He, Robert Wilson, carried a double size cot on safari to ac-
commodate any windfalls he might receive. He had hunted for a
certain clientele, the international, fast, sporting set, where the
women did not feel they were getting their money's worth unless they
had shared that cot with the white hunter. He despised them when
he was away from them although he liked some of them well enough
at the time, but he made his living by them; and their standards were
his standards as long as they were hiring him.

They were his standards in all except the shooting. He had his
own standards about the killing and they could live up to them or
get some one else to hunt them. He knew, too, that they all respected
him for this. This Macomber was an odd one though. Damned if he
wasn't. Now the wife. Well, the wife. Yes, the wife. Hm, the wife.
Well he'd dropped all that. He looked around at them. Macomber sat
grim and furious. Margot smiled at him. She looked younger today,
more innocent and fresher and not so professionally beautiful. What's
in her heart God knows, Wilson thought. She hadn't talked much last
night. At that it was a pleasure to see her.

The motor car climbed up a slight rise and went on through the
trees and then out into a grassy prairie-like opening and kept in the
shelter of the trees along the edge, the driver going slowly and Wilson

looking carefully out across the prairie and all along its far side. He stopped the car and studied the opening with his field glasses. Then he motioned to the driver to go on and the car moved slowly along, the driver avoiding wart-hog holes and driving around the mud castles ants had built. Then, looking across the opening, Wilson suddenly turned and said,

"By God, there they are!"

And looking where he pointed, while the car jumped forward and Wilson spoke in rapid Swahili to the driver, Macomber saw three huge, black animals looking almost cylindrical in their long heaviness, like big black tank cars, moving at a gallop across the far edge of the open prairie. They moved at a stiff-necked, stiff bodied gallop and he could see the upswept wide black horns on their heads as they galloped heads out; the heads not moving.

"They're three old bulls," Wilson said. "We'll cut them off before they get to the swamp."

The car was going a wild forty-five miles an hour across the open and as Macomber watched, the buffalo got bigger and bigger until he could see the gray, hairless, scabby look of one huge bull and how his neck was a part of his shoulders and the shiny black of his horns as he galloped a little behind the others that were strung out in that steady plunging gait; and then, the car swaying as though it had just jumped a road, they drew up close and he could see the plunging hugeness of the bull, and the dust in his sparsely haired hide, the wide boss of horn and his outstretched, wide-nostrilled muzzle, and he was raising his rifle when Wilson shouted, "Not from the car, you fool!" and he had no fear, only hatred of Wilson, while the brakes clamped on and the car skidded, plowing sideways to an almost stop and Wilson was out on one side and he on the other, stumbling as his feet hit the still speeding-by of the earth, and then he was shooting at the bull as he moved away, hearing the bullets whunk into him, emptying his rifle at him as he moved steadily away, finally remembering to get his shots forward into the shoulder, and as he fumbled to re-load, he saw the bull was down. Down on his knees, his big head tossing, and seeing the other two still galloping he shot at the leader and hit him. He shot again and missed and he heard the *carawonging* roar as Wilson shot and saw the leading bull slide forward onto his nose.

"Get that other," Wilson said. "Now you're shooting!"

But the other bull was moving steadily at the same gallop and he missed, throwing a spout of dirt, and Wilson missed and the dust rose in a cloud and Wilson shouted, "Come on. He's too far!" and grabbed his arm and they were in the car again, Macomber and Wilson hanging on the sides and rocketing swayingly over the uneven ground, drawing up on the steady, plunging, heavy-necked, straight-moving gallop of the bull.

They were behind him and Macomber was filling his rifle, dropping shells onto the ground, jamming it, clearing the jam, then they were almost up with the bull when Wilson yelled "Stop," and the car skidded so that it almost swung over and Macomber fell forward onto his feet, slammed his bolt forward and fired as far forward as he could aim into the galloping, rounded black back, aimed and shot again, then again, then again, and the bullets, all of them hitting, had no effect on the buffalo that he could see. Then Wilson shot, the roar deafening him, and he could see the bull stagger. Macomber shot again, aiming carefully, and down he came, onto his knees.

"All right," Wilson said. "Nice work. That's the three."

Macomber felt a drunken elation.

"How many times did you shoot?" he asked.

"Just three," Wilson said. "You killed the first bull. The biggest one. I helped you finish the other two. Afraid they might have got into cover. You had them killed. I was just mopping up a little. You shot damn well."

"Let's go to the car,'" said Macomber. "I want a drink."

"Got to finish off that buff first," Wilson told him. The buffalo was on his knees and he jerked his head furiously and bellowed in pig-eyed, roaring rage as they came toward him.

"Watch he doesn't get up," Wilson said. Then, "Get a little broadside and take him in the neck just behind the ear."

Macomber aimed carefully at the center of the huge, jerking, rage-driven neck and shot. At the shot the head dropped forward.

"That does it," said Wilson. "Got the spine. They're a hell of a looking thing, aren't they?"

"Let's get the drink," said Macomber. In his life he had never felt so good.

In the car Macomber's wife sat very white faced. "You were marvellous, darling," she said to Macomber. "What a ride."

"Was it rough?" Wilson asked.

"It was frightful. I've never been more frightened in my life."

"Let's all have a drink," Macomber said.

"By all means," said Wilson. "Give it to the Memsahib." She drank the neat whisky from the flask and shuddered a little when she swallowed. She handed the flask to Macomber who handed it to Wilson.

"It was frightfully exciting," she said. "It's given me a dreadful headache. I didn't know you were allowed to shoot them from cars though."

"No one shot from cars," said Wilson coldly.

"I mean chase them from cars."

"Wouldn't ordinarily," Wilson said. "Seemed sporting enough to me though while we were doing it. Taking more chance driving that way across the plain full of holes and one thing and another than hunting on foot. Buffalo could have charged us each time we shot if he liked. Gave him every chance. Wouldn't mention it to any one though. It's illegal if that's what you mean."

"It seemed very unfair to me," Margot said, "chasing those big helpless things in a motor car."

"Did it?" said Wilson.

"What would happen if they heard about it in Nairobi?"

"I'd lose my licence for one thing. Other unpleasantnesses," Wilson said, taking a drink from the flask. "I'd be out of business."

"Really?"

"Yes, really."

"Well," said Macomber, and he smiled for the first time all day. "Now she has something on you."

"You have such a pretty way of putting things, Francis," Margot Macomber said. Wilson looked at them both. If a four-letter man marries a five-letter woman, he was thinking, what number of letters would their children be? What he said was, "We lost a gun-bearer. Did you notice it?"

"My God, no," Macomber said.

"Here he comes," Wilson said. "He's all right. He must have fallen off when we left the first bull."

Approaching them was the middle-aged gun-bearer, limping along in his knitted cap, khaki tunic, shorts and rubber sandals, gloomy-faced and disgusted looking. As he came up he called out to Wilson in Swahili and they all saw the change in the white hunter's face.

"What does he say?" asked Margot.

"He says the first bull got up and went into the bush," Wilson said with no expression in his voice.

"Oh," said Macomber blankly.

"Then it's going to be just like the lion," said Margot, full of anticipation.

"It's not going to be a damned bit like the lion," Wilson told her. "Did you want another drink, Macomber?"

"Thanks, yes," Macomber said. He expected the feeling he had had about the lion to come back but it did not. For the first time in his life he really felt wholly without fear. Instead of fear he had a feeling of definite elation.

"We'll go and have a look at the second bull," Wilson said. "I'll tell the driver to put the car in the shade."

"What are you going to do?" asked Margaret Macomber.

"Take a look at the buff," Wilson said.

"I'll come."

"Come along."

The three of them walked over to where the second buffalo bulked blackly in the open, head forward on the grass, the massive horns swung wide.

"He's a very good head," Wilson said. "That's close to a fifty-inch spread."

Macomber was looking at him with delight.

"He's hateful looking," said Margot. "Can't we go into the shade?"

"Of course," Wilson said. "Look," he said to Macomber, and pointed. "See that patch of bush?"

"Yes."

"That's where the first bull went in. The gun-bearer said when he fell off the bull was down. He was watching us helling along and the other two buff galloping. When he looked up there was the bull up and looking at him. Gun-bearer ran like hell and the bull went off slowly into that bush."

"Can we go in after him now?" asked Macomber eagerly.

Wilson looked at him appraisingly. Damned if this isn't a strange one, he thought. Yesterday he's scared sick and today he's a ruddy fire eater.

"No, we'll give him a while."

"Let's please go into the shade," Margot said. Her face was white and she looked ill.

They made their way to the car where it stood under a single, wide-spreading tree and all climbed in.

"Chances are he's dead in there," Wilson remarked. "After a little we'll have a look."

Macomber felt a wild unreasonable happiness that he had never known before.

"By God, that was a chase," he said. "I've never felt any such feeling. Wasn't it marvellous, Margot?"

"I hated it."

"Why?"

"I hated it," she said bitterly. "I loathed it."

"You know I don't think I'd ever be afraid of anything again," Macomber said to Wilson. "Something happened in me after we first saw the buff and started after him. Like a dam bursting. It was pure excitement."

"Cleans out your liver," said Wilson. "Damn funny things happen to people."

Macomber's face was shining. "You know something did happen to me," he said. "I feel absolutely different."

His wife said nothing and eyed him strangely. She was sitting far back in the seat and Macomber was sitting forward talking to Wilson who turned sideways talking over the back of the front seat.

"You know, I'd like to try another lion," Macomber said. "I'm really not afraid of them now. After all, what can they do to you?"

"That's it," said Wilson. "Worst one can do is kill you. How does it go? Shakespeare. Damned good. See if I can remember. Oh, damned good. Used to quote it to myself at one time. Let's see. 'By my troth, I care not; a man can die but once; we owe God a death and let it go which way it will, he that dies this year is quit for the next.' Damned fine, eh?"

He was very embarrassed, having brought out this thing he had lived by, but he had seen men come of age before and it always moved him. It was not a matter of their twenty-first birthday.

It had taken a strange chance of hunting, a sudden precipitation into action without opportunity for worrying beforehand, to bring this about with Macomber, but regardless of how it had happened it had most certainly happened. Look at the beggar now, Wilson thought. It's that some of them stay little boys so long, Wilson thought. Sometimes all their lives. Their figures stay boyish when they're fifty. The great American boy-men. Damned strange people. But he liked this Macomber now. Damned strange fellow. Probably meant the end of cuckoldry too. Well, that would be a damned good thing. Damned good thing. Beggar had probably been afraid all his life. Don't know what started it. But over now. Hadn't had time to be afraid with the buff. That and being angry too. Motor car too. Motor cars made it familiar. Be a damn fire eater now. He'd seen it in the war work the same way. More of a change than any loss of virginity. Fear gone like an operation. Something else grew in its place. Main thing a man had. Made him into a man. Women knew it too. No bloody fear.

From the far corner of the seat Margaret Macomber looked at the two of them. There was no change in Wilson. She saw Wilson as she had seen him the day before when she had first realized what his great talent was. But she saw the change in Francis Macomber now.

"Do you have that feeling of happiness about what's going to happen?" Macomber asked, still exploring his new wealth.

"You're not supposed to mention it," Wilson said, looking in the other's face. "Much more fashionable to say you're scared. Mind you, you'll be scared too, plenty of times."

"But you *have* a feeling of happiness about action to come?"

"Yes," said Wilson. "There's that. Doesn't do to talk too much about all this. Talk the whole thing away. No pleasure in anything if you mouth it up too much."

"You're both talking rot," said Margot. "Just because you've chased some helpless animals in a motor car you talk like heroes."

"Sorry," said Wilson. "I have been gassing too much." She's worried about it already, he thought.

"If you don't know what we're talking about why not keep out of it?" Macomber asked his wife.

"You've gotten awfully brave, awfully suddenly," his wife said contemptuously, but her contempt was not secure. She was very afraid of something.

Macomber laughed, a very natural hearty laugh. "You know I *have*," he said. "I really have."

"Isn't it sort of late?" Margot said bitterly. Because she had done the best she could for many years back and the way they were together now was no one person's fault.

"Not for me," said Macomber.

Margot said nothing but sat back in the corner of the seat.

"Do you think we've given him time enough?" Macomber asked Wilson cheerfully.

"We might have a look," Wilson said. "Have you any solids left?"

"The gun-bearer has some."

Wilson called in Swahili and the older gun-bearer, who was skinning out one of the heads, straightened up, pulled a box of solids out of his pocket and brought them over to Macomber, who filled his magazine and put the remaining shells in his pocket.

"You might as well shoot the Springfield," Wilson said. "You're used to it. We'll leave the Mannlicher in the car with the Memsahib. Your gun-bearer can carry your heavy gun. I've this damned cannon. Now let me tell you about them." He had saved this until the last because he did not want to worry Macomber. "When a buff comes he comes with his head high and thrust straight out. The boss of the horns covers any sort of a brain shot. The only shot is straight into the nose. The only other shot is into his chest or, if you're to one side, into the neck or the shoulders. After they've been hit once they take a hell of a lot of killing. Don't try anything fancy. Take the easiest shot there is. They've finished skinning out that head now. Should we get started?"

He called to the gun-bearers, who came up wiping their hands, and the older one got into the back.

"I'll only take Kongoni," Wilson said. "The other can watch to keep the birds away."

As the car moved slowly across the open space toward the island of brushy trees that ran in a tongue of foliage along a dry water course that cut the open swale, Macomber felt his heart pounding and his mouth was dry again, but it was excitement, not fear.

"Here's where he went in," Wilson said. Then to the gun-bearer in Swahili, "Take the blood spoor."

The car was parallel to the patch of bush. Macomber, Wilson and the gun-bearer got down. Macomber, looking back, saw his wife, with the rifle by her side, looking at him. He waved to her and she did not wave back.

The brush was very thick ahead and the ground was dry. The middle-aged gun-bearer was sweating heavily and Wilson had his hat down over his eyes and his red neck showed just ahead of Macomber. Suddenly the gun-bearer said something in Swahili to Wilson and ran forward.

"He's dead in there," Wilson said. "Good work," and he turned to grip Macomber's hand and as they shook hands, grinning at each other, the gun-bearer shouted wildly and they saw him coming out of the bush sideways, fast as a crab, and the bull coming, nose out, mouth tight closed, blood dripping, massive head straight out, coming in a charge, his little pig eyes bloodshot as he looked at them. Wilson, who was ahead was kneeling shooting, and Macomber, as he fired, unhearing his shot in the roaring of Wilson's gun, saw fragments like slate burst from the huge boss of the horns, and the head jerked, he shot again at the wide nostrils and saw the horns jolt again and fragments fly, and he did not see Wilson now and, aiming carefully, shot again with the buffalo's huge bulk almost on him and his rifle almost level with the on-coming head, nose out, and he could see the little wicked eyes and the head started to lower and he felt a sudden white-hot, blinding flash explode inside his head and that was all he ever felt.

Wilson had ducked to one side to get in a shoulder shot. Macomber had stood solid and shot for the nose, shooting a touch high each time and hitting the heavy horns, splintering and chipping them like hitting a slate roof, and Mrs. Macomber, in the car, had shot at the buffalo with the 6.5 Mannlicher as it seemed about to gore Macomber and had hit her husband about two inches up and a little to one side of the base of his skull.

Francis Macomber lay now, face down, not two yards from where the buffalo lay on his side and his wife knelt over him with Wilson beside her.

"I wouldn't turn him over," Wilson said.

The woman was crying hysterically.

"I'd get back in the car," Wilson said. "Where's the rifle?"

She shook her head, her face contorted. The gun-bearer picked up the rifle.

"Leave it as it is," said Wilson. Then, "Go get Abdulla so that he may witness the manner of the accident."

He knelt down, took a handkerchief from his pocket, and spread it over Francis Macomber's crew-cropped head where it lay. The blood sank into the dry, loose earth.

Wilson stood up and saw the buffalo on his side, his legs out, his thinly-haired belly crawling with ticks. "Hell of a good bull," his brain registered automatically. "A good fifty inches, or better. Better." He called to the driver and told him to spread a blanket over the body and stay by it. Then he walked over to the motor car where the woman sat crying in the corner.

"That was a pretty thing to do," he said in a toneless voice. "He *would* have left you too."

"Stop it," she said.

"Of course it's an accident," he said. "I know that."

"Stop it," she said.

"Don't worry," he said. "There will be a certain amount of unpleasantness but I will have some photographs taken that will be very useful at the inquest. There's the testimony of the gun-bearers and the driver too. You're perfectly all right."

"Stop it," she said.

"There's a hell of a lot to be done," he said. "And I'll have to send a truck off to the lake to wireless for a plane to take the three of us into Nairobi. Why didn't you poison him? That's what they do in England."

"Stop it. Stop it. Stop it," the woman cried.

Wilson looked at her with his flat blue eyes.

"I'm through now," he said. "I was a little angry. I'd begun to like your husband."

"Oh, please stop it," she said. "Please, please stop it."

"That's better," Wilson said. "Please is much better. Now I'll stop."

Miss Mary's Lion

PART II

(*Sports Illustrated*—JANUARY 3, 1972)

I SAT by the fire in an old pair of pajamas from Idaho, tucked into a pair of worn mosquito boots made in Hong Kong and wearing a warm wool robe from Pendleton, Oregon and drank a whisky and soda made from a bottle of whisky Mr. Singh had given me as a present and boiled water from the stream that ran down from the mountain animated by a syphon cartridge made in Nairobi.

"I'm a stranger here," I thought. But the whisky said no and it was the time of day for the whisky to be right. Whisky can be as right as it can be wrong and it said I was not a stranger and I knew it was correct at this time of night. Anyway my boots had come home because they were made of ostrich hide and I remembered the place where I had found the leather in the bootmaker's in Hong Kong. No it was not me who found the leather. It was someone else and then I thought about who had found the leather and about those days and then I thought about different women and how they would be in Africa and how lucky I had been to have known fine women that loved Africa. I had known some really terrible ones who had only gone there to have been there and I had known some true bitches and several alcoholics to whom Africa had just been another place for more ample bitchery or fuller drunkenness. The bitches only hunted men although they shot other animals and the alcoholics blamed their rummyhood on the altitude. But they were just as drunk at sea level.

The alcoholics always had some great tragedy which had caused them to drink beyond reason but all of those I had known before their great tragedies had been rummies then too. The white male rummies in Africa were about as boring as the ex-rummies. With one exception I know no greater bore than the former alcoholic. Beside him the impotent man, the former forger, the retired panderer, the reformed card cheat, the ex-chief of police, the former Labor Government minister, a former noncareer ambassador to a Central American country, an aging official of Moral Re-Armament, an interim French Premier, ex-royalty, a former radio political commentator, a retired evangelist, a dedicated big game angler complete with statistics, an unfrocked priest or a professional ex-Communist are figures of blinding interest and charm.

I thought of that last former alcoholic I had met in Nairobi. He was very hearty and at once asked me to have a drink. They hang about bars at crowded hours taking up the place that might be occupied by an honest drinker and while they sip their tomato juice or barley water and nutmeg they look at the drinkers with that look of the ex-alcoholic which is compounded of Moral Re-Armament, crossed with one third marabou stork and a third of the curiosity of the fashionable undertaker who is a little overdrawn at his bank.

"Old Hem," my great old friend said. "Dear old boy. What are you drinking?"

"Whatever you are."

"But this is barley and nutmeg."

"What I've been needing. Bartender, a barley and nutmeg and a double pink gin."

"I don't think I'd mix them old boy."

"All right. I'll drink them separately. What do you hear from old Stevens?"

"Bad. Bad. Couldn't be worse. Shaking like a leaf. Went down the Tana and got up on an absolutely wonderful bull. Two hundred-pounder he said. You know it makes them all lie of course."

"Naturally."

"Missed the elephant completely at twenty yards. He's gone. Doubt if he'll ever go out again."

"Any word from old Dorch?"

"He's gone. Doesn't even know who he's with nor where. Tragic case. Saw him in Jamaica. He just stared at me. Thought I was your brother."

"Poor old Dorch. Nothing we can do for him?"

"You might do something for him."

"I'll think it over. I always liked old Dorch."

"Gone though. Absolutely extinguished. Doubt if he knows whether it's night or day."

"Well it could be night here and day there if he's in Jamaica."

"Quite. But he's not in Jamaica now. He's back in London."

The barley water and nutmeg came and I drank it. It had a heady quality but not too full-bodied.

"It is good. I see your point now." I drank a sip of the pink gin. "This cuts those long whiskers on the barley. Forgot how they stick in the throat."

"Are you feeling fit?" my dear old friend asked.

"Very."

"You look better than I'd heard."

"Splendid. Like a fiddler's bitch."

"I'd heard you'd been celebrating a bit."

"You mean you heard I was drunk?"

"No. Just celebrating a bit. The stuff's a deadly poison you know."

"Who told you?"

"The headwaiter."

"That's true. I was in here with young G.C. We *were* celebrating."

"An anniversary?"

"No. A recent event."

"Can you tell me?"

"No."

"Sorry. I didn't mean to be rude."

"Any word on old Hormones?"

"He's gone. He won't last three months. He may be gone already."

"We'd have heard. You get the *Telegraph* don't you? The air edition. Old Hormones would have been in it if he'd gone."

"True. You're right. It's my favorite paper actually. Any number of the oldtimers in it. Boozed their lives away."

"Not completely. I wouldn't say old Hormones did nothing but fondle the bottle."

"No," he said. "One mustn't be unfair."

"The Tempest wasn't exactly designed for drunkards. It weighed seven tons and it landed almost as fast as a Spitty flew."

"Not quite old boy. Not quite."

"Nowhere near. I was just trying to remind you."

"Great days," he said. "Great chaps. Surprising how they go though now. It is a poison you know. It's been proved. Not too late for you to stop it old Hem."

"Actually it's too bloody early for me to stop. I like it and I get good value from it. What are you having, because I have to run?"

"The same. Look, no offense, eh?"

"None."

"You'll get in touch with me if I can ever be of any help?"

"Absolutely."

"That must have been something interesting you and that youngster, what's his name, K.G., were celebrating eh?"

"It was the non-death of an elephant which was terrorizing the marble quarries which supply the tombstones for Nairobi."

"That must have been a show. Could you work me in on that type of show? What did the tusks go?"

"Not weighed yet."

"Go to the Game Department of course on a show like that. I'll see them there."

"I'd hold it up a little. You might have misunderstood me."

"I see," he said. "But be careful old boy. See if you can work me in."

"I count on you, Freddie," I said. I paid for the drinks and he slipped something into the pocket of my jacket.

"What's that?"

"Read them. Can't do any harm."

That was three months ago in the crowded, high-pitched, over-pistoled, pleasant noonday crush at the bar of The New Stanley and now, sitting by the fire, I thought God pity rummies but God please save us from the ex-rummy and from all tracts, for or against, deliver me.

I was very happy to have G.C. back in camp and so was Mary. He was happy to be back too because we had become a family and we always missed each other when we were apart. He loved his job and believed in it and its importance almost fanatically. He loved the game and wanted to care for it and protect it and that was

about all he believed in, I think, except a very stern and complicated system of ethics.

He was a little younger than my oldest son and if I had gone
to Addis Ababa to spend a year and write back in the middle Thirties as I had planned I would have known him when he was twelve
since his best friend then had been the son of the people I was
going out to stay with. But I had not gone because Mussolini's
armies had gone instead and my friend that I had been going out
to stay with had been moved to another diplomatic post and so I
had missed the chance to know G.C. when he was twelve. By the
time I met him he had a long, very difficult and unrewarding war
behind him plus the abandonment of a British Protectorate where
he had made the start of a fine career. He had commanded irregular
troops which is, if you are honest, the least rewarding way there
is to make a war. If an action is fought perfectly so that you have
almost no casualties and inflict large losses on the enemy it is regarded at Headquarters as an unjustified and reprehensible massacre. If you are forced to fight under unfavorable conditions and
at too great odds and win but have a large butcher bill the comment
is, "He gets too many men killed." There is no way for an honest
man commanding irregulars to get into anything but trouble. There
is some doubt as to whether any truly honest and talented soldier can
ever hope for anything except to be destroyed.

By the time I met G.C. he was well started in another career
in another British Colony. He was never bitter and he did not look
back at all. But he was intolerant of fools and of the British white
trash that sometimes come out to the Colonies posing as civil servants. There are many of these and they must be good enough at their
specialties or they would not have been graduated from the dreary
educational institutions which produce them. But they are not much
fun to be with after working hours. It is best never to attempt to joke
and for G.C. this was very cramping. He had always joked, as all
brave men do, and he had been well brought up and so knew that
bad words are used in the best of circles.

Over spaghetti and wine he told us of how he had been re-
proved by some newly arrived, bespectacled young bureau master
for, having come in from a patrol involving shooting with human
beings, using a bad word which might be overheard by this young

man's wife. I had seen the wife and felt that a few sound words of the type G.C. had uttered if put in practice by her husband might have done the marriage no end of good.

I explained this to G.C. and Mary gave him a list of words which let drop outside of the hearing of the husband might cause the wife to question him about their meaning and eventually, perhaps, produce some laudable action. We pictured the wife asking the husband what these strange terms meant and his embarrassment as he looked them up in the appropriate regulations. All of them were good words long hallowed in the language and G.C. was cheered at hearing them with Mary's clear diction.

I hated for G.C. to have to be bored by these people who, if you were to describe them, no one would believe. The old Pukka Sahib ones have often been described and caricatured. But no one has dealt much with these 1984s. I wished Orwell was alive and I told G.C. about the last time I had seen him in Paris in 1945 after the Bulge fight and how he had come in what looked something like civilian clothes to Room 117 of the Ritz where there was still a small arsenal to borrow a pistol because "they" were after him. He wanted a small pistol easily concealed and I found one but warned him that if he shot someone with it they probably would die eventually but that there might be a long interval. But a pistol was a pistol and he needed this one more as a talisman than a weapon I thought.

He was very gaunt and looked in bad shape and I asked him if he would not stay and eat. But he had to go. I told him I could give him a couple of people who would look after him if "they" were after him. That my characters were familiar with the local "theys" and would never bother him nor intrude on him. He said no, that the pistol was all he needed. We asked about a few mutual friends and he left. I sent two characters to pick him up at the door and tail him and check if anybody was after him. The next day their report was, "Papa, nobody is after him. He is a very chic type and knows Paris very well. We checked with so and so's brother and he says no one pursues him. He is in touch with the British Embassy but he is not an operative. This is only hearsay. Do you want the timetable of his movements?"

"No. Did he amuse himself?"

"Yes, Papa."

"I'm happy. We will not worry about him. He has the pistol."

"That worthless pistol," one of the characters said. "But you warned him against it, Papa?"

"Yes. He could have had any pistol he wished."

"Perhaps he would have been happier if you had given him a stinger."

"No," the other character said. "A stinger is too compromising. He was happy with that pistol."

We let it go at that.

G.C. did not sleep well and often would lie awake most of the night reading. He had a very good library at his house in Kajiado and I had a big duffel bag full of books that we had arranged in empty boxes in the mess tent as a library. There was an excellent bookstore near The New Stanley Hotel in Nairobi and another good one down Government Road. Whenever I had been in town I bought most of the new books that looked worth reading. Reading was the best palliative for G.C.'s insomnia. But it was no cure and I would often see his light on all night in his tent.

Mary and G.C. were talking happily about a city called London that I knew of largely by hearsay and knew concretely only under the most abnormal conditions and I was happy to let them talk of it. They knew very different parts and most of them I did not know at all. So I could listen to them talk and think about Paris. That was a city that I knew under almost all circumstances. I knew it and loved it so well that I never liked to talk about it except with people from the old days. In the old days we all had our own cafés where we went alone and knew no one except the waiters. These cafés were secret places and in the old days everyone who loved Paris had his own café. They were better than clubs and you received the mail there that you did not wish to have come to your flat. Usually you had two or three secret cafés. There would be one where you went to work and read the papers. You never gave the address of this café to anyone and you went there in the morning and had a café crème and brioche on the terrace and then, when they had cleaned the corner where your table was, inside and next to the window, you worked while the rest of the café was being cleaned and scrubbed and polished. It was nice to have other people working and it helped you to work. By the time the clients started to come to the café you would pay for your half bottle of Vichy and go out and walk down

the quay to where you would have an aperitif and then have lunch.
There were secret places to have lunch and also secret restaurants
where people went that you knew.

The best secret restaurants were always discovered by Mike
Ward. He knew Paris and loved her better than anyone I knew. As
soon as a Frenchman discovered a secret restaurant he would give a
huge party there to celebrate the secret. Mike and I hunted secret
places that had one or two good small wines and had a good cook,
usually a rummy, and were making a last effort to make things go
before having to sell out or go into bankruptcy. We did not want
any secret restaurants that were becoming successful or going up
in the world. That was what always happened with Charlie Sweeny's
secret restaurants. By the time he took you there the secret had been
so revealed that you had to stand in line to get a table.

But Charlie was very good about secret cafés and he had a
wonderful security consciousness about his own and yours. These
were of course our secondary or afternoon and early evening cafés.
This was a time of day when you might want to talk to someone
and sometimes I would go to his secondary café and sometimes he
would come to mine. He might say he wished to bring a girl he
wanted me to meet or I might tell him I would bring a girl. The
girls always worked. Otherwise they were not serious. No one, except
fools, kept a girl. You did not want her around in the daytime and
you did not want the problems she brought. If she wanted to be
your girl and worked then she was serious and then she owned
the nights when you wanted her and you fed her evenings and gave
her things when she needed them. I never brought many girls to
show them off to Charlie who always had beautiful and docile girls,
all of whom worked and all of whom were under perfect discipline,
because at that time my concierge was my girl. I had never known
a young concierge before and it was an inspiring experience. Her
greatest asset was that she could never go out, not only in society,
but at all. When I first knew her, as a *locataire,* she was in love with
a trooper in the Garde républicain. He was the horsetail-plumed,
metal-breastplate, mustached type and his barracks was not very far
away in that quarter. He had regular hours for his duty and he was
a fine figure of a man and whenever we met we always addressed
each other formally as "Monsieur."

I was not in love with my concierge but I was very lonely at

night at that time and the first time she came up the stairs and in
through the door, which had the key in it, and then up the ladder
that led to the sort of loft where the bed was beside the window
that gave such a lovely view over the Cemetery Montparnasse and
took off her felt-soled shoes and lay on the bed and asked me if I
loved her I answered, loyally, "Naturally."

"I knew it," she said. "I've known it too long."

She undressed very quickly and I looked out at the moonlight
on the cemetery.

She was clean and fragile out of sturdy but insufficient nourishment and we paid honor to the view which neither saw. I had it in
my mind however and when she said that the last tenant had entered and we lay and she told me that she could never love a member of the Garde républicain truly I said that I thought Monsieur
was a nice man, I said *un brave homme et très gentil,* and that he
must look very well on a horse. But she said that she was not a
horse and also that there were inconveniences.

So I was thinking this about Paris while they were talking of
London and I thought that we were all brought up differently and
it was good luck we got on so well and I wished G.C. was not lonely
nights and that I was too damned lucky to be married to somebody
as lovely as Mary and that I would straighten things out and try to
be a really good husband.

"You're being awfully silent, General," G.C. said. "Are we
boring you?"

"Young people never bore me. I love their careless chatter.
It keeps me from feeling old and unwanted."

"Balls to you," G.C. said. "What were you thinking about with
that semi-profound look? Not brooding are you or worrying about
what the morrow will bring?"

"When I start worrying about what the morrow will bring you'll
see a light burning in my tent late at night."

"Balls to you again, General," G.C. said.

"Don't use rough words, G.C.," Mary said. "My husband is a
delicate and sensitive man and they repugn him."

"I'm glad something repugns him," G.C. said. "I love to see
the good side of his character."

"He hides it carefully. What were you thinking about, darling?"

"A trooper in the Garde républicain."

"You see" G.C. said. "I always said he had a delicate side. It comes out completely unexpectedly. It's his Proustian side. Tell me was he very attractive? I try to be broad-minded."

"Papa and Proust used to live in the same hotel," Miss Mary said. "But Papa always claims it was at different times."

"God knows what really went on," G.C. said. He was very happy and not at all taut tonight and Mary with her wonderful memory for forgetting was happy too and without any problems. She could forget in the loveliest and most complete way of anyone I ever knew. She could carry a fight overnight but at the end of a week she could forget it completely and truly. She had a built-in selective memory and it was not built entirely in her favor. She forgave herself in her memory and she forgave you, too. She was a very strange girl and I loved her very much. She had, at the moment, only two defects. She was very short for honest lion hunting and she had too good a heart to be a killer and that, I had finally decided, made her either flinch or squeeze off a little when shooting at an animal. I found this attractive and was never exasperated by it. But she was exasperated by it because, in her head, she understood why we killed and the necessity for it and she had come to take pleasure in it, after thinking that she never would kill an animal as beautiful as an impala and would kill only ugly and dangerous beasts. In six months of daily hunting she had learned to love it, shameful though it is basically, and unshameful as it is if done cleanly, but there was something too good in her that worked subconsciously and made her pull off the target. I loved her for it in the same way that I could not love a woman who could work in the stockyards, or put dogs or cats out of their suffering, or destroy horses who had broken their legs at a racecourse.

"What was the trooper's name?" G.C. asked. "Albertine?"

"No, Monsieur."

"He's baffling us, Miss Mary," G.C. said.

They went on talking about London. So I started to think about London, too, and it was not unpleasant although much too noisy and not normal. I realized I knew nothing about London and so I started to think about Paris and in greater detail than before. Actually I was worried about Miss Mary's lion and so was G.C. and we were just handling it in different ways. It was always easy enough when it really happened. But Mary's lion had been going on for a long time and I wanted to get him the hell over with.

In the night I heard the lion roar several times. Then I went to sleep and Mwendi was pulling on the blanket at the foot of the cot.

"*Chai,* Bwana."

It was very dark outside but someone was building up the fire. I woke Mary with her tea but she did not feel well. She felt ill and had bad cramps.

"Do you want to cancel it, honey?"

"No. I feel just awful. After the tea maybe I'll be better."

"We can scrub it. It might be better to give him another day's rest."

"No. I want to go. But just let me try and feel better if I can."

I went out and washed in the cold water in the basin and washed my eyes with boric, dressed and went out to the fire. I could see G.C. shaving in front of his tent. He finished, dressed and came over.

"Mary feels rocky," I told him.

"Poor child."

"She wants to go anyway."

"Naturally."

"How'd you sleep?"

"Well. You?"

"Very well. What do you think he was doing last night?"

"I think he was just going walking about. And sounding off."

"He talks a lot. Want to split a bottle of beer?"

"It won't hurt us."

I went and got the beer and two glasses and waited for Mary. She came out of the tent and walked down the path to the latrine tent. She came back and then walked down again.

"How do you feel, honey?" I asked, when she came over to the table by the fire with her tea. Charo and Ngui were getting the guns and the binoculars and shell bags out from the tents and taking them to the hunting car.

"I don't feel good at all. Do we have anything for it?"

"Yes. But it makes you feel dopey. . . ."

She was in obvious pain and I could see it coming back on her again.

"Honey, we'll lay off him this morning and rest him. It's the best thing to do, anyway. You take it easy and take care of yourself. G.C. can stay a couple of more days anyway."

G.C. shook his hand, palm down, in negation. But Mary did not see him.

"He's your lion and you take your time and be in shape to shoot him and all the time we let him alone he will be getting more confident. If we don't go out at all this morning it's much better. . . ."

I went over to the car and said we were not going out. Then I went and found Keiti by the fire. He seemed to know all about it but he was very delicate and polite.

"Memsahib is sick."

"I know."

"Maybe spaghetti. Maybe dysentery."

"Yes," Keiti said. "I think spaghetti."

After we were sure that the lion would have left our bait if he had been on it G.C. and I went out to have a look at the country in his Land-Rover. Beasts were accustomed to seeing this vehicle and we thought the lion if he saw it might not connect it with the hunting car whose silhouette he knew. Many years ago I had discovered, or believed I had, that lions have no depth of vision and see only in silhouette. I had experimented with this, and later gambled on it in photographing wild lions at close range in the old days before the Serengeti was a game reserve and I was convinced that it was true. In those days I did not have the respect for lions that I should and Pop was along to back me up if I was wrong. Now I knew much more about lions and respected them much more but I still thought this was a valid theory. G.C. wanted to go in the Land-Rover anyway, so it did not make much difference.

Miss Mary said that what she wanted was to rest and be by herself. I had given her some chlorodyne in water and she had kept it down. She was also going to try some tea again. I wanted to stay with her but she hated being ill and if she were sick she wanted to be by herself.

"You and G.C. go. Please go. Mwendi will look after me. But

don't spook the lion. The only good thing about me being this way is that we give him a rest."

I promised her we wouldn't even get out at the bait and we started over to the Land-Rover and got in with G.C.'s head Game Scout and Ngui in the back. The head Game Scout was a tall, handsome, very soldierly Wakamba with a mustache. He was very good at his work and fanatically devoted to G.C. He was also devoted to Miss Mary and I always had a strong feeling that he thought I was not good enough for her. He would like to have seen her married to the Governor General at least. Ngui usually tried to look as unsmart as possible when he and the head Game Scout were together.

The grass seemed to have doubled in height in the night and it was a lovely clear cool morning with almost no wind. There seemed to be about three sorts of grass and one was a rather weedy sort that was growing faster than the others. There was more game than ever and we moved along the tire tracks as though through a park.

When we were about opposite where the bait had been taken well over to our right we hit the tracks of the big lion crossing the tire tracks to go into the woods across the dead grass field to our left. The tracks were fresh and there was no dew on them. Some of the weedy grass was bruised and the sap was fresh on the cracked stems. There were dry places on the tall grass where he had gone in shoulder high.

"How long ago?"

"An hour," Ngui said. "Not much more." He looked at the head Game Scout who nodded.

"They are very fresh," he said in English.

"He stayed out maybe an hour longer, G.C.," I said.

"We're getting him, Papa," G.C. said. "I don't think we'll go near the bait. It's all gone now. We'll feed him tonight same place."

"Good thing Mary doesn't know he crossed here in plenty good light."

"It's the best thing," G.C. said. "We're getting ahead of him now."

"Two more days."

"You said you could deal with him."

"We bloody well can, too."

"Don't be cross. You don't mind me being along though?"

"Let's not talk rot."

"Let's talk sense then. Suppose Miss Mary hits him and he doesn't come. If he comes I grant you kill him but you have your wife to think about and she has to stand where she is because if she runs he'll go for her. This is all fine. You play the heroic type and bring him down at your feet. Or he brings you down ass over apple cart. Is that the correct American expression?"

"Quite correct. Only now they say 'and then the shit went into the electric fan.' "

"I'll make a note of that."

"Be worthless. They'll be saying something else the next time you have Americans on your hands. People are hired to make up those expressions. They're called gag writers."

"O.K.," G.C. said. "You are my gag writer. Now you've entered the electric fan."

"Thanks."

"Now," G.C. said, "I'm not the contemplative type. I'm the strategic type."

"The hell you are. You're the emotional instant-decision type who's only alive because he shoots twice as fast as Wyatt Earp and Doc Holliday combined."

The Land-Rover was stopped now under some green and yellow trees with tall wide branches and in the shade we were both looking across the gray of the mud flats, dry now, toward the green of the papyrus swamp and the green-brown hills beyond.

"All right," G.C. said. "There isn't anything out there except just the usuals. So I can shoot faster than you. I'm glad to hear that admitted. But here you are the brusque, semi-heroic, outmoded miracle type who brings them down like the bowmen at Crécy. Now suppose Miss Mary hits this lion somewhere and instead of coming he has a little sense and breaks for better cover where you will have to go in and dig him out and every one of the miraculous shots that you throw after him throws dust behind his ass and he makes the island of thick cover."

"You know what I have to do then."

"Do you like it?"

"Not even with you."

"But we do it."

"I go in with the pump full of buckshot and you stay on his most likely exit route and Arap Maina on his next and Miss Mary is on the top of a truck whether she likes it or not. I go in with Ngui to see him for me, if he can see him, before he comes."

"Do you like it?"

"I'll buy it."

"What if all this starts at eighteen hundred hours and you have one half an hour light to complete the operation?"

"Do you have to get morbid?"

"No," G.C. said. "I'm the contemplative type and I was only contemplating."

"Let's get him so confident that he'll come out anytime."

"I couldn't agree more fully. Do you think we've earned a drink?"

"Beer."

"Did you really bring some?"

I asked Ngui for a bottle. It was wrapped in a wet sack and was still cold from the night and we sat in the Land-Rover in the shade of the tree and drank it out of the bottle and looked off across the dried mud flat and then watched the small Tommies and the black movement of the wildebeest and the zebra that looked a gray white in this light as they moved out across the flat to the grass on the far side and at the end toward the Chyulu hills. The hills were a dark blue this morning and looked very far away. Turning to look back at the great mountain it looked very close. It seemed to be just behind camp and the snow was heavy and bright in the sun.

"We could hunt Miss Mary on stilts," I said. "Then she could see him in the tall grass."

"There's nothing in the Game Laws against it."

"Or Charo could carry a stepladder such as they have in libraries for the higher stacks."

"That's brilliant," G.C. said. "We'd pad the rungs and she could take a rest with the rifle on the rung above where she stood."

"You don't think it would be too immobile?"

"It'd be up to Charo to make it mobile."

"It would be a beautiful sight," I said. "We could mount an electric fan on it."

"We could build it in the form of an electric fan," G.C. said happily. "But that would probably be considered a vehicle and illegal."

"If we rolled it forward and had Miss Mary keep climbing in it like a squirrel would it be illegal?"

"Anything that rolls is a vehicle," G.C. said judicially.

"I roll slightly when I walk."

"Then you're a vehicle. I'll run you in and you'll get six months and be shipped out of the Colony."

"We have to be careful, G.C."

"Care and moderation have been our watchwords, haven't they? Any more in that bottle?"

"We can share the dregs."

"A pair of dreg sharers out in the blue."

"The Chulis *are* blue."

They were very blue and very beautiful.

"*Chyulus,*" G.C. corrected. "Tell me what is The Wild Blue Yonder that your Air Force has a song about?"

"It is a Challenge to Man."

"I know a beautiful airline stewardess that is a Challenge to Man."

"She's probably the one they're talking about in the song."

Back in camp we found that Miss Mary was much better. But she was weak and she did not feel well and it was natural that she should not be in good temper. She was nearly always in wonderful temper in Africa and we had not had a fight since Fig Tree camp in the Magadi area where I had turned on the short-wave radio to listen to the World Series and then fallen asleep while listening. This was an irritating enough thing to do since we should have been sleeping soundly in order to get up rested and fresh before daylight to hunt the lion that Mary was even then engaged in pursuing instead of me lying asleep by a radio which kept Mary awake. Someone, undoubtedly me, had smashed the radio antenna and we had gone to meet the appointment, which the lion had not kept, with a certain amount of grimness. Several weeks later I found out how the Series came out. That night I had my cot moved out of the tent and slept in the open. This was fun. But Mary pointed out, quite right, that it left her in the tent at the mercy of any beast that wandered in.

We compromised finally, I believe, by putting my cot outside in a way that blocked the entrance of beasts by the front flap of the tent. . . .

On this day Mary was angry with me and I knew that I could do nothing right to offset all the wrong things I had probably done all my life. You did not mind or pretended you did not mind at such times and after a while you might be re-received into the status of a member of the human race. But it was best not to be too sure because you might yet be accused of those atrocities you had committed against a former wife. In some ways these atrocities, on which there was a certain difference of opinion, but on which Miss Mary had received the authorized version by the wife, might have been considered to have been, in a way, if not expiated at least to have come under some statute of limitations. But this was not so. They were as fresh and as alive as though they were in the morning mail if there had been a morning mail. They did not fade nor pale as the atrocities of the first war did and no matter how many times you had been convicted and fined for them they were as fresh as the first launching of the bayoneted Belgian babies.

So it was to be one of those days of, "Would you mind giving me that book? That happens to be the book that I am reading."

Or, "Do you know that the camp is completely out of meat due to your carelessness or incapacity? Everyone has complained to me about your thoughtlessness. We are allowed to have meat to feed the boys aren't we, G.C.?"

Or, "Did you take small envelopes out of this box? No?"

This to be followed by elaborate and obvious industry to show that there was someone around this camp who was serious and did not take their duties lightly or sloppily, frequent trips to the green tent at the edge of the fever trees, which, it is true, had not been built with possible dysentery in mind but had been placed there since it was the nearest shade and shelter apart from the clump of trees which shaded the camp and the lines. I felt terribly that Mary felt ill and I did not blame her for being in bad temper but for the moment there was nothing to do. The best thing was to get out of her sight but there is no place to go in Africa at high noon except the shade and so I took a chair in the mess tent which, with its heavy fly and the breeze that came through, was cool and comfortable. It would have been nice to take the road up the slope of the mountain to Loitokitok and sit in the back room of Mr. Singh's teahouse and saloon and read and listen to the sawmill. But that would have been desertion.

We had one of those lunches finally where the hostess is quietly heroic and wonderful to the guest and the husband would be better off eating in the lines. The shadow of all my sins, past, present and future lay spread across the table and catsup and mustard on the cheese did not help them. I had enjoyed my actual sins, those I had committed rather than those I had been accused of, and I could never be contrite about them because I knew I might well commit them again. I was not convinced, in the daylight, that they were sins and today I did not care very much. I knew we had prepared Miss Mary's lion for her as well as possible and I knew I was going to have to find and butcher meat when the sun was low in the afternoon and kill a bait. G.C. had to write his monthly report. Mary was going to help with the typing.

We were getting worried about Mary. G.C. and I agreed that she probably had the start of dysentery as well as ptomaine.

I went to see her and she asked if we had gotten any food for the camp. I said that we had. She inquired what and I told her.

"Did you shoot well?"

"Moderately."

"You can go into rhapsodies about it if you want."

"I've been out butchering for the camp. That's all."

"Then why talk so much about it? Wasn't everyone delighted and amused and overwhelmed by how wonderfully you shot?"

"They didn't mention it. Arap Maina kissed me."

"You'd gotten him drunk I suppose?"

"Actually not. He'd found the Jinny flask."

"I suppose you're drunk too?"

"No. Decidely not."

"But you will be."

"You may have something there."

"G.C. hasn't brought his report yet for me to type."

"He's another son of a bitch," I said. "The camp's full of them. Are you running any fever?"

"No. I just have bad cramps and feel awful."

"Do you feel as though you'd be going out tomorrow?"

"I'd go out no matter how I feel."

I went and found G.C. He was sitting under the fly of his tent working on the report. We had an absolute privacy rule so I left him.

"Forget it," he said. "Let's have a drink and watch the sunset. What are we doing in camp anyway?"

"I'm cheering up Miss Mary. But she isn't having any of it."

"Poor girl."

"I think she'll get the bastard tomorrow."

"She's going out in the morning?"

"Complete with handles."

"Splendid," G.C. said. "Lovely Miss Mary."

So on the next day Miss Mary killed her lion.

The day that Miss Mary shot her lion was a very beautiful day. That was about all that was beautiful about it. White flowers had blossomed in the night so that with the first daylight before the sun had risen all the meadows looked as though a full moon was shining on new snow through a mist. Mary was up and dressed long before first light. The right sleeve of her bush jacket was rolled up and she had checked all the rounds in her Mannlicher .256. She said she did not feel well and I believed her. She acknowledged G.C.'s and my greetings briefly and we were careful not to make any jokes. I did not know what she had against G.C. except his tendency to lightheartedness in the face of undeniably serious work. Her being angry at me was a sound reaction I thought. If she were in a bad mood I thought she might feel mean and shoot as deadly as I knew she knew how to shoot. This agreed with my last and greatest theory that she had too kind a heart to kill animals. Some people shoot easily and loosely; others shoot with a dreadful speed that is still so controlled that they have all the time they need to place the bullet as carefully as a surgeon would make his first incision; others are mechanical shots who are very deadly unless something happens to interfere with the mechanics of the shooting. This morning it looked as though Miss Mary was going out to shoot with grim resolution, contemptuous of all those who did not take things with appropriate seriousness, armored in her bad physical condition which provided an excuse if she missed, and full of rigid, concentrated do or die deadliness. It seemed fine to me. It was a new approach.

We waited by the hunting car for it to be light enough to start and we were all solemn and deadly. Ngui nearly always had an evil temper in the very early morning so he was solemn, deadly and sullen. Charo was solemn, deadly but faintly cheerful. He was like a man going to a funeral who did not really feel too deeply about the deceased. Muthoka was happy as always watching with his wonderful eyes for the lightening of the darkness.

We were all hunters and it was the start of that wonderful thing: the hunt. There is much mystic nonsense written about hunting but it is something that is probably much older than religion. Some are hunters and some are not. Miss Mary was a hunter and a brave and lovely one but she had come to it late instead of as a child and many of the things that had happened to her in hunting came as unexpectedly as being in heat for the first time to the kitten when she becomes a cat. She grouped all these new knowledges and changes as things we know and other people don't.

It was a good enough grouping and the four of us who had seen her go through these changes and had seen her now, for months, hunting something grimly and seriously against every possible sort of odds were like the cuadrilla of a very young matador. If the matador was serious the cuadrilla would be serious. They knew all the matador's defects and they were all well paid in different ways. All had lost completely any faith in the matador and all had regained it many times. As we sat in the car or moved around it waiting for it to be light enough to set out I was reminded very much of how it is before a bullfight.

Our matador was solemn; so we were solemn, since we loved our matador. Our matador was not well. This made it even more necessary that he be protected and given even a better chance in everything he chose to do. But as we sat and leaned and felt sleep drain from us we were as happy as hunters. Probably no one is as happy as hunters with the always new, fresh, unknowing day ahead and Mary was a hunter too. But she had set herself this task and being guided and trained and indoctrinated into the purity and virtue of killing a lion by Pop who had made her his last pupil and given her ethics he had never been able to impose on other women so that her killing of her lion must not be the way such things are done but the way such things should ideally be done; Pop finding finally in Mary the spirit of a fighting cock embodied in a woman; a loving and belated killer with the only defect that no one could say where the shot would go. Pop had given her the ethics and then it was necessary that he go away. She had the ethics now but she only had G.C. and me and neither of us was to be really trusted as Pop would have been. So now she was going out again to her corrida that always was postponed.

Muthoka nodded to me that the light was beginning to be possible and we started off through the fields of white flowers. As we came even with the trees of the forest with the high dead yellow grass on our left Muthoka slid the car to a quiet stop. He turned his head and I saw the arrow-shaped scar on his cheek and the slashes. He said nothing and I followed his eyes. The great black-maned lion, his head huge above the yellow grass, was coming out toward us. Only his head showed above the stiff tall yellow grass.

"What you say we circle easy back to camp?" I whispered to G.C.

"I quite agree," he whispered.

As we spoke the lion turned and moved back toward the forest. All you could see of him was the movements of the high grass.

When we got back to camp and had breakfast Mary understood why we had done what we did and agreed that it was right and necessary. But the corrida had been called off again when she was all set and tense for it and we were not popular. I felt so sorry that she felt ill and I wanted her to let down in tension if she could. There was no use going on talking about how the lion had made a mistake finally. Both G.C. and I were sure we had him now. He had not fed during the night and had come out to look for the bait in the morning. He had gone back into the forest again. He would lie up hungry and, if he were not disturbed, he should be out early in the evening; that is he should be. If he was not G.C. had to leave the next day no matter what happened and the lion would revert back to Mary and me on our own. But the lion had broken his pattern of behavior and made a very grave mistake and I did not worry any more about our getting him. I might have been happier to hunt him with Mary without G.C. but I loved to hunt with G.C. too and I was not so stupid as to want any sort of bad show to happen with me alone with Mary. G.C. had pointed out too well how it could be. I always had the great illusion of Mary hitting the lion exactly where she should and the lion rolling over like anything else, as I had seen them do so many times, and be as dead as only a lion can be. I was going to drive two into him if he rolled over alive and that was that. Miss Mary would have killed her lion and been happy about it always, and I would only have given him the puntilla and she would know it and love me very much forever world without end amen.

G.C.'s head Game Scout and Arap Maina went out to bring back the word. G.C. and I had wanted to go out but we had decided that two white men stinking up the ground with a smart lion was not worthwhile. Some people say lions have no sense of smell and some people can be wrong. We sat around and talked shop and made jokes and G.C. went to work on his report. I went over to see Miss Mary but she just felt bad and did not want company, and I went out to the lines and spoke to Keiti and the cook and we spoke of various things. Keiti had heard the lion roar in the night but in the direction of the forest. He had heard other lions hunting well to the north; toward the salt lick he thought. Keiti said he was sure we would get the big lion now and I told him my medicine had already told me so and that I expected Miss Mary to kill him this afternoon or evening. Keiti smiled and said nothing. Then he said, *"Mzuri."*

Everybody who had been up early was sleeping so I walked back to the mess tent to read a book by a man who had been very heroic in command of a submarine, then very lucky, then very insubordinate finally and wrote with false modesty and bitterness. That year you had the choice between escapers, climbers, underwater men, ex-RAF types, submariners of all nationalities, African adventurers, explainers of Mau Mau, and an exceptionally good book by Colonel, as he was then, Lindbergh which made him seem human and the air over the Atlantic a dangerous, strange and interesting place. There were also accounts of prisoners of the Japs, of buggery in Burma at platoon level, believable and unbelievable stories of elephants and those who hunted and trained them. It was not too bad a year for books. Fiction was almost uniformly worthless except for books about nasty characters who suffered heart attacks or were apprehended by the police in England, and about professors and instructors in American universities who did or did not live up to their ideals and were all brought down in the end by various committees. Chambers was emptying his pot; a man named

McCarthy was gathering a following and being attacked; some Lord had come out either for or against a man named Hiss; it was hard to determine. But none of us book readers cared too much for Hiss, McCarthy or Chambers. It was difficult to imagine them in the area.

Just then a Land-Rover, one of the new, larger and faster models we had never seen before, drove into camp through the wonderful field of white flowers that had been dust a month ago and mud one week before. This car was driven by a red-faced man of middle height who wore a faded khaki uniform of an officer in the Kenya police. He was dusty from the road and there were white smile wrinkles at the corners of his eyes that cracked the dust.

"Anybody home?" he asked coming into the mess tent and taking off his cap. Through the open, muslin-screened end that faced toward the mountain I had seen the car come up.

"Everybody home," I said. "How are you, Mr. Harry?"

"I'm quite well."

"Sit down and let me make you something. You can stay the night can't you . . . ?"

Harry Steele was shy, overworked, kind and ruthless. He was fond of Africans and understood them and he was paid to enforce the law and carry out orders. He was as gentle as he was tough and he was not revengeful nor a hater, nor was he ever stupid, nor sentimental. He did not hold grudges in a grudge-holding country, and I never saw him be petty about anything. He was administering the law in a time of corruption, hatreds, sadism and considerable hysteria and he worked himself each day past the limit that a man can possibly go; never working to seek promotion or advancement because he knew his worth at what he was doing. Miss Mary one time said that he was a portable fortress of a man.

Today he was a tired fortress and I thought of the first time I had ever seen him when he was only a shape at the wheel of a motor car on a very dark night in a vehicle which had not answered a challenge after curfew and G.C. had ordered me, "Shoot the man at the wheel," and I had covered him and taken up the slack on the trigger but had challenged again being sure something was wrong, and it had turned out to be Harry Steele with three converted Mau Mau with him. He had never been stuffy about that and had complimented G.C. on his efficiency. But he was the only man I had ever known that I had held a rifle on at twelve yards and started to squeeze off on who had been completely without bitterness.

On this day I knew that he had lost a sergeant that he felt about as I felt about Ngui; the sergeant chopped into pieces and mutilated in the last week. And we did not speak about this, not because of any traditions of good form or the stiff upper lip but because it does no good to talk about the death of those we love or care for deeply. If he wished to speak about it in any practical way of imparting knowledge he would do so. . . .

"Are you having fun here?"

"Very much."

"I've heard a little. What's this about your having to kill a leopard before the birthday of the Baby Jesus?"

"That's for that picture story for the magazine [Look] we were making the pictures for in September. We had a photographer and he took thousands of pictures and I've written a short article and captions for the pictures they use. They have a beautiful picture of a leopard and I shot him but he isn't mine."

"How does that work?"

"We were after a big lion that was very smart. It was over on the other side of the Ewaso Ngiro beyond Magadi under the escarpment."

"Well off my beat."

"We were trying to work up on this lion and this friend of mine climbed up a little rocky kopje with his gunbearer to look ahead to see if the lion had showed. The lion was for Mary because he and I had both killed lions. So we didn't know what the hell had happened when we heard him shoot and then something was down in the dust roaring. It was a leopard and the dust was so deep that it rose solid in a cloud and the leopard kept on roaring and nobody knew which direction he was coming out of the dust. This friend of mine, Mayito Menocal, had hit him twice from up above and I had shot into the moving center of the dust and ducked and moved to the right where it was natural he would break out. Then he showed his head up just once out of the dust still talking bad and I hit him in the neck and the dust started to settle. It was sort of like a gunfight in the dust outside of an old-time saloon out west. Except the leopard didn't have any gun but he was close enough to have mauled anyone. And he was awfully worked up. The photographer took pictures of

Mayito and him and of all of us and him and of me and him. He was Mayito's because Mayito hit him first and hit him again. So the best picture of him was the one with me and the magazine wanted to use it and I said they couldn't unless I killed a good leopard alone by myself. And so far I've failed three times."

"I didn't know the ethics were so rigid."

"Unfortunately they are. It's the law too. First blood and continuous pursuit."

"Is it perfectly all right if I don't understand you and G.C. completely?"

"I think something would be wrong if you did, Harry. Try to find out sometime if G.C. understands himself."

"Don't you understand him?"

"Hell, no. His ethics are too complicated for me."

"By God none of us are safe," Harry said. "But you're a writer. Writers are supposed to understand things. That's what they implied in the book of words."

"Africa is very complicated, Harry."

"You know," he said, "that idea had occurred to me. Perhaps I was just at the point of grasping it. You were good to put it so clearly."

I have many presentiments of things that do not happen. But I never thought ever that a day was going to be rougher than this day was going to be. Arap Maina and the head Game Scout had brought back the word that the two lionesses and the young lion had killed far up on the edge of the salt flat. Our bait had not been uncovered except where hyenas had pulled at it and the two scouts had recovered it carefully. There were birds in the trees around it that would surely draw the lion but the birds could not get at the remains of the zebra which were high enough to draw the lion surely. He had not fed nor killed in the night, and since he was hungry and had not been disturbed we might, almost surely, find him in the open in the evening. This was all good and my bad feeling came from something else.

"How do you feel, honey?" I asked Mary.

"I'm sorry, Big Kitten," she said. "I can make it to lunch all right. But I feel really awful."

"It's a lovely day and the lion should almost surely be out."

"I know it. That's what's so awful. I feel just terrible. I'm wearing that path out. The flowers are so beautiful and the mountain is so wonderful and I just feel too awful. . . ."

We had lunch and Mary was very cheerful and gracious with all of us. I believe she even asked me if I wanted any more of the cold meat. When I said no thank you I'd had enough, she said it would be good for me, that any man who drinks a great deal needs to eat. This was not only a very old truth but had been the basis of an article in the *Reader's Digest* that we had all read. That number of the *Digest* was down in the latrine tent now. I said that I had decided to run on a platform of true rummyhood and deceive none of my constituents. Churchill drank twice what I did if you could believe the accounts, and had just been awarded the Nobel Prize for Literature. I was simply trying to step up my drinking to a reasonable amount when I might win the prize myself; who knows?

G.C. said that the prize was as good as mine and that I ought to win it for bragging alone since Churchill had been awarded it, at least partially, for oratory. Harry said that he had not followed the prize awards as closely as he should but that he felt I might well be awarded for my work in the religious field and for my care of the natives. Miss Mary suggested that if I would try to write something, occasionally, I might win it for writing. This moved me very deeply and I said that once she had the lion I would do nothing but write; just to please her. She said that if I wrote even a little it would certainly please her. Harry asked me if I planned to write something about how mysterious Africa was and that if I planned to write in Swahili he could get me a book on up-country Swahili that might be invaluable to me. Miss Mary said that we already had the book and that she thought even with the book it would be better if I tried to write in English. I suggested that I might copy sections of the book to help me get an up-country style. Miss Mary said I could not write one correct sentence in Swahili nor speak one either and I agreed with her very sadly that this was true.

"Pop speaks it so beautifully and so does G.C. and so does Harry and you are a disgrace. I don't know how anyone can speak a language as badly as you do."

I wanted to say that at one time, years before, it had looked as though I were going to speak it quite well. But that I had been a fool not to have stayed on in Africa and instead gone back to America where I had killed my homesickness for Africa in different ways.

Then before I could get back came the Spanish war and I became involved in what was happening to the world and I had stayed with that for better and for worse until I had finally come back. It had not been easy to get back nor to break the chains of responsibility that are built up, seemingly as lightly as spider webs but that hold like steel cables. . . .

They were all having a good time now joking and making fun of one another and I joked a little but was careful to be very modest and contrite hoping to win back Miss Mary's favor and hoping to keep her in a good humor in case the lion would show. I had been drinking Bulmer's dry cider which I had found to be a marvelous drink. G.C. had brought some in from Kajiado from the stores. It was very light and refreshing and did not slow you down at all shooting. It came in full quarts and had screw-on tops and I used to drink it in the night when I woke instead of water. Mary's extremely nice cousin had given us two small square sacking-covered pillows filled with balsam needles. I always slept with mine under my neck or, if I slept on my side, with my ear on it. It was the smell of Michigan when I was a boy and I wished I could have had a sweet grass basket to keep it in when we traveled and to have under the mosquito net in the bed at night. The cider tasted like Michigan too, and I always remembered the cider mill and the door which was never locked but only fitted with a hasp and wooden pin, and the smell of the sacks used in the pressing and later spread to dry, and then spread over the deep tubs where the men who came to grind their wagon-loads of apples left the mill's share. Below the dam of the cider mill there was a deep pool where the eddy from the falling water in turning cut back in under the dam. You could always catch trout if you fished there patiently and whenever I caught one I would kill him and lay him in the big wicker creel that was in the shade and put a layer of fern leaves over him and then go into the cider mill and take the tin cup off the nail on the wall over the tubs and pull up the heavy sacking from one of the tubs and dip out a cup of cider and drink it. This cider that we had now reminded me of Michigan; especially with the pillow. . . .

Sitting now at the table I was pleased Mary seemed to be feeling better and I hoped the lion would show in the late afternoon and that she would kill him dead and be happy forever after. Then I hoped that I might get the leopard quickly and then that we might

all relax and have fun the way we knew how to have it. After Miss
Mary's lion we would start to have fun. I knew of three different
leopards in the area and there were probably more and if I hunted
intelligently I could certainly find one and if I didn't I would go
down to Fig Tree camp where I knew there was one that believed he
owned the country. I planned to go down with Ngui and Pop's gun-
bearer, maybe, and we would not need any camp but just hunt there
until we got him. If I could have stayed there one more day I am
quite sure I would have killed him. But no sentence that starts with
if is any good in Africa and most sentences start that way.

We finished lunch and everybody was cheerful and we all said
we would take a nap and I would call Miss Mary when it was time
to go look for the lion.

Mary went to sleep almost as soon as she lay down on her cot.
The back of the tent was propped open and a good cool breeze blew
down from the mountain and through the tent. We ordinarily slept
facing the open door of the tent but I took the pillows and placed
them at the opposite end of the cot and, doubling them over and
with the balsam pillow under my neck, lay on the cot with my boots
and trousers off and read with the good light behind me. I was reading a very good book by Gerald Hanley who had written another
good book called *The Consul at Sunset*. This book was about a lion
who made much trouble and killed practically all the characters in
the book. G.C. and I used to read this book in the mornings on the
latrine to inspire us. There were a few characters the lion did not
kill but they were all headed for some other sort of bad fate so we
did not really mind. Hanley wrote very well and it was an excellent
book and very inspiring when you were in the lion-hunting business.
I had seen a lion come at speed once and I had been very impressed
and am still impressed. On this afternoon I was reading the book
very slowly because it was such a good book and I did not want to
finish it. I was hoping the lion would kill the hero or the Old Major
because they were both very noble and nice characters and I had
gotten very fond of the lion and wanted him to kill some upper-
bracket characters. The lion was doing very well though and he had
just killed another very sympathetic and important character when I
decided it would be better to save the rest and got up and pulled
on my trousers and put my boots on without zipping them up and

went over to see if G.C. was awake. I coughed outside his tent the way The Informer always did outside the mess tent.

"Come in, General," G.C. said.

"No," I said. "A man's home is his castle. Are you feeling up to facing the deadly beasts?"

"It's too early yet. Did Mary sleep?"

"She's still sleeping. What are you reading?"

"Lindbergh. It's damned good. What were you reading?"

"*The Year of the Lion*. I'm sweating out the lion."

"You've been reading that for a month."

"Six weeks."

I finished talking to G.C. and went over to the tent to see Mary.

"Do you want to go out, honey? We're going out for a look in Harry's big new Land-Rover."

"I feel too badly."

"All right. We'll be careful not to disturb anything and if we see him we'll come back and get you."

"I'm worthless," she said. "And I feel terrible."

"Try to rest and take it as easy as you can."

"How can I rest and take it easy when my lion is going to come out and I'll not be there to meet him?"

"We'll be back for you if he's out."

"And he'll be gone back into the forest."

I walked over to where G.C. and Harry were waiting in the new car under the tree and climbed in the front with them. G.C. was driving and we went out through the meadow of white flowers to the airstrip. G.C. turned onto the tracks that were grown up with the flowers and drove the length of the strip toward the Kilimanjaro end and then made a turn and drove back beside his tracks. The flowers came up to the hubs of the wheels. It was late afternoon and when we had driven up the strip the mountain was huge and white beyond the dark green trees of camp. Now we were driving into the late sun with the mountain behind us. . . .

G.C. seemed sort of glazed with contentment with a new car and we moved off the airstrip speedway and onto what I thought of as The Great North Road; the tire tracks that paralleled the forest and led up toward the mud flats, the salt licks and the buffalo swamp. Ngui and G.C.'s head Game Scout were in back and they were watching for the lion. So was I and so were G.C. and Harry.

"If he's out," I told Harry, "really out, he'll be over in one of those clumps of trees on the right." We drove on, very slowly and quietly now with no one speaking. The sun was on our left over the hills behind the forest. G.C.'s Game Scout reached forward and put his hand on G.C.'s shoulder. He did not point but looked and G.C. very carefully stopped the car.

"There he is, Harry," he said very low.

"I see him."

I could not believe it when I saw him. Neither could Ngui. The lion lay on top of an anthill looking away from us. It was a broad-topped gray mound and the lion was molded on its top as though he were sculptured there. The mound was in the shade of a wide-topped thorn tree and I had never seen a lion look so big, nor so black. His great head was black and his mane swept in a black wedge over his back into the tawny gray of his flanks. I had never seen a lion looking that way except in a painting or a heroic sculpture. What was he doing there? He who had been so wary and so intelligent. Why had he gotten up in plain sight like that?

The wind was blowing toward us and he had not heard us nor seen us. G.C. let in the clutch very quietly and turned the car and we went back down the road and when we were out of sight of the lion he drove as fast as we could go for camp.

"What the hell put him up there?" I asked G.C.

"He got confident. He finally got confident. He went up there to look over his country and enjoy himself. It *is* his country."

"He's a hell of a lion," Harry said. "I can see why the Memsahib is worked up about him. Does he really kill cattle or did you just make that up to feed the troops?"

"He kills cattle," I said.

In camp I got Mary up while the gunbearer got Mary's rifle and my big gun from under the beds and checked the solids and the soft-nosed and then ran to the big Land-Rover.

"He's there, honey. He's there and you'll get him."

"It's late. Why didn't you take him? It's so damned late."

"Don't think about anything. Just get out in the car."

"I have to put my boots on. You know that."

I was helping her on with them.

"Where's my damned hat?"

"Here's your damned hat. Walk. Don't run to the nearest Land-Rover. Don't think about anything but hitting him."

"Don't talk to me so much. Leave me alone."

Mary and G.C. and Harry were in the front seat with Harry driving. Ngui, Charo and I were in the open back with the Game Scout. I was checking the cartridges in the barrel and the magazine of the .30-06, checking those in my pockets and cleaning the rear sight aperture of any dust with a toothpick. Mary was holding her rifle straight up and I had a fine view of the newly wiped dark barrel and the Scotch tape that held her rear sight leaves down, of the back of her head and her disreputable hat. The sun was just above the hills now and we were out of the flowers and going north on the old track that ran parallel to the woods. Somewhere on the right was the lion.

When we came up in sight of the high rounded cone of the anthill he was gone. The car stopped and everyone got out except Harry who stayed at the wheel. The lion's tracks went off to the right toward a clump of trees and brush on our side of the lone tree where the bait was covered by a pile of brush. He was not on the bait and there were no birds on it either. They were all up in the trees. I looked back at the sun and it did not have more than ten minutes before it would be behind the far hills to the west. Ngui had climbed the anthill and looked carefully over the top. He pointed with his hand held close by his face so that you could hardly see it move and then came fast down from the mound.

"*Yuko hapa,*" he said. "He's there. *Mzuri motokaa.*"

G.C. and I both looked at the sun again and G.C. waved his arm for Harry to come up. We climbed into the car and G.C. told Harry how he wanted him to go.

"But where is he?" Mary asked G.C.

G.C. put his hand on Harry's arm and Harry stopped the car.

"We leave the car back here," G.C. told Mary. "He must be in that far clump of trees and brush. Papa will take the left flank and block him off from breaking back to the forest. You and I will move straight in on him."

The sun was still above the hills as we moved up toward where the lion must be. Ngui was behind me and on our right Mary was walking a little ahead of G.C. Charo was behind G.C. They were walking straight toward the trees with the thin brush at their base. I could see the lion now and I kept working to the left; walking sideways and forward. The light showed the lion, huge black and long tawny gray gold and he was watching us. He was watching us and I thought what a bad place he had gotten himself into now. Every step I made I was blocking him worse from his safety that he had retreated into so many times. He had no choice now except to break toward me, to come out toward Mary and G.C., which he did not figure to do unless he were wounded, or to try for the next island of heavy cover, trees and thick brush that was four hundred and fifty yards away to the north. To reach that he would have to cross open flat plain.

Now I figured that I was far enough to the left and began moving in toward the lion. He stood there thigh deep in brush and I saw his head turn once to look toward me and then it swung back to watch Mary and G.C. His head was huge and dark but when he moved it the head did not look too big for his body. His body was heavy, great and long. I did not know how close G.C. would try to work Mary toward the lion. I did not watch them. I watched the lion and waited to hear the shot. I was as close as I needed to be now with room to take him if he came and I was sure that if he were wounded he would break toward me as his natural cover was behind me. Mary must take him soon, I thought. She can't get any closer. But maybe G.C. wants her closer. I looked at them from the corner of my eyes, my head down, not looking away from the lion. I could see Mary wanted to shoot and that G.C. was preventing her. They were not trying to work closer so I figured that from where they were there were some limbs of brush between Mary and the lion. I watched the lion and felt the change in his coloring as the first peak of the hills took the sun. It was good light to shoot in now but it would go fast. I watched the lion and he moved very slightly to his right and then looked at Mary and G.C. I could see his eyes. Still Mary did not shoot. Then the lion moved very slightly again and I heard Mary's rifle go and the dry whack of the bullet. She had hit him. The lion made a bound into the brush and then came out of the far side headed for the patch of heavy cover to the north. Mary was firing at him and I was sure she hit him. He was moving in long bounds his great head swinging. I shot and raised a puff of dirt behind him. I swung with him and squeezed off as I passed him and was behind him again. G.C.'s big double was firing and I saw the blossomings of dirt from it. I fired again picking up the lion in the sights and swung ahead of him and a bunch of dirt rose ahead of him. He was running heavy now and desperate but beginning to look small in the sights and almost certain to make the far cover when I had him in the sights again, very small now and going away fast, and swung gently ahead and lifting over him and squeezed as I passed him and no dirt rose and I saw him slide forward, his front feet plowing and his great head down before we heard the *thunk* of the bullet. Ngui banged me on the back and put his arm around me. The lion was trying to get up now and G.C. hit him and he rolled onto his side.

I went over to Mary and kissed her. She was happy but something was wrong.

"You shot before I did," she said.

"Don't say that, honey. You shot and hit him. How could I shoot before you when we'd waited all that time?"

"*Ndio*. Memsahib *piga*," Charo said. He had been right behind Mary.

"Of course you hit him. You hit him the first time in the foot I think. You hit him again too."

"But you killed him."

"We all had to keep him from getting into that thick stuff after he was hit."

"But you shot first. You know you did."

"I did not. Ask G.C."

It was a long walk and the lion grew larger and deader as we walked. We were all walking up to where the lion lay. With the sun gone it was getting dark fast. The shooting light was gone already. I felt wrung out inside and very tired. G.C. and I were both wet with sweat.

"Of course you hit him, Mary," G.C. told her. "Papa didn't shoot until he went into the open. You hit him twice."

"Why couldn't I have shot him when I wanted to when he was just standing there and looking at me?"

"There were branches that could have deflected the bullet or broken it up. That was why I made you wait."

"Then he moved."

"He had to move for you to shoot him."

"But did I really hit him first?"

"Of course you did. Nobody would have shot at him before you did."

"You're not just lying to make me happy?"

This was a scene that Charo had seen before.

"*PIGA!*" he said violently. "*Piga,* Memsahib. *PIGA.*"

I slapped Ngui on the hip with the side of my hand and looked toward Charo and he went over.

"*Piga,*" he said harshly. "*PIGA,* Memsahib. *Piga mbili.*"

G.C. came over to walk by me and I said, "What are *you* sweating for?"

"How far did you hold over him, you son of a bitch?"

"A foot and a half. Two feet. It was bow and arrow shooting."

"We'll pace it when we walk back."

"Nobody would ever believe it."

"We will. That's all that matters."

"Go over and make her realize she hit him."

"She believes the boys. You broke his back."

"I know."

"Did you hear how long it took for the sound of the bullet hitting to come back?"

"I did. Go over and talk to her. Here comes Harry with the car."

The Land-Rover pulled up behind us. Now we were there with the lion and he was Mary's and she knew it now and she saw how wonderful and long and dark and beautiful he was. The camel flies were crawling on him and his yellow eyes were not dull yet. I moved my hand through the heavy black of his mane. Harry had stopped the Land-Rover and come over and shaken Mary's hand. She was kneeling by him.

"He's a beautiful lion," Harry said. "I've never seen one so big or so dark." Then he saw the lorry coming out across the plain from camp. They had heard the shooting and Keiti had come out with everyone except two guards that they had left in camp. They were singing the lion song and when they piled out of the lorry, Mary had no more doubt about whose lion it was. I have seen many lions killed and many celebrations. But not one like this. I wanted Mary to have all of it. I was sure it was all right with her now and I walked on to the island of trees and thick brush the lion had been making for. He had nearly made it and I thought of what it would have been like if G.C. and I had had to go in there and dig him out. I wanted a look at it before the light was gone. He would have made it there in sixty more yards and it would have been dark when we got up to it. I thought about what could have happened and went back to the celebration and the picture-taking. The headlights of the lorry and the Land-Rover were centered on Mary and the lion, and G.C. was making the photographs. Ngui brought me the Jinny flask from the shellbag in the Land-Rover and I took a small swallow and handed it to Ngui. He took a small drink and shook his head and handed it to me.

"*Piga,*" he said and we both laughed. I took a long drink and felt warm and felt the strain slip off me like a snake shedding his skin. Until that moment I had not realized that we had the lion finally. I knew it technically when the unbelievable long bow and arrow shot had hit and broken him down and Ngui had hit me across the back. But then there had been Mary's worry and being upset and walking up to him we had been as unemotional and as detached as though it were the end of an attack. Now with the drink and celebrating going on and the photography, the hated and necessary photography, too late at night, no flash, no professionals to do it properly to make Miss Mary's lion immortal now on film, seeing her shining happy face in the glare of the headlights and the lion's great head that was too heavy for her to lift, proud of her and loving the lion, me feeling as empty inside as an empty room, seeing Keiti's gashed slant of a smile as he bent over Mary to touch the lion's unbelievable black mane, everyone cooing in Kamba like birds and each man individually proud of this our lion, ours and belonging to all of us and Mary's because she had hunted him for months and had hit him, in those barred phrases standing on her own two feet and when the chips were down, and how happy and shining in the headlights looking like a small, not quite deadly, bright angel and everyone loving her and this our lion, I began to relax and to have fun.

Charo and Ngui had told Keiti how it was and he came over to me and we shook hands and he said, "*Mzuri sana,* Bwana. *Shaitani tu.*"

"It was lucky," I said, which God knows it had to be.

"Not lucky," Keiti said. "*Mzuri. Mzuri. Shaitani mkubwa sana.*"

Then I remembered that I had given this afternoon for the lion's death and that it was all over now and that Mary had won and I talked with Ngui and Muthoka and Pop's gunbearer and the others of our religion and we shook our heads and laughed and Ngui wanted me to take another drink from the Jinny flask. They wanted to wait until we would get to camp for beer but they wanted me to drink now with them. They only touched the bottle with their lips. Mary stood up now after the photography and saw us drinking and she asked for the flask and drank from it and passed it to G.C. and to Harry. They passed it back and I drank and then lay down by the lion and talked to him very softly in Spanish and begged his pardon for having killed him and while I lay beside him I felt for the wounds. There were four. Mary had hit him in the foot and in one haunch. While I stroked his back I found where I had hit him in the spine and the larger hole G.C.'s bullet had made well forward in his flank behind the shoulder. All the time I was stroking him and talking to him in Spanish but many of the flat hard camel flies were shifting from him to me so I drew a fish in front of him with my forefinger in the dirt and then rubbed it out with the palm of my hand.

On the way into camp Ngui and Charo and I did not talk. I heard Mary once ask G.C. if I had not really shot before she did and heard him tell her that she had gotten her lion. That she had hit him first and that these things did not always go off ideally and that when an animal was wounded he had to be killed and that we were damned lucky and she should be happy. But I knew that her happiness came and went because it had not been as she had hoped and dreamed and feared and waited for all these months. I felt terribly about how she felt and I knew it made no difference to anyone else and it made all the difference in the world to her. But if we had to do it over again there was no way we could have done it differently. G.C. had taken her up closer than anyone but a great shot had a right to take her. If the lion had charged when she hit him G.C. would have had time for only one shot before the lion would have been on them. His big gun was as deadly and efficient if the lion came as it was a handicap if he had to shoot it at two and three hundred yards. We both knew that and had not even joked about it. Taking the lion at the range she did Mary had been in great danger and both G.C. and I knew that at the distance he had brought her to she had, recently, a possible error of fourteen inches on live game. This was not the time to talk about that but Ngui and Charo knew it too and I had slept with it for a long time. The lion, by deciding to make his fight in the thick cover where he was heavy odds on to get someone, had made his choice and had very nearly won. He was not a stupid lion and he was not cowardly. He simply had wanted to make his fight where the odds were in his favor.

We came into camp and sat in chairs by the fire and stretched our legs out and drank tall drinks. Who we needed was Pop and Pop was not here. I had told Keiti to break out some beer for the lines and then I waited for it to come. It came as suddenly as a dry stream bed filling with the high foam-crested roar of water from a cloud-burst. It had only taken time enough for them to decide who was to carry Miss Mary and then the wild, stooped dancing rush of Wakamba poured in from behind the tents all singing the lion song. The big mess boy and the truck driver had the chair and they put it down and Keiti, dancing and clapping his hands, led Miss Mary to it and they hoisted her up and started dancing around the fire with her and then out toward the lines and around the lion where he had been laid on the ground and then through the lines and around the cook fire and the men's fire and around the cars and the wood truck and in and out. The Game Scouts were all stripped to their shorts and so was everyone else except the old men. I watched Mary's bright head and the black strong fine bodies that were carrying her and crouching and stamping in the dance and then moving forward to reach up and touch her. It was a fine wild lion dance and at the end they put Mary down in the chair by her camp chair at the fire and everyone shook hands with her and the celebration was over.

In the night I woke and could not get back to sleep. I woke very suddenly and it was absolutely quiet. Then I heard Mary's regular, smooth breathing and I had a feeling of relief that we would not have to pit her against the lion every morning. Then I began to feel sorrow that the lion's death had not been as she hoped it would be and as she had planned it. With the celebration and the really wild dance and the love of all her friends and their allegiance to her the disappoint-ment that she felt had been anesthetized. But I was sure that after the more than a hundred mornings that she had gone out after a great lion the disappointment would return. She did not know the danger she had been in. Maybe she did and I did not know. Neither G.C. nor I wanted to tell her because we had both cut it too fine and we had not soaked in sweat that way in the cool of the evening for nothing. I remembered how the lion's eyes had looked when he had looked toward me and turned that down and then looked toward Mary and G.C. and how his eyes had never left them. I lay in the bed and thought how a lion can come one hundred yards from a standing start in just over three seconds. He comes low down to the ground and faster than a greyhound and he does not spring until he is on his prey. Mary's lion would weigh well over four hundred pounds and he was strong enough to have leaped out over a high thorn *boma* carrying a cow. He had been hunted for many years and he was very intelligent. But we had lulled him into making a mistake. I was happy that before he died he had lain on the high rounded mound with his tail down and his great paws comfortable before him and looked off across his country to the blue forest and the high white snows of the big mountain. Both G.C. and I wanted him to be killed by Mary's first shot or, wounded, charge. But he had played it his own way. The first shot could not have felt more than a sharp, slapping sting to him. The second that passed high through a leg muscle while he was bounding toward the heavy cover where he would make his fight would, at most, have felt like a hard slap. I did not like to think what my long running shot that was thrown at all of him hoping to rake him and bring him down must have felt like when it by chance took him in the spine. It was a two hundred and twenty grain solid bullet and I did not have to think how it would have felt. I had never yet broken my back and I did not know. I was glad G.C.'s wonderful distance shot had killed him instantly. He was dead now and we would miss hunting him too. But it was a great relief that he was dead because today I would have been hunting alone with Mary without G.C. and so there would have been nobody to block in the place I had blocked last evening. He was so crafty that something could always have gone wrong with him.

Mary was still breathing regularly and I looked out at the night and the glow of the coals of the fire when the breeze stirred the ashes and I was very glad the responsibility of hunting Mary on lion was over. There was nothing I could do about her disappointment when she woke. But maybe it would wear off. If it didn't she could kill another great lion some other time. But not right now, I thought, please not right now.

I tried to go to sleep but I started to think about the lion and what the moves would have been if he had reached the heavy cover, remembering other people's experiences under the same circumstances and then I thought the hell with all that. That's stuff for G.C. and I to talk over together and to talk with Pop. I wished Mary would wake and say, "I'm so glad I got my lion." But that was too much to expect and it was three o'clock in the morning. I remembered how Scott Fitzgerald had written that in the something something of the soul something something it is always three o'clock in the morning. Turning my memory back I remembered the quotation. It went like this: "In a real dark night of the soul it is always three o'clock in the morning, day after day."

And I thought sitting up awake in the African night that I knew nothing about the soul at all. People were always talking of it and writing of it but who knew about it? I did not know anyone who knew anything of it nor whether there was such a thing. It seemed a very strange belief and I knew I would have a very difficult time trying to explain it to Ngui and Muthoka and the others even if I knew anything about it. Before I woke I had been dreaming and in the dream I had a horse's body but a man's head and shoulders and I had wondered why no one had known this before. It was a very logical dream and it dealt with the precise moment at which the change came about in the body so that it was a human body. It seemed a very sound and good dream and I wondered what the others would think of it when I told it to them. I was awake now and the cider was cool and fresh but I could still feel the muscles I had in the dream when my body had been a horse's body. This was not helping me with the soul and I tried to think what it must be in the terms that I believed. Probably a spring of clear fresh water that never diminished in the drought and never froze in the winter was closest to what we had instead of the soul they all talked about. I remembered how when I was a boy the Chicago White Sox had a third baseman named Harry Lord who could foul off pitches down the third-base line until the opposing pitcher was worn out or it would get dark and the game be called. I was very young then and everything was exaggerated but I can remember it beginning to get dark, this was before there were lights in ball parks, and Harry still fouling them off and the crowd shouting, "Lord, Lord save your soul." This was the closest I had ever come to the soul. Once I had thought my own soul had been blown out of me when I was a boy and then that it had come back in again. But in those days I was very egotistical and I had heard so much talk about the soul and read so much about it that I had assumed that I had one. Then I began to think if Miss Mary or G.C. or Ngui or Charo or I had been killed by the lion would our souls have flown off somewhere? I could not believe it and I thought that we would all just have been dead, deader than the lion perhaps, and no one was worrying about his soul. The worst part would have been the trip to Nairobi and the inquiry although that would be easier because Harry Steele had been present and he was a policeman. But all I really knew was that it would have been very bad for G.C.'s career if Mary or I had been killed. It would have been bad luck for G.C. if he had been killed. It would have certainly been very bad for my writing if I had been killed. Neither Charo nor Ngui would have liked to be killed and if she had been killed it would have come as a great surprise to Miss Mary. It was something to be avoided and it was a relief to not have to put yourself in a position where it could happen day after day.

But what did this have to do with ". . . In a real dark night of the soul it is always three o'clock in the morning, day after day." ? Did Miss Mary and G.C. have souls? They had no religious beliefs as far as I knew. But if anybody had a soul they must have them. Charo was a very devout Mohammedan so we must credit him with a soul. That left only Ngui and me and the lion.

Now here it was three o'clock in the morning and I stretched my recent horse's legs and thought I would get up and go outside and sit by the coals of the fire and enjoy the rest of the night and the first light. I pulled on my mosquito boots and put on my bathrobe and buckled the pistol belt over it and went out to the remains of the fire. G.C. was sitting by it in his chair.

"What are we awake about?" he said very softly.

"I had a dream I was a horse. It was very vivid."

"Did you train well? Or had you been retired to stud?"

"There was something about stud. But I woke up before that."

"I had bloody nightmares."

"What kind?"

"I can't remember them."

"Do you think we're getting to be the nervous irascible type."

"You maybe. Me never."

"You're the home-loving, faithful husband, rather inarticulate type."

"Am I not?" said G.C. "Whose husband am I faithful to?"

"Miss Mary's."

"That bastard. What was it you dreamed you were? A horse's ass?"

"It will seem funny not to hunt the old bastard anymore."

"It will. . . ."

We sat and watched the fire that was burning brightly now and lighting the tents and the trees. It was half past three or a quarter to four by now or maybe four. I told G.C. about Scott Fitzgerald and the quotation I had remembered and asked him what he thought of it.

"Any hour can be a bad hour when you wake," he said. "I don't see why he picked three especially. It sounds quite good though."

"I think it is just fear and worry and remorse."

"We've both had enough of those haven't we?"

"Sure; to peddle. But I think what he meant was his conscience and despair."

"You don't ever have despair do you, Ernie?"

"Not yet."

"You'd probably have had it by now if you were going to have it."

"I've seen it close enough to touch it but I always turned it down."

Later, much later, I went into the tent to see if Mary was awake. But she was still sleeping heavily. She had awakened and drunk some of her tea and then gone back to sleep again.

"We'll let her sleep," I said to G.C. "It doesn't make any difference if we don't skin out until half past nine even. She should get all the sleep she can."

G.C. was reading the Lindbergh book but I had no stomach for *The Year of the Lion* this morning and so I read the bird book. It was a good new book called *Birds of Eastern and North Eastern Africa* and I knew that by hunting one beast too hard and concentrating on him I had missed much in not observing the birds properly.

If there had been no animals we could have been quite happy observing the birds but I knew that I had neglected them terribly.

Mary had been much better. She was always seeing birds that I did not notice or watching them in detail while I sat in my camp chair and just looked out across the country. Reading the bird book I felt how stupid I had been and how much time I had wasted.

At home sitting in the shade at the head of the pool it made me happy to see the kingbirds dip down to take insects off the water and to watch the gray white of their breasts show green from the reflection of the pool. I loved to watch the doves nesting in the alamo trees and to watch the mockingbirds as they sang. Seeing the migratory birds come through in the fall and the spring was an excitement and it made an afternoon happy to see the small bittern come to drink at the pool and watch him search the gutters for tree frogs. Now here in Africa there were beautiful birds around the camp all of the time. They were in the trees and in the thorn bushes and walking about on the ground and I only half saw them as moving bits of color while Mary loved and knew them all. I could not think how I had become so stupid and calloused about the birds and I was very ashamed.

For a long time I realized I had only paid attention to the predators, the scavengers and the birds that were good to eat and the birds that had to do with hunting. Then as I thought of which birds I did notice there came such a great long list of them that I did not feel quite as bad but I resolved to watch the birds around our camp more and to ask Mary about all the ones I did not know and most of all to really see them and not look past them.

This looking and not seeing things was a great sin, I thought, and one that was easy to fall into. It was always the beginning of something bad and I thought that we did not deserve to live in the world if we did not see it. I tried to think how I had gotten into not seeing the small birds around camp and I thought some of it was reading too much to take my mind off the concentration of the serious hunting and some was certainly drinking in camp to relax when we came in from hunting. I admired Mayito who drank almost nothing because he wanted to remember everything in Africa. But G.C. and I were drinkers and I knew it was not just a habit nor a way of escaping. It was a purposeful dulling of a receptivity that was so highly sensitized, as film can be, that if your receptiveness were always kept at the same level it would become unbearable. You make out quite a noble case for yourself, I thought, and you know too that you and G.C. drink because you love it too and Mary loves it the same way and we have such good fun drinking together. You better go in and see if she is awake now, I thought.

So I went in and she was still asleep. She always looked beautiful asleep. Her face, when she slept, was neither happy nor unhappy. It simply existed. But today the line of it was too finely drawn. I wished that I could make her happy but the only thing I knew to do was to let her keep on sleeping.

❋ PART V ❋

SPAIN AT WAR

From BY-LINE: ERNEST HEMINGWAY

The Chauffeurs of Madrid

FOR WHOM THE BELL TOLLS (CHAPTERS 1–2)

From THE FIFTH COLUMN AND FOUR STORIES
OF THE SPANISH CIVIL WAR

The Butterfly and the Tank
Under the Ridge

The Chauffeurs of Madrid

(NANA *Dispatch*—MAY 22, 1937)

WE had a lot of different chauffeurs in Madrid. The first one was named Tomás, was four feet eleven inches high and looked like a particularly unattractive, very mature dwarf out of Velásquez put into a suit of blue dungarees. He had several front teeth missing and seethed with patriotic sentiments. He also loved Scotch whisky.

We drove up from Valencia with Tomás and, as we sighted Madrid rising like a great white fortress across the plain from Alcalá de Henares, Tomás said, through missing teeth, "Long live Madrid, the Capital of my Soul!"

"And of my heart," I said, having had a couple myself. It had been a long cold ride.

"Hurray!" shouted Tomás and abandoned the wheel temporarily in order to clap me on the back. We just missed a lorry full of troops and a staff car.

"I am a man of sentiment," said Tomás.

"Me, too," I said, "but hang on to that wheel."

"Of the noblest sentiment," said Tomás.

"No doubt of it, comrade," I said, "but just try to watch where you are driving."

"You can place all confidence in me," said Tomás.

But the next day we were stalled on a muddy road up near Brihuega by a tank, which had lurched around a little too far on a hairpin bend, and held up six other tanks behind it. Three rebel planes sighted the tanks and decided to bomb them. The bombs hit the wet hillside above us, lifting mud geysers in sudden, clustered, bumping shocks. Nothing hit us and the planes went on over their own lines. In the field glasses, standing by the car, I could see the little Fiat fighter planes that protected the bombers, very shining looking, hanging up in the sun. We thought some more bombers were coming and everybody got away from there as fast as possible. But no more came.

Next morning Tomás couldn't get the car to start. And every day when anything of that sort happened, from then on, no matter how well the car had run coming home at night, Tomás never could start her in the morning. The way he felt about the front became sort of pitiful, finally, along with his size, his patriotism, and his general inefficiency, and we sent him back to Valencia, with a note to the press department thanking them for Tomás, a man of the noblest sentiments and the finest intentions; but could they send us something just a little braver.

So they sent one with a note certifying him as the bravest chauffeur in the whole department. I don't know what his name was because I never saw him. Sid Franklin (the Brooklyn bullfighter), who bought us all our food, cooked breakfasts, typed articles, wangled petrol, wangled cars, wangled chauffeurs, and covered Madrid and all its gossip like a human dictaphone, evidently instructed this chauffeur very strongly. Sid put forty liters of petrol in the car, and petrol was the correspondents' main problem, being harder to obtain than Chanel's and Molyneux's perfumes or Bols gin, took the chauffeur's name and address, and told him to hold himself ready to roll whenever he was called. We were expecting an attack.

Until we called him he was free to do whatever he wanted. But he must leave word at all times where we could reach him. We did not want to use up the precious petrol riding around Madrid in the car. We all felt good now, because we had transport.

The chauffeur was to check in at the hotel the next night at seven-thirty to see if there were any new orders. He didn't come and we called up his rooming house. He had left that same morning for Valencia with the car and the forty liters of petrol. He is in jail in Valencia now. I hope he likes it.

Then we got David. David was an Anarchist boy from a little town near Toledo. He used language that was so utterly and inconceivably foul that half the time you could not believe what your ears were hearing. Being with David has changed my whole conception of profanity.

He was absolutely brave and he had only one real defect as a chauffeur. He couldn't drive a car. He was like a horse which has only two gaits; walking and running away. David could sneak along, in second speed, and hit practically no one in the streets, due to his clearing a swathe ahead of him with his vocabulary. He could also drive with the car wide open, hanging to the wheel, in a sort of fatalism that was, however, never tinged with despair.

We solved the problem by driving for David ourselves. He liked this and it gave him a chance to work with his vocabulary. His vocabulary was terrific.

He liked the war and he thought shelling was beautiful. "Look at that! Olé! That's the stuff to give the unmentionable, unspeakable, absolutely unutterables," he would say in delight. "Come on, let's get closer!" He was watching his first battle in the Casa del Campo and it was like a super-fireworks show to him. The spouting clouds of stone and plaster dust that pulsed up as the Government shells landed on a house the Moors held with machine guns and the great, tremendous, slither automatic rifles, machine guns and rapid fire combine into at the moment of the assault moved David very deeply. "Ayee! Ayee!" he said. "That's war. That's really war!"

He liked the tearing rush of the incomers just as much as the crack and the chu-chu-chu-ing air-parting rustle of sound that came from the battery which was firing over our heads on to the rebel positions.

"Olé," said David as a 75 burst a little way down the street. "Listen," I said. "Those are the bad ones. Those are the ones that kill us."

"That's of no importance," David said. "Listen to that unspeakable unmentionable noise."

Well, I went back to the hotel, finally, to write a dispatch and we sent David around to a place near the Plaza Mayor to get some petrol. I had almost finished the dispatch when in came David.

"Come and look at the car," he said. "It's full of blood. It's a terrible thing." He was pretty shaky. He had a dark face and his lips trembled.

"What was it?"

"A shell hit a line of women waiting to buy food. It killed seven. I took three to the hospital."

"Good boy."

"But you can't imagine it," he said. "It's terrible. I did not know there were such things."

"Listen, David," I said. "You're a brave boy. You must remember that. But all day you have been being brave about noises. What you see now is what those noises do. Now you must be brave about the noises knowing what they can do."

"Yes, man," he said. "But it is a terrible thing just the same to see."

David was brave, though. I don't think he ever thought it was quite as beautiful again as he did that first day; but he never shirked any of it. On the other hand he never learned to drive a car. But he was a good, if fairly useless, kid and I loved to hear his awful language. The only thing that developed in David was his vocabulary. He went off to the village where the motion picture outfit was making a film and, after having one more particularly useless chauffeur that there is no point in going into, we got Hipolito. Hipolito is the point of this story.

Hipolito was not much taller than Tomás, but he looked carved out of a granite block. He walked with a roll, putting his feet down flat at each stride; and he had an automatic pistol so big it came halfway down his leg. He always said "Salud" with a rising inflection as though it were something you said to hounds. Good hounds that knew their business. He knew motors, he could drive and if you told him to show up at six a.m., he was there at ten minutes before the hour.

He had fought at the taking of Montana barracks in the first days of the war and he had never been a member of any political party. He was a trade union man for the last twenty years in the Socialist Union, the U.G.T. He said, when I asked him what he believed in, that he believed in the Republic.

He was our chauffeur in Madrid and at the front during a nineteen-day bombardment of the capital that was almost too bad to write anything about. All the time he was as solid as the rock he looked to be cut from, as sound as a good bell and as regular and accurate as a railway man's watch. He made you realize why Franco never took Madrid when he had the chance.

Hipolito and the others like him would have fought from street to street, and house to house, as long as any one of them was left alive; and the last ones left would have burned the town. They are tough and they are efficient. They are the Spaniards that once conquered the Western World. They are not romantic like the Anarchists and they are not afraid to die. Only they never mention it.

The Anarchists talk a little bit too much about it, the way the Italians do.

On the day we had over 300 shells come into Madrid so the main streets were a glass-strewn, brick-dust powdered, smoking shambles, Hipolito had the car parked in the lee of a building in a narrow street beside the hotel. It looked like a good safe place and after he had sat around the room while I was working until he was thoroughly bored, he said he'd go down and sit in the car. He hadn't been gone ten minutes when a six-inch shell hit the hotel just at the junction of the main floor and the sidewalk. It went deep in out of sight and didn't explode. If it had burst, there would not have been enough left of Hipolito and the car to take a picture of. They were about fifteen feet away from where the shell hit. I looked out of the window, saw he was all right, and then went downstairs.

"How are you?" I was fairly average breathless.

"Fine," he said.

"Put the car further down the street."

"Don't be foolish," he said. "Another one wouldn't drop there in a thousand years. Besides it didn't explode."

"Put it farther along the street."

"What's the matter with you?" he asked. "You getting windy?"

"You've got to be sensible."

"Go ahead and do your work," he said. "Don't worry about me."

The details of that day are a little confused because after nineteen days of heavy shelling some of the days get merged into others; but at one o'clock the shelling stopped and we decided to go to the Hotel Gran Via, about six blocks down, to get some lunch. I was going to walk by a very tortuous and extremely safe way I had worked out utilizing the angles of least danger, when Hipolito said, "Where are you going?"

"To eat."

"Get in the car."

"You're crazy."

"Come on, we'll drive down the Gran Via. It's stopped. They are eating their lunch too."

Four of us got into the car and drove down the Gran Via. It was solid with broken glass. There were great holes all down the sidewalks. Buildings were smashed and we had to walk around a heap of rubble and a smashed stone cornice to get into the hotel.

There was not a living person on either side of the street, which had been, always, Madrid's Fifth Avenue and Broadway combined. There were many dead. We were the only motor car.

Hipolito put the car up a side street and we all ate together. We were still eating when Hipolito finished and went up to the car. There was some more shelling sounding, in the hotel basement, like muffled blasting, and when we finished the lunch of bean soup, paper thin sliced sausage and an orange, we went upstairs, the streets were full of smoke and clouds of dust. There was new smashed cement work all over the sidewalk. I looked around a corner for the car. There was rubble scattered all down that street from a new shell that had hit just overhead. I saw the car. It was covered with dust and rubble.

"My God," I said, "they've got Hipolito."

He was lying with his head back in the driver's seat. I went up to him feeling very badly. I had got very fond of Hipolito.

Hipolito was asleep.

"I thought you were dead," I said. He woke and wiped a yawn on the back of his hand.

"Qué va, hombre," he said. "I am always accustomed to sleep after lunch if I have time."

"We are going to Chicote's Bar," I said.

"Have they got good coffee there?"

"Excellent."

"Come on," he said. "Let's go."

I tried to give him some money when I left Madrid.

"I don't want anything from you," he said.

"No," I said. "Take it. Go on. Buy something for the family."

"No," he said. "Listen, we had a good time, didn't we?"

You can bet on Franco, or Mussolini, or Hitler, if you want. But my money goes on Hipolito.

FOR WHOM
THE BELL TOLLS

(CHAPTERS 1–2)

1

HE lay flat on the brown, pine-needled floor of the forest, his chin
on his folded arms, and high overhead the wind blew in the tops
of the pine trees. The mountainside sloped gently where he lay; but
below it was steep and he could see the dark of the oiled road winding through the pass. There was a stream alongside the road and
far down the pass he saw a mill beside the stream and the falling
water of the dam, white in the summer sunlight.

"Is that the mill?" he asked.

"Yes."

"I do not remember it."

"It was built since you were here. The old mill is farther down;
much below the pass."

He spread the photostated military map out on the forest floor
and looked at it carefully. The old man looked over his shoulder.
He was a short and solid old man in a black peasant's smock and
gray iron-stiff trousers and he wore rope-soled shoes. He was breathing heavily from the climb and his hand rested on one of the two
heavy packs they had been carrying.

"Then you cannot see the bridge from here."

"No," the old man said. "This is the easy country of the pass
where the stream flows gently. Below, where the road turns out of
sight in the trees, it drops suddenly and there is a steep gorge——"

"I remember."

"Across this gorge is the bridge."

"And where are their posts?"

"There is a post at the mill that you see there."

The young man, who was studying the country, took his glasses from the pocket of his faded, khaki flannel shirt, wiped the lenses with a handkerchief, screwed the eyepieces around until the boards of the mill showed suddenly clearly and he saw the wooden bench beside the door; the huge pile of sawdust that rose behind the open shed where the circular saw was, and a stretch of the flume that brought the logs down from the mountainside on the other bank of the stream. The stream showed clear and smooth-looking in the glasses and, below the curl of the falling water, the spray from the dam was blowing in the wind.

"There is no sentry."

"There is smoke coming from the millhouse," the old man said. "There are also clothes hanging on a line."

"I see them but I do not see any sentry."

"Perhaps he is in the shade," the old man explained. "It is hot there now. He would be in the shadow at the end we do not see."

"Probably. Where is the next post?"

"Below the bridge. It is at the roadmender's hut at kilometer five from the top of the pass."

"How many men are here?" He pointed at the mill.

"Perhaps four and a corporal."

"And below?"

"More. I will find out."

"And at the bridge?"

"Always two. One at each end."

"We will need a certain number of men," he said. "How many men can you get?"

"I can bring as many men as you wish," the old man said. "There are many men now here in the hills."

"How many?"

"There are more than a hundred. But they are in small bands. How many men will you need?"

"I will let you know when we have studied the bridge."

"Do you wish to study it now?"

"No. Now I wish to go to where we will hide this explosive until it is time. I would like to have it hidden in utmost security at a distance no greater than half an hour from the bridge, if that is possible."

"That is simple," the old man said. "From where we are going, it will all be downhill to the bridge. But now we must climb a little in seriousness to get there. Are you hungry?"

"Yes," the young man said. "But we will eat later. How are you called? I have forgotten." It was a bad sign to him that he had forgotten.

"Anselmo," the old man said. "I am called Anselmo and I come from Barco de Avila. Let me help you with that pack."

The young man, who was tall and thin, with sun-streaked fair hair, and a wind- and sun-burned face, who wore the sun-faded flannel shirt, a pair of peasant's trousers and rope-soled shoes, leaned over, put his arm through one of the leather pack straps and swung the heavy pack up onto his shoulders. He worked his arm through the other strap and settled the weight of the pack against his back. His shirt was still wet from where the pack had rested.

"I have it up now," he said. "How do we go?"

"We climb," Anselmo said.

Bending under the weight of the packs, sweating, they climbed steadily in the pine forest that covered the mountainside. There was no trail that the young man could see, but they were working up and around the face of the mountain and now they crossed a small stream and the old man went steadily on ahead up the edge of the rocky stream bed. The climbing now was steeper and more difficult, until finally the stream seemed to drop down over the edge of a smooth granite ledge that rose above them and the old man waited at the foot of the ledge for the young man to come up to him.

"How are you making it?"

"All right," the young man said. He was sweating heavily and his thigh muscles were twitchy from the steepness of the climb.

"Wait here now for me. I go ahead to warn them. You do not want to be shot at carrying that stuff."

"Not even in a joke," the young man said. "Is it far?"

"It is very close. How do they call thee?"

"Roberto," the young man answered. He had slipped the pack off and lowered it gently down between two boulders by the stream bed.

"Wait here, then, Roberto, and I will return for you."

"Good," the young man said. "But do you plan to go down this way to the bridge?"

"No. When we go to the bridge it will be by another way. Shorter and easier."

"I do not want this material to be stored too far from the bridge."

"You will see. If you are not satisfied, we will take another place."

"We will see," the young man said.

He sat by the packs and watched the old man climb the ledge. It was not hard to climb and from the way he found hand-holds without searching for them the young man could see that he had climbed it many times before. Yet whoever was above had been very careful not to leave any trail.

The young man, whose name was Robert Jordan, was extremely hungry and he was worried. He was often hungry but he was not usually worried because he did not give any importance to what happened to himself and he knew from experience how simple it was to move behind the enemy lines in all this country. It was as simple to move behind them as it was to cross through them, if you had a good guide. It was only giving importance to what happened to you if you were caught that made it difficult; that and deciding whom to trust. You had to trust the people you worked with completely or not at all, and you had to make decisions about the trusting. He was not worried about any of that. But there were other things.

This Anselmo had been a good guide and he could travel wonderfully in the mountains. Robert Jordan could walk well enough himself and he knew from following him since before daylight that the old man could walk him to death. Robert Jordan trusted the man, Anselmo, so far, in everything except judgment. He had not yet had an opportunity to test his judgment, and, anyway, the judgment was his own responsibility. No, he did not worry about Anselmo and the problem of the bridge was no more difficult than many other problems. He knew how to blow any sort of bridge that you could name and he had blown them of all sizes and constructions. There was enough explosive and all equipment in the two packs to blow this bridge properly even if it were twice as big as Anselmo reported it, as he remembered it when he had walked over it on his way to La Granja on a walking trip in 1933, and as

Golz had read him the description of it night before last in that upstairs room in the house outside of the Escorial.

"To blow the bridge is nothing," Golz had said, the lamplight on his scarred, shaved head, pointing with a pencil on the big map. "You understand?"

"Yes, I understand."

"Absolutely nothing. Merely to blow the bridge is a failure."

"Yes, Comrade General."

"To blow the bridge at a stated hour based on the time set for the attack is how it should be done. You see that naturally. That is your right and how it should be done."

Golz looked at the pencil, then tapped his teeth with it.

Robert Jordan had said nothing.

"You understand that is your right and how it should be done," Golz went on, looking at him and nodding his head. He tapped on the map now with the pencil. "That is how I should do it. That is what we cannot have."

"Why, Comrade General?"

"Why?" Golz said, angrily. "How many attacks have you seen and you ask me why? What is to guarantee that my orders are not changed? What is to guarantee that the attack is not annulled? What is to guarantee that the attack is not postponed? What is to guarantee that it starts within six hours of when it should start? Has *any* attack ever been as it should?"

"It will start on time if it is your attack," Robert Jordan said.

"They are never my attacks," Golz said. "I make them. But they are not mine. The artillery is not mine. I must put in for it. I have never been given what I ask for even when they have it to give. That is the least of it. There are other things. You know how those people are. It is not necessary to go into all of it. Always there is something. Always some one will interfere. So now be sure you understand."

"So when is the bridge to be blown?" Robert Jordan had asked.

"After the attack starts. As soon as the attack has started and not before. So that no reinforcements will come up over that road." He pointed with his pencil. "I must know that nothing will come up over that road."

"And when is the attack?"

"I will tell you. But you are to use the date and hour only as an indication of a probability. You must be ready for that time. You will blow the bridge after the attack has started. You see?" he indicated with the pencil. "That is the only road on which they can bring up reinforcements. That is the only road on which they can get up tanks, or artillery, or even move a truck toward the pass which I attack. I must know that bridge is gone. Not before, so it can be repaired if the attack is postponed. No. It must go when the attack starts and I must know it is gone. There are only two sentries. The man who will go with you has just come from there. He is a very reliable man, they say. You will see. He has people in the mountains. Get as many men as you need. Use as few as possible, but use enough. I do not have to tell you these things."

"And how do I determine that the attack has started?"

"It is to be made with a full division. There will be an aerial bombardment as preparation. You are not deaf, are you?"

"Then I may take it that when the planes unload, the attack has started?"

"You could not always take it like that," Golz said and shook his head. "But in this case, you may. It is my attack."

"I understand it," Robert Jordan had said. "I do not say I like it very much."

"Neither do I like it very much. If you do not want to undertake it, say so now. If you think you cannot do it, say so now."

"I will do it," Robert Jordan had said. "I will do it all right."

"That is all I have to know," Golz said. "That nothing comes up over that bridge. That is absolute."

"I understand."

"I do not like to ask people to do such things and in such a way," Golz went on. "I could not order you to do it. I understand what you may be forced to do through my putting such conditions. I explain very carefully so that you understand and that you understand all of the possible difficulties and the importance."

"And how will you advance on La Granja if that bridge is blown?"

"We go forward prepared to repair it after we have stormed the pass. It is a very complicated and beautiful operation. As complicated and as beautiful as always. The plan has been manufactured in Madrid. It is another of Vicente Rojo, the unsuccessful professor's, masterpieces. I make the attack and I make it, as always, not in sufficient force. It is a very possible operation, in spite of that. I am much happier about it than usual. It can be successful with that bridge eliminated. We can take Segovia. Look, I show you how it goes. You see? It is not the top of the pass where we attack. We hold that. It is much beyond. Look— Here— Like this——"

"I would rather not know," Robert Jordan said.

"Good," said Golz. "It is less of baggage to carry with you on the other side, yes?"

"I would always rather not know. Then, no matter what can happen, it was not me that talked."

"It is better not to know," Golz stroked his forehead with the pencil. "Many times I wish I did not know myself. But you do know the one thing you must know about the bridge?"

"Yes. I know that."

"I believe you do," Golz said. "I will not make you any little speech. Let us now have a drink. So much talking makes me very thirsty, Comrade Hordan. You have a funny name in Spanish, Comrade Hordown."

"How do you say Golz in Spanish, Comrade General?"

"Hotze," said Golz grinning, making the sound deep in his throat as though hawking with a bad cold. "Hotze," he croaked. "Comrade Heneral Khotze. If I had known how they pronounced Golz in Spanish I would pick me out a better name before I come to war here. When I think I come to command a division and I can pick out any name I want and I pick out Hotze. Heneral Hotze. Now it is too late to change. How do you like *partizan* work?" It was the Russian term for guerilla work behind the lines.

"Very much," Robert Jordan said. He grinned. "It is very healthy in the open air."

"I like it very much when I was your age, too," Golz said. "They tell me you blow bridges very well. Very scientific. It is only hearsay. I have never seen you do anything myself. Maybe nothing ever happens really. You really blow them?" he was teasing now. "Drink this," he handed the glass of Spanish brandy to Robert Jordan. "You *really* blow them?"

"Sometimes."

"You better not have any sometimes on this bridge. No, let us not talk any more about this bridge. You understand enough now about that bridge. We are very serious so we can make very strong jokes. Look, do you have many girls on the other side of the lines?"

"No, there is no time for girls."

"I do not agree. The more irregular the service, the more irregular the life. You have very irregular service. Also you need a haircut."

"I have my hair cut as it needs it," Robert Jordan said. He would be damned if he would have his head shaved like Golz. "I have enough to think about without girls," he said sullenly.

"What sort of uniform am I supposed to wear?" Robert Jordan asked.

"None," Golz said. "Your haircut is all right. I tease you. You are very different from me," Golz had said and filled up the glasses again.

"You never think about only girls. I never think at all. Why should I? I am *Général Soviétique*. I never think. Do not try to trap me into thinking."

Some one on his staff, sitting on a chair working over a map on a drawing board, growled at him in the language Robert Jordan did not understand.

"Shut up," Golz had said, in English. "I joke if I want. I am so serious is why I can joke. Now drink this and then go. You understand, huh?"

"Yes," Robert Jordan had said. "I understand."

They had shaken hands and he had saluted and gone out to the staff car where the old man was waiting asleep and in that car they had ridden over the road past Guadarrama, the old man still asleep, and up the Navacerrada road to the Alpine Club hut where he, Robert Jordan, slept for three hours before they started.

That was the last he had seen of Golz with his strange white face that never tanned, his hawk eyes, the big nose and thin lips and the shaven head crossed with wrinkles and with scars. Tomorrow night they would be outside the Escorial in the dark along the road; the long lines of trucks loading the infantry in the darkness; the men, heavy loaded, climbing up into the trucks; the machinegun sections lifting their guns into the trucks; the tanks being run up on the skids onto the long-bodied tank trucks; pulling the Division out to move them in the night for the attack on the pass. He would not think about that. That was not his business. That was

Golz's business. He had only one thing to do and that was what he should think about and he must think it out clearly and take everything as it came along, and not worry. To worry was as bad as to be afraid. It simply made things more difficult.

He sat now by the stream watching the clear water flowing between the rocks and, across the stream, he noticed there was a thick bed of watercress. He crossed the stream, picked a double handful, washed the muddy roots clean in the current and then sat down again beside his pack and ate the clean, cool green leaves and the crisp, peppery-tasting stalks. He knelt by the stream and, pushing his automatic pistol around on his belt to the small of his back so that it would not be wet, he lowered himself with a hand on each of two boulders and drank from the stream. The water was achingly cold.

Pushing himself up on his hands he turned his head and saw the old man coming down the ledge. With him was another man, also in a black peasant's smock and the dark gray trousers that were almost a uniform in that province, wearing rope-soled shoes and with a carbine slung over his back. This man was bareheaded. The two of them came scrambling down the rock like goats.

They came up to him and Robert Jordan got to his feet.

"*Salud, Camarada,*" he said to the man with the carbine and smiled.

"*Salud,*" the other said, grudgingly. Robert Jordan looked at the man's heavy, beard-stubbled face. It was almost round and his head was round and set close on his shoulders. His eyes were small and set too wide apart and his ears were small and set close to his head. He was a heavy man about five feet ten inches tall and his hands and feet were large. His nose had been broken and his mouth was cut at one corner and the line of the scar across the upper lip and lower jaw showed through the growth of beard over his face.

The old man nodded his head at this man and smiled.

"He is the boss here," he grinned, then flexed his arms as though to make the muscles stand out and looked at the man with the carbine in a half-mocking admiration. "A very strong man."

"I can see it," Robert Jordan said and smiled again. He did not like the look of this man and inside himself he was not smiling at all.

"What have you to justify your identity?" asked the man with the carbine.

Robert Jordan unpinned a safety pin that ran through his pocket flap and took a folded paper out of the left breast pocket of his flannel shirt and handed it to the man, who opened it, looked at it doubtfully and turned it in his hands.

So he cannot read, Robert Jordan noted.

"Look at the seal," he said.

The old man pointed to the seal and the man with the carbine studied it, turning it in his fingers.

"What seal is that?"

"Have you never seen it?"

"No."

"There are two," said Robert Jordan. "One is S. I. M., the service of the military intelligence. The other is the General Staff."

"Yes, I have seen that seal before. But here no one commands but me," the other said sullenly. "What have you in the packs?"

"Dynamite," the old man said proudly. "Last night we crossed the lines in the dark and all day we have carried this dynamite over the mountain."

"I can use dynamite," said the man with the carbine. He handed back the paper to Robert Jordan and looked him over. "Yes. I have use for dynamite. How much have you brought me?"

"I have brought you no dynamite," Robert Jordan said to him evenly. "The dynamite is for another purpose. What is your name?"

"What is that to you?"

"He is Pablo," said the old man. The man with the carbine looked at them both sullenly.

"Good. I have heard much good of you," said Robert Jordan.

"What have you heard of me?" asked Pablo.

"I have heard that you are an excellent guerilla leader, that you are loyal to the republic and prove your loyalty through your acts, and that you are a man both serious and valiant. I bring you greetings from the General Staff."

"Where did you hear all this?" asked Pablo. Robert Jordan registered that he was not taking any of the flattery.

"I heard it from Buitrago to the Escorial," he said, naming all the stretch of country on the other side of the lines.

"I know no one in Buitrago nor in Escorial," Pablo told him.

"There are many people on the other side of the mountains who were not there before. Where are you from?"

"Avila. What are you going to do with the dynamite?"

"Blow up a bridge."

"What bridge?"

"That is my business."

"If it is in this territory, it is my business. You cannot blow bridges close to where you live. You must live in one place and operate in another. I know my business. One who is alive, now, after a year, knows his business."

"This is my business," Robert Jordan said. "We can discuss it together. Do you wish to help us with the sacks?"

"No," said Pablo and shook his head.

The old man turned toward him suddenly and spoke rapidly and furiously in a dialect that Robert Jordan could just follow. It was like reading Quevedo. Anselmo was speaking old Castilian and it went something like this, "Art thou a brute? Yes. Art thou a beast? Yes, many times. Hast thou a brain? Nay. None. Now we come for something of consummate importance and thee, with thy dwelling place to be undisturbed, puts thy fox-hole before the interests of humanity. Before the interests of thy people. I this and that in the this and that of thy father. I this and that and that in thy this. *Pick up that bag.*"

Pablo looked down.

"Every one has to do what he can do according to how it can be truly done," he said. "I live here and I operate beyond Segovia. If you make a disturbance here, we will be hunted out of these mountains. It is only by doing nothing here that we are able to live in these mountains. It is the principle of the fox."

"Yes," said Anselmo bitterly. "It is the principle of the fox when we need the wolf."

"I am more wolf than thee," Pablo said and Robert Jordan knew that he would pick up the sack.

"Hi. Ho . . . ," Anselmo looked at him. "Thou art more wolf than me and I am sixty-eight years old."

He spat on the ground and shook his head.

"You have that many years?" Robert Jordan asked, seeing that now, for the moment, it would be all right and trying to make it go easier.

"Sixty-eight in the month of July."

"If we should ever see that month," said Pablo. "Let me help you with the pack," he said to Robert Jordan. "Leave the other to the old man." He spoke, not sullenly, but almost sadly now. "He is an old man of great strength."

"I will carry the pack," Robert Jordan said.

"Nay," said the old man. "Leave it to this other strong man."

"I will take it," Pablo told him, and in his sullenness there was a sadness that was disturbing to Robert Jordan. He knew that sadness and to see it here worried him.

"Give me the carbine, then," he said and when Pablo handed it to him, he slung it over his back and, with the two men climbing ahead of him, they went heavily, pulling and climbing up the granite shelf and over its upper edge to where there was a green clearing in the forest.

They skirted the edge of the little meadow and Robert Jordan, striding easily now without the pack, the carbine pleasantly rigid over his shoulder after the heavy, sweating pack weight, noticed that the grass was cropped down in several places and signs that picket pins had been driven into the earth. He could see a trail through the grass where horses had been lead to the stream to drink and there was the fresh manure of several horses. They picket them here to feed at night and keep them out of sight in the timber in the daytime, he thought. I wonder how many horses this Pablo has?

He remembered now noticing, without realizing it, that Pablo's trousers were worn soapy shiny in the knees and thighs. I wonder if he has a pair of boots or if he rides in those *alpargatas*, he thought. He must have quite an outfit. But I don't like that sadness, he thought. That sadness is bad. That's the sadness they get before they quit or before they betray. That is the sadness that comes before the sell-out.

Ahead of them a horse whinnied in the timber and then, through the brown trunks of the pine trees, only a little sunlight coming down through their thick, almost-touching tops, he saw the corral made by roping around the tree trunks. The horses had their heads pointed toward the men as they approached, and at the foot of a tree, outside the corral, the saddles were piled together and covered with a tarpaulin.

As they came up, the two men with the packs stopped, and Robert Jordan knew it was for him to admire the horses.

"Yes," he said. "They are beautiful." He turned to Pablo. "You have your cavalry and all."

There were five horses in the rope corral, three bays, a sorrel, and a buckskin. Sorting them out carefully with his eyes after he had seen them first together, Robert Jordan looked them over individually. Pablo and Anselmo knew how good they were and while Pablo stood now proud and less sad-looking, watching them lovingly, the old man acted as though they were some great surprise that he had produced, suddenly, himself.

"How do they look to you?" he asked.

"All these I have taken," Pablo said and Robert Jordan was pleased to hear him speak proudly.

"That," said Robert Jordan, pointing to one of the bays, a big stallion with a white blaze on his forehead and a single white foot, the near front, "is much horse."

He was a beautiful horse that looked as though he had come out of a painting by Velásquez.

"They are all good," said Pablo. "You know horses?"

"Yes."

"Less bad," said Pablo. "Do you see a defect in one of these?"

Robert Jordan knew that now his papers were being examined by the man who could not read.

The horses all still had their heads up looking at the man. Robert Jordan slipped through between the double rope of the corral and slapped the buckskin on the haunch. He leaned back against the ropes of the enclosure and watched the horses circle the corral, stood watching them a minute more, as they stood still, then leaned down and came out through the ropes.

"The sorrel is lame in the off hind foot," he said to Pablo, not looking at him. "The hoof is split and although it might not get worse soon if shod properly, she could break down if she travels over much hard ground."

"The hoof was like that when we took her," Pablo said.

"The best horse that you have, the white-faced bay stallion, has a swelling on the upper part of the cannon bone that I do not like."

"It is nothing," said Pablo. "He knocked it three days ago. If it were to be anything it would have become so already."

He pulled back the tarpaulin and showed the saddles. There were two ordinary vaquero's or herdsman's saddles, like American stock saddles, one very ornate vaquero's saddle, with hand-tooled leather and heavy, hooded stirrups, and two military saddles in black leather.

"We killed a pair of *guardia civil*," he said, explaining the military saddles.

"That is big game."

"They had dismounted on the road between Segovia and Santa Maria del Real. They had dismounted to ask papers of the driver of a cart. We were able to kill them without injuring the horses."

"Have you killed many civil guards?" Robert Jordan asked.

"Several," Pablo said. "But only these two without injury to the horses."

"It was Pablo who blew up the train at Arevalo," Anselmo said. "That was Pablo."

"There was a foreigner with us who made the explosion," Pablo said. "Do you know him?"

"What is he called?"

"I do not remember. It was a very rare name."

"What did he look like?"

"He was fair, as you are, but not as tall and with large hands and a broken nose."

"Kashkin," Robert Jordan said. "That would be Kashkin."

"Yes," said Pablo. "It was a very rare name. Something like that. What has become of him?"

"He is dead since April."

"That is what happens to everybody," Pablo said, gloomily. "That is the way we will all finish."

"That is the way all men end," Anselmo said. "That is the way men have always ended. What is the matter with you, man? What hast thou in the stomach?"

"*They* are very strong," Pablo said. It was as though he were talking to himself. He looked at the horses gloomily. "You do not realize how strong they are. I see them always stronger, always better armed. Always with more material. Here am I with horses like these. And what can I look forward to? To be hunted and to die. Nothing more."

"You hunt as much as you are hunted," Anselmo said.

"No," said Pablo. "Not any more. And if we leave these mountains now, where can we go? Answer me that? Where now?"

"In Spain there are many mountains. There are the Sierra de Gredos if one leaves here."

"Not for me," Pablo said. "I am tired of being hunted. Here we are all right. Now if you blow a bridge here, we will be hunted. If they know we are here and hunt for us with planes, they will find us. If they send Moors to hunt us out, they will find us and we must go. I am tired of all this. You hear?" He turned to Robert Jordan. "What right have you, a foreigner, to come to me and tell me what I must do?"

"I have not told you anything you must do," Robert Jordan said to him.

"You will though," Pablo said. "There. There is the badness."

He pointed at the two heavy packs that they had lowered to the ground while they had watched the horses. Seeing the horses had seemed to bring this all to a head in him and seeing that Robert Jordan knew horses had seemed to loosen his tongue. The three of them stood now by the rope corral and the patchy sunlight shone on the coat of the bay stallion. Pablo looked at him and then pushed with his foot against the heavy pack. "There is the badness."

"I come only for my duty," Robert Jordan told him. "I come under orders from those who are conducting the war. If I ask you to help me, you can refuse and I will find others who will help me. I have not even asked you for help yet. I have to do what I am ordered to do and I can promise you of its importance. That I am a foreigner is not my fault. I would rather have been born here."

"To me, now, the most important is that we be not disturbed here," Pablo said. "To me, now, my duty is to those who are with me and to myself."

"Thyself. Yes," Anselmo said. "Thyself now since a long time. Thyself and thy horses. Until thou hadst horses thou wert with us. Now thou art another capitalist more."

"That is unjust," said Pablo. "I expose the horses all the time for the cause."

"Very little," said Anselmo scornfully. "Very little in my judgment. To steal, yes. To eat well, yes. To murder, yes. To fight, no."

"You are an old man who will make himself trouble with his mouth."

"I am an old man who is afraid of no one," Anselmo told him. "Also I am an old man without horses."

"You are an old man who may not live long."

"I am an old man who will live until I die," Anselmo said. "And I am not afraid of foxes."

Pablo said nothing but picked up the pack.

"Nor of wolves either," Anselmo said, picking up the other pack. "If thou art a wolf."

"Shut thy mouth," Pablo said to him. "Thou art an old man who always talks too much."

"And would do whatever he said he would do," Anselmo said, bent under the pack. "And who now is hungry. And thirsty. Go on, guerilla leader with the sad face. Lead us to something to eat."

It is starting badly enough, Robert Jordan thought. But Anselmo's a man. They are wonderful when they are good, he thought. There is no people like them when they are good and when they go bad there is no people that is worse. Anselmo must have known what he was doing when he brought us here. But I don't like it. I don't like any of it.

The only good sign was that Pablo was carrying the pack and that he had given him the carbine. Perhaps he is always like that, Robert Jordan thought. Maybe he is just one of the gloomy ones.

No, he said to himself, don't fool yourself. You do not know how he was before; but you do know that he is going bad fast and without hiding it. When he starts to hide it he will have made a decision. Remember that, he told himself. The first friendly thing he does, he will have made a decision. They are awfully good horses, though, he thought, beautiful horses. I wonder what could make me feel the way those horses make Pablo feel. The old man was right. The horses made him rich and as soon as he was rich he wanted to enjoy life. Pretty soon he'll feel bad because he can't join the Jockey Club, I guess, he thought. Pauvre Pablo. Il a manqué son Jockey.

That idea made him feel better. He grinned, looking at the two bent backs and the big packs ahead of him moving through the trees. He had not made any jokes with himself all day and now that he had made one he felt much better. You're getting to be as all the rest of them, he told himself. You're getting gloomy, too. He'd certainly been solemn and gloomy with Golz. The job had overwhelmed him a little. Slightly overwhelmed, he thought. Plenty overwhelmed. Golz was gay and he had wanted him to be gay too before he left, but he hadn't been.

All the best ones, when you thought it over, were gay. It was much better to be gay and it was a sign of something too. It was like having immortality while you were still alive. That was a complicated one. There were not many of them left though. No, there were not many of the gay ones left. There were very damned few of them left. And if you keep on thinking like that, my boy, you won't be left either. Turn off the thinking now, old timer, old comrade. You're a bridge-blower now. Not a thinker. Man, I'm hungry, he thought. I hope Pablo eats well.

2

THEY had come through the heavy timber to the cup-shaped upper end of the little valley and he saw where the camp must be under the rim-rock that rose ahead of them through the trees.

That was the camp all right and it was a good camp. You did not see it at all until you were up to it and Robert Jordan knew it could not be spotted from the air. Nothing would show from above. It was as well hidden as a bear's den. But it seemed to be little better guarded. He looked at it carefully as they came up.

There was a large cave in the rim-rock formation and beside the opening a man sat with his back against the rock, his legs stretched out on the ground and his carbine leaning against the rock. He was cutting away on a stick with a knife and he stared at them as they came up, then went on whittling.

"*Hola*," said the seated man. "What is this that comes?"

"The old man and a dynamiter," Pablo told him and lowered the pack inside the entrance to the cave. Anselmo lowered his pack, too, and Robert Jordan unslung the rifle and leaned it against the rock.

"Don't leave it so close to the cave," the whittling man, who had blue eyes in a dark, good-looking lazy gypsy face, the color of smoked leather, said. "There's a fire in there."

"Get up and put it away thyself," Pablo said. "Put it by that tree."

The gypsy did not move but said something unprintable, then, "Leave it there. Blow thyself up," he said lazily. " 'Twill cure thy diseases."

"What do you make?" Robert Jordan sat down by the gypsy. The gypsy showed him. It was a figure four trap and he was whittling the crossbar for it.

"For foxes," he said. "With a log for a dead-fall. It breaks their backs." He grinned at Jordan. "Like this, see?" He made a motion of the framework of the trap collapsing, the log falling, then shook his head, drew in his hand, and spread his arms to show the fox with a broken back. "Very practical," he explained.

"He catches rabbits," Anselmo said. "He is a gypsy. So if he catches rabbits he says it is foxes. If he catches a fox he would say it was an elephant."

"And if I catch an elephant?" the gypsy asked and showed his white teeth again and winked at Robert Jordan.

"You'd say it was a tank," Anselmo told him.

"I'll get a tank," the gypsy told him. "I will get a tank. And you can say it is what you please."

"Gypsies talk much and kill little," Anselmo told him.

The gypsy winked at Robert Jordan and went on whittling.

Pablo had gone in out of sight in the cave. Robert Jordan hoped he had gone for food. He sat on the ground by the gypsy and the afternoon sunlight came down through the tree tops and was warm on his outstretched legs. He could smell food now in the cave, the smell of oil and of onions and of meat frying and his stomach moved with hunger inside of him.

"We can get a tank," he said to the gypsy. "It is not too difficult."

"With this?" the gypsy pointed toward the two sacks.

"Yes," Robert Jordan told him. "I will teach you. You make a trap. It is not too difficult."

"You and me?"

"Sure," said Robert Jordan. "Why not?"

"Hey," the gypsy said to Anselmo. "Move those two sacks to where they will be safe, will you? They're valuable."

Anselmo grunted. "I am going for wine," he told Robert Jordan. Robert Jordan got up and lifted the sacks away from the cave entrance and leaned them, one on each side of a tree trunk. He knew what was in them and he never liked to see them close together.

"Bring a cup for me," the gypsy told him.

"Is there wine?" Robert Jordan asked, sitting down again by the gypsy.

"Wine? Why not? A whole skinful. Half a skinful, anyway."

"And what to eat?"

"Everything, man," the gypsy said. "We eat like generals."

"And what do gypsies do in the war?" Robert Jordan asked him.

"They keep on being gypsies."

"That's a good job."

"The best," the gypsy said. "How do they call thee?"

"Roberto. And thee?"

"Rafael. And this of the tank is serious?"

"Surely. Why not?"

Anselmo came out of the mouth of the cave with a deep stone basin full of red wine and with his fingers through the handles of three cups. "Look," he said. "They have cups and all." Pablo came out behind them.

"There is food soon," he said. "Do you have tobacco?"

Robert Jordan went over to the packs and opening one, felt inside an inner pocket and brought out one of the flat boxes of Russian cigarettes he had gotten at Golz's headquarters. He ran his thumbnail around the edge of the box and, opening the lid, handed them to Pablo who took half a dozen. Pablo, holding them in one of his huge hands, picked one up and looked at it against the light. They were long narrow cigarettes with pasteboard cylinders for mouthpieces.

"Much air and little tobacco," he said. "I know these. The other with the rare name had them."

"Kashkin," Robert Jordan said and offered the cigarettes to the gypsy and Anselmo, who each took one.

"Take more," he said and they each took another. He gave them each four more, they making a double nod with the hand holding the cigarettes so that the cigarette dipped its end as a man salutes with a sword, to thank him.

"Yes," Pablo said. "It was a rare name."

"Here is the wine." Anselmo dipped a cup out of the bowl and handed it to Robert Jordan, then dipped for himself and the gypsy.

"Is there no wine for me?" Pablo asked. They were all sitting together by the cave entrance.

Anselmo handed him his cup and went into the cave for another. Coming out he leaned over the bowl and dipped the cup full and they all touched cup edges.

The wine was good, tasting faintly resinous from the wineskin, but excellent, light and clean on his tongue. Robert Jordan drank it slowly, feeling it spread warmly through his tiredness.

"The food comes shortly," Pablo said. "And this foreigner with the rare name, how did he die?"

"He was captured and he killed himself."

"How did that happen?"

"He was wounded and he did not wish to be a prisoner."

"What were the details?"

"I don't know," he lied. He knew the details very well and he knew they would not make good talking now.

"He made us promise to shoot him in case he were wounded at the business of the train and should be unable to get away," Pablo said. "He spoke in a very rare manner."

He must have been jumpy even then, Robert Jordan thought. Poor old Kashkin.

"He had a prejudice against killing himself," Pablo said. "He told me that. Also he had a great fear of being tortured."

"Did he tell you that, too?" Robert Jordan asked him.

"Yes," the gypsy said. "He spoke like that to all of us."

"Were you at the train, too?"

"Yes. All of us were at the train."

"He spoke in a very rare manner," Pablo said. "But he was very brave."

Poor old Kashkin, Robert Jordan thought. He must have been doing more harm than good around here. I wish I would have known he was that jumpy as far back as then. They should have pulled him out. You can't have people around doing this sort of work and talking like that. That is no way to talk. Even if they accomplish their mission they are doing more harm than good, talking that sort of stuff.

"He was a little strange," Robert Jordan said. "I think he was a little crazy."

"But very dexterous at producing explosions," the gypsy said. "And very brave."

"But crazy," Robert Jordan said. "In this you have to have very much head and be very cold in the head. That was no way to talk."

"And you," Pablo said. "If you are wounded in such a thing as this bridge, you would be willing to be left behind?"

"Listen," Robert Jordan said and, leaning forward, he dipped himself another cup of the wine. "Listen to me clearly. If ever I should have any little favors to ask of any man, I will ask him at the time."

"Good," said the gypsy approvingly. "In this way speak the good ones. Ah! Here it comes."

"You have eaten," said Pablo.

"And I can eat twice more," the gypsy told him. "Look now who brings it."

The girl stooped as she came out of the cave mouth carrying the big iron cooking platter and Robert Jordan saw her face turned at an angle and at the same time saw the strange thing about her. She smiled and said, "*Hola,* Comrade," and Robert Jordan said, "*Salud,*" and was careful not to stare and not to look away. She set down the flat iron platter in front of him and he noticed her handsome brown hands. Now she looked him full in the face and smiled. Her teeth were white in her brown face and her skin and her eyes were the same golden tawny brown. She had high cheekbones, merry eyes and a straight mouth with full lips. Her hair was the golden brown of a grain field that has been burned dark in the sun but it was cut short all over her head so that it was but little longer than the fur on a beaver pelt. She smiled in Robert Jordan's face and put her brown hand up and ran it over her head, flattening the hair which rose again as her hand passed. She has a beautiful face, Robert Jordan thought. She'd be beautiful if they hadn't cropped her hair.

"That is the way I comb it," she said to Robert Jordan and laughed. "Go ahead and eat. Don't stare at me. They gave me this haircut in Valladolid. It's almost grown out now."

She sat down opposite him and looked at him. He looked back at her and she smiled and folded her hands together over her knees. Her legs slanted long and clean from the open cuffs of the trousers as she sat with her hands across her knees and he could see the shape of her small, up-tilted breasts under the gray shirt. Every time

Robert Jordan looked at her he could feel a thickness in his throat.

"There are no plates," Anselmo said. "Use your own knife." The girl had leaned four forks, tines down, against the sides of the iron dish.

They were all eating out of the platter, not speaking, as is the Spanish custom. It was rabbit cooked with onions and green peppers and there were chick peas in the red wine sauce. It was well cooked, the rabbit meat flaked off the bones, and the sauce was delicious. Robert Jordan drank another cup of wine while he ate. The girl watched him all through the meal. Every one else was watching his food and eating. Robert Jordan wiped up the last of the sauce in front of him with a piece of bread, piled the rabbit bones to one side, wiped the spot where they had been for sauce, then wiped his fork clean with the bread, wiped his knife and put it away and ate the bread. He leaned over and dipped his cup full of wine and the girl still watched him.

Robert Jordan drank half the cup of wine but the thickness still came in his throat when he spoke to the girl.

"How art thou called?" he asked. Pablo looked at him quickly when he heard the tone of his voice. Then he got up and walked away.

"Maria. And thee?"

"Roberto. Have you been long in the mountains?"

"Three months."

"Three months?" he looked at her hair, that was as thick and short and rippling when she passed her hand over it, now in embarrassment, as a grain field in the wind on a hillside. "It was shaved," she said. "They shaved it regularly in the prison at Valladolid. It has taken three months to grow to this. I was on the train. They were taking me to the south. Many of the prisoners were caught after the train was blown up but I was not. I came with these."

"I found her hidden in the rocks," the gypsy said. "It was when we were leaving. Man, but this one was ugly. We took her along but many times I thought we would have to leave her."

"And the other who was with them at the train?" asked Maria. "The other blond one. The foreigner. Where is he?"

"Dead," Robert Jordan said. "In April."

"In April? The train was in April."

"Yes," Robert Jordan said. "He died ten days after the train."

"Poor man," she said. "He was very brave. And you do that same business?"

"Yes."

"You have done trains, too?"

"Yes. Three trains."

"Here?"

"In Estremadura," he said. "I was in Estremadura before I came here. We do very much in Estremadura. There are many of us working in Estremadura."

"And why do you come to these mountains now?"

"I take the place of the other blond one. Also I know this country from before the movement."

"You know it well?"

"No, not really well. But I learn fast. I have a good map and I have a good guide."

"The old man," she nodded. "The old man is very good."

"Thank you," Anselmo said to her and Robert Jordan realized suddenly that he and the girl were not alone and he realized too that it was hard for him to look at her because it made his voice change so. He was violating the second rule of the two rules for getting on well with people that speak Spanish; give the men tobacco and leave the women alone; and he realized, very suddenly, that he did not care. There were so many things that he had not to care about, why should he care about that?

"You have a very beautiful face," he said to Maria. "I wish I would have had the luck to see you before your hair was cut."

"It will grow out," she said. "In six months it will be long enough."

"You should have seen her when we brought her from the train. She was so ugly it would make you sick."

"Whose woman are you?" Robert Jordan asked, trying now to pull out of it. "Are you Pablo's?"

She looked at him and laughed, then slapped him on the knee.

"Of Pablo? You have seen Pablo?"

"Well, then, of Rafael. I have seen Rafael."

"Of Rafael neither."

"Of no one," the gypsy said. "This is a very strange woman. Is of no one. But she cooks well."

"Really of no one?" Robert Jordan asked her.

"Of no one. No one. Neither in joke nor in seriousness. Nor of thee either."

"No?" Robert Jordan said and he could feel the thickness coming in his throat again. "Good. I have no time for any woman. That is true."

"Not fifteen minutes?" the gypsy asked teasingly. "Not a quarter of an hour?" Robert Jordan did not answer. He looked at the girl, Maria, and his throat felt too thick for him to trust himself to speak.

Maria looked at him and laughed, then blushed suddenly but kept on looking at him.

"You are blushing," Robert Jordan said to her. "Do you blush much?"

"Never."

"You are blushing now."

"Then I will go into the cave."

"Stay here, Maria."

"No," she said and did not smile at him. "I will go into the cave now." She picked up the iron plate they had eaten from and the four forks. She moved awkwardly as a colt moves, but with that same grace as of a young animal.

"Do you want the cups?" she asked.

Robert Jordan was still looking at her and she blushed again.

"Don't make me do that," she said. "I do not like to do that."

"Leave them," the gypsy said to her. "Here," he dipped into the stone bowl and handed the full cup to Robert Jordan who watched the girl duck her head and go into the cave carrying the heavy iron dish.

"Thank you," Robert Jordon said. His voice was all right again, now that she was gone. "This is the last one. We've had enough of this."

"We will finish the bowl," the gypsy said. "There is over half a skin. We packed it in on one of the horses."

"That was the last raid of Pablo," Anselmo said. "Since then he has done nothing."

"How many are you?" Robert Jordan asked.

"We are seven and there are two women."

"Two?"

"Yes. The *mujer* of Pablo."

"And she?"

"In the cave. The girl can cook a little. I said she cooks well to please her. But mostly she helps the *mujer* of Pablo."

"And how is she, the *mujer* of Pablo?"

"Something barbarous," the gypsy grinned. "Something *very* barbarous. If you think Pablo is ugly you should see his woman. But brave. A hundred times braver than Pablo. But something barbarous."

"Pablo was brave in the beginning," Anselmo said. "Pablo was something serious in the beginning."

"He killed more people than the cholera," the gypsy said. "At the start of the movement, Pablo killed more people than the typhoid fever."

"But since a long time he is *muy flojo*," Anselmo said. "He is very flaccid. He is very much afraid to die."

"It is possible that it is because he has killed so many at the beginning," the gypsy said philosophically. "Pablo killed more than the bubonic plague."

"That and the riches," Anselmo said. "Also he drinks very much. Now he would like to retire like a *matador de toros*. Like a bull fighter. But he cannot retire."

"If he crosses to the other side of the lines they will take his horses and make him go in the army," the gypsy said. "In me there is no love for being in the army either."

"Nor is there in any other gypsy," Anselmo said.

"Why should there be?" the gypsy asked. "Who wants to be in an army? Do we make the revolution to be in an army? I am willing to fight but not to be in an army."

"Where are the others?" asked Robert Jordan. He felt comfortable and sleepy now from the wine and lying back on the floor of the forest he saw through the tree tops the small afternoon clouds of the mountains moving slowly in the high Spanish sky.

"There are two asleep in the cave," the gypsy said. "Two are on guard above where we have the gun. One is on guard below. They are probably all asleep."

Robert Jordan rolled over on his side.

"What kind of a gun is it?"

"A very rare name," the gypsy said. "It has gone away from me for the moment. It is a machine gun."

It must be an automatic rifle, Robert Jordan thought.

"How much does it weigh?" he asked.

"One man can carry it but it is heavy. It has three legs that fold. We got it in the last serious raid. The one before the wine."

"How many rounds have you for it?"

"An infinity," the gypsy said. "One whole case of an unbelievable heaviness."

Sounds like about five hundred rounds, Robert Jordan thought.

"Does it feed from a pan or a belt?"

"From round iron cans on the top of the gun."

Hell, it's a Lewis gun, Robert Jordan thought.

"Do you know anything about a machine gun?" he asked the old man.

"*Nada*," said Anselmo. "Nothing."

"And thou?" to the gypsy.

"That they fire with much rapidity and become so hot the barrel burns the hand that touches it," the gypsy said proudly.

"Every one knows that," Anselmo said with contempt.

"Perhaps," the gypsy said. "But he asked me to tell what I know about a *máquina* and I told him." Then he added, "Also, unlike an ordinary rifle, they continue to fire as long as you exert pressure on the trigger."

"Unless they jam, run out of ammunition or get so hot they melt," Robert Jordan said in English.

"What do you say?" Anselmo asked him.

"Nothing," Robert Jordan said. "I was only looking into the future in English."

"That is something truly rare," the gypsy said. "Looking into the future in *Ingles*. Can you read in the palm of the hand?"

"No," Robert Jordan said and he dipped another cup of wine. "But if thou canst I wish thee would read in the palm of my hand and tell me what is going to pass in the next three days."

"The *mujer* of Pablo reads in the hands," the gypsy said. "But she is so irritable and of such a barbarousness that I do not know if she will do it."

Robert Jordan sat up now and took a swallow of the wine.

"Let us see the *mujer* of Pablo now," he said. "If it is that bad let us get it over with."

"I would not disturb her," Rafael said. "She has a strong hatred for me."

"Why?"

"She treats me as a time waster."

"What injustice," Anselmo taunted.

"She is against gypsies."

"What an error," Anselmo said.

"She has gypsy blood," Rafael said. "She knows of what she speaks." He grinned. "But she has a tongue that scalds and that bites like a bull whip. With this tongue she takes the hide from any one. In strips. She is of an unbelievable barbarousness."

"How does she get along with the girl, Maria?" Robert Jordan asked.

"Good. She likes the girl. But let any one come near her seriously—" He shook his head and clucked with his tongue.

"She is very good with the girl," Anselmo said. "She takes good care of her."

"When we picked the girl up at the time of the train she was very strange," Rafael said. "She would not speak and she cried all the time and if any one touched her she would shiver like a wet dog. Only lately has she been better. Lately she has been much better. Today she was fine. Just now, talking to you, she was very good. We would have left her after the train. Certainly it was not worth being delayed by something so sad and ugly and apparently worthless. But the old woman tied a rope to her and when the girl thought she could not go further, the old woman beat her with the end of the rope to make her go. Then when she could not really go further, the old woman carried her over her shoulder. When the old woman could not carry her, I carried her. We were going up that hill breast high in the gorse and heather. And when I could no longer carry her, Pablo carried her. But what the old woman had to say to us to make us do it!" He shook his head at the memory. "It is true that the girl is long in the legs but is not heavy. The bones are light and she weighs little. But she weighs enough when we had to carry her and stop to fire and then carry her again with the old woman lashing at Pablo with the rope and carrying his rifle, putting it in his hand when he would drop the girl, making him pick her up again and loading the gun for him while she cursed him; taking the shells from his pouches and shoving them down into the magazine and cursing him. The dusk was coming well on then and when the night came it was all right. But it was lucky that they had no cavalry."

"It must have been very hard at the train," Anselmo said. "I was not there," he explained to Robert Jordan. "There was the band of Pablo, of El Sordo, whom we will see tonight, and two other bands of these mountains. I had gone to the other side of the lines."

"In addition to the blond one with the rare name—" the gypsy said.

"Kashkin."

"Yes. It is a name I can never dominate. We had two with a machine gun. They were sent also by the army. They could not get the gun away and lost it. Certainly it weighed no more than that girl and if the old woman had been over them they would have gotten it away." He shook his head remembering, then went on. "Never in my life have I seen such a thing as when the explosion was produced. The train was coming steadily. We saw it far away. And I had an excitement so great that I cannot tell it. We saw steam from it and then later came the noise of the whistle. Then it came chu-chu-chu-chu-chu-chu steadily larger and larger and then, at the moment of the explosion, the front wheels of the engine rose up and all of the earth seemed to rise in a great cloud of blackness and a roar and the engine rose high in the cloud of dirt and of the wooden ties rising in the air as in a dream and then it fell onto its side like a great wounded animal and there was an explosion of white steam before the clods of the other explosion had ceased to fall on us and the *máquina* commenced to speak ta-tat-tat-ta!" went the gypsy shaking his two clenched fists up and down in front of him, thumbs up, on an imaginary machine gun. "Ta! Ta! Tat! Tat! Tat! Ta!" he exulted. "Never in my life have I seen such a thing, with the troops running from the train and the *máquina* speaking into them and the men falling. It was then that I put my hand on the *máquina* in my excitement and discovered that the barrel burned and at that moment the old woman slapped me on the side of the face and said, 'Shoot, you fool! Shoot or I will kick your brains in!' Then I commenced to shoot but it was very hard to hold my gun steady and the troops were running up the far hill. Later, after we had been down at the train to see what there was to take, an officer forced some troops back toward us at the point of a pistol. He kept waving the pistol and shouting at them and we were all shooting at him but no one hit him. Then some troops lay down and commenced firing and the officer walked up and down behind them with his pistol and still we could not hit him and the *máquina* could not fire on him because of the position of the train. This officer shot two men as they lay and still they would not get up and he was cursing them and finally they got up, one two and three at a time and came running toward us and the train. Then they lay flat again and fired. Then we left, with the *máquina* still speaking over us as we left. It was then I found the girl where she had run from the train to the rocks and she ran with us. It was those troops who hunted us until that night."

"It must have been something very hard," Anselmo said. "Of much emotion."

"It was the only good thing we have done," said a deep voice. "What are you doing now, you lazy drunken obscene unsayable son of an unnameable unmarried gypsy obscenity? What are you doing?"

Robert Jordan saw a woman of about fifty almost as big as Pablo, almost as wide as she was tall, in black peasant skirt and waist, with heavy wool socks on heavy legs, black rope-soled shoes and a brown face like a model for a granite monument. She had big but nice looking hands and her thick curly black hair was twisted into a knot on her neck.

"Answer me," she said to the gypsy, ignoring the others.

"I was talking to these comrades. This one comes as a dynamiter."

"I know all that," the *mujer* of Pablo said. "Get out of here now and relieve Andrés who is on guard at the top."

"*Me voy*," the gypsy said. "I go." He turned to Robert Jordan. "I will see thee at the hour of eating."

"Not even in a joke," said the woman to him. "Three times you have eaten today according to my count. Go now and send me Andrés.

"*Hola*," she said to Robert Jordan and put out her hand and smiled. "How are you and how is everything in the Republic?"

"Good," he said and returned her strong hand grip. "Both with me and with the Republic."

"I am happy," she told him. She was looking into his face and smiling and he noticed she had fine gray eyes. "Do you come for us to do another train?"

"No," said Robert Jordan, trusting her instantly. "For a bridge."

"No es nada," she said. "A bridge is nothing. When do we do another train now that we have horses?"

"Later. This bridge is of great importance."

"The girl told me your comrade who was with us at the train is dead."

"Yes."

"What a pity. Never have I seen such an explosion. He was a man of talent. He pleased me very much. It is not possible to do another train now? There are many men here now in the hills. Too many. It is already hard to get food. It would be better to get out. And we have horses."

"We have to do this bridge."

"Where is it?"

"Quite close."

"All the better," the *mujer* of Pablo said. "Let us blow all the bridges there are here and get out. I am sick of this place. Here is too much concentration of people. No good can come of it. Here is a stagnation that is repugnant."

She sighted Pablo through the trees.

"Borracho!" she called to him. "Drunkard. Rotten drunkard!" She turned back to Robert Jordan cheerfully. "He's taken a leather wine bottle to drink alone in the woods," she said. "He's drinking all the time. This life is ruining him. Young man, I am very content that you have come." She clapped him on the back. "Ah," she said. "You're bigger than you look," and ran her hand over his shoulder, feeling the muscle under the flannel shirt. "Good. I am very content that you have come."

"And I equally."

"We will understand each other," she said. "Have a cup of wine."

"We have already had some," Robert Jordan said. "But, will you?"

"Not until dinner," she said. "It gives me heartburn." Then she sighted Pablo again. *"Borracho!"* she shouted. "Drunkard!" She turned to Robert Jordan and shook her head. "He was a very good man," she told him. "But now he is terminated. And listen to me about another thing. Be very good and careful about the girl. The Maria. She has had a bad time. Understandest thou?"

"Yes. Why do you say this?"

"I saw how she was from seeing thee when she came into the cave. I saw her watching thee before she came out."

"I joked with her a little."

"She was in a very bad state," the woman of Pablo said. "Now she is better, she ought to get out of here."

"Clearly, she can be sent through the lines with Anselmo."

"You and the Anselmo can take her when this terminates."

Robert Jordan felt the ache in his throat and his voice thickening. "That might be done," he said.

The *mujer* of Pablo looked at him and shook her head. "Ayee. Ayee," she said. "Are all men like that?"

"I said nothing. She is beautiful, you know that."

"No she is not beautiful. But she begins to be beautiful, you mean," the woman of Pablo said. "Men. It is a shame to us women that we make them. No. In seriousness. Are there not homes to care for such as her under the Republic?"

"Yes," said Robert Jordan. "Good places. On the coast near Valencia. In other places too. There they will treat her well and she can work with children. There are the children from evacuated villages. They will teach her the work."

"That is what I want," the *mujer* of Pablo said. "Pablo has a sickness for her already. It is another thing which destroys him. It lies on him like a sickness when he sees her. It is best that she goes now."

"We can take her after this is over."

"And you will be careful of her now if I trust you? I speak to you as though I knew you for a long time."

"It is like that," Robert Jordan said, "when people understand one another."

"Sit down," the woman of Pablo said. "I do not ask any promise because what will happen, will happen. Only if you will *not* take her out, then I ask a promise."

"Why if I would not take her?"

"Because I do not want her crazy here after you will go. I have had her crazy before and I have enough without that."

"We will take her after the bridge," Robert Jordan said. "If we are alive after the bridge, we will take her."

"I do not like to hear you speak in that manner. That manner of speaking never brings luck."

"I spoke in that manner only to make a promise," Robert Jordan said. "I am not of those who speak gloomily."

"Let me see thy hand," the woman said. Robert Jordan put his hand out and the woman opened it, held it in her own big hand, rubbed her thumb over it and looked at it, carefully, then dropped it. She stood up. He got up too and she looked at him without smiling.

"What did you see in it?" Robert Jordan asked her. "I don't believe in it. You won't scare me."

"Nothing," she told him. "I saw nothing in it."

"Yes you did. I am only curious. I do not believe in such things."

"In what do you believe?"

"In many things but not in that."

"In what?"

"In my work."

"Yes, I saw that."

"Tell me what else you saw."

"I saw nothing else," she said bitterly. "The bridge is very difficult you said?"

"No. I said it is very important."

"But it can be difficult?"

"Yes. And now I go down to look at it. How many men have you here?"

"Five that are any good. The gypsy is worthless although his intentions are good. He has a good heart. Pablo I no longer trust."

"How many men has El Sordo that are good?"

"Perhaps eight. We will see tonight. He is coming here. He is a very practical man. He also has some dynamite. Not very much, though. You will speak with him."

"Have you sent for him?"

"He comes every night. He is a neighbor. Also a friend as well as a comrade."

"What do you think of him?"

"He is a very good man. Also very practical. In the business of the train he was enormous."

"And in the other bands?"

"Advising them in time, it should be possible to unite fifty rifles of a certain dependability."

"How dependable?"

"Dependable within the gravity of the situation."

"And how many cartridges per rifle?"

"Perhaps twenty. Depending how many they would bring for this business. If they would come for this business. Remember thee that in this of a bridge there is no money and no loot and in thy reservations of talking, much danger, and that afterwards there must be a moving from these mountains. Many will oppose this of the bridge."

"Clearly."

"In this way it is better not to speak of it unnecessarily."

"I am in accord."

"Then after thou hast studied thy bridge we will talk tonight with El Sordo."

"I go down now with Anselmo."

"Wake him then," she said. "Do you want a carbine?"

"Thank you," he told her. "It is good to have but I will not use it. I go to look, not to make disturbances. Thank you for what you have told me. I like very much your way of speaking."

"I try to speak frankly."

"Then tell me what you saw in the hand."

"No," she said and shook her head. "I saw nothing. Go now to thy bridge. I will look after thy equipment."

"Cover it and that no one should touch it. It is better there than in the cave."

"It shall be covered and no one shall touch it," the woman of Pablo said. "Go now to thy bridge."

"Anselmo," Robert Jordan said, putting his hand on the shoulder of the old man who lay sleeping, his head on his arms.

The old man looked up. "Yes," he said. "Of course. Let us go."

The Butterfly and the Tank

On this evening I was walking home from the censorship office to the Florida Hotel and it was raining. So about halfway home I got sick of the rain and stopped into Chicote's for a quick one. It was the second winter of shelling in the siege of Madrid and everything was short including tobacco and people's tempers and you were a little hungry all the time and would become suddenly and unreasonably irritated at things you could do nothing about such as the weather. I should have gone on home. It was only five blocks more, but when I saw Chicote's doorway I thought I would get a quick one and then do those six blocks up the Gran Via through the mud and rubble of the streets broken by the bombardment.

The place was crowded. You couldn't get near the bar and all the tables were full. It was full of smoke, singing, men in uniform, and the smell of wet leather coats, and they were handing drinks over a crowd that was three deep at the bar.

A waiter I knew found a chair from another table and I sat down with a thin, white-faced, Adam's-appled German I knew who was working at the censorship and two other people I did not know. The table was in the middle of the room a little on your right as you go in.

You couldn't hear yourself talk for the singing and I ordered a gin and angostura and put it down against the rain. The place was really packed and everybody was very jolly; maybe getting just a little bit too jolly from the newly made Catalan liquor most of them were drinking. A couple of people I did not know slapped me on the back and when the girl at our table said something to me, I couldn't hear it and said, "Sure."

She was pretty terrible looking now I had stopped looking around and was looking at our table; really pretty terrible. But it turned out, when the waiter came, that what she had asked me was to have a drink. The fellow with her was not very forceful

657

looking but she was forceful enough for both of them. She had
one of those strong, semi-classical faces and was built like a lion
tamer; and the boy with her looked as though he ought to be wearing an old school tie. He wasn't though. He was wearing a leather
coat just like all the rest of us. Only it wasn't wet because they had
been there since before the rain started. She had on a leather coat
too and it was becoming to the sort of face she had.

By this time I was wishing I had not stopped into Chicote's
but had gone straight on home where you could change your clothes
and be dry and have a drink in comfort on the bed with your feet
up, and I was tired of looking at both of these young people. Life
is very short and ugly women are very long and sitting there at the
table I decided that even though I was a writer and supposed to have
an insatiable curiosity about all sorts of people, I did not really care
to know whether these two were married, or what they saw in each
other, or what their politics were, or whether he had a little money,
or she had a little money, or anything about them. I decided they
must be in the radio. Any time you saw really strange looking
civilians in Madrid they were always in the radio. So to say something I raised my voice above the noise and asked, "You in the
radio?"

"We are," the girl said. So that was that. They were in the
radio.

"How are you comrade?" I said to the German.

"Fine. And you?"

"Wet," I said, and he laughed with his head on one side.

"You haven't got a cigarette?" he asked. I handed him my next
to the last pack of cigarettes and he took two. The forceful girl
took two and the young man with the old school tie face took one.

"Take another," I shouted.

"No thanks," he answered and the German took it instead.

"Do you mind?" he smiled.

"Of course not," I said. I really minded and he knew it. But he
wanted the cigarettes so badly that it did not matter. The singing
had died down momentarily, or there was a break in it as there is
sometimes in a storm, and we could all hear what we said.

"You been here long?" the forceful girl asked me. She pronounced it bean as in bean soup.

"Off and on," I said.

"We must have a serious talk," the German said. "I want to have a talk with you. When can we have it?"

"I'll call you up," I said. This German was a very strange German indeed and none of the good Germans liked him. He lived under the delusion that he could play the piano, but if you kept him away from pianos he was all right unless he was exposed to liquor, or the opportunity to gossip, and nobody had ever been able to keep him away from those two things yet.

Gossip was the best thing he did and he always knew something new and highly discreditable about anyone you could mention in Madrid, Valencia, Barcelona, and other political centers.

Just then the singing really started in again, and you cannot gossip very well shouting, so it looked like a dull afternoon at Chicote's and I decided to leave as soon as I should have bought a round myself.

Just then it started. A civilian in a brown suit, a white shirt, black tie, his hair brushed straight back from a rather high forehead, who had been clowning around from table to table, squirted one of the waiters with a flit gun. Everybody laughed except the waiter who was carrying a tray full of drinks at the time. He was indignant.

"*No hay derecho*," the waiter said. This means, "You have no right to do that," and is the simplest and the strongest protest in Spain.

The flit gun man, delighted with his success, and not seeming to give any importance to the fact that it was well into the second year of the war, that he was in a city under siege where everyone was under a strain, and that he was one of only four men in civilian clothes in the place, now squirted another waiter.

I looked around for a place to duck to. This waiter, also, was indignant and the flit gun man squirted him twice more, lightheartedly. Some people still thought it was funny, including the forceful girl. But the waiter stood, shaking his head. His lips were trembling. He was an old man and he had worked in Chicote's for ten years that I knew of.

"*No hay derecho*," he said with dignity.

People had laughed, however, and the flit gun man, not noticing how the singing had fallen off, squirted his flit gun at the back of a waiter's neck. The waiter turned, holding his tray.

"No hay derecho," he said. This time it was no protest. It was an indictment and I saw three men in uniform start from a table for the flit gun man and the next thing all four of them were going out the revolving door in a rush and you heard a smack when someone hit the flit gun man on the mouth. Somebody else picked up the flit gun and threw it out the door after him.

The three men came back in looking serious, tough and very righteous. Then the door revolved and in came the flit gun man. His hair was down in his eyes, there was blood on his face, his necktie was pulled to one side and his shirt was torn open. He had the flit gun again and as he pushed, wild-eyed and white-faced, into the room he made one general, unaimed, challenging squirt with it, holding it toward the whole company.

I saw one of the three men start for him and I saw this man's face. There were more men with him now and they forced the flit gun man back between two tables on the left of the room as you go in, the flit gun man struggling wildly now, and when the shot went off I grabbed the forceful girl by the arm and dove for the kitchen door.

The kitchen door was shut and when I put my shoulder against it it did not give.

"Get down here behind the angle of the bar," I said. She knelt there.

"Flat," I said and pushed her down. She was furious.

Every man in the room except the German, who lay behind a table, and the public-school-looking boy who stood in a corner drawn up against the wall, had a gun out. On a bench along the wall three over-blonde girls, their hair dark at the roots, were standing on tiptoe to see and screaming steadily.

"I'm not afraid," the forceful one said. "This is ridiculous."

"You don't want to get shot in a café brawl," I said. "If that flit king has any friends here this can be very bad."

But he had no friends, evidently, because people began putting their pistols away and somebody lifted down the blonde screamers and everyone who had started over there when the shot came, drew back away from the flit man who lay, quietly, on his back on the floor.

"No one is to leave until the police come," someone shouted from the door.

Two policemen with rifles, who had come in off the street patrol, were standing by the door and at this announcement I saw six men form up just like the line-up of a football team coming out of a huddle and head out through the door. Three of them were the men who had first thrown the flit king out. One of them was the man who shot him. They went right through the policemen with the rifles like good interference taking out an end and a tackle. And as they went out one of the policemen got his rifle across the door and shouted, "No one can leave. Absolutely no one."

"Why did those men go? Why hold us if anyone's gone?"

"They were mechanics who had to return to their air field," someone said.

"But if anyone's gone it's silly to hold the others."

"Everyone must wait for the Seguridad. Things must be done legally and in order."

"But don't you see that if any person has gone it is silly to hold the others?"

"No one can leave. Everyone must wait."

"It's comic," I said to the forceful girl.

"No it's not. It's simply horrible."

We were standing up now and she was staring indignantly at where the flit king was lying. His arms were spread wide and he had one leg drawn up.

"I'm going over to help that poor wounded man. Why has no one helped him or done anything for him?"

"I'd leave him alone," I said. "You want to keep out of this."

"But it's simply inhuman. I've nurse's training and I'm going to give him first aid."

"I wouldn't," I said. "Don't go near him."

"Why not?" She was very upset and almost hysterical.

"Because he's dead," I said.

When the police came they held everybody there for three hours. They commenced by smelling of all the pistols. In this manner they would detect one which had been fired recently. After about forty pistols they seemed to get bored with this and anyway all you could smell was wet leather coats. Then they sat at a table placed directly behind the late flit king, who lay on the floor looking like a grey wax caricature of himself, with grey wax hands and a grey wax face, and examined people's papers.

With his shirt ripped open you could see the flit king had no undershirt and the soles of his shoes were worn through. He looked very small and pitiful lying there on the floor. You had to step over him to get to the table where two plain clothes policemen sat and examined everyone's identification papers. The husband lost and found his papers several times with nervousness. He had a safe conduct pass somewhere but he had mislaid it in a pocket but he kept on searching and perspiring until he found it. Then he would put it in a different pocket and have to go searching again. He perspired heavily while doing this and it made his hair very curly and his face red. He now looked as though he should have not only an old school tie but one of those little caps boys in the lower forms wear. You have heard how events age people. Well this shooting had made him look about ten years younger.

While we were waiting around I told the forceful girl I thought the whole thing was a pretty good story and that I would write it sometime. The way the six had lined up in single file and rushed that door was very impressive. She was shocked and said that I could not write it because it would be prejudicial to the cause of the Spanish Republic. I said that I had been in Spain for a long time and that they used to have a phenomenal number of shootings in the old days around Valencia under the monarchy, and that for hundreds of years before the Republic people had been cutting each other with large knives called Navajas in Andalucia, and that if I saw a comic shooting in Chicote's during the war I could write about it just as though it had been in New York, Chicago, Key West or Marseilles. It did not have anything to do with politics. She said I shouldn't. Probably a lot of other people will say I shouldn't too. The German seemed to think it was a pretty good story however, and I gave him the last of the Camels. Well, anyway, finally, after about three hours the police said we could go.

They were sort of worried about me at the Florida because in those days, with the shelling, if you started for home on foot and didn't get there after the bars were closed at seven-thirty, people worried. I was glad to get home and I told the story while we were cooking supper on an electric stove and it had quite a success.

Well, it stopped raining during the night, and the next morning it was a fine, bright, cold early winter day and at twelve forty-five I pushed open the revolving doors at Chicote's to try a little gin and tonic before lunch. There were very few people there at that hour and two waiters and the manager came over to the table. They were all smiling.

"Did they catch the murderer?" I asked.

"Don't make jokes so early in the day," the manager said. "Did *you* see him shot?"

"Yes," I told him.

"Me too," he said. "I was just here when it happened." He pointed to a corner table. "He placed the pistol right against the man's chest when he fired."

"How late did they hold people?"

"Oh until past two this morning."

"They only came for the *fiambre*," using the Spanish slang word for corpse, the same used on menus for cold meat, "at eleven o'clock this morning."

"But you don't know about it yet," the manager said.

"No. He doesn't know," a waiter said.

"It is a very rare thing," another waiter said. *"Muy raro."*

"And sad too," the manager said. He shook his head.

"Yes. Sad and curious," the waiter said. "Very sad."

"Tell me."

"It is a very rare thing," the manager said.

"Tell me. Come on tell me."

The manager leaned over the table in great confidence.

"In the flit gun, you know," he said. "He had *eau de cologne*. Poor fellow."

"It was not a joke in such bad taste, you see?" the waiter said.

"It was really just gaiety. No one should have taken offense," the manager said. "Poor fellow."

"I see," I said. "He just wanted everyone to have a good time."

"Yes," said the manager. "It was really just an unfortunate misunderstanding."

"And what about the flit gun?"

"The police took it. They have sent it around to his family."

"I imagine they will be glad to have it," I said.

"Yes," said the manager. "Certainly. A flit gun is always useful."

"Who was he?"

"A cabinet maker."

"Married?"

"Yes, the wife was here with the police this morning."

"What did she say?"

"She dropped down by him and said, 'Pedro, what have they done to thee, Pedro? Who has done this to thee? Oh Pedro.' "

"Then the police had to take her away because she could not control herself," the waiter said.

"It seems he was feeble of the chest," the manager said. "He fought in the first days of the movement. They said he fought in the Sierra but he was too weak in the chest to continue."

"And yesterday afternoon he just went out on the town to cheer things up," I suggested.

"No," said the manager. "You see it is very rare. Everything is *muy raro.* This I learn from the police who are very efficient if given time. They have interrogated comrades from the shop where he worked. This they located from the card of his syndicate which was in his pocket. Yesterday he bought the flit gun and *agua de colonia* to use for a joke at a wedding. He had announced this intention. He bought them across the street. There was a label on the cologne bottle with the address. The bottle was in the washroom. It was there he filled the flit gun. After buying them he must have come in here when the rain started."

"I remember when he came in," a waiter said.

"In the gaiety, with the singing, he became gay too."

"He was gay all right," I said. "He was practically floating around."

The manager kept on with the relentless Spanish logic.

"That is the gaiety of drinking with a weakness of the chest," he said.

"I don't like this story very well," I said.

"Listen," said the manager. "How rare it is. His gaiety comes in contact with the seriousness of the war like a butterfly—"

"Oh very like a butterfly," I said. "Too much like a butterfly."

"I am not joking," said the manager. "You see it? Like a butterfly and a tank."

This pleased him enormously. He was getting into the real Spanish metaphysics.

"Have a drink on the house," he said. "You must write a story about this."

I remembered the flit gun man with his grey wax hands and his grey wax face, his arms spread wide and his legs drawn up and he did look a little like a butterfly; not too much, you know. But he did not look very human either. He reminded me more of a dead sparrow.

"I'll take gin and Schweppes quinine tonic water," I said.

"You must write a story about it," the manager said. "Here. Here's luck."

"Luck," I said. "Look, an English girl last night told me I shouldn't write about it. That it would be very bad for the cause."

"What nonsense," the manager said. "It it very interesting and important, the misunderstood gaiety coming in contact with the deadly seriousness that is here always. To me it is the rarest and most interesting thing which I have seen for some time. You must write it."

"All right," I said. "Sure. Has he any children?"

"No," he said. "I asked the police. But you must write it and you must call it The Butterfly and the Tank."

"All right," I said. "Sure. But I don't like the title much."

"The title is very elegant," the manager said. "It is pure literature."

"All right," I said. "Sure. That's what we'll call it. The Butterfly and the Tank."

And I sat there on that bright cheerful morning, the place smelling clean and newly aired and swept, with the manager who was an old friend and who was now very pleased with the literature we were making together and I took a sip of the gin and tonic water and looked out the sandbagged window and thought of the wife kneeling there and saying, "Pedro. *Pedro, who has done this to thee, Pedro?*" And I thought that the police would never be able to tell her that even if they had the name of the man who pulled the trigger.

Under the Ridge

In the heat of the day with the dust blowing, we came back, dry-mouthed, nose-clogged and heavy-loaded, down out of the battle to the long ridge above the river where the Spanish troops lay in reserve.

I sat down with my back against the shallow trench, my shoulders and the back of my head against the earth, clear now from even stray bullets, and looked at what lay below us in the hollow. There was the tank reserve, the tanks covered with branches chopped from olive trees. To their left were the staff cars, mud-daubed and branch-covered, and between the two a long line of men carrying stretchers wound down through the gap to where, on the flat at the foot of the ridge, ambulances were loading. Commissary mules loaded with sacks of bread and kegs of wine, and a train of ammunition mules, led by their drivers, were coming up the gap in the ridge, and men with empty stretchers were walking slowly up the trail with the mules.

To the right, below the curve of the ridge, I could see the entrance to the cave where the brigade staff was working, and their signaling wires ran out of the top of the cave and curved on over the ridge in the shelter of which we lay.

Motorcyclists in leather suits and helmets came up and down the cut on their cycles or, where it was too steep, walking them, and leaving them beside the cut, walked over to the entrance to the cave and ducked inside. As I watched, a big Hungarian cyclist that I knew came out of the cave, tucked some papers in his leather wallet, walked over to his motorcycle and, pushing it up through the stream of mules and stretcher-bearers, threw a leg over the saddle and roared on over the ridge, his machine churning a storm of dust.

Below, across the flat where the ambulances were coming and going, was the green foliage that marked the line of the river. There was a large house with a red tile roof and there was a gray stone mill, and from the trees around the big house beyond the river came the flashes of our guns. They were firing straight at us and there were the twin flashes, then the throaty, short *bung-bung* of the three-inch pieces and then the rising cry of the shells coming toward us and going on over our heads. As always, we were short of artillery. There were only four batteries down there, when there should have been forty, and they were firing only two guns at a time. The attack had failed before we came down.

"Are you Russians?" a Spanish soldier asked me.

"No, Americans," I said. "Have you any water?"

"Yes, comrade." He handed over a pigskin bag. These troops in reserve were soldiers only in name and from the fact that they were in uniform. They were not intended to be used in the attack, and they sprawled along this line under the crest of the ridge, huddled in groups, eating, drinking and talking, or simply sitting dumbly, waiting. The attack was being made by an International Brigade.

We both drank. The water tasted of asphalt and pig bristles.

"Wine is better," the soldier said. "I will get wine."

"Yes. But for the thirst, water."

"There is no thirst like the thirst of battle. Even here, in reserve, I have much thirst."

"That is fear," said another soldier. "Thirst is fear."

"No," said another. "With fear there is thirst, always. But in battle there is much thirst even when there is no fear."

"There is always fear in battle," said the first soldier.

"For you," said the second soldier.

"It is normal," the first soldier said.

"For you."

"Shut your dirty mouth," said the first soldier. "I am simply a man who tells the truth."

It was a bright April day and the wind was blowing wildly so that each mule that came up the gap raised a cloud of dust, and the two men at the ends of a stretcher each raised a cloud of dust that blew together and made one, and below, across the flat, long streams of dust moved out from the ambulances and blew away in the wind.

I felt quite sure I was not going to be killed on that day now, since we had done our work well in the morning, and twice during the early part of the attack we should have been killed and were not; and this had given me confidence. The first time had been when we had gone up with the tanks and picked a place from which to film the attack. Later I had a sudden distrust for the place and we had moved the cameras about two hundred yards to the left. Just before leaving, I had marked the place in quite the oldest way there is of marking a place, and within ten minutes a six-inch shell had lit on the exact place where I had been and there was no trace of any human being ever having been there. Instead, there was a large and clearly blasted hole in the earth.

Then, two hours later, a Polish officer, recently detached from the battalion and attached to the staff, had offered to show us the positions the Poles had just captured and, coming from under the lee of a fold of hill, we had walked into machine-gun fire that we had to crawl out from under with our chins tight to the ground and dust in our noses, and at the same time made the sad discovery that the Poles had captured no positions at all that day but were a little further back than the place they had started from. And now, lying in the shelter of the trench, I was wet with sweat, hungry and thirsty and hollow inside from the now-finished danger of the attack.

"You are sure you are not Russians?" asked a soldier. "There are Russians here today."

"Yes. But we are not Russians."

"You have the face of a Russian."

"No," I said. "You are wrong, comrade. I have quite a funny face but it is not the face of a Russian."

"He has the face of a Russian," pointing at the other one of us who was working on a camera.

"Perhaps. But still he is not Russian. Where you from?"

"Extremadura," he said proudly.

"Are there any Russians in Extremadura?" I asked.

"No," he told me, even more proudly. "There are no Russians in Extremadura, and there are no Extremadurans in Russia."

"What are your politics?"

"I hate all foreigners," he said.

"That's a broad political program."

"I hate the Moors, the English, the French, the Italians, the Germans, the North Americans and the Russians."

"You hate them in that order?"

"Yes. But perhaps I hate the Russians the most."

"Man, you have very interesting ideas," I said. "Are you a Fascist?"

"No. I am an Extremaduran and I hate foreigners."

"He has very rare ideas," said another soldier. "Do not give him too much importance. Me, I like foreigners. I am from Valencia. Take another cup of wine, please."

I reached up and took the cup, the other wine still brassy in my mouth. I looked at the Extremaduran. He was tall and thin. His face was haggard and unshaven, and his cheeks were sunken. He stood straight up in his rage, his blanket cape around his shoulders.

"Keep your head down," I told him. "There are many lost bullets coming over."

"I have no fear of bullets and I hate all foreigners," he said fiercely.

"You don't have to fear bullets," I said, "but you should avoid them when you are in reserve. It is not intelligent to be wounded when it can be avoided."

"I am not afraid of anything," the Extremaduran said.

"You are very lucky, comrade."

"It's true," the other, with the wine cup, said. "He has no fear, not even of the *aviones*."

"He is crazy," another soldier said. "Everyone fears planes. They kill little but make much fear."

"I have no fear. Neither of planes nor of nothing," the Extremaduran said. "And I hate every foreigner alive."

Down the gap, walking beside two stretcher-bearers and seeming to pay no attention at all to where he was, came a tall man in International Brigade uniform with a blanket rolled over his shoulder and tied at his waist. His head was held high and he looked like a man walking in his sleep. He was middle-aged. He was not carrying a rifle and, from where I lay, he did not look wounded.

I watched him walking alone down out of the war. Before he

came to the staff cars he turned to the left and his head still held
high in that strange way, he walked over the edge of the ridge and
out of sight.

The one who was with me, busy changing film in the hand
cameras, had not noticed him.

A single shell came in over the ridge and fountained in dirt
and black smoke just short of the tank reserve.

Someone put his head out of the cave where Brigade headquarters was and then disappeared inside. I thought it looked like
a good place to go, but knew they would all be furious in there because the attack was a failure, and I did not want to face them.
If an operation was successful they were happy to have motion
pictures of it. But if it was a failure everyone was in such a rage
there was always a chance of being sent back under arrest.

"They may shell us now," I said.

"That makes no difference to me," said the Extremaduran. I
was beginning to be a little tired of the Extremaduran.

"Have you any more wine to spare?" I asked. My mouth was
still dry.

"Yes, man. There are gallons of it," the friendly soldier said.
He was short, big-fisted and very dirty, with a stubble of beard about
the same length as the hair on his cropped head. "Do you think they
will shell us now?"

"They should," I said. "But in this war you can never tell."

"What is the matter with this war?" asked the Extremaduran
angrily. "Don't you like this war?"

"Shut up!" said the friendly soldier. "I command here, and
these comrades are our guests."

"Then let him not talk against our war," said the Extremaduran.
"No foreigners shall come here and talk against our war."

"What town are you from, comrade?" I asked the Extremaduran.

"Badajoz," he said. "I am from Badajoz. In Badajoz, we have
been sacked and pillaged and our women violated by the English, the French and now the Moors. What the Moors have done
now is no worse than what the English did under Wellington. You
should read history. My great-grandmother was killed by the English. The house where my family lived was burned by the English."

"I regret it," I said. "Why do you hate the North Americans?"

"My father was killed by the North Americans in Cuba while he was there as a conscript."

"I am sorry for that, too. Truly sorry. Believe me. And why do you hate the Russians?"

"Because they are the representatives of tyranny and I hate their faces. You have the face of a Russian."

"Maybe we better get out of here," I said to the one who was with me and who did not speak Spanish. "It seems I have the face of a Russian and it's getting me into trouble."

"I'm going to sleep," he said. "This is a good place. Don't talk so much and you won't get into trouble."

"There's a comrade here that doesn't like me. I think he's an anarchist."

"Well, watch out he doesn't shoot you, then. I'm going to sleep."

Just then two men in leather coats, one short and stocky, the other of medium height, both with civilian caps, flat, high-cheek-boned faces, wooden-holstered Mauser pistols strapped to their legs, came out of the gap and headed toward us.

The taller of them spoke to me in French. "Have you seen a French comrade pass through here?" he asked. "A comrade with a blanket tied around his shoulders in the form of a bandoleer? A comrade of about forty-five or fifty years old? Have you seen such a comrade going in the direction away from the front?"

"No," I said. "I have not seen such a comrade."

He looked at me a moment and I noticed his eyes were a grayish-yellow and that they did not blink at all.

"Thank you, comrade," he said, in his odd French, and then spoke rapidly to the other man with him in a language I did not understand. They went off and climbed the highest part of the ridge, from where they could see down all the gullies.

"There is the true face of Russians," the Extremaduran said.

"Shut up!" I said. I was watching the two men in the leather coats. They were standing there, under considerable fire, looking carefully over all the broken country below the ridge and toward the river.

Suddenly one of them saw what he was looking for, and pointed. Then the two started to run like hunting dogs, one straight down over the ridge, the other at an angle as though to cut someone off. Before the second one went over the crest I could see him drawing his pistol and holding it ahead of him as he ran.

"And how do you like that?" asked the Extremaduran.

"No better than you," I said.

Over the crest of the parallel ridge I heard the Mausers' jerky barking. They kept it up for more than a dozen shots. They must have opened fire at too long a range. After all the burst of shooting there was a pause and then a single shot.

The Extremaduran looked at me sullenly and said nothing. I thought it would be simpler if the shelling started. But it did not start.

The two in the leather coats and civilian caps came back over the ridge, walking together, and then down to the gap, walking downhill with that odd bent-kneed way of the two-legged animal coming down a steep slope. They turned up the gap as a tank came whirring and clanking down and moved to one side to let it pass.

The tanks had failed again that day, and the drivers coming down from the lines in their leather helmets, the tank turrets open now as they came into the shelter of the ridge, had the straight-ahead stare of football players who have been removed from a game for yellowness.

The two flat-faced men in the leather coats stood by us on the ridge to let the tank pass.

"Did you find the comrade you were looking for?" I asked the taller one of them in French.

"Yes, comrade. Thank you," he said and looked me over very carefully.

"What does he say?" the Extremaduran asked.

"He says they found the comrade they were looking for," I told him. The Extremaduran said nothing.

We had been all that morning in the place the middle-aged Frenchman had walked out of. We had been there in the dust, the smoke, the noise, the receiving of wounds, the death, the fear of death, the bravery, the cowardice, the insanity and failure of an unsuccessful attack. We had been there on that plowed field men could not cross and live. You dropped and lay flat; making a mound to shield your head; working your chin into the dirt; waiting for the order to go up that slope no man could go up and live.

We had been with those who lay there waiting for the tanks

that did not come; waiting under the inrushing shriek and roaring crash of the shelling; the metal and the earth thrown like clods from a dirt fountain; and overhead the cracking, whispering fire like a curtain. We knew how those felt, waiting. They were as far forward as they could get. And men could not move further and live, when the order came to move ahead.

We had been there all morning in the place the middle-aged Frenchman had come walking away from. I understood how a man might suddenly, seeing clearly the stupidity of dying in an unsuccessful attack; or suddenly seeing it clearly, as you can see clearly and justly before you die; seeing its hopelessness, seeing its idiocy, seeing how it really was, simply get back and walk away from it as the Frenchman had done. He could walk out of it not from cowardice, but simply from seeing too clearly; knowing suddenly that he had to leave it; knowing there was no other thing to do.

The Frenchman had come walking out of the attack with great dignity and I understood him as a man. But, as a soldier, these other men who policed the battle had hunted him down, and the death he had walked away from had found him when he was just over the ridge, clear of the bullets and the shelling, and walking toward the river.

"And that," the Extremaduran said to me, nodding toward the battle police.

"Is war," I said. "In war, it is necessary to have discipline."

"And to live under that sort of discipline we should die?"

"Without discipline everyone will die anyway."

"There is one kind of discipline and another kind of discipline," the Extremaduran said. "Listen to me. In February we were here where we are now and the Fascists attacked. They drove us from the hills that you Internationals tried to take today and that you could not take. We fell back to here; to this ridge. Internationals came up and took the line ahead of us."

"I know that," I said.

"But you do not know this," he went on angrily. "There was a boy from my province who became frightened during the bombardment, and he shot himself in the hand so that he could leave the line because he was afraid."

The other soldiers were all listening now. Several nodded.

"Such people have their wounds dressed and are returned at once to the line," the Extremaduran went on. "It is just."

"Yes," I said. "That is as it should be."

"That is as it should be," said the Extremaduran. "But this boy shot himself so badly that the bone was all smashed and there surged up an infection and his hand was amputated."

Several soldiers nodded.

"Go on, tell him the rest," said one.

"It might be better not to speak of it," said the cropped-headed, bristly-faced man who said he was in command.

"It is my duty to speak," the Extremaduran said.

The one in command shrugged his shoulders. "I did not like it either," he said. "Go on, then. But I do not like to hear it spoken of either."

"This boy remained in the hospital in the valley since February," the Extremaduran said. "Some of us have seen him in the hospital. All say he was well liked in the hospital and made himself as useful as a man with one hand can be useful. Never was he under arrest. Never was there anything to prepare him."

The man in command handed me the cup of wine again without saying anything. They were all listening; as men who cannot read or write listen to a story.

"Yesterday, at the close of day, before we knew there was to be an attack. Yesterday, before the sun set, when we thought today was to be as any other day, they brought him up the trail in the gap there from the flat. We were cooking the evening meal and they brought him up. There were only four of them. Him, the boy Paco, those two you have just seen in the leather coats and the caps, and an officer from the Brigade. We saw the four of them climbing together up the gap, and we saw Paco's hands were not tied, nor was he bound in any way.

"When we saw him we all crowded around and said, 'Hello, Paco. How are you, Paco? How is everything, Paco, old boy, old Paco?'

"Then he said, 'Everything's all right. Everything is good except this'—and showed us the stump.

"Paco said, 'That was a cowardly and foolish thing. I am sorry that I did that thing. But I try to be useful with one hand. I will do what I can with one hand for the Cause.' "

"Yes," interrupted a soldier. "He said that. I heard him say that."

"We spoke with him," the Extremaduran said. "And he spoke with us. When such people with the leather coats and the pistols come it is always a bad omen in a war, as is the arrival of people with map cases and field glasses. Still we thought they had brought him for a visit, and all of us who had not been to the hospital were happy to see him, and as I say, it was the hour of the evening meal and the evening was clear and warm."

"This wind only rose during the night," a soldier said.

"Then," the Extremaduran went on somberly, "one of *them* said to the officer in Spanish, 'Where is the place?'

" 'Where is the place this Paco was wounded?' asked the officer."

"I answered him," said the man in command. "I showed the place. It is a little further down than where you are."

"Here is the place," said a soldier. He pointed, and I could see it was the place. It showed clearly that it was the place.

"Then one of them led Paco by the arm to the place and held him there by the arm while the other spoke in Spanish. He spoke in Spanish, making many mistakes in the language. At first we wanted to laugh, and Paco started to smile. I could not understand all the speech, but it was that Paco must be punished as an example, in order that there would be no more self-inflicted wounds, and that all others would be punished in the same way.

"Then, while the one held Paco by the arm; Paco, looking very ashamed to be spoken of this way when he was already ashamed and sorry; the other took his pistol out and shot Paco in the back of the head without any word to Paco. Nor any word more."

The soldiers all nodded.

"It was thus," said one. "You can see the place. He fell with his mouth there. You can see it."

I had seen the place clearly enough from where I lay.

"He had no warning and no chance to prepare himself," the one in command said. "It was very brutal."

"It is for this that I now hate Russians as well as all other foreigners," said the Extremaduran. "We can give ourselves no illusions about foreigners. If you are a foreigner, I am sorry. But for myself, now, I can make no exceptions. You have eaten bread and drunk wine with us. Now I think you should go."

"Do not speak in that way," the man in command said to the Extremaduran. "It is necessary to be formal."

"I think we had better go," I said.

"You are not angry?" the man in command said. "You can stay in this shelter as long as you wish. Are you thirsty? Do you wish more wine?"

"Thank you very much," I said. "I think we had better go."

"You understand my hatred?" asked the Extremaduran.

"I understand your hatred," I said.

"Good," he said and put out his hand. "I do not refuse to shake hands. And that you, personally, have much luck."

"Equally to you," I said. "Personally, and as a Spaniard."

I woke the one who took the pictures and we started down the ridge toward Brigade headquarters. The tanks were all coming back now and you could hardly hear yourself talk for the noise.

"Were you talking all that time?"

"Listening."

"Hear anything interesting?"

"Plenty."

"What do you want to do now?"

"Get back to Madrid."

"We should see the General."

"Yes," I said. "We must."

The General was coldly furious. He had been ordered to make the attack as a surprise with one brigade only, bringing everything up before daylight. It should have been made by at least a division. He had used three battalions and held one in reserve. The French tank commander had got drunk to be brave for the attack and finally was too drunk to function. He was to be shot when he sobered up.

The tanks had not come up in time and finally had refused to advance, and two of the battalions had failed to attain their objectives. The third had taken theirs, but it formed an untenable salient. The only real result had been a few prisoners, and these had been confided to the tank men to bring back and the tank men had killed them. The General had only failure to show, and they had killed his prisoners.

"What can I write on it?" I asked.

"Nothing that is not in the official communiqué. Have you any whisky in that long flask?"

"Yes."

He took a drink and licked his lips carefully. He had once been a captain of Hungarian Hussars, and he had once captured a gold train in Siberia when he was a leader of irregular cavalry with the Red Army and held it all one winter when the thermometer went down to forty below zero. We were good friends and he loved whisky, and he is now dead.

"Get out of here now," he said. "Have you transport?"

"Yes."

"Did you get any pictures?"

"Some. The tanks."

"The tanks," he said bitterly. "The swine. The cowards. Watch out you don't get killed," he said. "You are supposed to be a writer."

"I can't write now."

"Write it afterwards. You can write it all afterwards. And don't get killed. Especially, don't get killed. Now, get out of here."

He could not take his own advice because he was killed two months later. But the oddest thing about that day was how marvelously the pictures we took of the tanks came out. On the screen they advanced over the hill irresistibly, mounting the crests like great ships, to crawl clanking on toward the illusion of victory we screened.

The nearest any man was to victory that day was probably the Frenchman who came, with his head held high, walking out of the battle. But his victory only lasted until he had walked halfway down the ridge. We saw him lying stretched out there on the slope of the ridge, still wearing his blanket, as we came walking down the cut to get into the staff car that would take us to Madrid.

❀ PART VI ❀

ON THE WATER

From BY-LINE: ERNEST HEMINGWAY
The Great Blue River

THE OLD MAN AND THE SEA

ISLANDS IN THE STREAM (PART III)

The Great Blue River

(*Holiday*—JULY 1949)

PEOPLE ask you why you live in Cuba and you say it is because you like it. It is too complicated to explain about the early morning in the hills above Havana where every morning is cool and fresh on the hottest day in summer. There is no need to tell them that one reason you live there is because you can raise your own fighting cocks, train them on the place, and fight them anywhere that you can match them and that this is all legal.

Maybe they do not like cockfighting anyway.

You do not tell them about the strange and lovely birds that are on the farm the year around, nor about all the migratory birds that come through, nor that quail come in the early mornings to drink at the swimming pool, nor about the different types of lizards that live and hunt in the thatched arbor at the end of the pool, nor the eighteen different kinds of mangoes that grow on the long slope up to the house. You do not try to explain about our ball team— hardball, not softball—where, if you are over forty, you can have a boy run for you and still stay in the game, nor which are the boys in our town that are really the fastest on the base paths.

You do not tell them about the shooting club just down the road, where we used to shoot the big live-pigeon matches for the large money, with Winston Guest, Tommy Shevlin, Thorwald Sanchez and Pichon Aguilera, and where we used to shoot matches against the Brooklyn Dodgers when they had fine shots like Curt Davis, Billy Herman, Augie Galan and Hugh Casey. Maybe they think live-pigeon shooting is wrong. Queen Victoria did and barred it in England. Maybe they are right. Maybe it is wrong. It certainly is a miserable spectator sport. But with strong, really fast birds it is still the best participant sport for betting I know; and where we live it is legal.

You could tell them that you live in Cuba because you only have to put shoes on when you come into town, and that you can plug the bell in the party-line telephone with paper so that you won't have to answer, and that you work as well there in those cool early mornings as you ever have worked anywhere in the world. But those are professional secrets.

There are many other things you do not tell them. But when they talk to you about salmon fishing and what it costs them to fish the Restigouche, then, if they have not talked too much about how much it costs, and have talked well, or lovingly, about the salmon fishing, you tell them the biggest reason you live in Cuba is the great, deep blue river, three quarters of a mile to a mile deep and sixty to eighty miles across, that you can reach in thirty minutes from the door of your farmhouse, riding through beautiful country to get to it, that has, when the river is right, the finest fishing I have ever known.

When the Gulf Stream is running well, it is a dark blue and there are whirlpools along the edges. We fish in a forty-foot cabin cruiser with a flying bridge equipped with topside controls, oversize outriggers big enough to skip a ten-pound bait in summer, and we fish four rods.

Sometimes we keep Pilar, the fishing boat, in Havana harbor, sometimes in Cojimar, a fishing village seven miles east of Havana, with a harbor that is safe in summer and imminently unsafe in winter when there are northers or nor'westers. Pilar was built to be a fishing machine that would be a good sea boat in the heaviest kind of weather, have a minimum cruising range of five hundred miles, and sleep seven people. She carries three hundred gallons of gasoline in her tanks and one hundred and fifty gallons of water. On a long trip she can carry another hundred gallons of gas in small drums in her forward cockpit and the same extra amount of water in demijohns. She carries, when loaded full, 2400 pounds of ice.

Wheeler Shipyard, of New York, built her hull and modified it to our specifications, and we have made various changes in her since. She is a really sturdy boat, sweet in any kind of sea, and she has a very low-cut stern with a large wooden roller to bring big fish over. The flying bridge is so sturdy and so reinforced below you can fight fish from the top of the house.

Ordinarily, fishing out of Havana, we get a line out with a Japanese feather squid and a strip of pork rind on the hook, while we are still running out of the harbor. This is for tarpon, which feed around the fishing smacks anchored along the Morro Castle-Cabañas side of the channel, and for kingfish, which are often in the mouth of the main ship channel and over the bar, where the bottom fishermen catch snappers just outside the Morro.

This bait is fished on a twelve-foot No. 10 piano-wire leader from a 6/0 reel, full of fifteen-thread line and from a nine-ounce Tycoon tip. The biggest tarpon I ever caught with this rig weighed 135 pounds. We have hooked some that were much bigger but lost them to outgoing or incoming ships, to port launches, to bumboats and to the anchor chains of the fishing smacks. You can plead with or threaten launches and bumboats when you have a big fish on and they are headed so that they will cut him off. But there is nothing you can do when a big tanker, or a cargo ship, or a liner is coming down the channel. So we usually put out this line when we can see the channel is clear and nothing is coming out; or after seven o'clock in the evening when ships will usually not be entering the harbor due to the extra port charges made after that hour.

Coming out of the harbor I will be on the flying bridge steering and watching the traffic and the line that is fishing the feather astern. As you go out, seeing friends along the water front—lottery-ticket sellers you have known for years, policemen you have given fish to and who have done favors in their turn, bumboatmen who lose their earnings standing shoulder to shoulder with you in the betting pit at the jai-alai fronton, and friends passing in motorcars along the harbor and ocean boulevard who wave and you wave to but cannot recognize at that distance, although they can see the Pilar and you on her flying bridge quite clearly—your feather jig is fishing all the time.

Behind the boulevards are the parks and buildings of old Havana and on the other side you are passing the steep slopes and walls of the fortress of Cabañas, the stone weathered pink and yellow, where most of your friends have been political prisoners at one time or another; and then you pass the rocky headland of the Morro, with O'Donnell, 1844, on the tall white light tower and then, two hundred yards beyond the Morro, when the stream is running well, is the great river.

Sometimes as you leave the gray-green harbor water and Pilar's bows dip into the dark blue water a covey of flying fish will rise from under her bows and you will hear the slithering, silk-tearing noise they make when they leave the water.

If they are the usual size flying fish it does not mean so much as a sign, unless you see a man-of-war hawk working, dipping down after them if they go up again; but if they are the big three-pound, black-winged Bahian flyers that come out of the water as though they were shot out, and at the end of their soaring flight drop their tails to give the flight a new impulse and fly again and again, then it is a very good sign. Seeing the big Bahian flyers is as sure a sign as any, except seeing fish themselves.

By now, Gregorio, the mate, has gotten the meat line out. The meat line is a new trick that I'll tell about later because once it is out, and he wants to get it out fast to cover this patch of bottom before we get outside of the hundred-fathom curve, he must get outrigger baits out, since marlin will come in over this bottom any time the stream is running and the water is blue and clear.

Gregorio Fuentes has been mate on Pilar since 1938. He is fifty years old this summer and went to sea in sail from Lanzarote, one of the smaller Canary Islands, when he was four. I met him at Dry Tortugas when he was captain of a fishing smack and we were both stormbound there in a very heavy northeast gale in 1928. We went on board his smack to get some onions. We wanted to buy the onions, but he gave them to us, and some rum as well, and I remember thinking he had the cleanest ship that I had ever seen. Now after ten years I know that he would rather keep a ship clean, and paint and varnish, than he would fish. But I know, too, that he would rather fish than eat or sleep.

We had a great mate before Gregorio, named Carlos Gutierrez, but someone hired him away from me when I was away at the Spanish Civil War. It was wonderful luck to find Gregorio, and his seamanship has saved Pilar in three hurricanes. So far, knocking on wood, we have never had to put in a claim on the all-risk marine insurance policy carried on her; and Gregorio was the only man to stay on board a small craft in the October, 1944, hurricane when it blew 180 mph true, and small craft and Navy vessels were blown up onto the harbor boulevard and up onto the small hills around the harbor. He also rode out the 1948 hurricane on her.

By now, as you have cleared the harbor, Gregorio has the meat line out and is getting the outrigger baits out and, it being a good day, you are getting flying fish up and pushing to the eastward into the breeze. The first marlin you see can show within ten minutes of leaving your moorings, and so close to the Morro that you can still see the curtains on the light.

He may come behind the big, white wooden teaser that is zig-zagging and diving between the two inside lines. He may show behind an outrigger bait that is bouncing and jumping over the water. Or he may come racing from the side, slicing a wake through the dark water, as he comes for the feather.

When you see him from the flying bridge he will look first brown and then dark purple as he rises in the water, and his pectoral fins, spread wide as he comes to feed, will be a light lavender color and look like widespread wings as he drives just under the surface. He will look, in the sea, more like a huge submarine bird than a fish.

Gregorio, if he sees him first will shout, "Feesh! Feesh, Papa, feesh!"

If you see him first you leave the wheel, or turn it over to Mary, your wife, and go to the stern end of the house and say "Feesh" as calmly as possible to Gregorio, who has always seen him by then, too, and you lean over and he hands you up the rod the marlin is coming for, or, if he is after the teaser, he hands you up the rod with the feather and pork rind on.

All right, he is after the teaser and you are racing-in the feather. Gregorio is keeping the teaser, a tapering, cylindrical piece of wood two feet long, with a curve cut in its head that makes it dive and dance when towed, away from the marlin. The marlin is rushing it and trying to grab it. His bill comes out of water as he drives toward it. But Gregorio keeps it just out of his reach. If he pulled it all the way in, the fish might go down. So he is playing him as a bullfighter might play a bull, keeping the lure just out of his range, and yet never denying it to him, while you race-in the feather.

Mary is saying, "Isn't he beautiful? Oh, Papa, look at his stripes and that color and the color of his wings. Look at him!"

"I'm looking at him," you say, and you have the feather now abreast of the teaser, and Gregorio sees it and flicks the teaser clear, and the marlin sees the feather. The big thing that he chased, and that looked and acted like a crippled fish, is gone. But here is a squid, his favorite food, instead.

The marlin's bill comes clear out of water as he hits the feather and you see his open mouth and, as he hits it, you lower the rod that you have held as high as you could, so the feather goes out of sight into his mouth. You see it go in, and the mouth shuts and you see him turn, shining silver, his stripes showing as he turns.

As he turns his head you hit him, striking hard, hard and hard again, to set the hook. Then, if he starts to run instead of jumping, you hit him three or four times more to make sure, because he might just be holding feather, hook and all, tight in his jaws and running away with it, still unhooked. Then he feels the hook and jumps clear. He will jump straight up all clear of the water, shaking himself. He will jump straight and stiff as a beaked bar of silver. He will jump high and long, shedding drops of water as he comes out, and making a splash like a shell hitting when he enters the water again. And he will jump, and jump, and jump, sometimes on one side of the boat, then crossing to the other so fast you see the belly of the line whipping through the water, fast as a racing ski turn.

Sometimes he will get the leader over his shoulder (the hump on his back behind his head) and go off greyhounding over the water, jumping continuously and with such an advantage in pull, with the line in that position, that you cannot stop him, and so Mary has to back Pilar fast and then turn, gunning both motors, to chase him.

You lose plenty of line making the turn to chase him. But he is jumping against the friction of the belly of the line in the water which keeps it taut, and when, reeling, you recover that belly and have the fish now broadside, then astern again, you have control of him once more. He will sound now and circle, and then you will gradually work him closer and closer and then in to where Gregorio can gaff him, club him and take him on board.

That is the way it should go ideally; he should sound, circle, and you should work him gradually alongside or on either quarter of the stern, and then gaff him, club him and bring him on board. But it doesn't always go that way. Sometimes when he gets up to the boat he will start the whole thing all over again and head out for the northwest, jumping again as fresh, seemingly, as when he was first hooked, and you have to chase him again.

Sometimes, if he is a big striped marlin, you will get him within thirty feet of the boat and he will come no farther, swimming, with his wings spread, at whatever speed and direction you elect to move. If you don't move, he will be up and under the boat. If you move away from him, he will stay there, refusing to come in one inch, as strong a fish for his weight as any in the world and as stubborn.

(Bonefish angler, on your way! You never saw a bonefish in mile-deep water, nor up against the tackle striped marlin have to face sometimes. Nor did you know how your bonefish would act after he had jumped forty-three times clean out of water. Your bone-fish is a smart fish, very conservative, very strong too. Too smart by far to jump, even if he could. I do not think he can, myself. And the only nonjumping fish that has a patent of nobility in our books is the wahoo. He *can* jump, too, if he wants to. He will do it some-times when he takes the bait. Also, bonefish angler, your fish might be as fat and as short of wind, at four hundred pounds, as some of the overstuffed Nova Scotia tuna are. But do not shoot, bonefish angler; at four hundred pounds, your fish might be the strongest thing in the sea, the strongest fish that ever lived; so strong no one would ever want to hook into one. But tell me confidentially: would he jump . . . ? Thank you very much. I thought not.)

This dissertation has not helped you any if you have a strong, male, striped marlin on and he decides he won't be lifted any closer. Of course you could loosen up the drag and work away from him and wear him out that way. But that is the way sharks get fish. We like to fight them close to the boat and take them while they are still strong. We will gaff an absolutely green fish, one that has not been tired at all, if by any fluke we can get him close enough.

Since 1931, when I learned that was how to keep fish from being hit by sharks, I have never lost a marlin nor a tuna to a shark, no matter how shark-infested the waters fished. We try to fight them fast, but never rough. The secret is for the angler never to rest. Any time he rests the fish is resting. That gives the fish a chance to get strong again, or to get down to a greater depth; and the odds lengthen that something may close in on him.

So now, say, you have this marlin down thirty feet, pulling as strong as a horse. All you have to do is stay with him. Play him just this side of breaking strain, but do it softly. Never jerk on him. Jerking will only hurt him or anger him. Either or both will make him pull harder. He is as strong as a horse. Treat him like a horse.

Keep your maximum possible strain on him and you will convince him and bring him in. Then you gaff him, club him for kindness and for safety, and bring him on board.

You do not have to kill a horse to break him. You have to convince him, and that is what you have to do with a truly strong, big fish after the first jumps, which correspond to a wild horse's bucking, are over. To do this, you have to be in good condition.

There is tackle made now, and there are fishing guides expert in ways of cheating with it, by which anybody who can walk up three flights of stairs, carrying a quart bottle of milk in each hand, can catch game fish over five hundred pounds without even having to sweat much.

There is old-fashioned tackle with which you can catch really big fish in short time, thus ensuring they will not be attacked by sharks. But you have to be a fisherman or, at least, in very good shape to use it. But this is the tackle that will give you the greatest amount of sport with the smaller and medium-sized marlin. You don't need to be an athlete to use it. You ought to be in good condition. If you are not, two or three fish will put you in condition. Or they may make you decide marlin fishing in the Gulf Stream is not your sport.

In almost any other sport requiring strength and skill to play or practice, those practicing the sport expect to know how to play it, to have at least moderate ability and to be in some sort of condition. In big-game fishing they will come on board in ghastly shape, incapable of reeling in 500 yards of line, simply line, with no question of there being a fish on it, and yet full of confidence that they can catch a fish weighing twice or three times their weight.

They are confident because it has been done. But it was never done honestly, to my knowledge, by completely inexperienced and untrained anglers, without physical assistance from the guides, mates and boatmen, until the present winch reels, unbreakable rods and other techniques were invented which made it possible for any angler, no matter how incompetent, to catch big fish if he could hold and turn the handle of a winch.

The International Game Fish Association, under the auspices of the American Museum of Natural History, has tried to set a standard of sporting fishing and to recognize records of fish taken honestly and sportingly according to these standards. It has had considerable success in these and other fields. But as long as charter boats are extremely expensive, and both guides and their anglers want results above everything else, big-game fishing will be closer to total war against big fish than to sport. Of course, it could never be considered an equal contest unless the angler had a hook in his mouth, as well as the fish. But insistence on that might discourage the sporting fishermen entirely.

Education as to what makes a big fish legitimately caught has been slow, but it has progressed steadily. Very few guides or anglers shoot or harpoon hooked fish any more. Nor is the flying gaff much used.

The use of wire line, our meat line, is a deadly way of fishing, and no fish caught that way could possibly be entered as a sporting record. But we use it as a way of finding out at what depths fish are when they are not on the surface. It is a scientific experiment, the results are carefully noted, and what it catches are classed in our books as fish caught commercially. Its carefully recorded results will surely provide valuable information for the commercial fisherman, and its use is justified for that end. It is also a very rough, tough, punishing way to catch big fish and it puts the angler who practices it, fishing standing up, not sitting in a chair, into the condition he needs to be able to fight fish honestly with the sporting tackle that allows the fish to run, leap and sound to his fullest ability and still be caught within an hour by the angler, if the angler knows how to handle big fish.

Fighting a really big fish, fast and unaided, never resting, nor letting the fish rest, is comparable to a ten-round fight in the ring in its requirements for good physical condition. Two hours of the same, not resting, not letting the fish rest, is comparable to a twenty-round fight. Most honest and skillful anglers who lose big fish do so because the fish whips them, and they cannot hold him when he decides, toward the end of the fight, to sound and, sounding, dies.

Once the fish is dead, sharks will eat him if any are about. If he is not hit by sharks, bringing him up, dead, from a great depth is one of the most difficult phases of fishing for big fish in deep water.

We have tried to work out tackle which would give the maximum sport with the different fish, small, medium, large and oversize, at the different months of the year when they run. Since their runs overlap it has been necessary to try to have always a margin of

safety in the quantity of line. In a section at the end of the article
this tackle is described. It would not suit purists, or members of some
light-tackle clubs; but remember we fish five months out of the year
in water up to a mile deep, in a current that can make a very big sea
with the trade wind blowing against it, and in waters that are occasionally infested with sharks. We could catch fish with the very
lightest tackle, I believe. It would prove nothing, since others have
done it, and we would break many fish off to die. Our ideal is to
catch the fish with tackle that you can really pull on and which still
permits the fish to jump and run as freely as possible.

Then, altogether apart from that ideal, there is the meat line.
This is 800 yards of monel wire of eighty-five-pound test which,
fished from an old Hardy six-inch reel and old Hardy No. 5 rod,
will sink a feather jib down so that it can be trolled in thirty-five
fathoms if you put enough wire out. When there are no fish on the
surface at all, this goes down where they are. It catches everything:
wahoo out of their season when no one has caught one on the surface for months; big grouper; huge dog snappers, red snappers, big
kingfish; and it catches marlin when they are deep and not coming
up at all. With it we eat, and fill the freezing unit, on days when you
would not have caught a fish surface-trolling. The fight on the wire
which actually tests no more than thirty-nine-thread line but is definitely wire, not line, is rugged, muscle-straining, punishing, short and
anything but sweet. It is in a class with steer bulldogging, bronc riding and other ungentle sports. The largest marlin caught in 1948 on
the meat line was a 210-pound striped fish. We caught him when we
had fished three days on the surface and not seen a thing.

Now we are anxious to see what the meat line will dredge into
during those days in August and September, when there are flat
calms, and the huge fish are down deep and will not come up. When
you hook a marlin on the wire he starts shaking his head, then he
bangs it with his bill, then he sees if he can outpull you. Then if he
can't, he finally comes up to see what is the matter. What we are
anxious to find out is what happens if he ever gets the wire over his
shoulder and starts to go. They can go, if they are big enough, wire
and all. We plan to try to go with him. There is a chance we could
make it, if Pilar makes the turn fast enough. That will be up to
Mary.

The really huge fish always head out to the northwest when they make their first run. If you are ever flying across between Havana and Miami, and looking down on the blue sea, and you see something making splashes such as a horse dropped off a cliff might make, and behind these splashes a black boat with green topside and decks is chasing, leaving a white wake behind her—that will be us.

If the splashes look sizable from the height that you are flying, and they are going out to the northwest, then wish us plenty of luck. Because we will need it.

In the meantime, what we always hope for is fish feeding on the surface, up after the big flying fish, and that whoever is a guest on the boat, unless he or she has fished before, will hook something under one hundred and fifty pounds to start with. Any marlin from thirty pounds up, on proper tackle, will give a new fisherman all the excitement and all the exercise he can assimilate, and off the marlin grounds along the north Cuban coast he might raise twenty to thirty in a day, when they are running well. The most I ever caught in one day was seven. But Pepe Gomez-Mena and Martin Menocal caught twelve together in one day, and I would hate to bet that record would not be beaten by them, or by some of the fine resident and visiting sportsmen who love and know the marlin fishing of the great river that moves along Cuba's northern coast.

ERNEST HEMINGWAY'S TACKLE SPECIFICATIONS

WHITE MARLIN RUN: *April–May–Early June.*

Gear for the feather jig, fished astern, with pork-rind strip on the hook:

Rod, 9 oz. or 12 oz. tip; Reel, 6/0; 500 yards #15 thread line; 12-foot piano-wire leader #9 or #10; 8/0 or 9/0 O'Shaughnessy hook, or 8/0 Mustad, smallest type of Japanese feather jig (white) and three-inch strip of pork rind attached. (This gives a beautiful motion in the water. Of white marlin hooked we average six out of ten on the feather compared to the baits.)

First rod (light for smaller bait) of the two outrigger rods:

Rod, 14 oz. tip; Reel, 9/0; 600 yards of #18 thread line; 14-foot piano-wire leader #10 or #11; 10/0 Mustad hook.

Baits: small mullet, strip bait, boned needle fish, small cero mackerel, small or medium size flying fish, fresh squid and cut baits.

Second rod of two outriggers:

14 oz. tip; Reel, 9/0; 400 yards of #18 thread line, spliced to 150 yards of #21 thread, on the outside for when the fish is close to the boat. 14-foot piano-wire leader #11; 11/0 or 12/0 Mustad hook.

Baits: big cero mackerel, medium and large mullet, large strip baits, flying fish and good-sized squid.

Above rod is designed to attract any big fish that might be mixed in with the smaller run.

BIG MARLIN RUN: *July–August–September–October.*
(Fish from 250 to over 1000 pounds.)

Feather is fished same as ever, since after white marlin are gone it will catch school tuna, albacore, bonito and dolphin. An extra rod is in readiness, equipped with feather jig in case schools of above fish are encountered.

Outrigger rods: Either 22 or 24 oz. tips. (The best I have found, outside of the old Hardy Hickory-Palakona bamboo #5, are those made by Frank O'Brien of Tycoon Tackle, Inc. His rods are incomparably the best I know made today.)

Reels. 12/0 or 14/0 Hardy, and two 14/0 Finor for guests. If inexperienced anglers want to catch big fish they need the advantage the Finor changeable gear ratio reel gives them.

Line: all the reels will hold without jamming of either 36 or 39 thread good Ashaway linen line. We use this line for years, testing it, discarding any rotted by the sun, and splicing on more as needed.

Leaders are 14½ foot stainless-steel cable.

Hooks: 14/0 Mustad, bent in the crook of the shank to give the point an offset hooking drive.

Baits: Albacore and bonito, whole, up to seven pounds and barracuda, whole, up to five and six pounds. These are the best. Alternative baits are large cero mackerel, squid, big mullet and yellow jacks, runners and big needlefish. Of all baits, the whole bonito and albacore have proved, with us, the best for attracting really big marlin.

The wire line has been described in the article.

THE OLD MAN
AND THE SEA

HE was an old man who fished alone in a skiff in the Gulf Stream and he had gone eighty-four days now without taking a fish. In the first forty days a boy had been with him. But after forty days without a fish the boy's parents had told him that the old man was now definitely and finally *salao,* which is the worst form of unlucky, and the boy had gone at their orders in another boat which caught three good fish the first week. It made the boy sad to see the old man come in each day with his skiff empty and he always went down to help him carry either the coiled lines or the gaff and harpoon and the sail that was furled around the mast. The sail was patched with flour sacks and, furled, it looked like the flag of permanent defeat.

The old man was thin and gaunt with deep wrinkles in the back of his neck. The brown blotches of the benevolent skin cancer the sun brings from its reflection on the tropic sea were on his cheeks. The blotches ran well down the sides of his face and his hands had the deep-creased scars from handling heavy fish on the cords. But none of these scars were fresh. They were as old as erosions in a fish-less desert.

Everything about him was old except his eyes and they were the same color as the sea and were cheerful and undefeated.

"Santiago," the boy said to him as they climbed the bank from where the skiff was hauled up. "I could go with you again. We've made some money."

The old man had taught the boy to fish and the boy loved him.

"No," the old man said. "You're with a lucky boat. Stay with them."

"But remember how you went eighty-seven days without fish and then we caught big ones every day for three weeks."

"I remember," the old man said. "I know you did not leave me because you doubted."

"It was papa made me leave. I am a boy and I must obey him."

"I know," the old man said. "It is quite normal."

"He hasn't much faith."

"No," the old man said. "But we have. Haven't we?"

"Yes," the boy said. "Can I offer you a beer on the Terrace and then we'll take the stuff home."

"Why not?" the old man said. "Between fishermen."

They sat on the Terrace and many of the fishermen made fun of the old man and he was not angry. Others, of the older fishermen, looked at him and were sad. But they did not show it and they spoke politely about the current and the depths they had drifted their lines at and the steady good weather and of what they had seen. The successful fishermen of that day were already in and had butchered their marlin out and carried them laid full length across two planks, with two men staggering at the end of each plank, to the fish house where they waited for the ice truck to carry them to the market in Havana. Those who had caught sharks had taken them to the shark factory on the other side of the cove where they were hoisted on a block and tackle, their livers removed, their fins cut off and their hides skinned out and their flesh cut into strips for salting.

When the wind was in the east a smell came across the harbour from the shark factory; but today there was only the faint edge of the odour because the wind had backed into the north and then dropped off and it was pleasant and sunny on the Terrace.

"Santiago," the boy said.

"Yes," the old man said. He was holding his glass and thinking of many years ago.

"Can I go out to get sardines for you for tomorrow?"

"No. Go and play baseball. I can still row and Rogelio will throw the net."

"I would like to go. If I cannot fish with you, I would like to serve in some way."

"You bought me a beer," the old man said. "You are already a man."

"How old was I when you first took me in a boat?"

"Five and you nearly were killed when I brought the fish in too green and he nearly tore the boat to pieces. Can you remember?"

"I can remember the tail slapping and banging and the thwart breaking and the noise of the clubbing. I can remember you throwing me into the bow where the wet coiled lines were and feeling the whole boat shiver and the noise of you clubbing him like chopping a tree down and the sweet blood smell all over me."

"Can you really remember that or did I just tell it to you?"

"I remember everything from when we first went together."

The old man looked at him with his sunburned, confident loving eyes.

"If you were my boy I'd take you out and gamble," he said. "But you are your father's and your mother's and you are in a lucky boat."

"May I get the sardines? I know where I can get four baits too."

"I have mine left from today. I put them in salt in the box."

"Let me get four fresh ones."

"One," the old man said. His hope and his confidence had never gone. But now they were freshening as when the breeze rises.

"Two," the boy said.

"Two," the old man agreed. "You didn't steal them?"

"I would," the boy said. "But I bought these."

"Thank you," the old man said. He was too simple to wonder when he had attained humility. But he knew he had attained it and he knew it was not disgraceful and it carried no loss of true pride.

"Tomorrow is going to be a good day with this current," he said.

"Where are you going?" the boy asked.

"Far out to come in when the wind shifts. I want to be out before it is light."

"I'll try to get him to work far out," the boy said. "Then if you hook something truly big we can come to your aid."

"He does not like to work too far out."

"No," the boy said. "But I will see something that he cannot see such as a bird working and get him to come out after dolphin."

"Are his eyes that bad?"

"He is almost blind."

"It is strange," the old man said. "He never went turtle-ing. That is what kills the eyes."

"But you went turtle-ing for years off the Mosquito Coast and your eyes are good."

"I am a strange old man."

"But are you strong enough now for a truly big fish?"

"I think so. And there are many tricks."

"Let us take the stuff home," the boy said. "So I can get the cast net and go after the sardines."

They picked up the gear from the boat. The old man carried the mast on his shoulder and the boy carried the wooden box with the coiled, hard-braided brown lines, the gaff and the harpoon with its shaft. The box with the baits was under the stern of the skiff along with the club that was used to subdue the big fish when they were brought alongside. No one would steal from the old man but it was better to take the sail and the heavy lines home as the dew was bad for them and, though he was quite sure no local people would steal from him, the old man thought that a gaff and a harpoon were needless temptations to leave in a boat.

They walked up the road together to the old man's shack and went in through its open door. The old man leaned the mast with its wrapped sail against the wall and the boy put the box and the other gear beside it. The mast was nearly as long as the one room of the shack. The shack was made of the tough budshields of the royal palm which are called *guano* and in it there was a bed, a table, one chair, and a place on the dirt floor to cook with charcoal. On the brown walls of the flattened, overlapping leaves of the sturdy fibered *guano* there was a picture in color of the Sacred Heart of Jesus and another of the Virgin of Cobre. These were relics of his wife. Once there had been a tinted photograph of his wife on the wall but he had taken it down because it made him too lonely to see it and it was on the shelf in the corner under his clean shirt.

"What do you have to eat?" the boy asked.

"A pot of yellow rice with fish. Do you want some?"

"No. I will eat at home. Do you want me to make the fire?"

"No. I will make it later on. Or I may eat the rice cold."

"May I take the cast net?"

"Of course."

There was no cast net and the boy remembered when they had sold it. But they went through this fiction every day. There was no pot of yellow rice and fish and the boy knew this too.

"Eighty-five is a lucky number," the old man said. "How would you like to see me bring one in that dressed out over a thousand pounds?"

"I'll get the cast net and go for sardines. Will you sit in the sun in the doorway?"

"Yes. I have yesterday's paper and I will read the baseball."

The boy did not know whether yesterday's paper was a fiction too. But the old man brought it out from under the bed.

"Perico gave it to me at the *bodega*," he explained.

"I'll be back when I have the sardines. I'll keep yours and mine together on ice and we can share them in the morning. When I come back you can tell me about the baseball."

"The Yankees cannot lose."

"But I fear the Indians of Cleveland."

"Have faith in the Yankees my son. Think of the great DiMaggio."

"I fear both the Tigers of Detroit and the Indians of Cleveland."

"Be careful or you will fear even the Reds of Cincinnati and the White Sox of Chicago."

"You study it and tell me when I come back."

"Do you think we should buy a terminal of the lottery with an eighty-five? Tomorrow is the eighty-fifth day."

"We can do that," the boy said. "But what about the eighty-seven of your great record?"

"It could not happen twice. Do you think you can find an eighty-five?"

"I can order one."

"One sheet. That's two dollars and a half. Who can we borrow that from?"

"That's easy. I can always borrow two dollars and a half."

"I think perhaps I can too. But I try not to borrow. First you borrow. Then you beg."

"Keep warm old man," the boy said. "Remember we are in September."

"The month when the great fish come," the old man said. "Anyone can be a fisherman in May."

"I go now for the sardines," the boy said.

When the boy came back the old man was asleep in the chair and the sun was down. The boy took the old army blanket off the bed and spread it over the back of the chair and over the old man's shoulders. They were strange shoulders, still powerful although very old, and the neck was still strong too and the creases did not show so much when the old man was asleep and his head fallen forward. His shirt had been patched so many times that it was like the sail and the patches were faded to many different shades by the sun. The old man's head was very old though and with his eyes closed there was no life in his face. The newspaper lay across his knees and the weight of his arm held it there in the evening breeze. He was barefooted.

The boy left him there and when he came back the old man was still asleep.

"Wake up old man," the boy said and put his hand on one of the old man's knees.

The old man opened his eyes and for a moment he was coming back from a long way away. Then he smiled.

"What have you got?" he asked.

"Supper," said the boy. "We're going to have supper."

"I'm not very hungry."

"Come on and eat. You can't fish and not eat."

"I have," the old man said getting up and taking the newspaper and folding it. Then he started to fold the blanket.

"Keep the blanket around you," the boy said. "You'll not fish without eating while I'm alive."

"Then live a long time and take care of yourself," the old man said. "What are we eating?"

"Black beans and rice, fried bananas, and some stew."

The boy had brought them in a two-decker metal container from the Terrace. The two sets of knives and forks and spoons were in his pocket with a paper napkin wrapped around each set.

"Who gave this to you?"

"Martin. The owner."

"I must thank him."

"I thanked him already," the boy said. "You don't need to thank him."

"I'll give him the belly meat of a big fish," the old man said. "Has he done this for us more than once?"

"I think so."

"I must give him something more than the belly meat then. He is very thoughtful for us."

"He sent two beers."

"I like the beer in cans best."

"I know. But this is in bottles, Hatuey beer, and I take back the bottles."

"That's very kind of you," the old man said. "Should we eat?"

"I've been asking you to," the boy told him gently. "I have not wished to open the container until you were ready."

"I'm ready now," the old man said. "I only needed time to wash."

Where did you wash? the boy thought. The village water supply was two streets down the road. I must have water here for him, the boy thought, and soap and a good towel. Why am I so thoughtless? I must get him another shirt and a jacket for the winter and some sort of shoes and another blanket.

"Your stew is excellent," the old man said.

"Tell me about the baseball," the boy asked him.

"In the American League it is the Yankees as I said," the old man said happily.

"They lost today," the boy told him.

"That means nothing. The great DiMaggio is himself again."

"They have other men on the team."

"Naturally. But he makes the difference. In the other league, between Brooklyn and Philadelphia I must take Brooklyn. But then I think of Dick Sisler and those great drives in the old park."

"There was nothing ever like them. He hits the longest ball I have ever seen."

"Do you remember when he used to come to the Terrace? I wanted to take him fishing but I was too timid to ask him. Then I asked you to ask him and you were too timid."

"I know. It was a great mistake. He might have gone with us. Then we would have that for all of our lives."

"I would like to take the great DiMaggio fishing," the old man said. "They say his father was a fisherman. Maybe he was as poor as we are and would understand."

"The great Sisler's father was never poor and he, the father, was playing in the Big Leagues when he was my age."

"When I was your age I was before the mast on a square rigged ship that ran to Africa and I have seen lions on the beaches in the evening."

"I know. You told me."

"Should we talk about Africa or about baseball?"

"Baseball I think," the boy said. "Tell me about the great John J. McGraw." He said *Jota* for J.

"He used to come to the Terrace sometimes too in the older days. But he was rough and harsh-spoken and difficult when he was drinking. His mind was on horses as well as baseball. At least he carried lists of horses at all times in his pocket and frequently spoke the names of horses on the telephone."

"He was a great manager," the boy said. "My father thinks he was the greatest."

"Because he came here the most times," the old man said. "If Durocher had continued to come here each year your father would think him the greatest manager."

"Who is the greatest manager, really, Luque or Mike Gonzalez?"

"I think they are equal."

"And the best fisherman is you."

"No. I know others better."

"*Qué va,*" the boy said. "There are many good fishermen and some great ones. But there is only you."

"Thank you. You make me happy. I hope no fish will come along so great that he will prove us wrong."

"There is no such fish if you are still strong as you say."

"I may not be as strong as I think," the old man said. "But I know many tricks and I have resolution."

"You ought to go to bed now so that you will be fresh in the morning. I will take the things back to the Terrace."

"Good night, then. I will wake you in the morning."

"You're my alarm clock," the boy said.

"Age is my alarm clock," the old man said. "Why do old men wake so early? Is it to have one longer day?"

"I don't know," the boy said. "All I know is that young boys sleep late and hard."

"I can remember it," the old man said. "I'll waken you in time."

"I do not like for him to waken me. It is as though I were inferior."

"I know."

"Sleep well old man."

The boy went out. They had eaten with no light on the table and the old man took off his trousers and went to bed in the dark. He rolled his trousers up to make a pillow, putting the newspaper inside them. He rolled himself in the blanket and slept on the other old newspapers that covered the springs of the bed.

He was asleep in a short time and he dreamed of Africa when he was a boy and the long golden beaches and the white beaches, so white they hurt your eyes, and the high capes and the great brown mountains. He lived along that coast now every night and in his dreams he heard the surf roar and saw the native boats come riding through it. He smelled the tar and oakum of the deck as he slept and he smelled the smell of Africa that the land breeze brought at morning.

Usually when he smelled the land breeze he woke up and dressed to go and wake the boy. But tonight the smell of the land breeze came very early and he knew it was too early in his dream and went on dreaming to see the white peaks of the Islands rising from the sea and then he dreamed of the different harbours and roadsteads of the Canary Islands.

He no longer dreamed of storms, nor of women, nor of great occurrences, nor of great fish, nor fights, nor contests of strength, nor of his wife. He only dreamed of places now and of the lions on the beach. They played like young cats in the dusk and he loved them as he loved the boy. He never dreamed about the boy. He simply woke, looked out the open door at the moon and unrolled his trousers and put them on. He urinated outside the shack and then went up the road to wake the boy. He was shivering with the morning cold. But he knew he would shiver himself warm and that soon he would be rowing.

The door of the house where the boy lived was unlocked and he opened it and walked in quietly with his bare feet. The boy was asleep on a cot in the first room and the old man could see him clearly with the light that came in from the dying moon. He took hold of one foot gently and held it until the boy woke and turned and looked at him. The old man nodded and the boy took his trousers from the chair by the bed and, sitting on the bed, pulled them on.

The old man went out the door and the boy came after him. He was sleepy and the old man put his arm across his shoulders and said, "I am sorry."

"*Qué va,*" the boy said. "It is what a man must do."

They walked down the road to the old man's shack and all along the road, in the dark, barefoot men were moving, carrying the masts of their boats.

When they reached the old man's shack the boy took the rolls of line in the basket and the harpoon and gaff and the old man carried the mast with the furled sail on his shoulder.

"Do you want coffee?" the boy asked.

"We'll put the gear in the boat and then get some."

They had coffee from condensed milk cans at an early morning place that served fishermen.

"How did you sleep old man?" the boy asked. He was waking up now although it was still hard for him to leave his sleep.

"Very well, Manolin," the old man said. "I feel confident today."

"So do I," the boy said. "Now I must get your sardines and mine and your fresh baits. He brings our gear himself. He never wants anyone to carry anything."

"We're different," the old man said. "I let you carry things when you were five years old."

"I know it," the boy said. "I'll be right back. Have another coffee. We have credit here."

He walked off, bare-footed on the coral rocks, to the ice house where the baits were stored.

The old man drank his coffee slowly. It was all he would have all day and he knew that he should take it. For a long time now eating had bored him and he never carried a lunch. He had a bottle of water in the bow of the skiff and that was all he needed for the day.

The boy was back now with the sardines and the two baits wrapped in a newspaper and they went down the trail to the skiff, feeling the pebbled sand under their feet, and lifted the skiff and slid her into the water.

"Good luck old man."

"Good luck," the old man said. He fitted the rope lashings of the oars onto the thole pins and, leaning forward against the thrust of the blades in the water, he began to row out of the harbour in the dark. There were other boats from the other beaches going out to sea and the old man heard the dip and push of their oars even though he could not see them now the moon was below the hills.

Sometimes someone would speak in a boat. But most of the boats were silent except for the dip of the oars. They spread apart after they were out of the mouth of the harbour and each one headed for the part of the ocean where he hoped to find fish. The old man knew he was going far out and he left the smell of the land behind and rowed out into the clean early morning smell of the ocean. He saw the phosphorescence of the Gulf weed in the water as he rowed over the part of the ocean that the fishermen called the great well because there was a sudden deep of seven hundred fathoms where all sorts of fish congregated because of the swirl the current made against the steep walls of the floor of the ocean. Here there were concentrations of shrimp and bait fish and sometimes schools of squid in the deepest holes and these rose close to the surface at night where all the wandering fish fed on them.

In the dark the old man could feel the morning coming and as he rowed he heard the trembling sound as flying fish left the water and the hissing that their stiff set wings made as they soared away in the darkness. He was very fond of flying fish as they were his principal friends on the ocean. He was sorry for the birds, especially the small delicate dark terns that were always flying and looking and almost never finding, and he thought, the birds have a harder life than we do except for the robber birds and the heavy strong ones. Why did they make birds so delicate and fine as those sea swallows when the ocean can be so cruel? She is kind and very beautiful. But she can be so cruel and it comes so suddenly and such birds that fly, dipping and hunting, with their small sad voices are made too delicately for the sea.

He always thought of the sea as *la mar* which is what people call her in Spanish when they love her. Sometimes those who love her say bad things of her but they are always said as though she were a woman. Some of the younger fishermen, those who used buoys as floats for their lines and had motorboats, bought when the shark livers had brought much money, spoke of her as *el mar* which is masculine. They spoke of her as a contestant or a place or even an enemy. But the old man always thought of her as feminine and as something that gave or withheld great favours, and if she did wild or wicked things it was because she could not help them. The moon affects her as it does a woman, he thought.

He was rowing steadily and it was no effort for him since he kept well within his speed and the surface of the ocean was flat except for the occasional swirls of the current. He was letting the current do a third of the work and as it started to be light he saw he was already further out than he had hoped to be at this hour.

I worked the deep wells for a week and did nothing, he thought. Today I'll work out where the schools of bonito and albacore are and maybe there will be a big one with them.

Before it was really light he had his baits out and was drifting with the current. One bait was down forty fathoms. The second was at seventy-five and the third and fourth were down in the blue water at one hundred and one hundred and twenty-five fathoms. Each bait hung head down with the shank of the hook inside the bait fish, tied and sewed solid and all the projecting part of the hook, the curve and the point, was covered with fresh sardines. Each sardine was hooked through both eyes so that they made a half-garland on the projecting steel. There was no part of the hook that a great fish could feel which was not sweet smelling and good tasting.

The boy had given him two fresh small tunas, or albacores, which hung on the two deepest lines like plummets and, on the others, he had a big blue runner and a yellow jack that had been used before; but they were in good condition still and had the excellent sardines to give them scent and attractiveness. Each line, as thick around as a big pencil, was looped onto a green-sapped stick so that any pull or touch on the bait would make the stick dip and each line had two forty-fathom coils which could be made fast to the other spare coils so that, if it were necessary, a fish could take out over three hundred fathoms of line.

Now the man watched the dip of the three sticks over the side of the skiff and rowed gently to keep the lines straight up and down and at their proper depths. It was quite light and any moment now the sun would rise.

The sun rose thinly from the sea and the old man could see the other boats, low on the water and well in toward the shore, spread out across the current. Then the sun was brighter and the glare came on the water and then, as it rose clear, the flat sea sent it back at his eyes so that it hurt sharply and he rowed without looking into it. He looked down into the water and watched the lines that went straight down into the dark of the water. He kept them straighter than anyone did, so that at each level in the darkness of the stream there would be a bait waiting exactly where he wished it to be for any fish that swam there. Others let them drift with the current and sometimes they were at sixty fathoms when the fishermen thought they were at a hundred.

But, he thought, I keep them with precision. Only I have no luck any more. But who knows? Maybe today. Every day is a new day. It is better to be lucky. But I would rather be exact. Then when luck comes you are ready.

The sun was two hours higher now and it did not hurt his eyes so much to look into the east. There were only three boats in sight now and they showed very low and far inshore.

All my life the early sun has hurt my eyes, he thought. Yet they are still good. In the evening I can look straight into it without getting the blackness. It has more force in the evening too. But in the morning it is painful.

Just then he saw a man-of-war bird with his long black wings circling in the sky ahead of him. He made a quick drop, slanting down on his back-swept wings, and then circled again.

"He's got something," the old man said aloud. "He's not just looking."

He rowed slowly and steadily toward where the bird was circling. He did not hurry and he kept his lines straight up and down. But he crowded the current a little so that he was still fishing correctly though faster than he would have fished if he was not trying to use the bird.

The bird went higher in the air and circled again, his wings motionless. Then he dove suddenly and the old man saw flying fish spurt out of the water and sail desperately over the surface.

"Dolphin," the old man said aloud. "Big dolphin."

He shipped his oars and brought a small line from under the bow. It had a wire leader and a medium-sized hook and he baited it with one of the sardines. He let it go over the side and then made it fast to a ring bolt in the stern. Then he baited another line and left it coiled in the shade of the bow. He went back to rowing and to watching the long-winged black bird who was working, now, low over the water.

As he watched the bird dipped again slanting his wings for the dive and then swinging them wildly and ineffectually as he followed the flying fish. The old man could see the slight bulge in the water that the big dolphin raised as they followed the escaping fish. The dolphin were cutting through the water below the flight of the fish and would be in the water, driving at speed, when the fish dropped. It is a big school of dolphin, he thought. They are widespread and the flying fish have little chance. The bird has no chance. The flying fish are too big for him and they go too fast.

He watched the flying fish burst out again and again and the ineffectual movements of the bird. That school has gotten away from me, he thought. They are moving out too fast and too far. But perhaps I will pick up a stray and perhaps my big fish is around them. My big fish must be somewhere.

The clouds over the land now rose like mountains and the coast was only a long green line with the gray blue hills behind it. The water was a dark blue now, so dark that it was almost purple. As he looked down into it he saw the red sifting of the plankton in the dark water and the strange light the sun made now. He watched his lines to see them go straight down out of sight into the water and he was happy to see so much plankton because it meant fish. The strange light the sun made in the water, now that the sun was higher, meant good weather and so did the shape of the clouds over the land. But the bird was almost out of sight now and nothing showed on the surface of the water but some patches of yellow, sun-bleached Sargasso weed and the purple, formalized, iridescent, gelatinous bladder of a Portuguese man-of-war floating close beside the boat. It turned on its side and then righted itself. It floated cheerfully as a bubble with its long deadly purple filaments trailing a yard behind it in the water.

"*Agua mala,*" the man said. "You whore."

From where he swung lightly against his oars he looked down into the water and saw the tiny fish that were coloured like the trailing filaments and swam between them and under the small shade the bubble made as it drifted. They were immune to its poison. But men were not and when some of the filaments would catch on a line and rest there slimy and purple while the old man was working a fish, he would have welts and sores on his arms and hands of the sort that poison ivy or poison oak can give. But these poisonings from the *agua mala* came quickly and struck like a whiplash.

The iridescent bubbles were beautiful. But they were the falsest thing in the sea and the old man loved to see the big turtles eating them. The turtles saw them, approached them from the front, then shut their eyes so they were completely carapaced and ate them filaments and all. The old man loved to see the turtles eat them and he loved to walk on them on the beach after a storm and hear them pop when he stepped on them with the horny soles of his feet.

He loved green turtles and hawk-bills with their elegance and speed and their great value and he had a friendly contempt for the huge, stupid loggerheads, yellow in their armour-plating, strange in their love-making, and happily eating the Portuguese men-of-war with their eyes shut.

He had no mysticism about turtles although he had gone in turtle boats for many years. He was sorry for them all, even the great trunk backs that were as long as the skiff and weighed a ton. Most people are heartless about turtles because a turtle's heart will beat for hours after he has been cut up and butchered. But the old man thought, I have such a heart too and my feet and hands are like theirs. He ate the white eggs to give himself strength. He ate them all through May to be strong in September and October for the truly big fish.

He also drank a cup of shark liver oil each day from the big drum in the shack where many of the fishermen kept their gear. It was there for all fishermen who wanted it. Most fishermen hated the taste. But it was no worse than getting up at the hours that they rose and it was very good against all colds and grippes and it was good for the eyes.

Now the old man looked up and saw that the bird was circling again.

"He's found fish," he said aloud. No flying fish broke the surface and there was no scattering of bait fish. But as the old man watched, a small tuna rose in the air, turned and dropped head first into the water. The tuna shone silver in the sun and after he had dropped back into the water another and another rose and they were jumping in all directions, churning the water and leaping in long jumps after the bait. They were circling it and driving it.

If they don't travel too fast I will get into them, the old man thought, and he watched the school working the water white and the bird now dropping and dipping into the bait fish that were forced to the surface in their panic.

"The bird is a great help," the old man said. Just then the stern line came taut under his foot, where he had kept a loop of the line, and he dropped his oars and felt the weight of the small tuna's shivering pull as he held the line firm and commenced to haul it in. The shivering increased as he pulled in and he could see the blue back of the fish in the water and the gold of his sides before he swung him over the side and into the boat. He lay in the stern in the sun, compact and bullet shaped, his big, unintelligent eyes staring as he thumped his life out against the planking of the boat with the quick shivering strokes of his neat, fast-moving tail. The old man hit him on the head for kindness and kicked him, his body still shuddering, under the shade of the stern.

"Albacore," he said aloud. "He'll make a beautiful bait. He'll weigh ten pounds."

He did not remember when he had first started to talk aloud when he was by himself. He had sung when he was by himself in the old days and he had sung at night sometimes when he was alone steering on his watch in the smacks or in the turtle boats. He had probably started to talk aloud, when alone, when the boy had left. But he did not remember. When he and the boy fished together they usually spoke only when it was necessary. They talked at night or when they were storm-bound by bad weather. It was considered a virtue not to talk unnecessarily at sea and the old man had always considered it so and respected it. But now he said his thoughts aloud many times since there was no one that they could annoy.

"If the others heard me talking out loud they would think that I am crazy," he said aloud. "But since I am not crazy, I do not care. And the rich have radios to talk to them in their boats and to bring them the baseball."

Now is no time to think of baseball, he thought. Now is the time to think of only one thing. That which I was born for. There might be a big one around that school, he thought. I picked up only a straggler from the albacore that were feeding. But they are working far out and fast. Everything that shows on the surface today travels very fast and to the north-east. Can that be the time of day? Or is it some sign of weather that I do not know?

He could not see the green of the shore now but only the tops of the blue hills that showed white as though they were snow-capped and the clouds that looked like high snow mountains above them. The sea was very dark and the light made prisms in the water. The myriad flecks of the plankton were annulled now by the high sun and it was only the great deep prisms in the blue water that the old man saw now with his lines going straight down into the water that was a mile deep.

The tuna, the fisherman called all the fish of that species tuna and only distinguished among them by their proper names when they came to sell them or to trade them for baits, were down again. The sun was hot now and the old man felt it on the back of his neck and felt the sweat trickle down his back as he rowed.

I could just drift, he thought, and sleep and put a bight of line around my toe to wake me. But today is eighty-five days and I should fish the day well.

Just then, watching his lines, he saw one of the projecting green sticks dip sharply.

"Yes," he said. "Yes," and shipped his oars without bumping the boat. He reached out for the line and held it softly between the thumb and forefinger of his right hand. He felt no strain nor weight and he held the line lightly. Then it came again. This time it was a tentative pull, not solid nor heavy, and he knew exactly what it was. One hundred fathoms down a marlin was eating the sardines that covered the point and the shank of the hook where the hand-forged hook projected from the head of the small tuna.

The old man held the line delicately, and softly, with his left hand, unleashed it from the stick. Now he could let it run through his fingers without the fish feeling any tension.

This far out, he must be huge in his mouth, he thought. Eat them, fish. Eat them. Please eat them. How fresh they are and you down there six hundred feet in that cold water in the dark. Make another turn in the dark and come back and eat them.

He felt the light delicate pulling and then a harder pull when a sardine's head must have been more difficult to break from the hook. Then there was nothing.

"Come on," the old man said aloud. "Make another turn. Just smell them. Aren't they lovely? Eat them good now and then there is the tuna. Hard and cold and lovely. Don't be shy, fish. Eat them."

He waited with the line between his thumb and his finger, watching it and the other lines at the same time for the fish might have swum up or down. Then came the same delicate pulling touch again.

"He'll take it," the old man said aloud. "God help him to take it."

He did not take it though. He was gone and the old man felt nothing.

"He can't have gone," he said. "Christ knows he can't have gone. He's making a turn. Maybe he has been hooked before and he remembers something of it."

Then he felt the gentle touch on the line and he was happy.

"It was only his turn," he said. "He'll take it."

He was happy feeling the gentle pulling and then he felt something hard and unbelievably heavy. It was the weight of the fish and he let the line slip down, down, down, unrolling off the first of the two reserve coils. As it went down, slipping lightly through the old man's fingers, he still could feel the great weight, though the pressure of his thumb and finger were almost imperceptible.

"What a fish," he said. "He has it sideways in his mouth now and he is moving off with it."

Then he will turn and swallow it, he thought. He did not say that because he knew that if you said a good thing it might not happen. He knew what a huge fish this was and he thought of him moving away in the darkness with the tuna held crosswise in his mouth. At that moment he felt him stop moving but the weight was still there. Then the weight increased and he gave more line. He tightened the pressure of his thumb and finger for a moment and the weight increased and was going straight down.

"He's taken it," he said. "Now I'll let him eat it well."

He let the line slip through his fingers while he reached down with his left hand and made fast the free end of the two reserve coils to the loop of the two reserve coils of the next line. Now he was ready. He had three forty-fathom coils of line in reserve now, as well as the coil he was using.

"Eat it a little more," he said. "Eat it well."

Eat it so that the point of the hook goes into your heart and kills you, he thought. Come up easy and let me put the harpoon into you. All right. Are you ready? Have you been long enough at table?

"Now!" he said aloud and struck hard with both hands, gained a yard of line and then struck again and again, swinging with each arm alternately on the cord with all the strength of his arms and the pivoted weight of his body.

Nothing happened. The fish just moved away slowly and the

old man could not raise him an inch. His line was strong and made for heavy fish and he held it against his back until it was so taut that beads of water were jumping from it. Then it began to make a slow hissing sound in the water and he still held it, bracing himself against the thwart and leaning back against the pull. The boat began to move slowly off toward the north-west.

The fish moved steadily and they travelled slowly on the calm water. The other baits were still in the water but there was nothing to be done.

"I wish I had the boy," the old man said aloud. "I'm being towed by a fish and I'm the towing bitt. I could make the line fast. But then he could break it. I must hold him all I can and give him line when he must have it. Thank God he is travelling and not going down."

What I will do if he decides to go down, I don't know. What I'll do if he sounds and dies I don't know. But I'll do something. There are plenty of things I can do.

He held the line against his back and watched its slant in the water and the skiff moving steadily to the north-west.

This will kill him, the old man thought. He can't do this forever. But four hours later the fish was still swimming steadily out to sea, towing the skiff, and the old man was still braced solidly with the line across his back.

"It was noon when I hooked him," he said. "And I have never seen him."

He had pushed his straw hat hard down on his head before he hooked the fish and it was cutting his forehead. He was thirsty too and he got down on his knees and, being careful not to jerk on the line, moved as far into the bow as he could get and reached the water bottle with one hand. He opened it and drank a little. Then he rested against the bow. He rested sitting on the unstepped mast and sail and tried not to think but only to endure.

Then he looked behind him and saw that no land was visible. That makes no difference, he thought. I can always come in on the glow from Havana. There are two more hours before the sun sets and maybe he will come up before that. If he doesn't maybe he will come up with the moon. If he does not do that maybe he will come up with the sunrise. I have no cramps and I feel strong. It is he that has the hook in his mouth. But what a fish to pull like that. He must have his mouth shut tight on the wire. I wish I could see him. I wish I could see him only once to know what I have against me.

The fish never changed his course nor his direction all that night as far as the man could tell from watching the stars. It was cold after the sun went down and the old man's sweat dried cold on his back and his arms and his old legs. During the day he had taken the sack that covered the bait box and spread it in the sun to dry. After the sun went down he tied it around his neck so that it hung down over his back and he cautiously worked it down under the line that was across his shoulders now. The sack cushioned the line and he had found a way of leaning forward against the bow so that he was almost comfortable. The position actually was only somewhat less intolerable; but he thought of it as almost comfortable.

I can do nothing with him and he can do nothing with me, he thought. Not as long as he keeps this up.

Once he stood up and urinated over the side of the skiff and looked at the stars and checked his course. The line showed like a phosphorescent streak in the water straight out from his shoulders. They were moving more slowly now and the glow of Havana was not so strong, so that he knew the current must be carrying them to the eastward. If I lose the glare of Havana we must be going more to the eastward, he thought. For if the fish's course held true I must see it for many more hours. I wonder how the baseball came out in the grand leagues today, he thought. It would be wonderful to do this with a radio. Then he thought, think of it always. Think of what you are doing. You must do nothing stupid.

Then he said aloud, "I wish I had the boy. To help me and to see this."

No one should be alone in their old age, he thought. But it is unavoidable. I must remember to eat the tuna before he spoils in order to keep strong. Remember, no matter how little you want to, that you must eat him in the morning. Remember, he said to himself.

During the night two porpoises came around the boat and he could hear them rolling and blowing. He could tell the difference between the blowing noise the male made and the sighing blow of the female.

"They are good," he said. "They play and make jokes and love one another. They are our brothers like the flying fish."

Then he began to pity the great fish that he had hooked. He is wonderful and strange and who knows how old he is, he thought. Never have I had such a strong fish nor one who acted so strangely. Perhaps he is too wise to jump. He could ruin me by jumping or by a wild rush. But perhaps he has been hooked many times before and he knows that this is how he should make his fight. He cannot know that it is only one man against him, nor that it is an old man. But what a great fish he is and what will he bring in the market if the flesh is good. He took the bait like a male and he pulls like a male and his fight has no panic in it. I wonder if he has any plans or if he is just as desperate as I am?

He remembered the time he had hooked one of a pair of marlin. The male fish always let the female fish feed first and the hooked fish, the female, made a wild, panic-stricken, despairing fight that soon exhausted her, and all the time the male had stayed with her, crossing the line and circling with her on the surface. He had stayed so close that the old man was afraid he would cut the line with his tail which was sharp as a scythe and almost of that size and shape. When the old man had gaffed her and clubbed her, holding the rapier bill with its sandpaper edge and clubbing her across the top of her head until her colour turned to a colour almost like the backing of mirrors, and then, with the boy's aid, hoisted her aboard, the male fish had stayed by the side of the boat. Then, while the old man was clearing the lines and preparing the harpoon, the male fish jumped high into the air beside the boat to see where the female was and then went down deep, his lavender wings, that were his pectoral fins, spread wide and all his wide lavender stripes showing. He was beautiful, the old man remembered, and he had stayed.

That was the saddest thing I ever saw with them, the old man thought. The boy was sad too and we begged her pardon and butchered her promptly.

"I wish the boy was here," he said aloud and settled himself against the rounded planks of the bow and felt the strength of the great fish through the line he held across his shoulders moving steadily toward whatever he had chosen.

When once, through my treachery, it had been necessary to him to make a choice, the old man thought.

His choice had been to stay in the deep dark water far out beyond all snares and traps and treacheries. My choice was to go there to find him beyond all people. Beyond all people in the world. Now we are joined together and have been since noon. And no one to help either one of us.

Perhaps I should not have been a fisherman, he thought. But that was the thing that I was born for. I must surely remember to eat the tuna after it gets light.

Some time before daylight something took one of the baits that were behind him. He heard the stick break and the line begin to rush out over the gunwale of the skiff. In the darkness he loosened his sheath knife and taking all the strain of the fish on his left shoulder he leaned back and cut the line against the wood of the gunwale. Then he cut the other line closest to him and in the dark made the loose ends of the reserve coils fast. He worked skillfully with the one hand and put his foot on the coils to hold them as he drew his knots tight. Now he had six reserve coils of line. There were two from each bait he had severed and the two from the bait the fish had taken and they were all connected.

After it is light, he thought, I will work back to the forty-fathom bait and cut it away too and link up the reserve coils. I will have lost two hundred fathoms of good Catalan *cardel* and the hooks and leaders. That can be replaced. But who replaces this fish if I hook some fish and it cuts him off? I don't know what that fish was that took the bait just now. It could have been a marlin or a broadbill or a shark. I never felt him. I had to get rid of him too fast.

Aloud he said, "I wish I had the boy."

But you haven't got the boy, he thought. You have only yourself and you had better work back to the last line now, in the dark or not in the dark, and cut it away and hook up the two reserve coils.

So he did it. It was difficult in the dark and once the fish made a surge that pulled him down on his face and made a cut below his eye. The blood ran down his cheek a little way. But it coagulated and dried before it reached his chin and he worked his way back to the bow and rested against the wood. He adjusted the sack and carefully worked the line so that it came across a new part of his shoulders and, holding it anchored with his shoulders, he carefully felt the pull of the fish and then felt with his hand the progress of the skiff through the water.

I wonder what he made that lurch for, he thought. The wire

must have slipped on the great hill of his back. Certainly his back cannot feel as badly as mine does. But he cannot pull this skiff forever, no matter how great he is. Now everything is cleared away that might make trouble and I have a big reserve of line; all that a man can ask.

"Fish," he said softly, aloud, "I'll stay with you until I am dead."

He'll stay with me too, I suppose, the old man thought and he waited for it to be light. It was cold now in the time before daylight and he pushed against the wood to be warm. I can do it as long as he can, he thought. And in the first light the line extended out and down into the water. The boat moved steadily and when the first edge of the sun rose it was on the old man's right shoulder.

"He's headed north," the old man said. The current will have set us far to the eastward, he thought. I wish he would turn with the current. That would show that he was tiring.

When the sun had risen further the old man realized that the fish was not tiring. There was only one favorable sign. The slant of the line showed he was swimming at a lesser depth. That did not necessarily mean that he would jump. But he might.

"God let him jump," the old man said. "I have enough line to handle him."

Maybe if I can increase the tension just a little it will hurt him and he will jump, he thought. Now that it is daylight let him jump so that he'll fill the sacks along his backbone with air and then he cannot go deep to die.

He tried to increase the tension, but the line had been taut up to the very edge of the breaking point since he had hooked the fish and he felt the harshness as he leaned back to pull and knew he could put no more strain on it. I must not jerk it ever, he thought. Each jerk widens the cut the hook makes and then when he does jump he might throw it. Anyway I feel better with the sun and for once I do not have to look into it.

There was yellow weed on the line but the old man knew that only made an added drag and he was pleased. It was the yellow Gulf weed that had made so much phosphorescence in the night.

"Fish," he said, "I love you and respect you very much. But I will kill you dead before this day ends."

Let us hope so, he thought.

A small bird came toward the skiff from the north. He was a warbler and flying very low over the water. The old man could see that he was very tired.

The bird made the stern of the boat and rested there. Then he flew around the old man's head and rested on the line where he was more comfortable.

"How old are you?" the old man asked the bird. "Is this your first trip?"

The bird looked at him when he spoke. He was too tired even to examine the line and he teetered on it as his delicate feet gripped it fast.

"It's steady," the old man told him. "It's too steady. You shouldn't be that tired after a windless night. What are birds coming to?"

The hawks, he thought, that come out to sea to meet them. But he said nothing of this to the bird who could not understand him anyway and who would learn about the hawks soon enough.

"Take a good rest, small bird," he said. "Then go in and take your chance like any man or bird or fish."

It encouraged him to talk because his back had stiffened in the night and it hurt truly now.

"Stay at my house if you like, bird," he said. "I am sorry I cannot hoist the sail and take you in with the small breeze that is rising. But I am with a friend."

Just then the fish gave a sudden lurch that pulled the old man down onto the bow and would have pulled him overboard if he had not braced himself and given some line.

The bird had flown up when the line jerked and the old man had not even seen him go. He felt the line carefully with his right hand and noticed his hand was bleeding.

"Something hurt him then," he said aloud and pulled back on the line to see if he could turn the fish. But when he was touching the breaking point he held steady and settled back against the strain of the line.

"You're feeling it now, fish," he said. "And so, God knows, am I."

He looked around for the bird now because he would have liked him for company. The bird was gone.

You did not stay long, the man thought. But it is rougher where you are going until you make the shore. How did I let the fish cut me with that one quick pull he made? I must be getting very stupid. Or perhaps I was looking at the small bird and thinking of him. Now I will pay attention to my work and then I must eat the tuna so that I will not have a failure of strength.

"I wish the boy were here and that I had some salt," he said aloud.

Shifting the weight of the line to his left shoulder and kneeling carefully he washed his hand in the ocean and held it there, submerged, for more than a minute watching the blood trail away and the steady movement of the water against his hand as the boat moved.

"He has slowed much," he said.

The old man would have liked to keep his hand in the salt water longer but he was afraid of another sudden lurch by the fish and he stood up and braced himself and held his hand up against the sun. It was only a line burn that had cut his flesh. But it was in the working part of his hand. He knew he would need his hands before this was over and he did not like to be cut before it started.

"Now," he said, when his hand had dried, "I must eat the small tuna. I can reach him with the gaff and eat him here in comfort."

He knelt down and found the tuna under the stern with the gaff and drew it toward him keeping it clear of the coiled lines. Holding the line with his left shoulder again, and bracing on his left hand and arm, he took the tuna off the gaff hook and put the gaff back in place. He put one knee on the fish and cut strips of dark red meat longitudinally from the back of the head to the tail. They were wedge-shaped strips and he cut them from next to the back bone down to the edge of the belly. When he had cut six strips he spread them out on the wood of the bow, wiped his knife on his trousers, and lifted the carcass of the bonito by the tail and dropped it overboard.

"I don't think I can eat an entire one," he said and drew his knife across one of the strips. He could feel the steady hard pull of the line and his left hand was cramped. It drew up tight on the heavy cord and he looked at it in disgust.

"What kind of a hand is that," he said. "Cramp then if you want. Make yourself into a claw. It will do you no good."

Come on, he thought and looked down into the dark water at the slant of the line. Eat it now and it will strengthen the hand. It is not the hand's fault and you have been many hours with the fish. But you can stay with him forever. Eat the bonito now.

He picked up a piece and put it in his mouth and chewed it slowly. It was not unpleasant.

Chew it well, he thought, and get all the juices. It would not be bad to eat with a little lime or with lemon or with salt.

"How do you feel, hand?" he asked the cramped hand that was almost as stiff as rigor mortis. "I'll eat some more for you."

He ate the other part of the piece that he had cut in two. He chewed it carefully and then spat out the skin.

"How does it go, hand? Or is it too early to know?"

He took another full piece and chewed it.

"It is a strong full-blooded fish," he thought. "I was lucky to get him instead of dolphin. Dolphin is too sweet. This is hardly sweet at all and all the strength is still in it."

There is no sense in being anything but practical though, he thought. I wish I had some salt. And I do not know whether the sun will rot or dry what is left, so I had better eat it all although I am not hungry. The fish is calm and steady. I will eat it all and then I will be ready.

"Be patient, hand," he said. "I do this for you."

I wish I could feel the fish, he thought. He is my brother. But I must kill him and keep strong to do it. Slowly and conscientiously he ate all of the wedge-shaped strips of fish.

He straightened up, wiping his hand on his trousers.

"Now," he said. "You can let the cord go, hand, and I will handle him with the right arm alone until you stop that nonsense." He put his left foot on the heavy line that the left hand had held and lay back against the pull against his back.

"God help me to have the cramp go," he said. "Because I do not know what the fish is going to do."

But he seems calm, he thought, and following his plan. But what is his plan, he thought. And what is mine? Mine I must improvise to his because of his great size. If he will jump I can kill him. But he stays down forever. Then I will stay down with him forever.

He rubbed the cramped hand against his trousers and tried to gentle the fingers. But it would not open. Maybe it will open with the sun, he thought. Maybe it will open when the strong raw tuna is digested. If I have to have it, I will open it, cost whatever it costs. But I do not want to open it now by force. Let it open by itself and come back of its own accord. After all I abused it much in the night when it was necessary to free and untie the various lines.

He looked across the sea and knew how alone he was now. But he could see the prisms in the deep dark water and the line stretching ahead and the strange undulation of the calm. The clouds were building up now for the trade wind and he looked ahead and saw a flight of wild ducks etching themselves against the sky over the water, then blurring, then etching again and he knew no man was ever alone on the sea.

He thought of how some men feared being out of sight of land in a small boat and knew they were right in the months of sudden bad weather. But now they were in hurricane months and, when there are no hurricanes, the weather of hurricane months is the best of all the year.

If there is a hurricane you always see the signs of it in the sky for days ahead, if you are at sea. They do not see it ashore because they do not know what to look for, he thought. The land must make a difference too, in the shape of the clouds. But we have no hurricane coming now.

He looked at the sky and saw the white cumulus build like friendly piles of ice cream and high above were the thin feathers of the cirrus against the high September sky.

"Light *brisa*," he said. "Better weather for me than for you, fish."

His left hand was still cramped, but he was unknotting it slowly.

I hate a cramp, he thought. It is a treachery of one's own body. It is humiliating before others to have a diarrhoea from ptomaine poisoning or to vomit from it. But a cramp, he thought of it as a *calambre,* humiliates oneself especially when one is alone.

If the boy were here he could rub it for me and loosen it down from the forearm, he thought. But it will loosen up.

Then, with his right hand he felt the difference in the pull of the line before he saw the slant change in the water. Then, as he leaned against the line and slapped his left hand hard and fast against his thigh he saw the line slanting slowly upward.

"He's coming up," he said. "Come on hand. Please come on."

The line rose slowly and steadily and then the surface of the ocean bulged ahead of the boat and the fish came out. He came out unendingly and water poured from his sides. He was bright in the sun and his head and back were dark purple and in the sun the stripes on his sides showed wide and a light lavender. His sword was as long as a baseball bat and tapered like a rapier and he rose his full length from the water and then re-entered it, smoothly, like a diver and the old man saw the great scythe-blade of his tail go under and the line commenced to race out.

"He is two feet longer than the skiff," the old man said. The line was going out fast but steadily and the fish was not panicked. The old man was trying with both hands to keep the line just inside of breaking strength. He knew that if he could not slow the fish with a steady pressure the fish could take out all the line and break it.

He is a great fish and I must convince him, he thought. I must never let him learn his strength nor what he could do if he made his run. If I were him I would put in everything now and go until something broke. But, thank God, they are not as intelligent as we who kill them; although they are more noble and more able.

The old man had seen many great fish. He had seen many that weighed more than a thousand pounds and he had caught two of that size in his life, but never alone. Now alone, and out of sight of land, he was fast to the biggest fish that he had ever seen and bigger than he had ever heard of, and his left hand was still as tight as the gripped claws of an eagle.

It will uncramp though, he thought. Surely it will uncramp to help my right hand. There are three things that are brothers: the fish and my two hands. It must uncramp. It is unworthy of it to be cramped. The fish had slowed again and was going at his usual pace.

I wonder why he jumped, the old man thought. He jumped almost as though to show me how big he was. I know now, anyway, he thought. I wish I could show him what sort of man I am. But then he would see the cramped hand. Let him think I am more man than I am and I will be so. I wish I was the fish, he thought, with everything he has against only my will and my intelligence.

He settled comfortably against the wood and took his suffering as it came and the fish swam steadily and the boat moved slowly through the dark water. There was a small sea rising with the wind coming up from the east and at noon the old man's left hand was uncramped.

"Bad news for you, fish," he said and shifted the line over the sacks that covered his shoulders.

He was comfortable but suffering, although he did not admit the suffering at all.

"I am not religious," he said. "But I will say ten Our Fathers and ten Hail Marys that I should catch this fish, and I promise to make a pilgrimage to the Virgin of Cobre if I catch him. That is a promise."

He commenced to say his prayers mechanically. Sometimes he would be so tired that he could not remember the prayer and then he would say them fast so that they would come automatically. Hail Marys are easier to say than Our Fathers, he thought.

"Hail Mary full of Grace the Lord is with thee. Blessed art thou among women and blessed is the fruit of thy womb, Jesus. Holy Mary, Mother of God, pray for us sinners now and at the hour of our death. Amen." Then he added, "Blessed Virgin, pray for the death of this fish. Wonderful though he is."

With his prayers said, and feeling much better, but suffering exactly as much, and perhaps a little more, he leaned against the wood of the bow and began, mechanically, to work the fingers of his left hand.

The sun was hot now although the breeze was rising gently.

"I had better re-bait that little line out over the stern," he said. "If the fish decides to stay another night I will need to eat again and the water is low in the bottle. I don't think I can get anything but a dolphin here. But if I eat him fresh enough he won't be bad. I wish a flying fish would come on board tonight. But I have no light to attract them. A flying fish is excellent to eat raw and I would not have to cut him up. I must save all my strength now. Christ, I did not know he was so big.

"I'll kill him though," he said. "In all his greatness and his glory."

Although it is unjust, he thought. But I will show him what a man can do and what a man endures.

"I told the boy I was a strange old man," he said. "Now is when I must prove it."

The thousand times that he had proved it meant nothing. Now he was proving it again. Each time was a new time and he never thought about the past when he was doing it.

I wish he'd sleep and I could sleep and dream about the lions, he thought. Why are the lions the main thing that is left? Don't think, old man, he said to himself. Rest gently now against the wood and think of nothing. He is working. Work as little as you can.

It was getting into the afternoon and the boat still moved slowly and steadily. But there was an added drag now from the easterly breeze and the old man rode gently with the small sea and the hurt of the cord across his back came to him easily and smoothly.

Once in the afternoon the line started to rise again. But the fish only continued to swim at a slightly higher level. The sun was on the old man's left arm and shoulder and on his back. So he knew the fish had turned east of north.

Now that he had seen him once, he could picture the fish swimming in the water with his purple pectoral fins set wide as wings and the great erect tail slicing through the dark. I wonder how much he sees at that depth, the old man thought. His eye is huge and a horse, with much less eye, can see in the dark. Once I could see quite well in the dark. Not in the absolute dark. But almost as a cat sees.

The sun and his steady movement of his fingers had uncramped his left hand now completely and he began to shift more of the strain to it and he shrugged the muscles of his back to shift the hurt of the cord a little.

"If you're not tired, fish," he said aloud, "you must be very strange."

He felt very tired now and he knew the night would come soon and he tried to think of other things. He thought of the Big Leagues, to him they were the *Gran Ligas,* and he knew that the Yankees of New York were playing the *Tigres* of Detroit

This is the second day now that I do not know the result of the *Juegos,* he thought. But I must have confidence and I must be worthy of the great DiMaggio who does all things perfectly even with the pain of the bone spur in his heel. What is a bone spur? he asked himself. *Un espuela de hueso.* We do not have them. Can it be as painful as the spur of a fighting cock in one's heel? I do not think I could endure that or the loss of the eye and of both eyes and continue to fight as the fighting cocks do. Man is not much beside the great birds and beasts. Still I would rather be that beast down there in the darkness of the sea.

"Unless sharks come," he said aloud. "If sharks come, God pity him and me."

Do you believe the great DiMaggio would stay with a fish as long as I will stay with this one? he thought. I am sure he would and more since he is young and strong. Also his father was a fisherman. But would the bone spur hurt him too much?

"I do not know," he said aloud. "I never had a bone spur."

As the sun set he remembered, to give himself more confidence, the time in the tavern at Casablanca when he had played the hand game with the great Negro from Cienfuegos who was the strongest man on the docks. They had gone one day and one night with their elbows on a chalk line on the table and their forearms straight up and their hands gripped tight. Each one was trying to force the other's hand down onto the table. There was much betting and people went in and out of the room under the kerosene lights and he had looked at the arm and hand of the Negro and at the Negro's face. They changed the referees every four hours after the first eight so that the referees could sleep. Blood came out from under the fingernails of both his and the Negro's hands and they looked each other in the eye and at their hands and forearms and the bettors went in and out of the room and sat on high chairs against the wall and watched. The walls were painted bright blue and were of wood and the lamps threw their shadows against them. The Negro's shadow was huge and it moved on the wall as the breeze moved the lamps.

The odds would change back and forth all night and they fed the Negro rum and lighted cigarettes for him. Then the Negro, after the rum, would try for a tremendous effort and once he had the old man, who was not an old man then but was Santiago *El Campeón,* nearly three inches off balance. But the old man had raised his hand up to dead even again. He was sure then that he had the Negro, who was a fine man and a great athlete, beaten. And at daylight when the bettors were asking that it be called a draw and the referee was shaking his head, he had unleashed his effort and forced the hand of the Negro down and down until it rested on the wood. The match had started on a Sunday morning and ended on a Monday morning. Many of the bettors had asked for a draw because they had to go to work on the docks loading sacks of sugar or at the Havana Coal Company. Otherwise everyone would have wanted it to go to a finish. But he had finished it anyway and before anyone had to go to work.

For a long time after that everyone had called him The Champion and there had been a return match in the spring. But not much money was bet and he had won it quite easily since he had broken the confidence of the Negro from Cienfuegos in the first match. After that he had a few matches and then no more. He decided that he could beat anyone if he wanted to badly enough and he decided that it was bad for his right hand for fishing. He had tried a few practice matches with his left hand. But his left hand had always been a traitor and would not do what he called on it to do and he did not trust it.

The sun will bake it out well now, he thought. It should not cramp on me again unless it gets too cold in the night. I wonder what this night will bring.

An airplane passed overhead on its course to Miami and he watched its shadow scaring up the schools of flying fish.

"With so much flying fish there should be dolphin," he said, and leaned back on the line to see if it was possible to gain any on his fish. But he could not and it stayed at the hardness and waterdrop shivering that preceded breaking. The boat moved ahead slowly and he watched the airplane until he could no longer see it.

It must be very strange in an airplane, he thought. I wonder what the sea looks like from that height? They should be able to see the fish well if they do not fly too high. I would like to fly very slowly at two hundred fathoms high and see the fish from above. In the turtle boats I was in the cross-trees of the mast-head and even at that height I saw much. The dolphin look greener from there and you can see their stripes and their purple spots and you can see all of the school as they swim. Why is it that all the fast-moving fish of the dark current have purple backs and usually purple stripes or spots? The dolphin looks green of course because he is really golden. But when he comes to feed, truly hungry, purple stripes show on his sides as on a marlin. Can it be anger, or the greater speed he makes that brings them out? ·

Just before it was dark, as they passed a great island of Sargasso weed that heaved and swung in the light sea as though the ocean were making love with something under a yellow blanket, his small line was taken by a dolphin. He saw it first when it jumped in the air, true gold in the last of the sun and bending and flapping wildly in the air. It jumped again and again in the acrobatics of its fear and he worked his way back to the stern and crouching and holding the big line with his right hand and arm, he pulled the dolphin in with his left hand, stepping on the gained line each time with his bare left foot. When the fish was at the stern, plunging and cutting from side to side in desperation, the old man leaned over the stern and lifted the burnished gold fish with its purple spots over the stern. Its jaws were working convulsively in quick bites against the hook and it pounded the bottom of the skiff with its long flat body, its tail and its head until he clubbed it across the shining golden head until it shivered and was still.

The old man unhooked the fish, re-baited the line with another sardine and tossed it over. Then he worked his way slowly back to the bow. He washed his left hand and wiped it on his trousers. Then he shifted the heavy line from his right hand to his left and washed his right hand in the sea while he watched the sun go into the ocean and the slant of the big cord.

"He hasn't changed at all," he said. But watching the movement of the water against his hand he noted that it was perceptibly slower.

"I'll lash the two oars together across the stern and that will slow him in the night," he said. "He's good for the night and so am I."

It would be better to gut the dolphin a little later to save the blood in the meat, he thought. I can do that a little later and lash the oars to make a drag at the same time. I had better keep the fish quiet now and not disturb him too much at sunset. The setting of the sun is a difficult time for all fish.

He let his hand dry in the air then grasped the line with it and eased himself as much as he could and allowed himself to be pulled forward against the wood so that the boat took the strain as much, or more, than he did.

I'm learning how to do it, he thought. This part of it anyway. Then too, remember he hasn't eaten since he took the bait and he is huge and needs much food. I have eaten the whole bonito. Tomorrow I will eat the dolphin. He called it *dorado*. Perhaps I should eat some of it when I clean it. It will be harder to eat than the bonito. But, then, nothing is easy.

"How do you feel, fish?" he asked aloud. "I feel good and my left hand is better and I have food for a night and a day. Pull the boat, fish."

He did not truly feel good because the pain from the cord across his back had almost passed pain and gone into a dullness that he mistrusted. But I have had worse things than that, he thought. My hand is only cut a little and the cramp is gone from the other. My legs are all right. Also now I have gained on him in the question of sustenance.

It was dark now as it becomes dark quickly after the sun sets in September. He lay against the worn wood of the bow and rested all that he could. The first stars were out. He did not know the name of Rigel but he saw it and knew soon they would all be out and he would have all his distant friends.

"The fish is my friend too," he said aloud. "I have never seen or heard of such a fish. But I must kill him. I am glad we do not have to try to kill the stars."

Imagine if each day a man must try to kill the moon, he thought. The moon runs away. But imagine if a man each day should have to try to kill the sun? We were born lucky, he thought.

Then he was sorry for the great fish that had nothing to eat and his determination to kill him never relaxed in his sorrow for him. How many people will he feed, he thought. But are they worthy to eat him? No, of course not. There is no one worthy of eating him from the manner of his behaviour and his great dignity.

I do not understand these things, he thought. But it is good that we do not have to try to kill the sun or the moon or the stars. It is enough to live on the sea and kill our true brothers.

Now, he thought, I must think about the drag. It has its perils and its merits. I may lose so much line that I will lose him, if he makes his effort and the drag made by the oars is in place and the boat loses all her lightness. Her lightness prolongs both our suffering but it is my safety since he has great speed that he has never yet employed. No matter what passes I must gut the dolphin so he does not spoil and eat some of him to be strong.

Now I will rest an hour more and feel that he is solid and steady before I move back to the stern to do the work and make the decision. In the meantime I can see how he acts and if he shows any changes. The oars are a good trick; but it has reached the time to play for safety. He is much fish still and I saw that the hook was in the corner of his mouth and he has kept his mouth tight shut. The punishment of the hook is nothing. The punishment of hunger, and that he is against something that he does not comprehend, is everything. Rest now, old man, and let him work until your next duty comes.

He rested for what he believed to be two hours. The moon did not rise now until late and he had no way of judging the time. Nor was he really resting except comparatively. He was still bearing the pull of the fish across his shoulders but he placed his left hand on the gunwale of the bow and confided more and more of the resistance to the fish to the skiff itself.

How simple it would be if I could make the line fast, he thought. But with one small lurch he could break it. I must cushion the pull of the line with my body and at all times be ready to give line with both hands.

"But you have not slept yet, old man," he said aloud. "It is half a day and a night and now another day and you have not slept. You must devise a way so that you sleep a little if he is quiet and steady. If you do not sleep you might become unclear in the head."

I'm clear enough in the head, he thought. Too clear. I am as clear as the stars that are my brothers. Still I must sleep. They sleep and the moon and the sun sleep and even the ocean sleeps sometimes on certain days when there is no current and a flat calm.

But remember to sleep, he thought. Make yourself do it and devise some simple and sure way about the lines. Now go back and prepare the dolphin. It is too dangerous to rig the oars as a drag if you must sleep.

I could go without sleeping, he told himself. But it would be too dangerous.

He started to work his way back to the stern on his hands and knees, being careful not to jerk against the fish. He may be half asleep himself, he thought. But I do not want him to rest. He must pull until he dies.

Back in the stern he turned so that his left hand held the strain of the line across his shoulders and drew his knife from its sheath with his right hand. The stars were bright now and he saw the dolphin clearly and he pushed the blade of his knife into his head and drew him out from under the stern. He put one of his feet on the fish and slit him quickly from the vent up to the tip of his lower jaw. Then he put his knife down and gutted him with his right hand, scooping him clean and pulling the gills clear. He felt the maw heavy and slippery in his hands and he slid it open. There were two flying fish inside. They were fresh and hard and he laid them side by side and dropped the guts and the gills over the stern. They sank leaving a trail of phosphorescence in the water. The dolphin was cold and a leprous gray-white now in the starlight and the old man skinned one side of him while he held his right foot on the fish's head. Then he turned him over and skinned the other side and cut each side off from the head down to the tail.

He slid the carcass overboard and looked to see if there was any swirl in the water. But there was only the light of its slow descent. He turned then and placed the two flying fish inside the two fillets of fish and putting his knife back in its sheath, he worked his way slowly back to the bow. His back was bent with the weight of the line across it and he carried the fish in his right hand.

Back in the bow he laid the two fillets of fish out on the wood with the flying fish beside them. After that he settled the line across his shoulders in a new place and held it again with his left hand resting on the gunwale. Then he leaned over the side and washed the flying fish in the water, noting the speed of the water against his hand. His hand was phosphorescent from skinning the fish and he watched the flow of the water against it. The flow was less strong and as he rubbed the side of his hand against the planking of the skiff, particles of phosphorus floated off and drifted slowly astern.

"He is tiring or he is resting," the old man said. "Now let me get through the eating of this dolphin and get some rest and a little sleep."

Under the stars and with the night colder all the time he ate half of one of the dolphin fillets and one of the flying fish, gutted and with its head cut off.

"What an excellent fish dolphin is to eat cooked," he said. "And what a miserable fish raw. I will never go in a boat again without salt or limes."

If I had brains I would have splashed water on the bow all day and drying, it would have made salt, he thought. But then I did not hook the dolphin until almost sunset. Still it was a lack of preparation. But I have chewed it all well and I am not nauseated.

The sky was clouding over to the east and one after another the stars he knew were gone. It looked now as though he were moving into a great canyon of clouds and the wind had dropped.

"There will be bad weather in three or four days," he said. "But not tonight and not tomorrow. Rig now to get some sleep, old man, while the fish is calm and steady."

He held the line tight in his right hand and then pushed his thigh against his right hand as he leaned all his weight against the wood of the bow. Then he passed the line a little lower on his shoulders and braced his left hand on it.

My right hand can hold it as long as it is braced, he thought. If it relaxes in sleep my left hand will wake me as the line goes out. It is hard on the right hand. But he is used to punishment. Even if I sleep twenty minutes or a half an hour it is good. He lay forward cramping himself against the line with all of his body, putting all his weight onto his right hand, and he was asleep.

He did not dream of the lions but instead of a vast school of porpoises that stretched for eight or ten miles and it was in the time of their mating and they would leap high into the air and return into the same hole they had made in the water when they leaped.

Then he dreamed that he was in the village on his bed and there was a norther and he was very cold and his right arm was asleep because his head had rested on it instead of a pillow.

After that he began to dream of the long yellow beach and he saw the first of the lions come down onto it in the early dark and then the other lions came and he rested his chin on the wood of the bows where the ship lay anchored with the evening off-shore breeze and he waited to see if there would be more lions and he was happy.

The moon had been up for a long time but he slept on and the fish pulled on steadily and the boat moved into the tunnel of clouds.

He woke with the jerk of his right fist coming up against his face and the line burning out through his right hand. He had no feeling of his left hand but he braked all he could with his right and the line rushed out. Finally his left hand found the line and he leaned back against the line and now it burned his back and his left hand, and his left hand was taking all the strain and cutting badly. He looked back at the coils of line and they were feeding smoothly. Just then the fish jumped making a great bursting of the ocean and then a heavy fall. Then he jumped again and again and the boat was going fast although line was still racing out and the old man was raising the strain to breaking point and raising it to breaking point again and again. He had been pulled down tight onto the bow and his face was in the cut slice of dolphin and he could not move.

This is what we waited for, he thought. So now let us take it.

Make him pay for the line, he thought. Make him pay for it.

He could not see the fish's jumps but only heard the breaking of the ocean and the heavy splash as he fell. The speed of the line was cutting his hands badly but he had always known this woul 1 happen and he tried to keep the cutting across the calloused parts and not let the line slip into the palm nor cut the fingers.

If the boy was here he would wet the coils of line, he thought. Yes. If the boy were here. If the boy were here.

The line went out and out and out but it was slowing now and he was making the fish earn each inch of it. Now he got his head up from the wood and out of the slice of fish that his cheek had crushed. Then he was on his knees and then he rose slowly to his feet. He was ceding line but more slowly all the time. He worked back to where he could feel with his foot the coils of line that he could not see. There was plenty of line still and now the fish had to pull the friction of all that new line through the water.

Yes, he thought. And now he has jumped more than a dozen times and filled the sacks along his back with air and he cannot go down deep to die where I cannot bring him up. He will start circling soon and then I must work on him. I wonder what started him so suddenly? Could it have been hunger that made him desperate, or was he frightened by something in the night? Maybe he suddenly felt fear. But he was such a calm, strong fish and he seemed so fearless and so confident. It is strange.

"You better be fearless and confident yourself, old man," he said. "You're holding him again but you cannot get line. But soon he has to circle."

The old man held him with his left hand and his shoulders now and stooped down and scooped up water in his right hand to get the crushed dolphin flesh off of his face. He was afraid that it might nauseate him and he would vomit and lose his strength. When his face was cleaned he washed his right hand in the water over the side and then let it stay in the salt water while he watched the first light come before the sunrise. He's headed almost east, he thought. That means he is tired and going with the current. Soon he will have to circle. Then our true work begins.

After he judged that his right hand had been in the water long enough he took it out and looked at it.

"It is not bad," he said. "And pain does not matter to a man."

He took hold of the line carefully so that it did not fit into any of the fresh line cuts and shifted his weight so that he could put his left hand into the sea on the other side of the skiff.

"You did not do so badly for something worthless," he said to his left hand. "But there was a moment when I could not find you."

Why was I not born with two good hands? he thought. Perhaps it was my fault in not training that one properly. But God knows he has had enough chances to learn. He did not do so badly in the night, though, and he has only cramped once. If he cramps again let the line cut him off.

When he thought that he knew that he was not being clear-headed and he thought he should chew some more of the dolphin. But I can't, he told himself. It is better to be light-headed than to lose your strength from nausea. And I know I cannot keep it if I eat it since my face was in it. I will keep it for an emergency until it goes bad. But it is too late to try for strength now through nourishment. You're stupid, he told himself. Eat the other flying fish.

It was there, cleaned and ready, and he picked it up with his left hand and ate it chewing the bones carefully and eating all of it down to the tail.

It has more nourishment than almost any fish, he thought. At least the kind of strength that I need. Now I have done what I can, he thought. Let him begin to circle and let the fight come.

The sun was rising for the third time since he had put to sea when the fish started to circle.

He could not see by the slant of the line that the fish was circling. It was too early for that. He just felt a faint slackening of the pressure of the line and he commenced to pull on it gently with his right hand. It tightened, as always, but just when he reached the point where it would break, line began to come in. He slipped his shoulders and head from under the line and began to pull in line steadily and gently. He used both of his hands in a swinging motion and tried to do the pulling as much as he could with his body and his legs. His old legs and shoulders pivoted with the swinging of the pulling.

"It is a very big circle," he said. "But he is circling."

Then the line would not come in any more and he held it until he saw the drops jumping from it in the sun. Then it started out and the old man knelt down and let it go grudgingly back into the dark water.

"He is making the far part of his circle now," he said. I must hold all I can, he thought. The strain will shorten his circle each time. Perhaps in an hour I will see him. Now I must convince him and then I must kill him.

But the fish kept on circling slowly and the old man was wet with sweat and tired deep into his bones two hours later. But the circles were much shorter now and from the way the line slanted he could tell the fish had risen steadily while he swam.

For an hour the old man had been seeing black spots before his eyes and the sweat salted his eyes and salted the cut over his eye and on his forehead. He was not afraid of the black spots. They were normal at the tension that he was pulling on the line. Twice, though, he had felt faint and dizzy and that had worried him.

"I could not fail myself and die on a fish like this," he said. "Now that I have him coming so beautifully, God help me endure. I'll say a hundred Our Fathers and a hundred Hail Marys. But I cannot say them now."

Consider them said, he thought. I'll say them later.

Just then he felt a sudden banging and jerking on the line he held with his two hands. It was sharp and hard-feeling and heavy.

He is hitting the wire leader with his spear, he thought. That was bound to come. He had to do that. It may make him jump though and I would rather he stayed circling now. The jumps were necessary for him to take air. But after that each one can widen the opening of the hook wound and he can throw the hook.

"Don't jump, fish," he said. "Don't jump."

The fish hit the wire several times more and each time he shook his head the old man gave up a little line.

I must hold his pain where it is, he thought. Mine does not matter. I can control mine. But his pain could drive him mad.

After a while the fish stopped beating at the wire and started circling slowly again. The old man was gaining line steadily now. But he felt faint again. He lifted some sea water with his left hand and put it on his head. Then he put more on and rubbed the back of his neck.

"I have no cramps," he said. "He'll be up soon and I can last. You have to last. Don't even speak of it."

He kneeled against the bow and, for a moment, slipped the line over his back again. I'll rest now while he goes out on the circle and then stand up and work on him when he comes in, he decided.

It was a great temptation to rest in the bow and let the fish make one circle by himself without recovering any line. But when the strain showed the fish had turned to come toward the boat, the old man rose to his feet and started the pivoting and the weaving pulling that brought in all the line he gained.

I'm tireder than I have ever been, he thought, and now the trade wind is rising. But that will be good to take him in with. I need that badly.

"I'll rest on the next turn as he goes out," he said. "I feel much better. Then in two or three turns more I will have him."

His straw hat was far on the back of his head and he sank down into the bow with the pull of the line as he felt the fish turn.

You work now, fish, he thought. I'll take you at the turn.

The sea had risen considerably. But it was a fair-weather breeze and he had to have it to get home.

"I'll just steer south and west," he said. "A man is never lost at sea and it is a long island."

It was on the third turn that he saw the fish first.

He saw him first as a dark shadow that took so long to pass under the boat that he could not believe its length.

"No," he said. "He can't be that big."

But he was that big and at the end of this circle he came to the surface only thirty yards away and the man saw his tail out of water. It was higher than a big scythe blade and a very pale lavender above the dark blue water. It raked back and as the fish swam just below the surface the old man could see his huge bulk and the purple stripes that banded him. His dorsal fin was down and his huge pectorals were spread wide.

On this circle the old man could see the fish's eye and the two gray sucking fish that swam around him. Sometimes they attached themselves to him. Sometimes they darted off. Sometimes they would swim easily in his shadow. They were each over three feet long and when they swam fast they lashed their whole bodies like eels.

The old man was sweating now but from something else besides the sun. On each calm placid turn the fish made he was gaining line and he was sure that in two turns more he would have a chance to get the harpoon in.

But I must get him close, close, close, he thought. I mustn't try for the head. I must get the heart.

"Be calm and strong, old man," he said.

On the next circle the fish's back was out but he was a little too far from the boat. On the next circle he was still too far away but he was higher out of water and the old man was sure that by gaining some more line he could have him alongside.

He had rigged his harpoon long before and its coil of light rope was in a round basket and the end was made fast to the bitt in the bow.

The fish was coming in on his circle now calm and beautiful looking and only his great tail moving. The old man pulled on him all that he could to bring him closer. For just a moment the fish turned a little on his side. Then he straightened himself and began another circle.

"I moved him," the old man said. "I moved him then."

He felt faint again now but he held on the great fish all the strain that he could. I moved him, he thought. Maybe this time I can get him over. Pull, hands, he thought. Hold up, legs. Last for me, head. Last for me. You never went. This time I'll pull him over.

But when he put all of his effort on, starting it well out before the fish came alongside and pulling with all his strength, the fish pulled part way over and then righted himself and swam away.

"Fish," the old man said. "Fish, you are going to have to die anyway. Do you have to kill me too?"

That way nothing is accomplished, he thought. His mouth was too dry to speak but he could not reach for the water now. He must get him alongside this time, he thought. I am not good for many more turns. Yes you are, he told himself. You're good for ever.

On the next turn, he nearly had him. But again the fish righted himself and swam slowly away.

You are killing me, fish, the old man thought. But you have a right to. Never have I seen a greater, or more beautiful, or a calmer or more noble thing than you, brother. Come on and kill me. I do not care who kills who.

Now you are getting confused in the head, he thought. You must keep your head clear. Keep your head clear and know how to suffer like a man. Or a fish, he thought.

"Clear up, head," he said in a voice he could hardly hear. "Clear up."

Twice more it was the same on the turns.

I do not know, the old man thought. He had been on the point of feeling himself go each time. I do not know. But I will try it once more.

He tried it once more and he felt himself going when he turned the fish. The fish righted himself and swam off again slowly with the great tail weaving in the air.

I'll try it again, the old man promised, although his hands were mushy now and he could only see well in flashes.

He tried it again and it was the same. So he thought, and he felt himself going before he started; I will try it once again.

He took all his pain and what was left of his strength and his long gone pride and he put it against the fish's agony and the fish came over onto his side and swam gently on his side, his bill almost touching the planking of the skiff and started to pass the boat, long, deep, wide, silver and barred with purple and interminable in the water.

The old man dropped the line and put his foot on it and lifted the harpoon as high as he could and drove it down with all his strength, and more strength he had just summoned, into the fish's side just behind the great chest fin that rose high in the air to the altitude of the man's chest. He felt the iron go in and he leaned on it and drove it further and then pushed all his weight after it.

Then the fish came alive, with his death in him, and rose high out of the water showing all his great length and width and all his power and his beauty. He seemed to hang in the air above the old man in the skiff. Then he fell into the water with a crash that sent spray over the old man and over all of the skiff.

The old man felt faint and sick and he could not see well. But he cleared the harpoon line and let it run slowly through his raw hands and, when he could see, he saw the fish was on his back with his silver belly up. The shaft of the harpoon was projecting at an angle from the fish's shoulder and the sea was discolouring with the red of the blood from his heart. First it was dark as a shoal in the blue water that was more than a mile deep. Then it spread like a cloud. The fish was silvery and still and floated with the waves.

The old man looked carefully in the glimpse of vision that he had. Then he took two turns of the harpoon line around the bitt in the bow and laid his head on his hands.

"Keep my head clear," he said against the wood of the bow. "I am a tired old man. But I have killed this fish which is my brother and now I must do the slave work."

Now I must prepare the nooses and the rope to lash him alongside, he thought. Even if we were two and swamped her to load him and bailed her out, this skiff would never hold him. I must prepare everything, then bring him in and lash him well and step the mast and set sail for home.

He started to pull the fish in to have him alongside so that he could pass a line through his gills and out his mouth and make his head fast alongside the bow. I want to see him, he thought, and to touch and to feel him. He is my fortune, he thought. But that is not why I wish to feel him. I think I felt his heart, he thought. When I pushed on the harpoon shaft the second time. Bring him in now and make him fast and get the noose around his tail and another around his middle to bind him to the skiff.

"Get to work, old man," he said. He took a very small drink of the water. "There is very much slave work to be done now that the fight is over."

He looked up at the sky and then out to his fish. He looked at the sun carefully. It is not much more than noon, he thought. And the trade wind is rising. The lines all mean nothing now. The boy and I will splice them when we are home.

"Come on, fish," he said. But the fish did not come. Instead he lay there wallowing now in the seas and the old man pulled the skiff up onto him.

When he was even with him and had the fish's head against the bow he could not believe his size. But he untied the harpoon rope from the bitt, passed it through the fish's gills and out his jaws, made a turn around his sword then passed the rope through the other gill, made another turn around the bill and knotted the double rope and made it fast to the bitt in the bow. He cut the rope then and went astern to noose the tail. The fish had turned silver from his original purple and silver, and the stripes showed the same pale violet colour as his tail. They were wider than a man's hand with his fingers spread and the fish's eye looked as detached as the mirrors in a periscope or as a saint in a procession.

"It was the only way to kill him," the old man said. He was feeling better since the water and he knew he would not go away and his head was clear. He's over fifteen hundred pounds the way he is, he thought. Maybe much more. If he dresses out two-thirds of that at thirty cents a pound?

"I need a pencil for that," he said. "My head is not that clear. But I think the great DiMaggio would be proud of me today. I had no bone spurs. But the hands and the back hurt truly." I wonder what a bone spur is, he thought. Maybe we have them without knowing of it.

He made the fish fast to bow and stern and to the middle thwart. He was so big it was like lashing a much bigger skiff alongside. He cut a piece of line and tied the fish's lower jaw against his bill so his mouth would not open and they would sail as cleanly as possible. Then he stepped the mast and, with the stick that was his gaff and with his boom rigged, the patched sail drew, the boat began to move, and half lying in the stern he sailed south-west.

He did not need a compass to tell him where south-west was. He only needed the feel of the trade wind and the drawing of the sail. I better put a small line out with a spoon on it and try and get something to eat and drink for the moisture. But he could not find a spoon and his sardines were rotten. So he hooked a patch of yellow Gulf weed with the gaff as they passed and shook it so that the small shrimps that were in it fell onto the planking of the skiff. There were more than a dozen of them and they jumped and kicked like sand fleas. The old man pinched their heads off with his thumb and forefinger and ate them chewing up the shells and the tails. They were very tiny but he knew they were nourishing and they tasted good.

The old man still had two drinks of water in the bottle and he used half of one after he had eaten the shrimps. The skiff was sailing well considering the handicaps and he steered with the tiller under his arm. He could see the fish and he had only to look at his hands and feel his back against the stern to know that this had truly happened and was not a dream. At one time when he was feeling so badly toward the end, he had thought perhaps it was a dream. Then when he had seen the fish come out of the water and hang motionless in the sky before he fell, he was sure there was some great strangeness and he could not believe it. Then he could not see well, although now he saw as well as ever.

Now he knew there was the fish and his hands and back were no dream. The hands cure quickly, he thought. I bled them clean and the salt water will heal them. The dark water of the true gulf is the greatest healer that there is. All I must do is keep the head clear.

The hands have done their work and we sail well. With his mouth shut and his tail straight up and down we sail like brothers. Then his head started to become a little unclear and he thought, is he bringing me in or am I bringing him in? If I were towing him behind there would be no question. Nor if the fish were in the skiff, with all dignity gone, there would be no question either. But they were sailing together lashed side by side and the old man thought, let him bring me in if it pleases him. I am only better than him through trickery and he meant me no harm.

They sailed well and the old man soaked his hands in the salt water and tried to keep his head clear. There were high cumulus clouds and enough cirrus above them so that the old man knew the breeze would last all night. The old man looked at the fish constantly to make sure it was true. It was an hour before the first shark hit him.

The shark was not an accident. He had come up from deep down in the water as the dark cloud of blood had settled and dispersed in the mile deep sea. He had come up so fast and absolutely without caution that he broke the surface of the blue water and was in the sun. Then he fell back into the sea and picked up the scent and started swimming on the course the skiff and the fish had taken.

Sometimes he lost the scent. But he would pick it up again, or have just a trace of it, and he swam fast and hard on the course. He was a very big Mako shark built to swim as fast as the fastest fish in the sea and everything about him was beautiful except his jaws. His back was as blue as a sword fish's and his belly was silver and his hide was smooth and handsome. He was built as a sword fish except for his huge jaws which were tight shut now as he swam fast, just under the surface with his high dorsal fin knifing through the water without wavering. Inside the closed double lip of his jaws all of his eight rows of teeth were slanted inwards. They were not the ordinary pyramid-shaped teeth of most sharks. They were shaped like a man's fingers when they are crisped like claws. They were nearly as long as the fingers of the old man and they had razor-sharp cutting edges on both sides. This was a fish built to feed on all the fishes in the sea, that were so fast and strong and well armed that they had no other enemy. Now he speeded up as he smelled the fresher scent and his blue dorsal fin cut the water.

When the old man saw him coming he knew that this was a

shark that had no fear at all and would do exactly what he wished. He prepared the harpoon and made the rope fast while he watched the shark come on. The rope was short as it lacked what he had cut away to lash the fish.

The old man's head was clear and good now and he was full of resolution but he had little hope. It was too good to last, he thought. He took one look at the great fish as he watched the shark close in. It might as well have been a dream, he thought. I cannot keep him from hitting me but maybe I can get him. *Dentuso,* he thought. Bad luck to your mother.

The shark closed fast astern and when he hit the fish the old man saw his mouth open and his strange eyes and the clicking chop of the teeth as he drove forward in the meat just above the tail. The shark's head was out of water and his back was coming out and the old man could hear the noise of skin and flesh ripping on the big fish when he rammed the harpoon down onto the shark's head at a spot where the line between his eyes intersected with the line that ran straight back from his nose. There were no such lines. There was only the heavy sharp blue head and the big eyes and the clicking, thrusting all-swallowing jaws. But that was the location of the brain and the old man hit it. He hit it with his blood mushed hands driving a good harpoon with all his strength. He hit it without hope but with resolution and complete malignancy.

The shark swung over and the old man saw his eye was not alive and then he swung over once again, wrapping himself in two loops of the rope. The old man knew that he was dead but the shark would not accept it. Then, on his back, with his tail lashing and his jaws clicking, the shark plowed over the water as a speedboat does. The water was white where his tail beat it and three-quarters of his body was clear above the water when the rope came taut, shivered, and then snapped. The shark lay quietly for a little while on the surface and the old man watched him. Then he went down very slowly.

"He took about forty pounds," the old man said aloud. He took my harpoon too and all the rope, he thought, and now my fish bleeds again and there will be others.

He did not like to look at the fish anymore since he had been mutilated. When the fish had been hit it was as though he himself were hit.

But I killed the shark that hit my fish, he thought. And he was the biggest *dentuso* that I have ever seen. And God knows that I have seen big ones.

It was too good to last, he thought. I wish it had been a dream now and that I had never hooked the fish and was alone in bed on the newspapers.

"But man is not made for defeat," he said. "A man can be destroyed but not defeated." I am sorry that I killed the fish though, he thought. Now the bad time is coming and I do not even have the harpoon. The *dentuso* is cruel and able and strong and intelligent. But I was more intelligent than he was. Perhaps not, he thought. Perhaps I was only better armed.

"Don't think, old man," he said aloud. "Sail on this course and take it when it comes."

But I must think, he thought. Because it is all I have left. That and baseball. I wonder how the great DiMaggio would have liked the way I hit him in the brain? It was no great thing, he thought. Any man could do it. But do you think my hands were as great a handicap as the bone spurs? I cannot know. I never had anything wrong with my heel except the time the sting ray stung it when I stepped on him when swimming and paralyzed the lower leg and made the unbearable pain.

"Think about something cheerful, old man," he said. "Every minute now you are closer to home. You sail lighter for the loss of forty pounds."

He knew quite well the pattern of what could happen when he reached the inner part of the current. But there was nothing to be done now.

"Yes there is," he said aloud. "I can lash my knife to the butt of one of the oars."

So he did that with the tiller under his arm and the sheet of the sail under his foot.

"Now," he said. "I am still an old man. But I am not unarmed."

The breeze was fresh now and he sailed on well. He watched only the forward part of the fish and some of his hope returned.

It is silly not to hope, he thought. Besides I believe it is a sin. Do not think about sin, he thought. There are enough problems now without sin. Also I have no understanding of it.

I have no understanding of it and I am not sure that I believe in it. Perhaps it was a sin to kill the fish. I suppose it was even though

I did it to keep me alive and feed many people. But then everything is a sin. Do not think about sin. It is much too late for that and there are people who are paid to do it. Let them think about it. You were born to be a fisherman as the fish was born to be a fish. San Pedro was a fisherman as was the father of the great DiMaggio.

But he liked to think about all things that he was involved in and since there was nothing to read and he did not have a radio, he thought much and he kept on thinking about sin. You did not kill the fish only to keep alive and to sell for food, he thought. You killed him for pride and because you are a fisherman. You loved him when he was alive and you loved him after. If you love him, it is not a sin to kill him. Or is it more?

"You think too much, old man," he said aloud.

But you enjoyed killing the *dentuso,* he thought. He lives on the live fish as you do. He is not a scavenger nor just a moving appetite as some sharks are. He is beautiful and noble and knows no fear of anything.

"I killed him in self-defense," the old man said aloud. "And I killed him well."

Besides, he thought, everything kills everything else in some way. Fishing kills me exactly as it keeps me alive. The boy keeps me alive, he thought. I must not deceive myself too much.

He leaned over the side and pulled loose a piece of the meat of the fish where the shark had cut him. He chewed it and noted its quality and its good taste. It was firm and juicy, like meat, but it was not red. There was no stringiness in it and he knew that it would bring the highest price in the market. But there was no way to keep its scent out of the water and the old man knew that a very bad time was coming.

The breeze was steady. It had backed a little further into the north-east and he knew that meant that it would not fall off. The old man looked ahead of him but he could see no sails nor could he see the hull nor the smoke of any ship. There were only the flying fish that went up from his bow sailing away to either side and the yellow patches of Gulf weed. He could not even see a bird.

He had sailed for two hours, resting in the stern and sometimes chewing a bit of the meat from the marlin, trying to rest and to be strong, when he saw the first of the two sharks.

"*Ay,*" he said aloud. There is no translation for this word and perhaps it is just a noise such as a man might make, involuntarily, feeling the nail go through his hands and into the wood.

"*Galanos*," he said aloud. He had seen the second fin now coming up behind the first and had identified them as shovel-nosed sharks by the brown, triangular fin and the sweeping movements of the tail. They had the scent and were excited and in the stupidity of their great hunger they were losing and finding the scent in their excitement. But they were closing all the time.

The old man made the sheet fast and jammed the tiller. Then he took up the oar with the knife lashed to it. He lifted it as lightly as he could because his hands rebelled at the pain. Then he opened and closed them on it lightly to loosen them. He closed them firmly so they would take the pain now and would not flinch and watched the sharks come. He could see their wide, flattened, shovel-pointed heads now and their white-tipped wide pectoral fins. They were hateful sharks, bad smelling, scavengers as well as killers, and when they were hungry they would bite at an oar or the rudder of a boat. It was these sharks that would cut the turtles' legs and flippers off when the turtles were asleep on the surface, and they would hit a man in the water, if they were hungry, even if the man had no smell of fish blood nor of fish slime on him.

"*Ay*," the old man said. "*Galanos*. Come on *galanos*."

They came. But they did not come as the Mako had come. One turned and went out of sight under the skiff and the old man could feel the skiff shake as he jerked and pulled on the fish. The other watched the old man with his slitted yellow eyes and then came in fast with his half circle of jaws wide to hit the fish where he had already been bitten. The line showed clearly on the top of his brown head and back where the brain joined the spinal cord and the old man drove the knife on the oar into the juncture, withdrew it, and drove it in again into the shark's yellow cat-like eyes. The shark let go of the fish and slid down, swallowing what he had taken as he died.

The skiff was still shaking with the destruction the other shark was doing to the fish and the old man let go the sheet so that the skiff would swing broadside and bring the shark out from under. When he saw the shark he leaned over the side and punched at him. He hit only meat and the hide was set hard and he barely got the knife in. The blow hurt not only his hands but his shoulder too. But the shark came up fast with his head out and the old man hit him squarely in the center of his flat-topped head as his nose came out of water and lay against the fish. The old man withdrew the blade and punched the shark exactly in the same spot again. He still hung to the fish with his jaws hooked and the old man stabbed him in his left eye. The shark still hung there.

"No?" the old man said and he drove the blade between the vertebrae and the brain. It was an easy shot now and he felt the cartilage sever. The old man reversed the oar and put the blade between the shark's jaws to open them. He twisted the blade and as the shark slid loose he said, "Go on, *galano*. Slide down a mile deep. Go see your friend, or maybe it's your mother."

The old man wiped the blade of his knife and laid down the oar. Then he found the sheet and the sail filled and he brought the skiff onto her course.

"They must have taken a quarter of him and of the best meat," he said aloud. "I wish it were a dream and that I had never hooked him. I'm sorry about it, fish. It makes everything wrong." He stopped and he did not want to look at the fish now. Drained of blood and awash he looked the colour of the silver backing of a mirror and his stripes still showed.

"I shouldn't have gone out so far, fish," he said. "Neither for you nor for me. I'm sorry, fish."

Now, he said to himself. Look to the lashing on the knife and see if it has been cut. Then get your hand in order because there still is more to come.

"I wish I had a stone for the knife," the old man said after he had checked the lashing on the oar butt. "I should have brought a stone." You should have brought many things, he thought. But you did not bring them, old man. Now is no time to think of what you do not have. Think of what you can do with what there is.

"You give me much good counsel," he said aloud. "I'm tired of it."

He held the tiller under his arm and soaked both his hands in the water as the skiff drove forward.

"God knows how much that last one took," he said. "But she's much lighter now." He did not want to think of the mutilated underside of the fish. He knew that each of the jerking bumps of the shark had been meat torn away and that the fish now made a trail for all sharks as wide as a highway through the sea.

He was a fish to keep a man all winter, he thought. Don't think of that. Just rest and try to get your hands in shape to defend what is left of him. The blood smell from my hands means nothing now with all that scent in the water. Besides they do not bleed much. There is nothing cut that means anything. The bleeding may keep the left from cramping.

What can I think of now? he thought. Nothing. I must think of nothing and wait for the next ones. I wish it had really been a dream, he thought. But who knows? It might have turned out well.

The next shark that came was a single shovelnose. He came like a pig to the trough if a pig had a mouth so wide that you could put your head in it. The old man let him hit the fish and then drove the knife on the oar down into his brain. But the shark jerked backwards as he rolled and the knife blade snapped.

The old man settled himself to steer. He did not even watch the big shark sinking slowly in the water, showing first life-size, then small, then tiny. That always fascinated the old man. But he did not even watch it now.

"I have the gaff now," he said. "But it will do no good. I have the two oars and the tiller and the short club."

Now they have beaten me, he thought. I am too old to club sharks to death. But I will try it as long as I have the oars and the short club and the tiller.

He put his hands in the water again to soak them. It was getting late in the afternoon and he saw nothing but the sea and the sky. There was more wind in the sky than there had been, and soon he hoped that he would see land.

"You're tired, old man," he said. "You're tired inside."

The sharks did not hit him again until just before sunset.

The old man saw the brown fins coming along the wide trail the fish must make in the water. They were not even quartering on the scent. They were headed straight for the skiff swimming side by side.

He jammed the tiller, made the sheet fast and reached under the stern for the club. It was an oar handle from a broken oar sawed off to about two and a half feet in length. He could only use it effectively with one hand because of the grip of the handle and he took good hold of it with his right hand, flexing his hand on it, as he watched the sharks come. They were both *galanos*.

I must let the first one get a good hold and hit him on the point of the nose or straight across the top of the head, he thought.

The two sharks closed together and as he saw the one nearest him open his jaws and sink them into the silver side of the fish, he raised the club high and brought it down heavy and slamming onto the top of the shark's broad head. He felt the rubbery solidity as the club came down. But he felt the rigidity of bone too and he struck the shark once more hard across the point of the nose as he slid down from the fish.

The other shark had been in and out and now came in again with his jaws wide. The old man could see pieces of the meat of the fish spilling white from the corner of his jaws as he bumped the fish and closed his jaws. He swung at him and hit only the head and the shark looked at him and wrenched the meat loose. The old man swung the club down on him again as he slipped away to swallow and hit only the heavy solid rubberiness.

"Come on, *galano*," the old man said. "Come in again."

The shark came in a rush and the old man hit him as he shut his jaws. He hit him solidly and from as high up as he could raise the club. This time he felt the bone at the base of the brain and he hit him again in the same place while the shark tore the meat loose sluggishly and slid down from the fish.

The old man watched for him to come again but neither shark showed. Then he saw one on the surface swimming in circles. He did not see the fin of the other.

I could not expect to kill them, he thought. I could have in my time. But I have hurt them both badly and neither one can feel very good. If I could have used a bat with two hands I could have killed the first one surely. Even now, he thought.

He did not want to look at the fish. He knew that half of him had been destroyed. The sun had gone down while he had been in the fight with the sharks.

"It will be dark soon," he said. "Then I should see the glow of Havana. If I am too far to the eastward I will see the lights of one of the new beaches."

I cannot be too far out now, he thought. I hope no one has been too worried. There is only the boy to worry, of course. But I am sure he would have confidence. Many of the older fishermen will worry. Many others too, he thought. I live in a good town.

He could not talk to the fish anymore because the fish had been ruined too badly. Then something came into his head.

"Half fish," he said. "Fish that you were. I am sorry that I went too far out. I ruined us both. But we have killed many sharks, you and I, and ruined many others. How many did you ever kill, old fish? You do not have that spear on your head for nothing."

He liked to think of the fish and what he could do to a shark if he were swimming free. I should have chopped the bill off to fight them with, he thought. But there was no hatchet and then there was no knife.

But if I had, and could have lashed it to an oar butt, what a weapon. Then we might have fought them together. What will you do now if they come in the night? What can you do?

"Fight them," he said. "I'll fight them until I die."

But in the dark now and no glow showing and no lights and only the wind and the steady pull of the sail he felt that perhaps he was already dead. He put his two hands together and felt the palms. They were not dead and he could bring the pain of life by simply opening and closing them. He leaned his back against the stern and knew he was not dead. His shoulders told him.

I have all those prayers I promised if I caught the fish, he thought. But I am too tired to say them now. I better get the sack and put it over my shoulders.

He lay in the stern and steered and watched for the glow to come in the sky. I have half of him, he thought. Maybe I'll have the luck to bring the forward half in. I should have some luck. No, he said. You violated your luck when you went too far outside.

"Don't be silly," he said aloud. "And keep awake and steer. You may have much luck yet.

"I'd like to buy some if there's any place they sell it," he said.

What could I buy it with? he asked himself. Could I buy it with a lost harpoon and a broken knife and two bad hands?

"You might," he said. "You tried to buy it with eighty-four days at sea. They nearly sold it to you too."

I must not think nonsense, he thought. Luck is a thing that comes in many forms and who can recognize her? I would take some though in any form and pay what they asked. I wish I could see the glow from the lights, he thought. I wish too many things. But that is the thing I wish for now. He tried to settle more comfortably to steer and from his pain he knew he was not dead.

He saw the reflected glare of the lights of the city at what must have been around ten o'clock at night. They were only perceptible at first as the light is in the sky before the moon rises. Then they were steady to see across the ocean which was rough now with the increasing breeze. He steered inside of the glow and he thought that now, soon, he must hit the edge of the stream.

Now it is over, he thought. They will probably hit me again. But what can a man do against them in the dark without a weapon?

He was stiff and sore now and his wounds and all of the strained parts of his body hurt with the cold of the night. I hope I do not have to fight again, he thought. I hope so much I do not have to fight again.

But by midnight he fought and this time he knew the fight was useless. They came in a pack and he could only see the lines in the water that their fins made and their phosphorescence as they threw themselves on the fish. He clubbed at heads and heard the jaws chop and the shaking of the skiff as they took hold below. He clubbed desperately at what he could only feel and hear and he felt something seize the club and it was gone.

He jerked the tiller free from the rudder and beat and chopped with it, holding it in both hands and driving it down again and again. But they were up to the bow now and driving in one after the other and together, tearing off the pieces of meat that showed glowing below the sea as they turned to come once more.

One came, finally, against the head itself and he knew that it was over. He swung the tiller across the shark's head where the jaws were caught in the heaviness of the fish's head which would not tear. He swung it once and twice and again. He heard the tiller break and he lunged at the shark with the splintered butt. He felt it go in and knowing it was sharp he drove it in again. The shark let go and rolled away. That was the last shark of the pack that came. There was nothing more for them to eat.

The old man could hardly breathe now and he felt a strange taste in his mouth. It was coppery and sweet and he was afraid of it for a moment. But there was not much of it.

He spat into the ocean and said, "Eat that, *galanos*. And make a dream you've killed a man."

He knew he was beaten now finally and without remedy and he went back to the stern and found the jagged end of the tiller would fit in the slot of the rudder well enough for him to steer. He settled the sack around his shoulders and put the skiff on her course. He sailed lightly now and he had no thoughts nor any feelings of any kind. He was past everything now and he sailed the skiff to make his home port as well and as intelligently as he could. In the night sharks hit the carcass as someone might pick up crumbs from the table. The old man paid no attention to them and did not pay any attention to anything except steering. He only noticed how lightly and how well the skiff sailed now there was no great weight beside her.

She's good, he thought. She is sound and not harmed in any way except for the tiller. That is easily replaced.

He could feel he was inside the current now and he could see the lights of the beach colonies along the shore. He knew where he was now and it was nothing to get home.

The wind is our friend, anyway, he thought. Then he added, sometimes. And the great sea with our friends and our enemies. And bed, he thought. Bed is my friend. Just bed, he thought. Bed will be a great thing. It is easy when you are beaten, he thought. I never knew how easy it was. And what beat you, he thought.

"Nothing," he said aloud. "I went out too far."

When he sailed into the little harbour the lights of the Terrace were out and he knew everyone was in bed. The breeze had risen steadily and was blowing strongly now. It was quiet in the harbour though and he sailed up onto the little patch of shingle below the rocks. There was no one to help him so he pulled the boat up as far as he could. Then he stepped out and made her fast to a rock.

He unstepped the mast and furled the sail and tied it. Then he shouldered the mast and started to climb. It was then he knew the depth of his tiredness. He stopped for a moment and looked back and saw in the reflection from the street light the great tail of the fish standing up well behind the skiff's stern. He saw the white naked line of his backbone and the dark mass of the head with the projecting bill and all the nakedness between.

He started to climb again and at the top he fell and lay for some time with the mast across his shoulder. He tried to get up. But it was too difficult and he sat there with the mast on his shoulder and looked at the road. A cat passed on the far side going about its business and the old man watched it. Then he just watched the road.

Finally he put the mast down and stood up. He picked the mast up and put in on his shoulder and started up the road. He had to sit down five times before he reached his shack.

Inside the shack he leaned the mast against the wall. In the dark he found a water bottle and took a drink. Then he lay down on the bed. He pulled the blanket over his shoulders and then over his back and legs and he slept face down on the newspapers with his arms out straight and the palms of his hands up.

He was asleep when the boy looked in the door in the morning. It was blowing so hard that the drifting-boats would not be going out and the boy had slept late and then come to the old man's shack as he had come each morning. The boy saw that the old man was breathing and then he saw the old man's hands and he started to cry. He went out very quietly to go to bring some coffee and all the way down the road he was crying.

Many fishermen were around the skiff looking at what was lashed beside it and one was in the water, his trousers rolled up, measuring the skeleton with a length of line.

The boy did not go down. He had been there before and one of the fishermen was looking after the skiff for him.

"How is he?" one of the fishermen shouted.

"Sleeping," the boy called. He did not care that they saw him crying. "Let no one disturb him."

"He was eighteen feet from nose to tail," the fisherman who was measuring him called.

"I believe it," the boy said.

He went into the Terrace and asked for a can of coffee.

"Hot and with plenty of milk and sugar in it."

"Anything more?"

"No. Afterwards I will see what he can eat."

"What a fish it was," the proprietor said. "There has never been such a fish. Those were two fine fish you took yesterday too."

"Damn my fish," the boy said and he started to cry again.

"Do you want a drink of any kind?" the proprietor asked.

"No," the boy said. "Tell them not to bother Santiago. I'll be back."

"Tell him how sorry I am."

"Thanks," the boy said.

The boy carried the hot can of coffee up to the old man's shack and sat by him until he woke. Once it looked as though he were waking. But he had gone back into heavy sleep and the boy had gone across the road to borrow some wood to heat the coffee.

Finally the old man woke.

"Don't sit up," the boy said. "Drink this." He poured some of the coffee in a glass.

The old man took it and drank it.

"They beat me, Manolin," he said. "They truly beat me."

"He didn't beat you. Not the fish."

"No. Truly. It was afterwards."

"Pedrico is looking after the skiff and the gear. What do you want done with the head?"

"Let Pedrico chop it up to use in fish traps."

"And the spear?"

"You keep it if you want it."

"I want it," the boy said. "Now we must make our plans about the other things."

"Did they search for me?"

"Of course. With coast guard and with planes."

"The ocean is very big and a skiff is small and hard to see," the old man said. He noticed how pleasant it was to have someone to talk to instead of speaking only to himself and to the sea. "I missed you," he said. "What did you catch?"

"One the first day. One the second and two the third."

"Very good."

"Now we fish together again."

"No. I am not lucky. I am not lucky anymore."

"The hell with luck," the boy said. "I'll bring the luck with me."

"What will your family say?"

"I do not care. I caught two yesterday. But we will fish together now for I still have much to learn."

"We must get a good killing lance and always have it on board. You can make the blade from a spring leaf from an old Ford. We can grind it in Guanabacoa. It should be sharp and not tempered so it will break. My knife broke."

"I'll get another knife and have the spring ground. How many days of heavy *brisa* have we?"

"Maybe three. Maybe more."

"I will have everything in order," the boy said. "You get your hands well old man."

"I know how to care for them. In the night I spat something strange and felt something in my chest was broken."

"Get that well too," the boy said. "Lie down, old man, and I will bring you your clean shirt. And something to eat."

"Bring any of the papers of the time that I was gone," the old man said.

"You must get well fast for there is much that I can learn and you can teach me everything. How much did you suffer?"

"Plenty," the old man said.

"I'll bring the food and the papers," the boy said. "Rest well, old man. I will bring stuff from the drugstore for your hands."

"Don't forget to tell Pedrico the head is his."

"No. I will remember."

As the boy went out the door and down the worn coral rock road he was crying again.

That afternoon there was a party of tourists at the Terrace and looking down in the water among the empty beer cans and dead barracudas a woman saw a great long white spine with a huge tail at the end that lifted and swung with the tide while the east wind blew a heavy steady sea outside the entrance to the harbour.

"What's that?" she asked a waiter and pointed to the long backbone of the great fish that was now just garbage waiting to go out with the tide.

"Tiburon," the waiter said. "Eshark." He was meaning to explain what had happened.

"I didn't know sharks had such handsome, beautifully formed tails."

"I didn't either," her male companion said.

Up the road, in his shack, the old man was sleeping again. He was still sleeping on his face and the boy was sitting by him watching him. The old man was dreaming about the lions.

ISLANDS IN THE STREAM

PART III

AT SEA

1

THERE was a long white beach with coconut palms behind it. The reef lay across the entrance to the harbor and the heavy east wind made the sea break on it so that the entrance was easy to see once you had opened it up. There was no one on the beach and the sand was so white that it hurt his eyes to look at it.

The man on the flying bridge studied the shore. There were no shacks where the shacks should have been and there were no boats anchored in the lagoon that he could see.

"You've been in here before," he said to his mate.

"Yes."

"Weren't the shacks over there?"

"They were over there and it shows a village on the chart."

"They sure as hell aren't here now," the man said. "Can you make out any boats up in the mangroves?"

"There's nothing that I can see."

"I'm going to take her in and anchor," the man said. "I know this cut. It's about eight times as deep as it looks."

He looked down into the green water and saw the size of the shadow of his ship on the bottom.

"There's good holding ground east from where the village used to be," his mate said.

"I know. Break out the starboard anchor and stand by. I'm going to lay off there. With this wind blowing day and night there will be no insects."

"No sir."

They anchored and the boat, not big enough to be called a ship except in the mind of the man who was her master, lay with her bow into the wind with the waves breaking white and green on the reef.

The man on the bridge watched that she swung well and held solidly. Then he looked ashore and cut his motors. He continued to look at the shore and he could not figure it out at all.

"Take three men in and have a look," he said. "I'm going to lie down a while. Remember you're scientists."

When they were scientists no weapons showed and they wore machetes and wide straw hats such as Bahaman spongers wear. These the crew referred to as *"sombreros científicos."* The larger they were the more scientific they were considered.

"Someone has stolen my scientific hat," a heavy-shouldered Basque with thick eyebrows that came together over his nose said. "Give me a bag of frags for science's sake."

"Take my scientific hat," another Basque said. "It's twice as scientific as yours."

"What a scientific hat," the widest of the Basques said. "I feel like Einstein in this one. Thomas, can we take specimens?"

"No," the man said. "Antonio knows what I want him to do. You keep your damned scientific eyes open."

"I'll look for water."

"It's behind where the village was," the man said. "See how it is. We had probably better fill."

"H₂O," the Basque said. "That scientific stuff. Hey, you worthless scientist. You hat stealer. Give us four five-gallon jugs so we won't waste the trip."

The other Basque put four wicker-covered jugs in the dinghy.

The man heard them talking, "Don't hit me in the back with that damned scientific oar."

"I do it only for science."

"Fornicate science and his brother."

"Science's sister."

"Penicilina is her name."

The man watched them rowing toward the too white beach. I should have gone in, he thought. But I was up all night and I've steered twelve hours. Antonio can size it up as well as I can. But I wonder what the hell has happened.

He looked once at the reef and then at the shore and at the

current of clean water running against the side and making little eddies in the lee. Then he shut his eyes and turned on his side and went to sleep.

He woke as the dinghy came alongside and he knew it was something bad when he saw their faces. His mate was sweating as he always did with trouble or bad news. He was a dry man and he did not sweat easily.

"Somebody burned the shacks," he said. "Somebody tried to put them out and there are bodies in the ashes. You can't smell them from here because of the wind."

"How many bodies?"

"We counted nine. There could be more."

"Men or women?"

"Both."

"Are there any tracks?"

"Nothing. It's rained since. Heavy rain. The sand is still pitted with it."

The wide-shouldered Basque whose name was Ara said, "They've been dead a week anyway. Birds haven't worked on them but the land crabs are working on them."

"How do you know they have been dead a week?"

"No one can say exactly," Ara said. "But they have been dead about a week. From the land crab trails the rain was about three days ago."

"How was the water?"

"It looked all right."

"Did you bring it?"

"Yes."

"I don't see why they would have poisoned the water," Ara said. "It smelled good so I tasted it and brought it."

"You shouldn't have tasted it."

"It smelled good and there was no reason to believe it was poisoned."

"Who killed the people?"

"Anybody."

"Didn't you check?"

"No. We came to tell you. You are the skipper."

"All right," said Thomas Hudson. He went below and buckled

on his revolver. There was a sheath knife on the other side of the belt, the side that rode high, and the weight of the gun was on his leg. He stopped in the galley and took a spoon and put it in his pocket.

"Ara, you and Henry come ashore. Willie come in with the dinghy and then see if you can get some conches. Let Peters sleep." To his mate he said, "Check the engines, please, and all tanks."

The water was clear and lovely over the white sand bottom and he could see every ridge and wrinkle in the sand. As they waded ashore when the dinghy grounded on a ridge of sand he felt small fish playing around his toes and looked down and saw they were tiny pompano. Maybe they are not true pompano, he thought. But they look exactly like them and they are most friendly.

"Henry," he said when they were ashore. "You take the windward beach and walk it all the way up to the mangroves. Watch for tracks or anything else. Meet we here. Ara, you take the other beach and do the same."

He did not have to ask where the bodies were. He saw the tracks that led to them and heard the rattle of the land crabs in the dry brush. He looked out at his ship and the line of the breakers and Willie in the stern of the skiff with a water glass looking over the side for conches while the skiff drifted.

Since I have to do it I might as well get it over with, he thought. But this day was built for something else. It is strange how they had such a rain here where there was no need for it and we had nothing. How long is it now that we have seen the rains go by on either side and never had a drop?

The wind was blowing heavily and had blown now, day and night, for more than fifty days. It had become a part of the man and it did not make him nervous. It fortified him and gave him strength and he hoped that it would never stop.

We wait always for something that does not come, he thought. But it is easier waiting with the wind than in a calm or with the capriciousness and malignancy of squalls. There is always water somewhere. Let it stay dry. We can always find it. There is water on all these keys if you know how to look for it.

Now, he thought to himself. Go in and get it over with.

The wind helped him to get it over with. As he crouched under the scorched sea-grape bushes and sifted the sand in double handfuls the wind blew the scent of what was just ahead of him away. He found nothing in the sand and he was puzzled but he looked in all the sand to windward of the burned shacks before he moved in. He had hoped to find what he looked for the easier way. But there was nothing.

Then, with the wind at his back, so that he turned and gulped it and then held his breath again he went to work with his knife probing into the charred deliquescence that the land crabs were feeding on. He touched a sudden hardness that rolled against a bone and dug it out with the spoon. He laid it on the sand with the spoon and probed and dug and found three more in the pile. Then he turned into the wind and cleaned the knife and the spoon in the sand. He took the four bullets in a handful of sand and with the knife and the spoon in his left hand made his way back through the brush.

A big land crab, obscenely white, reared back and lifted his claws at him.

"You on the way in, boy?" the man said to him. "I'm on the way out."

The crab stood his ground with his claws raised high and the points open sharply.

"You're getting pretty big for yourself," the man said. He put his knife slowly in its sheath and the spoon in his pocket. Then he shifted the handful of sand with the four bullets in it to his left hand. He wiped his right hand on his shorts carefully. Then he drew the sweat-darkened, well-oiled .357 Magnum.

"You still have a chance," he said to the land crab. "Nobody blames you. You're having your pleasure and doing your duty."

The crab did not move and his claws were held high. He was a big crab, nearly a foot across, and the man shot him between his eyes and the crab disintegrated.

"Those damn .357's are hard to get now because draftdodging FBI's have to use them to hunt down draftdodgers," the man said. "But a man has to fire a shot sometime or he doesn't know how he is shooting."

Poor old crab, he thought. All he was practicing was his trade. But he ought to have shuffled along.

He came out onto the beach and saw where his ship was riding and the steady line of the surf and Willie anchored now and diving for conches. He cleaned his knife properly and scrubbed the spoon and washed it and then washed the four bullets. He held them in his hand and looked at them as a man who was panning for gold, expecting only flakes, would look at four nuggets in his pan. The four bullets had black noses. Now the meat was out of them, the short twist rifling showed clearly. They were 9mm standard issue for the Schmeisser machine pistol.

They made the man very happy.

They picked up all the hulls, he thought. But they left these as plain as calling cards. Now I must try to think it out. We know two things. They left nobody on the Cay and the boats are gone. Go on from there, boy. You're supposed to be able to think.

But he did not think. Instead he lay back on the sand with his pistol pulled over so it lay between his legs and he watched the sculpture that the wind and sand had made of a piece of driftwood. It was gray and sanded and it was embedded in the white, floury sand. It looked as though it were in an exhibition. It should be in the Salon d'Automne.

He heard the breaking roar of the seas on the reef and he thought, I would like to paint this. He lay and looked at the sky which had nothing but east wind in it and the four bullets were in the buttoned-down change pocket of his shorts. He knew they were the rest of his life. But he did not wish to think about them now nor make all the practical thinking that he must make. I will enjoy the gray wood, he thought. Now we know that we have our enemies and that they cannot escape. Neither can we. But there is no necessity to think about it until Ara and Henry are back. Ara will find something. There is something to be found and he is not a fool. A beach tells many lies but somewhere the truth is always written. He felt the bullets in his change pocket and then he elbowed his way back to where the sand was drier and even whiter, if there could be a comparison in such whiteness, and he lay with his head against the gray piece of driftwood and his pistol between his legs.

"How long have you been my girl?" he said to the pistol.

"Don't answer," he said to the pistol. "Lie there good and I will see you kill something better than land crabs when the time comes."

2

HE was lying there looking out at the line of the surf and he had it pretty well thought out by the time he saw Ara and Henry coming down the beach. He saw them and then looked away from them and out to sea again. He had tried not to think about it and to relax but it had been impossible. Now he would relax until they came and he would think of nothing but the sea on the reef. But there was not time. They came too fast.

"What did you find?" he asked Ara who sat down by the gray driftwood. Henry sat beside him.

"I found one. A young man. Dead."

"He was a German all right," Henry said. "He only had on shorts and he had very long hair, blond and sun-streaked, and he was face down in the sand."

"Where was he shot?"

"At the base of the spine and in the back of the neck," Ara said. "*Rematado*. Here are the bullets. I washed them."

"Yes," said Thomas Hudson. "I have four like them."

"They're 9mm Luger aren't they?" Henry asked. "It's the same caliber as our .38's."

"These with the black ends are for the machine pistol," Thomas Hudson said. "Thanks for digging them out, doctor."

"At your orders," Ara said. "The neck one had gone clean through and I found it in the sand. Henry cut out the other one."

"I didn't mind it," Henry said. "The wind and the sun had sort of dried him. It was like cutting into a pie. He wasn't like those in there. Why did they kill him, Tom?"

"I don't know."

"What do you think?" Ara asked. "Did they come in here to make repairs?"

"No. They've lost their boat."

"Yes," Ara said. "They took the boats."

"Why was the sailor killed?" Henry asked. "You forgive me if I don't sound too intelligent, Tom. But you know how much I want to do what I can and I'm so happy we have contact."

"We haven't contact," Thomas Hudson said. "But Christ we've got a lovely scent."

"Breast high?" Henry asked hopefully.

"Don't mention that word to me."

"But Tom, who killed the sailor and why?"

"Family trouble," Thomas Hudson said. "Did you ever see a man shot in the base of the spine for kindness? Afterwards whoever did it was kind and shot him in the neck."

"Maybe there were two," said Ara.

"Did you find the hulls?"

"No," Ara said. "I looked where they would be. Even if it was a machine pistol it would not have thrown them further than I looked."

"It could be the same methodical bastard that picked up the other ones."

"Where would they go?" Ara asked. "Where would they make for with the boats?"

"They have to go south," Thomas said. "You know damned well they can't go north."

"And we?"

"I'm trying to think in their heads," Thomas Hudson said. "I haven't many facts to go on."

"You have the deads and the boats gone," Henry said. "You can think it out, Tom."

"And one known weapon and where did they lose their undersea boat and how many are they? Stir that and add we couldn't raise Guantánamo last night and add how many keys there are south of here plus when we have to fill our tanks. Add Peters and serve."

"It will be all right, Tom."

"Sure," Thomas Hudson said. "All right and all wrong are identical twins in this business."

"You're confident we will get them though, aren't you?"

"Of course," Thomas Hudson said. "Now go and flag Willie in and let Antonio get started on his conches. We will have chowder. Ara, you load all the water you can in the next three hours. Tell Antonio to go ahead on the motors. I want to get out of here before dark. Was there nothing on the island? No pigs nor any fowl?"

"Nothing," Ara told him. "They took everything."

"Well, they will have to eat them. They have no feed for them and no ice. They are Germans so they are capable and they can get turtle in these months. I think we will find them at Lobos. It is logical they should take Lobos. Have Willie fill the ice-well with conches and we will take only enough water to the next key."

He stopped and reconsidered, "No, I'm sorry. I was wrong. Fill water until sundown and I will take her out at moonrise. We lose three hours but we save six later on."

"Did you taste the water?" Ara asked.

"Yes," he said. "It was clean and good. You were quite right."

"Thank you," Ara said. "I will go now to call in Willie. He has been diving many."

"Tom," Henry asked. "Do you want me to stay with you or to carry water or what?"

"Carry water until you are too tired and then get some sleep. I want you on the bridge with me tonight."

"Can I bring you a shirt or a sweater?" Henry asked.

"Bring me a shirt and one of the very light blankets," Thomas Hudson said. "I can sleep now in the sun and the sand is dry. But later on it will be cool with the wind."

"Isn't the sand wonderful? I've never known such dry or powdery sand."

"The wind has beaten it for many years."

"Will we get them, Tommy?"

"Of course," Thomas Hudson said. "There is no doubt of it at all."

"Please forgive me if I am ever stupid," Henry said.

"You were forgiven when you were born," Thomas Hudson said. "You are a very brave boy, Henry, and I am fond of you and trust you. You're not stupid either."

"You truly think we will have a fight?"

"I know it. Do not think about that. Think about details. Think about all the things you should do and how we should be a happy ship until we fight. I'll think about the fight."

"I will go and do my duty as well as I can," Henry said. "I wish we could practice the fight so I could do my part better."

Thomas Hudson said, "You'll do it all right. I do not see any way that we can miss it."

"It's been so very long," Henry said.

"But everything is long," Thomas Hudson told him. "And pursuit is the longest."

"Get some sleep," Henry said. "You never sleep any more."

"I'll sleep," Thomas Hudson said.

"Where do you suppose they lost their own boat, Tom?" Ara asked.

"They got these boats here and they did away with these people a week ago, say. So they must be the one that Camagüey claimed. But they got somewhere close to here before they lost her. They didn't sail any rubber boats into that wind."

"Then they must have lost her east of here."

"Naturally. And they were damned well in the clear when they lost her," Thomas Hudson said.

"It was still a long way home," Henry said.

"It is going to be a longer way home now," Ara said.

"They're funny people," Thomas Hudson said. "They're all brave and some of them are so damned admirable. Then they have mean ones like this."

"We better go and do our work," Ara said. "We can talk tonight on watch to keep awake. You get some rest, Tom."

"Get some sleep," Henry said.

"Rest is as good as sleep."

"No it isn't," Ara said. "You need sleep, Tom."

"I'll try to get some," Thomas Hudson said. But when they were gone he could not sleep.

What did they have to do this rotten thing here for? he thought. We will get them anyway. All these people would have done was tell us how many they were and how they were armed. I suppose that was worth killing for, from their standpoint. Especially if they thought of these people as Negroes. But all that shows something about them. To have killed like that they must have some plan and they must have some hope of being picked up. Also there must have been dissension about the plan or they would not have done this murdering here of the sailor. That could be an execution for anything, though. He might have let her go down when she could have been kept up to make the try to get home.

Where does that bring us? he thought. You can't bank on that. It is only a possibility. But if it was true it would mean she went down in sight of land and fast. That would mean they would not have much stuff. Maybe the boy did not do it and was falsely accused.

You don't know how many boats they have because there could
be a boat or two boats from here out turtling. There is nothing to
do but think around it and check your keys.

But suppose they have crossed the Old Bahama channel and
hit the Cuban coast? Sure, he thought. Why didn't you think of
that before? That's the best thing for them to do.

If they do that they can make for home on a Spanish boat out
of Havana. There is a screening at Kingston. But that is an easier
chance to take and you know plenty of people have beaten it. That
damned Peters with his radio out. FCC, he thought. Frankly Can't
Communicate. Then we got the beauty big one and it was too much
radio for him. I don't know how he has fucked it. But he couldn't get
Guantánamo last night on our call hour and if he doesn't get her
tonight we are on our own. The hell with it, he thought. There are
worse places to be than on your own. Get some sleep now, he said
to himself. There is nothing you can do now that is sounder than
that.

He moved his shoulders against the sand and went to sleep with
the roaring of the surf on the reef.

3

WHILE Thomas Hudson was asleep he dreamed that his son Tom
was not dead and that the other boys were all right and that the war
was over. He dreamed that Tom's mother was sleeping with him and
she was sleeping on top of him as she liked to do sometimes. He felt
all of this and the tangibility of her legs against his legs and her
body against his and her breasts against his chest and her mouth was
playing against his mouth. Her hair hung down and lay heavy and
silky on his eyes and on his cheeks and he turned his lips away from
her searching ones and took the hair in his mouth and held it. Then
with one hand he moistened the .357 Magnum and slipped it easily
and sound asleep where it should be. Then he lay under her weight
with her silken hair over his face like a curtain and moved slowly
and rhythmically.

That was when Henry put the light blanket over him and
Thomas Hudson said, asleep, "Thank you for being so moist and

lovely and for pressing on me so hard. Thank you for coming back so quickly and for not being too thin."

"The poor son of a bitch," Henry said and covered him carefully. He went away carrying two wicker five-gallon demijohns on his shoulders.

"I thought you wanted me thin, Tom," the woman said in the dream. "You said I felt like a young goat when I was thin and that nothing felt better than a young goat."

"You," he said. "Who's going to make love to who?"

"Both of us," she said. "Unless you want it differently."

"You make love to me. I'm tired."

"You're just lazy. Let me take the pistol off and put it by your leg. The pistol's in the way of everything."

"Lay it by the bed," he said. "And make everything the way it should be."

Then it was all the way it should be and she said, "Should I be you or you be me?"

"You have first choice."

"I'll be you."

"I can't be you. But I can try."

"It's fun. You try it. Don't try to save yourself at all. Try to lose everything and take everything too."

"All right."

"Are you doing it?"

"Yes," he said. "It's wonderful."

"Do you know now what we have?"

"Yes," he said. "Yes I know. It's easy to give up."

"Will you give up everything? Are you glad I brought back the boys and that I come and be a devil in the night?"

"Yes. I'm glad of everything and will you swing your hair across my face and give me your mouth please and hold me so tight it kills me?"

"Of course. And you'll do it for me?"

When he woke he touched the blanket and he did not know, for an instant, that it was a dream. Then he lay on his side and felt the pistol holster between his legs and how it was really and all the hollownesses in him were twice as hollow and there was a new one from the dream. He saw it was still light and he saw the dinghy carrying water to his ship and he saw the white pounding of the surf on the reef. He turned on his side and tucked the blanket around himself and slept on his arms. He was asleep when they came to wake him and he had not dreamed at all this time.

4

HE steered all that night and he had Ara on the flying bridge with him until midnight and then Henry. They were running with a heavy beam sea and steering was like riding a horse downhill, he thought. It is all downhill and sometimes it is across the side of a hill. The sea is many hills and in here it is a broken country like the badlands.

"Talk to me," he said to Ara.

"What about, Tom?"

"Anything."

"Peters couldn't raise Guantánamo again. He has ruined it. The new big one."

"I know," Thomas Hudson said and tried to roll her as little as he could, riding the side of the hill. "He's burnt out something that he can't repair."

"He's listening," Ara said. "Willie is keeping him awake."

"Who's keeping Willie awake?"

"He's awake good," Ara said. "He doesn't sleep any better than you."

"How about you?"

"I'm good for all night if you want. Don't you want me to steer?"

"No. I haven't anything else to do."

"Tom, how badly do you feel?"

"I don't know. How badly can you feel?"

"It's useless," Ara said. "Would you like the wineskin?"

"No. Bring me up a bottle of cold tea and check on Peters and Willie. Check on everything."

Ara went down and Thomas Hudson was alone with the night and the sea and he still rode it like a horse going downhill too fast across broken country.

Henry came up with the bottle of cold tea.

"How are we, Tom?" he asked.

"We're perfect."

"Peters has the Miami police department on the old radio. All the prowl cars. Willie wants to talk to them. But I told him he couldn't."

"Correct."

"On the UHF, Peters has something squirting in German but he says it is way up with the wolf packs."

"He couldn't hear it then."

"It's a very funny night, Tom."

"It's not that funny."

"I don't know. I'm just telling you. Give me the course and let me take her and you go down."

"Has Peters logged it?"

"Of course."

"Tell Juan to give me a fix and have Peters log it. When was the son of a bitch squirting?"

"When I came up."

"Tell Juan to get the fix and log it right away."

"Yes, Tom."

"How are all the comic characters?"

"Sleeping. Gil, too."

"Get the rag out and have Peters log the fix."

"Do you want it?"

"I know too damn well where we are."

"Yes, Tom," Henry said. "Take it easy if you can."

Henry came up but Thomas Hudson did not feel like talking and Henry stood by him on the flying bridge and braced himself against the roll. After an hour he said, "There's a light, Tom. Off our starboard bow about twenty degrees."

"That's right."

When he was abeam of it he changed the course and the sea was astern.

"Now she is headed home to pasture," he said to Henry. "We're in the channel now. Wake Juan and get him up here and really keep your eyes open. You were late on the light."

"I'm sorry, Tom. I'll get Juan. Wouldn't you like a four-man watch?"

"Not until just before daylight," Thomas Hudson said. "I'll give you the word."

They might have cut across the banks, Thomas Hudson was thinking. But I don't think they would. They wouldn't want to cross at night and in daytime the banks wouldn't look good to deep-water sailors. They'd make their turn where I did. Then they would edge across comfortably the way we are going to do and they would probably hit for the highest part of the Cuban coast that showed. They don't want to get into any port so they will run with the wind. They will keep outside of Confites because they know there is a radio station there. But they have to get food and they have to get water. Actually they would do best to try to get as close to Havana as they could to land somewhere around Bacuranao and then infiltrate in from there. I'll send a signal from Confites. I won't ask him what to do. That will hold us up if he's away. I'll tell him what it is and what I'm doing. He can make his own dispositions. Guantánamo can make theirs and Camagüey can make theirs and La Fe theirs and the FBI theirs and maybe something will happen in a week.

Hell, he thought. I'll get them this week. They've got to stop for water and to cook what they have before the animals starve and rot. There's a good chance they will only run at nights and lay up daytimes. That would be logical. That's what I would do if I were them. Try to think like an intelligent German sailor with the problems this undersea boat commander has.

He has problems all right, Thomas Hudson thought. And the worst problem he has is us and he doesn't even know about us. We don't look dangerous to him. We look good to him.

Don't take it in any bloodthirsty way, he thought. Nothing of this is going to bring back anything. Use your head and be glad to have something to do and good people to do it with.

"Juan," he said. "What do you see, boy?"

"All bloody ocean."

"You other gentlemen see anything?"

"Bloody nothing," Gil said.

"My bloody belly sees coffee. But it doesn't come any closer," Ara said.

"I see land," Henry said. He had seen it that instant, a low square smudge as though a man's thumb had daubed weak ink against the lightening sky.

"That's behind Romano," Thomas Hudson said. "Thank you,

Henry. Now you characters go down for coffee and send up four other desperate men to see strange and amusing things."

"Do you want coffee, Tom?" Ara asked.

"No. I'll take tea when it's made."

"We've only been on watch a couple of hours," Gil said. "We don't need to go off, Tom."

"Go on down and get coffee and give the other desperate men a chance for glory."

"Tom, didn't you say you thought they were at Lobos?"

"Yes. But I changed my mind."

The others had gone down and four were coming up.

"Gentlemen," Thomas Hudson said. "Split the four quadrants up amongst you. Is there coffee below?"

"Plenty," his mate said. "And tea. The engines are good and she didn't make any more water than you would expect in the cross sea."

"How is Peters?"

"He drank his own whisky in the night. The one with the little lamb on it. But he stayed awake. Willie kept him awake and drank his whisky," his mate said.

"We have to fill gas at Confites and take on anything else there is."

"They can load fast and I can kill a pig and scald and scrape him," his mate said. "I'll give them a quarter at the radio station to help me and I can butcher him while you are running. You get some sleep while we load. Would you like me to steer?"

"No. I only have to send three signals at Confites and you load and I will sleep. Then we will pursue."

"Toward home?"

"Of course. They may avoid us for a time. But they cannot escape us. Later we will talk about it. How are they?"

"You know them. We will talk about it later. Steer in a little more, Tom. With the countercurrent you'll shorten it."

"Did you lose much with rolling?"

"Nothing that matters. It was a bitch of a beam sea," his mate said.

"*Ya lo creo,*" said Thomas Hudson. "I believe it."

"There should only be the people of this one undersea boat around here. She must surely be the one they claimed sunk. Now they are off La Guayra and above Kingston and on all the petrol lanes. Also they are with the wolf packs."

"Also they are here sometimes."

"Yes, for our sins."

"And for theirs."

"On this thing we will pursue well and intelligently."

"Let us get it started," Thomas Hudson said.

"There has been no delay."

"It goes slowly for me."

"Yes," his mate said. "But get some sleep in Confites and I promise everything will go faster than you could hope."

5

THOMAS HUDSON saw the high lookout post on the sandy key and the tall signalling mast. They were painted white and were the first things that showed. Then he saw the stumpy radio masts and the high cocked wreck of the ship that lay on the rocks and obscured the view of the radio shack. The key was not handsome from his side.

The sun was behind him and it was easy to find the first big pass through the reef and then, skirting the shoals and the coral heads, to come up on the leeward shelter. There was a sandy half-moon of beach and the island was covered with dry grass on this side and was rocky and flat on its windward end. The water was clear and green over the sand and Thomas Hudson came in close to the center of the beach and anchored with his bow almost against the shore. The sun was up and the Cuban flag was flying over the radio shack and the outbuildings. The signalling mast was bare in the wind. There was no one in sight and the Cuban flag, new and brightly clean, was snapping in the wind.

"Maybe they had a relief," Thomas Hudson said. "The old flag was pretty worn when we left."

He looked and saw his drums of gas where he had left them and the marks of digging in the sand where his blocks of ice should be buried. The sand was high like new-made graves and over the island sooty terns were flying in the wind. They nested in the rocks up at the windward end and a few nested in the grass of the lee. They were flying now, falling off with the wind, cutting sharply into it, and dipping down toward the grass and the rocks. They were all calling, sadly and desperately.

Must be somebody out getting eggs for breakfast, Thomas Hudson thought. Just then he smelled ham frying in the galley and he went astern and called down that he would take his breakfast on the bridge. He studied the island carefully. They might be here, he thought. They could have taken this.

But when a man in shorts came down the path that ran from the radio shack to the beach, it was the Lieutenant. He was very brown and cheerful and he had not cut his hair in three months and he called out, "How was your trip?"

"Good," said Thomas Hudson. "Will you come aboard for a beer?"

"Later," the Lieutenant said. "They brought your ice and supplies and some beer two days ago. We buried the ice. The other things are at the house."

"What news do you have?"

"The aviation were supposed to have sunk a submarine off Guinchos ten days ago. But that was before you left."

"Yes," Thomas Hudson said. "That was two weeks ago. Is that the same one?"

"Yes."

"Any other news?"

"Another submarine was supposed to have shot down a blimp off Cayo Sal day before yesterday."

"Is that confirmed?"

"We heard so. Then there was your pig."

"Yes?"

"The same day of the blimp they brought a pig for you with your supplies and he swam out to sea the next morning and was drowned. We had fed him, too."

"*¡Qué puerco más suicido!*" Thomas Hudson said.

The Lieutenant laughed. He had a very cheerful brown face and he was not stupid. He was acting because it amused him. He had orders to do anything he could for Hudson and to ask him nothing. Thomas Hudson had orders to use any facilities the station could give and tell nothing to anyone.

"Any more news?" he asked. "Have you seen any Bahaman sponging or turtle boats?"

"What would they be doing here when they have all the turtle and sponge over there? But there were two Bahaman turtle boats came by here this week. They turned off the point and tacked to come in. But they ran for Cayo Cruz instead."

"I wonder what they were doing here?"

"I don't know. You cruise those waters for scientific purposes. Why should turtle boats leave the best turtling grounds to come here?"

"How many men could you see?"

"We could only see the men at the tiller. The boats had palm branches spread over the deck. They were built up like a shack. It could be to give shade for the turtles."

"Were the helmsmen white or black?"

"White and sunburned."

"Could you make out any numbers or names on the boats?"

"No. They were too far away. I put the key in a state of defense that night and the next day and night and there was nothing."

"When did they go by?"

"The day before your ice and groceries and your suicidal pig arrived. Eleven days after the sub was reported sunk by your aviation. Three days before you arrived here. Are they friends of yours?"

"You signalled them, of course?"

"Naturally. And I have heard nothing."

"Can you send three messages for me?"

"Of course. Send them in as soon as they are ready."

"I will start to load gas and ice and put the supplies aboard. Was there anything in them you can use?"

"I don't know. There is a list. I signed for it but I could not read it in English."

"Didn't they send any chickens or turkeys?"

"Yes," the Lieutenant said. "I was saving them for a surprise."

"We'll split them," Thomas Hudson said. "We'll split the beer, too."

"Let my people help you load the gas and ice."

"Good. Thank you very much. I would like to be gone in two hours."

"I understand. Our relief has been put off another month."

"Again?"

"Again."

"How do your people take it?"

"They're all here on a disciplinary basis."

"Thank you very much for your help. The whole world of science is grateful."

"Guantánamo, too?"

"Guantánamo, the Athens of science."

"I think they may have holed up somewhere."

"So do I," said Thomas Hudson.

"The shelters were of coconut palm and they were still green."

"Tell me anything else."

"I don't know anything else. Send in the messages. I don't want to come on board to take up any of your time or be a nuisance."

"If anything perishable comes out while I am gone, use it before it spoils."

"Thank you. I'm sorry your pig committed such suicide."

"Thank you," said Thomas Hudson. "We all have our small problems."

"I'll tell the men not to come on board but only to help load at the stern and help alongside."

"Thank you," Thomas Hudson said. "Can you remember anything more about the turtle boats?"

"They were typical. One was almost exactly the same as the other. They looked as though they had been built by the same builder. They turned the point of the reef and made to tack in here. Then they ran before the wind for Cayo Cruz."

"Inside the reef?"

"Inside until they were out of sight."

"And the sub off Cayo Sal?"

"Stayed on the surface and shot it out with the blimp."

"I'd stay in a state of defense if I were you."

"I am," the Lieutenant said. "That's why you haven't seen anybody."

"I saw the birds moving."

"The poor birds," the Lieutenant said.

6

THEY were running to the westward inside the reef with the wind astern. The tanks had been filled, the ice stowed, and below one watch was picking and cleaning chickens. The other was cleaning weapons. The canvas that shielded the flying bridge to waist height was laced on and the two long boards that announced in twelve-inch block letters the scientific mission of the boat were in place. Looking over the side watching the depth of water Thomas Hudson saw the patches of chicken feathers floating out onto the following sea.

"Take her in just as close as we can get without hitting any of those sandbars," he told Ara. "You know this coast."

"I know it's no good," Ara said. "Where are we going to anchor?"

"I want to check up at the head of Cayo Cruz."

"We can check there but I don't think it will be much use. You don't think they would stay there, do you?"

"No. But there might be fishermen in there who would have seen them. Or charcoal burners."

"I wish this wind would fail," Ara said. "I'd like to have a couple of days of flat calm."

"It's squally over Romano."

"I know. But this wind blows through here like through a pass in the mountains. We'll never catch them if this wind keeps up."

"We've been right so far," Thomas Hudson said. "And maybe we'll get some luck. They could have taken Lobos and used the radio there to call up that other sub to take them off."

"That shows they didn't know the other sub was there."

"Must be. They move a lot in ten days."

"When they want to," Ara said. "Let's stop thinking, Tom. It gives me a headache. I'd rather handle gas drums. You think and tell me where you want me to steer."

"Just as she goes and watch for the no-good Minerva. Keep well inside of that and outside the sandspits."

"Good."

Do you suppose she lost her radio when she got smacked? Thomas Hudson thought. She must have had an emergency radio that she could have used. But Peters never picked her up on the UHF after she was smacked. Still, that doesn't necessarily prove anything. Nothing proves anything except that those two boats were seen on the course we are on three days ago. Did I ask him if they had their dinghys on deck? No, I forgot to. But they must have because he said they were ordinary Bahaman turtling boats except for the shelters they had rigged with the palm branches.

How many people? You don't know. Any wounded? You don't know. How armed? All you know is a machine pistol. Their course? We are on it until now.

Maybe we will find something between Cayo Cruz and Mégano, he thought. What you'll probably find is lots of willets and iguana tracks in the sand toward the water hole.

Well, it keeps your mind off things. What things? There aren't any things any more. Oh yes, there are. There is this ship and the people on her and the sea and the bastards you are hunting. Afterwards you will see your animals and go into town and get drunk as you can and your ashes dragged and then get ready to go out and do it again.

Maybe this time you will get these characters. You did not destroy their undersea boat but you were faintly instrumental in its destruction. If you can round up the crew, it will be extremely useful.

Then why don't you care anything about anything? he asked himself. Why don't you think of them as murderers and have the righteous feelings that you should have? Why do you just pound and pound on after it like a riderless horse that is still in the race? Because we are all murderers, he told himself. We all are on both sides, if we are any good, and no good will come of any of it.

But you have to do it. Sure, he said. But I don't have to be proud of it. I only have to do it well. I didn't hire out to like it. You did not even hire out, he told himself. That makes it even worse.

"Let me take her, Ara," he said.

Ara gave him the wheel.

"Keep a good lookout to starboard. But don't let the sun blind you."

"I'll get my glasses. Look, Tom. Why don't you let me steer and get a good four-man lookout up here? You're tired and you didn't rest at all at the key."

"We don't need a four-man lookout in here. Later on we will."

"But you're tired."

"I'm not sleepy. Look, if they run nights along here close in to shore they are going to get in trouble. Then they will have to lay up to make repairs and we will find them."

"That's no reason for you never to rest, Tom."

"I'm not doing it to show off," Thomas Hudson said.

"No one has ever thought so."

"How do you feel about these bastards?"

"Only that we will catch them and kill what is necessary and bring the others in."

"What about the massacre?"

"I don't say we would have done the same thing. But they thought it was necessary. They did not do it for pleasure," Ara said.

"And their dead man?"

"Henry has wanted to kill Peters several times. I have wanted to kill him myself sometimes."

"Yes," Thomas Hudson agreed. "It is not an uncommon feeling."

"I don't think of any of these things and so I don't worry. Why don't you not worry, and read when you relax the way you always did?"

"I'm going to sleep tonight. After we anchor I'll read and then sleep. We've gained four days on them, though it does not show. Now we must search carefully."

"We will get them or we will drive them into other people's hands," Ara said. "What difference does it make? We have our pride but we have another pride people know nothing of."

"That is what I had forgotten," Thomas Hudson said.

"It is a pride without vanity," Ara continued. "Failure is its brother and shit is its sister and death is its wife."

"It must be a big pride."

"It is," Ara said. "You must not forget it, Tom, and you must not destroy yourself. Everyone in the ship has that pride, including Peters. Although I do not like Peters."

"Thanks for telling me," Thomas Hudson said. "I feel fuck-all discouraged about things sometimes."

"Tom," Ara said. "All a man has is pride. Sometimes you have it so much it is a sin. We have all done things for pride that we knew were impossible. We didn't care. But a man must implement his pride with intelligence and care. Now that you have ceased to be careful of yourself I must ask you to be, please. For us and for the ship."

"Who is us?"

"All of us."

"OK," Thomas Hudson said. "Ask for your dark glasses."

"Tom, please understand."

"I understand. Thanks very much. I'll eat a hearty supper and sleep like a child."

Ara did not think it was funny and he always thought funny things were funny.

"You try it, Tom," he said.

7

THEY anchored in the lee of Cayo Cruz in the sandy bight between the two keys.

"We'll put out another anchor to lay here," Thomas Hudson called to his mate. "I don't like this bottom."

The mate shrugged his shoulders and bent down to the second anchor and Thomas Hudson eased her ahead against the tide, watching the grass from the banks riding by in the current. He came astern until his second anchor was well dug in. The boat lay with her bow into the wind and the tide running past her. There was much wind even in this lee and he knew that when the tide changed she would swing broadside to the swell.

"The hell with it," he said. "Let her roll."

But his mate had lowered the dinghy already and they were running out a stern anchor. Thomas Hudson watched them drop the little Danforth where it would hold her into the wind when the tide came aflood.

"Why don't you put out a couple more?" he called. "Then maybe we could sell her for a goddam spider."

The mate grinned at him.

"Get the outboard on her. I'm going in."

"No, Tom," his mate said. "Let Ara and Willie go in. I'll take them in and another party to Mégano. Do you want them to take the niños?"

"No. Be scientists."

I'm accepting a lot of handling, he thought. That must mean I really do need some rest. The thing is I am neither tired nor sleepy.

"Antonio," he said.

"Yes," said his mate.

"I'll take the air mattress and two cushions and a big drink."

"What kind of drink?"

"Gin and coconut water with Angostura and lime."

"A *Tomini?*" his mate said, pleased that he was drinking again.

"Double quantity."

Henry threw the air mattress up and climbed after it with a book and a magazine.

"You're out of the wind here," he said. "Do you want me to open any of this canvas for ventilation?"

"Since when did I rate all this?"

"Tom, we talked of it and we all agreed that you need some rest. You've been driving yourself past what a man can stand. You are past it now."

"Shit," said Thomas Hudson.

"Maybe," said Henry. "I said I thought you were OK and could go quite a lot more and hold the pace. But the others were worried and they convinced me. You can deconvince me. But take it easy now, Tom."

"I never felt better. I just don't give a damn."

"That's what it's about. You won't come down off the bridge. You want to stand all the watches steering. And you don't give a damn about anything."

"OK," said Thomas Hudson. "I get the picture. But I still command."

"I didn't mean it in any bad way, truly."

"Forget it," Thomas Hudson said. "I'm resting. You know how to search a key, don't you?"

"I should."

"See what there is on Mégano."

"That's mine. Willie and Ara have gone in already. I'm just waiting with the other party for Antonio to come back with the dinghy."

"How is Peters?"

"He's been working hard on the big radio all afternoon. He thinks he has it fixed OK."

"That would be wonderful. If I'm asleep, wake me as soon as you get back."

"Yes, Tom." Henry reached down and took something that was handed to him. It was a big glass full of ice and a rusty-colored liquid and it was wrapped in a double thickness of paper towel held fast by a rubber band.

"A double *Tomini*," Henry said. "Drink it and read and go to sleep. You can put the glass in one of the big frag slots."

Thomas Hudson took a long sip.

"I like it," he said.

"You used to. Everything will be fine, Tom."

"Everything we can do damn well better be."

"Just get a good rest."

"I will."

Henry went down and Thomas Hudson heard the hum of the outboard coming in. It stopped and there was talking and then he heard the hum of it going away. He waited a little, listening. Then he took the drink and threw it high over the side and let the wind take it astern. He settled the glass in the hole it fitted best in the triple rack and lay face down on the rubber mattress with his two arms around it.

I think they had wounded under the shelters, he thought. Of course it could be to conceal many people. But I do not believe that. They would have come in here the first night. I should have gone ashore. I will from now on. But Ara and Henry could not be better and Willie is very good. I must try to be very good. Try hard tonight, he told himself. And chase hard and good and with no mistakes and do not overrun them.

8

HE felt a hand on his shoulder. It was Ara and he said, "We got one, Tom. Willie and I."

Thomas Hudson swung down and Ara was with him. The German lay on the stern wrapped in a blanket. His head was on two cushions. Peters was sitting on the deck beside him with a glass of water.

"Look what we got," he said.

The German was thin and there was a blond beard on his chin and on his sunken cheeks. His hair was long and uncombed and in the late afternoon light, with the sun almost down, he looked like a saint.

"He can't talk," Ara said. "Willie and I tried him. You better keep to windward of him, too."

"I smelled it coming down," Thomas Hudson said. "Ask him if he wants anything," he said to Peters.

The radio operator spoke to him in German and the German looked toward him but he did not speak nor move his head. Thomas Hudson heard the humming of the outboard motor, and looked across the bight at the dinghy coming out of the sunset. It was loaded down to the water line. He looked down at the German again.

"Ask him how many they are. Tell him we must know how many they are. Tell him this is important."

Peters spoke to the German softly and it seemed to Thomas Hudson almost lovingly.

The German said three words with great effort.

"He says nothing is important," Peters said.

"Tell him he is wrong. I have to know. Ask him if he wants morphine."

The German looked at Thomas Hudson kindly and said three words.

"He says it doesn't hurt anymore," Peters said. He spoke rapidly in German and again Thomas Hudson caught the loving tone; or, perhaps it was only the loving sound of the language.

"Shut up, Peters," Thomas Hudson said. "Translate only and exactly what I say. Did you hear me?"

"Yes, sir," Peters said.

"Tell him I can make him tell."

Peters spoke to the German and he turned his eyes toward Thomas Hudson. They were old eyes now but they were in a young man's face gone old as driftwood and nearly as gray.

"*Nein*," the German said slowly.

"He says no," Peters translated.

"Yeah, I got that part of it," Thomas Hudson said. "Get him some warm soup, Willie, and bring some cognac. Peters, ask him if he wouldn't like some morphine really if he doesn't have to talk. Tell him we have plenty."

Peters translated and the German looked toward Thomas Hudson and smiled a thin, northern smile.

He spoke almost inaudibly to Peters.

"He says thank you but he doesn't need it and it's better to save it."

Then he said something softly to Peters who translated, "He says he could have used it last week."

"Tell him I admire him," Thomas Hudson said.

Antonio, his mate, was alongside in the dinghy with Henry and the rest of the Mégano party.

"Come aboard easy," Thomas Hudson said to them. "Keep away from the stern. We got a Kraut dying on the stern that I want to have die easy. What did you find?"

"Nothing," Henry said. "Absolutely nothing."

"Peters," Thomas Hudson said. "Talk to him all you want. You might get something. I'm going forward with Ara and Willie to get a drink."

Below, he said, "How's your soup, Willie?"

"The first one I put my hands on was clam broth," Willie said. "It's about hot enough."

"Why didn't you give him oxtail or mulligatawny?" Thomas Hudson said. "They're more deadly in his condition. Where the hell is the chicken?"

"I didn't want to give him the chicken. That's Henry's."

"Quite right, too," Henry said. "Why should we coddle him?"

"I don't think we really are. When I ordered it I thought some soup and a drink might help him talk. But he isn't going to talk. Give me a gin, will you, Ara?"

"They made a shelter for him, Tom, and he had a good bed made from branches and plenty of water and food in a crock. They tried to make him comfortable and they ditched the sand for drainage. There were many good tracks from the beach and I would say they were eight or ten. Not more. Willie and I were very careful carrying him. Both his wounds are gangrenous and the gangrene is very high toward the right thigh. Perhaps we should not have brought him but instead have come for you and Peters to question him in his shelter. If so, it is my fault."

"Did he have a weapon?"

"No. Nor any identification."

"Give me my drink," Thomas Hudson said. "When would you say the branches for the shelter were cut?"

"Not later than yesterday morning, I would say. But I could not be sure."

"Did he speak at all?"

"No. He looked as though made of wood when he saw us with the pistols. He looked afraid of Willie once. When he saw his eye, I think. Then he smiled when we lifted him."

"To show he could," Willie said.

"Then he went away," Ara said. "How long do you think it will take him to die, Tom?"

"I don't know."

"Well, let's go out and take the drinks," Henry said. "I don't trust Peters."

"Let's drink the clam broth up," Willie said. "I'm hungry. I can heat him a can of Henry's chicken if he says it is OK."

"If it will help to make him talk," Henry said. "Of course."

"It probably won't," Willie said. "But it's kind of shitty to give him clam broth the way he is. Take him out the cognac, Henry. Maybe he really likes that, like you and me."

"Don't bother him," Thomas Hudson said. "He's a good Kraut."

"Sure," Willie said. "They're all good Krauts when they fold up."

"He hasn't folded up," Thomas Hudson said. "He's just dying."

"With much style," Ara said.

"You getting to be a Kraut-lover, too?" Willie asked him. "That makes you and Peters."

"Shut up, Willie," Thomas Hudson said.

"What's the matter with you?" Willie said to Thomas Hudson. "You're just the exhausted leader of a little group of earnest Kraut-lovers."

"Come up forward, Willie," Thomas Hudson said. "Ara, take the soup astern when it is warm. The rest of you go watch the Kraut die, if you want. But don't crowd him."

Antonio started to follow as Thomas Hudson and Willie went forward but Thomas Hudson shook his head at him and the big man went back to the galley.

They were in the forward cockpit and it was almost dark. Thomas Hudson could just see Willie's face. It looked better in this light and he was on the side of the good eye. Thomas Hudson looked at Willie and then at his two anchor lines and at a tree he could still see on the beach. It's a tricky sandy bottom, he thought; and he said, "All right, Willie. Say the rest of it."

"You," Willie said. "Flogging yourself to death up there because your kid is dead. Don't you know everybody's kids die?"

"I know it. What else?"

"That fucking Peters and a fucking Kraut stinking up the fantail and what kind of a ship is it where the cook is the mate?"

"How does he cook?"

"He cooks wonderful and he knows more about small-boat handling than all of us put together, including you."

"Much more."

"Shit, Tom. I'm not blowing my top. I got no goddam top to blow. I'm used to doing things a different way. I like it on the ship and I like everybody except that half-cunt Peters. Only you quit flogging yourself."

"I'm not really," Thomas Hudson said. "I don't think about anything except work."

"You're so noble you ought to be stuffed and crucified," Willie said. "Think about cunt."

"We're headed toward it."

"That's the way to talk."

"Willie, are you OK now?"

"Sure. Why the hell wouldn't I be? That Kraut got me, I guess. They had him fixed up nice like we wouldn't fix up anybody. Or maybe we would if we had time. But they took time. They don't know how close we are. But they got to know somebody's chasing. Everybody's after them now. But they fixed him up just as nice as anybody could be fixed in the condition he was."

"Sure," Thomas Hudson said. "They fixed up those people back on the key nice, too."

"Yeah," said Willie. "Isn't that the hell of it?"

Just then Peters came in. He always held himself as a Marine even when he was not at his best and he was proudest of the real discipline without the formalities of discipline which was the rule of the ship. He was the one who took the greatest advantage of it. Now he stopped, came to attention, saluted, which showed he was drunk, and said, "Tom, I mean, sir. He is dead."

"Who's dead?"

"The prisoner, sir."

"OK," Thomas Hudson said. "Get your generator going and see if you can get Guantánamo."

They ought to have something for us, he thought.

"Did the prisoner talk?" he asked Peters.

"No sir."

"Willie," he asked. "How do you feel?"

"Fine."

"Get some flashbulbs and take two, in profile of the face, lying on the stern. Take the blanket off and his shorts off and take one full-length lying as he is across the stern. Shoot one full-face of his head and one full-face lying down."

"Yes sir," Willie said.

Thomas Hudson went up on the flying bridge. He heard the motor of the generator start and saw the sudden flashes of the bulbs. ONI, up where they evaluate, won't believe we even have this much of a Kraut, he thought. There isn't any proof. Somebody will claim it is a stiff they pushed out that we picked up. I should have photographed him sooner. The hell with them. Maybe we will get the others tomorrow.

Ara came up.

"Tom, who do you want to have take him ashore and bury him?"

"Who's worked the least today?"

"Everybody has worked hard. I'll take Gil in and we will do it. We can bury him in the sand just above high water."

"Maybe a little higher."

"I'll send Willie up and you tell him how you want the board lettered. I have a board from a box in stores."

"Send Willie up."

"Do we sew him up?"

"No. Just wrap him in his own blanket. Send Willie up."

"What was it that you wanted?" Willie asked.

"Letter the board, 'Unknown German Sailor' and put the date underneath."

"OK, Tom. Do you want me to go in with the burial detail?"

"No. Ara and Gil are going in. Letter the board and take it easy and have a drink."

"As soon as Peters gets Guantánamo, I'll send it up. Don't you want to come down?"

"No. I'm taking it easy up here."

"What's it like on the bridge of a big ship like this, full of responsibility and horseshit?"

"Just about the same as lettering that board."

When the signal came from Guantánamo it read, decoded, CONTINUE SEARCHING CAREFULLY WESTWARD.

That's us, said Thomas Hudson to himself. He lay down and was asleep immediately and Henry covered him with a light blanket.

9

AN hour before daylight he was below and had checked his glass. It was four-tenths lower and he woke his mate and showed it to him.

The mate looked at him and nodded.

"You saw the squalls over Romano yesterday," he whispered. "She is going into the south."

"Make me some tea, will you, please," Thomas Hudson asked.

"I have some cold in a bottle on the ice."

He went astern and found a mop and a bucket and scrubbed the deck of the stern. It had been scrubbed before but he scrubbed it again and rinsed the mop. Then he took his bottle of cold tea up on the flying bridge and waited for it to get light.

Before it was light his mate got in the stern anchor and then with Ara brought in the starboard anchor and they and Gil hoisted the dinghy aboard. Then his mate pumped the bilges and checked his motors.

He put his head up and said, "Any time."

"Why did she make that much water?"

"Just a stuffing box. I tightened it a little. But I'd rather she made a little water than run hot."

"All right. Send up Ara and Henry. We'll get going."

They got in the anchor and he turned to Ara. "Show me the tree again."

Ara pointed it out just above the line of beach they were leaving and Thomas Hudson made a small pencilled cross on the chart.

"Peters never did get Guantánamo again?"

"No. He burned out once more."

"Well, we are behind them and they have other people ahead of them and we've got orders."

"Do you think the wind will really go into the south, Tom?" Henry asked.

"The glass shows it will. We can tell better when it starts to get up."

"It fell off to almost nothing about four o'clock."

"Did the sand flies hit you?"

"Only at daylight."

"You might as well go down and Flit them all out. There's no sense our carrying them around with us."

It was a lovely day and looking back at the bight where they had anchored and at the beach and the scrub trees of Cayo Cruz that they both knew so well, Thomas Hudson and Ara saw the high, piled clouds over the land. Cayo Romano rose so that it was like the mainland and the clouds were high above it with their promise of south wind or calm and land squalls.

"What would you think if you were a German, Ara?" Thomas Hudson asked. "What would you think if you saw that and knew that you were going to lose your wind?"

"I'd try to get inside," Ara said. "I think that's what I'd do."

"You'd need a guide for inside."

"I'd get me a guide," Ara said.

"Where would you get him?"

"From fishermen up at Antón or inside at Romano. Or at Coco. There must be fishermen salting fish along there now. There might even be a live-well boat at Antón."

"We'll try Antón," Thomas Hudson said. "It's nice to wake up in the morning and steer with the sun behind you."

"If you always steered with the sun behind you and on a day like this, what a place the ocean would be."

The day was like true summer and in the morning the squalls had not yet built. The day was all gentle promise and the sea lay smooth and clear. They could see bottom clearly until they ran out of soundings, and then far out and just where it should be was the Minerva with the sea breaking restfully on its coral rocks. It was the swell that was left from the two months of unremitting heavy trade wind. But it broke gently and kindly and with a passive regularity.

It is as though she were saying we are all friends now and there will never be any trouble nor any wildness again, Thomas Hudson thought. Why is she so dishonest? A river can be treacherous and cruel and kind and friendly. A stream can be completely friendly and you can trust it all your life if you do not abuse it. But the ocean always has to lie to you before she does it.

He looked again at her gentle rise and fall that showed the Minervas as regularly and attractively as though she were trying to sell them as a choice location.

"Want to get me a sandwich?" he asked Ara. "Corned beef and raw onion or ham and egg and raw onion. After you get breakfast, bring a four-man watch up here and check all the binoculars. I'm going outside before we go in to Antón."

"Yes, Tom."

I wonder what I would do without that Ara, Thomas Hudson thought. You had a wonderful sleep, he told himself, and you couldn't feel better. We've got orders and we are right on their tails and pushing them toward other people. You're following your orders and look what a beautiful morning you have to follow them in. But things look too damned good.

They moved down the channel keeping a good lookout, but there was nothing but the calm, early morning sea with its friendly undulations and the long green line of Romano inland with the many keys between.

"They won't sail very far in this," Henry said.

"They won't sail at all," Thomas Hudson said.

"Are we going in to Antón?"

"Sure. And work all of that out."

"I like Antón," Henry said. "There's a good place to lay to, if it's calm, so they won't eat us up."

"Inside they'd carry you away," Ara said.

A small seaplane showed ahead, flying low and coming toward them. It was white and minute with the sun on it.

"Plane," Thomas Hudson said. "Pass the word to get the big flag out."

The plane came on until it buzzed them. Then it circled them twice and went off flying on down to the eastward.

"He wouldn't have it so good if he found one," Henry said. "They'd shoot him down."

"He could send the location and Cayo Francés would pick it up."

"Maybe," Ara said. The two other Basques said nothing. They stood back to back and searched their quadrants.

After a while the Basque they called George because his name was Eugenio and Peters could not always say Eugenio said, "Plane's coming back to the eastward between the outer keys and Romano."

"He's going home to breakfast," Ara said.

"He'll report us," Thomas Hudson said. "So in a month maybe everybody will know where we were at this time today."

"If he doesn't get the location mixed up on his chart," Ara said. "Paredón Grande, Tom. Bearing approximately twenty degrees off the port bow."

"You've got good eyes," Thomas Hudson said. "That's her, all right. I better take her in and find the channel in to Antón."

"Turn port ninety degrees and I think you'll have her."

"I'll hit the bank anyway and we can run along it until we find that damned canal."

They came in toward the line of green keys that showed like black hedges sticking up from the water and then acquired shape and greenness and finally sandy beaches. Thomas Hudson came in with reluctance from the open channel, the promising sea, and the beauty of the morning on deep water, to the business of searching the inner keys. But the plane working the coast in this direction, turning to run over it with the sun behind it, should mean no one had picked the boats up to the eastward. It could be only a routine patrol, too. But it was logical that it should mean the other. A routine patrol would have been out over the channel both ways.

He saw Antón, which was well wooded and a pleasant island, growing before him and he watched ahead for his marks while he worked in toward the bank. He must take the highest tree on the head of the island and fit it squarely into the little saddle on Romano. On that bearing, he could come in even if the sun were in his eyes and the water had the glare of a burning glass.

Today he did not need it. But he did it for practice and when he found his tree, thinking, I should have something more permanent for a bearing on a hurricane coast, he eased along the bank until he fitted the tree carefully into the slot of the saddle, then turned sharp in. He was in the canal between marly banks that were barely covered with water and he said to Ara, "Ask Antonio to put a feather out. We might pick up something to eat. This channel has a wonderful bar on the bottom."

Then he steered straight in on his bearing. He was tempted not to look at the banks but to push it straight through. But then he knew that was one of the things of too much pride Ara had spoken of and he piloted carefully on the starboard bank and made his turn to starboard when it came by the banks and not by the second bearing that he had. It was like running in the regular streets of a new subdivision and the tide was racing in. It came in brown at first, then pure and clean. Just before he came into the part that he thought of as the turning basin where he planned to anchor, he heard Willie shout, "Feesh! Feesh!!" Looking astern, he saw a tarpon shaking himself high in the sun. His mouth was open and he was huge and the sun shone on his silvered scales and on the long green whip of his dorsal fin. He shook himself desperately in the sun and came down in a splash of water.

"*Sábalo*," Antonio called up disgustedly.

"Worthless *sábalo*," the Basques said.

"Can I play him, Tom?" Henry asked. "I'd like to catch him even if he is no good to eat."

"Take him from Antonio if Willie hasn't got him. Tell Antonio to get the hell forward. I'm going to anchor."

The excitement and the leaping of the big tarpon continued astern, with no one paying attention to it except to grin, while they anchored.

"Do you want to put out another?" Thomas Hudson called forward. His mate shook his head. When they swung well to the anchor, his mate came up on the bridge.

"She'll hold in anything, Tom," he said. "Any kind of a squall. Anything. And it doesn't make any difference how she swings, we can't have any motion."

"What time will we get the squalls."

"After two," his mate said, looking at the sky.

"Get the dinghy over," Thomas Hudson said. "And give me an extra can of gas with the outboard. We have to get the hell **going**."

"Who's going with you?"

"Just Ara and Willie and I. I want her to travel fast."

10

IN the dinghy the three of them had their raincoats wrapped around the *niños*. These were the Thompson submachine guns in their full-length sheep-wool cases. The cases were cut and sewn by Ara, who was not a tailor, and Thomas Hudson had impregnated the clipped wool on the inside with a protective oil which had a faintly carbolic smell. It was because the guns nestled in their sheep-lined cradles, and because the cradles swung when they were strapped open inside the branch of the flying bridge, that the Basques had nicknamed them "little children."

"Give us a bottle of water," Thomas Hudson said to his mate. When Antonio brought it, heavy and cold with the wide, screw-on top, he passed it to Willie, who stowed it forward. Ara loved to steer the outboard and he was in the stern. Thomas Hudson was in the center and Willie crouched in the bow.

Ara headed her straight in for the key and Thomas Hudson watched the clouds piling up over the land.

As they came into the shallow water, Thomas Hudson could see the grayish humps of conches bulging from the sand. Ara leaned forward to say, "Do you want to look at the beach, Tom?"

"Maybe we'd better before the rain."

Aran ran the dinghy ashore, tilting his motor up just at the last rush. The tide had undercut the sand to make a little channel at the point and he drove the boat in, slanting her up onto the sand.

"Home again," Willie said. "What's this bitch's name?"

"Antón."

"Not Antón Grande or Antón Chico or Antón El Cabrón?"

"Just Antón. You take it up to that point to the eastward and then keep going. We'll pick you up. I'll work along this beach fast and Ara will leave the dinghy down somewhere past the next point and work on ahead. I'll pick him up in the dinghy and we'll come back around for you."

Willie had his *niño* wrapped in his raincoat and put it on his shoulder.

"If I find any Krauts, can I kill them?"

"The Colonel said all but one," Thomas Hudson said. "Try to save a smart one."

"I'll give them all IQ tests before I open up."

"Give yourself one."

"Mine's goddam low or I wouldn't be here," Willie said, and he set out. He walked contemptuously and he watched the beach and the country ahead as carefully as a man could watch.

Thomas Hudson told Ara in Spanish what they were going to do and then shoved the dinghy off. He started down the beach with his *niño* under his arm and he felt the sand between his bare toes. Ahead, the dinghy was rounding the small point.

He was glad that he had come ashore and he walked as fast as he could go and still check the beach. It was a pleasant beach and he had no forebodings about it as he had had earlier in the day on the sea.

It was spooky this morning, he thought. Maybe it was just the calm. Ahead he could see the clouds still building up. But nothing had started to come out. There were no sand flies now in the hot sun and no mosquitoes and ahead of him he saw a tall white heron standing looking down in the shallow water with his head, neck, and beak poised. He had not flown when Ara passed with the dinghy.

We have to search it carefully even though I do not believe there is anything here, he thought. They are becalmed today so we lose nothing and it would be criminal to overrun them. Why don't I know more about them? he thought. It is my own fault. I should have gone in and looked at the hut they built and at the tracks. I questioned Willie and Ara and they are both truly good. But I should have gone in myself.

It is the repugnance that I feel toward meeting them, he thought. It is my duty and I want to get them and I will. But I have a sort of fellow death-house feeling about them. Do people who are in the death house hate each other? I don't believe they do unless they are insane.

Just then the heron rose and flew further up the beach. Braking widely with his great white wings, and then taking a few awkward steps, he landed. I am sorry I disturbed him, Thomas Hudson thought.

He checked all of the beach above high tide. But there were no tracks except where one turtle had crawled twice. She had made a wide track to the sea and back and a wallowing depression where she had laid.

I haven't time to dig for the eggs, he thought. The clouds were beginning to darken and to move out.

If they had been on this side of the key they certainly would have dug for them. He looked ahead but he could not see the dinghy because there was another curving point.

He walked along just where the sand was firm from the dampness of the high tide and he saw the hermit crabs carrying their shells and the ghost crabs that slipped across the stretch of sand and into the water. To his right, in the shallow channel, he saw the grayness that a school of mullet made and their shadow on the sand bottom as they moved. He saw the shadow of a very big barracuda that was stalking the mullet and then he saw the lines of the fish, long, pale, and gray, and seeming not to move. He walked steadily and soon he was past the fish and was coming up on the heron again.

I'll see if I can pass him without making him fly, he thought. But just when he was coming almost even with the heron, the school of mullet burst from the water jumping stiffly, big-eyed and blunt-headed, silvery in the sun but not beautiful. Thomas Hudson turned to watch them and to try to see the barracuda who was cutting into them. He could not see the predatory fish; only the wild leaping of the frightened mullet. Then he saw that the school was re-formed into a gray moving mass and when he turned his head the heron was gone. He saw him flying with his white wings over the green water and ahead was the yellow sand beach and the line of the trees along the point. The clouds were beginning to darken behind Romano and he walked faster to round the point and see where Ara had left the dinghy.

Walking faster gave him an erection and he thought there can't be any Krauts around. That wouldn't happen if there were any Krauts around. I don't know, he thought. It could happen if you were wrong enough and didn't know it.

At the end of the point there was a patch of bright white sand and he thought, I'd like to lie down here. This would be a good place. Then he saw the dinghy at the end of the long beach and he thought, the hell with it. I'll sleep tonight and I will love the air mattress or the deck. I might as well love the deck. We have been around together long enough to get married. There is probably a lot of talk about you and the flying bridge now, he thought. You ought to do right by her. And all you do is step on her and stand on her. What sort of a way is that to act? And spill cold tea on her, too. That's not nice. What are you saving her for anyway? To die on her? She would certainly appreciate that. Walk on her, stand on her, and die on her. Treat her really nice. One thing practical you can do now is cut out this crap and get this beach checked and pick up Ara.

He walked on down the beach and he tried not to think at all but only to notice things. He knew his duty very well and he had tried never to shirk it. But today he had come ashore when someone else could have done it just as well, but when he stayed aboard and they found nothing, he felt guilty. He watched everything. But he could not keep from thinking.

Maybe Willie's side is hotter, he thought. Maybe Ara will have hit something. I know damn well this is where I would come if I were they. It is the first good place. They might have passed it and gone straight on. Or they might have turned in between Paredón and Cruz. But I don't believe they would because somebody would see them from the light and they never could get in and through there at night, guide or no guide. I think they will have gone further down. Maybe we will find them down by Coco. Maybe we'll find them right in behind here. There's another key that we ought to work out. I must remember that they are always working on the chart. That is, unless they picked up a fisherman here. I haven't seen any smoke from anybody burning charcoal. Well, I am glad we will get this key worked out before the rain. I love doing it, he thought. I just don't like the end.

He shoved off the dinghy and stepped into her, washing the sand off his feet as he got in. He stowed the *niño,* in its rubber coat, where he could reach it and started the motor. He had no love for the outboard as Ara had and he never started it without remembering blowing out and sucking out clogged fuel lines and remembering shorted plugs and other delights of the small motor. But Ara never had ignition trouble. When the motor misfunctioned, he regarded it as a chess player might admire a brilliant move on the part of his opponent.

Thomas Hudson steered along the beach but Ara was far ahead and he could not see him. He must be halfway to Willie, he thought.

But when he saw him he was nearly to the mangrove bay where the sand stopped and the mangroves grew heavy and green into the water, their roots showing like tangled brown sticks.

Then he noticed the mast sticking up out of the mangroves. It was all he could see. But he could see Ara was lying behind a small sand dune so that he could just see over the top.

He could feel his scalp prickle as it does when you meet a car coming fast, suddenly, on the wrong side of the road. But Ara heard the motor and turned his head, and waved him in. Thomas came in on a tangent behind Ara.

The Basque came aboard carrying his raincoated *niño,* barrel first, over the right shoulder of his old striped beach shirt. He looked pleased.

"Get as far out as the channel will let you," he said. "We'll find Willie."

"Is it one of the boats?"

"Sure," Ara said. "But I'm sure it's abandoned. It's going to rain, Tom."

"Did you see anything?"

"Nothing."

"Me either."

"It's a nice key. I found an old trail to water. But it wasn't used."

"There's water on Willie's side, too."

"There's Willie," Ara said. He was sitting on the sand. His legs were drawn up and his *niño* was in his lap. Thomas Hudson ran the dinghy in to him. Willie looked at them, his black hair down over his forehead and wet with sweat and his good eye blue and mean.

"Where you two fuck-offs been?" he asked.

"When were they here, Willie?"

"Yesterday by the turds," Willie said. "Or should I say their excrement?"

"How many?"

"Eight that could excremenate and three of these with the bubbleshits."

"What else?"

"They got a guide or a pilot or whatever his rating is."

The guide they had picked up was a fisherman who had a palm-thatched shelter and had been salting barracuda strips on a rack to sell them later to the Chinese who bought fish for the Chinese retail grocers who would sell the dried fish in their shops as codfish. The fisherman had salted and dried a good quantity of fish by the looks of the rack.

"Krauts eat 'em plenty codfish now on in," Willie said.

"What language is that?"

"My own," Willie said. "Everybody has a private language around here, like Basque or something. You got an objection if I speak mine?"

"Tell me the rest."

"Sleepum here one smoke," Willie said. "Eatum pig meat. All samee from Massacre Key. Kraut master no gottum tin goods or save 'em."

"Cut out the shit and tell it straight."

"Ole Massa Hudson going to lose all afternoon anyway due huge rainfall accompanied squall winds all along same. Might as well listen alongside Willie all same famous scout of the Pampas. Willie tell his own way."

"Cut it out."

"Listen, Tom, who found Krauts twice?"

"What about the boat?"

"Boat all same finish. She alongside too many rotten planks. One drop out by stern."

"They hit something coming in with a bad light."

"I guess so. Well, I'll cut out the shit. They've gone on into the westward sun. Eight men and a guide. Maybe nine if the captain couldn't shit on account of his great responsibilities like our own leader himself has trouble sometimes and now it is starting to rain. The boat they left was stunk up and beshat with pigs and chickens and that comrade we buried. There's one other guy is wounded but it doesn't look bad from the dressing."

"Pussy?"

"Yeah. But clean pus. You want to see it all or you take my word for it?"

"I take your word on all of it but I want to see it."

He saw everything, the tracks, the fire, where they had slept and cooked, the dressing, the part of the brush they had used as a latrine, and the groove the turtle boat had made in the sand when they beached her. It was raining hard now and the first gusts of the squall were coming.

"Put on the coats and put the *niños* under them," Ara said. "I have to take them down tonight anyway."

"I'll help you," Willie said. "We're breathing down their necks, Tom."

"There's an awful lot of country and they have someone with local knowledge now."

"You just keep thinking the way you are," Willie said. "What local knowledge has he got that we haven't got?"

"Certainly he'll have plenty."

"The hell with him. I'm going to wash on the stern with soap. Jesus, I want to feel that fresh water and that soap."

It was raining so hard now that it was hard to see the ship as they came around the point. The squall had moved out toward the ocean and it was so violent and the rain so heavy that trying to see the ship was like looking at an object from behind a falls. Her tanks will fill like nothing with this, Thomas Hudson thought. She'll probably be running off through the galley faucets and the head right now.

"How many days since it rained, Tom?" Willie asked.

"We'll have to check with the log. It's something over fifty."

"It's like the goddam monsoon breaking," Willie said. "Give me a gourd so I can bail."

"Keep the cover on your *niño* dry."

"Her butt is in my crotch and her nose is under the left shoulder of my coat," Willie said. "She never had it better in her life. Give me the gourd."

On the stern they were all bathing naked. They soaped themselves and stood on one foot and another, bending against the lashing of the rain as they soaped and then leaning back into it. They were really all brown but they looked white in this strange light. Thomas Hudson thought of the canvas of the bathers by Cézanne and then he thought he would like to have Eakins paint it. Then he thought that he should be painting it himself with the ship against the roaring white of the surf that came through the driving gray outside with the black of the new squall coming out and the sun breaking through momentarily to make the driving rain silver and to shine on the bathers in the stern.

He brought the dinghy up and Ara tossed a line and they were home.

11

THAT night after the rain had stopped and he had checked all leaks from the long dry spell, and seen that pans were put under them, and the point of actual leakage, not the drip, was pencilled, the watches were set, the duties apportioned, and everything discussed and agreed on with his mate and Ara. Then when the supper was ended and the poker game underway, he went up on the flying bridge. He had a Flit gun with him and his air mattress and a light blanket.

He thought that he would lie down and think about nothing. Sometimes he could do this. Sometimes he could think about the stars without wondering about them and the ocean without problems and the sunrise without what it would bring.

He felt clean from his scalp to his feet from the soaping in the rain that had beaten down on the stern and he thought, I will just lie here and feel clean. He knew there was no use thinking of the girl who had been Tom's mother nor all the things they had done and the places they had been nor how they had broken up. There was no use thinking about Tom. He had stopped that as soon as he had heard.

There was no use thinking about the others. He had lost them, too, and there was no use thinking about them. He had traded in remorse for another horse that he was riding now. So lie here now and feel clean from the soap and the rain and do a good job at nonthinking. You learned to do it quite well for a while. Maybe you will go to sleep and have funny or good dreams. Just lie quiet and watch the night and don't think. Ara or Henry will wake you if Peters gets anything.

He was asleep in a little while. He was a boy again and riding up a steep canyon. The canyon opened out and there was a sandbar by the clear river that was so clear he could see the pebbles in the bed of the stream and then watch the cutthroat trout at the foot of the pool as they rose to flies that floated down the current. He was sitting on his horse and watching the trout rise when Ara woke him.

The message read CONTINUE SEARCH CAREFULLY WESTWARD with the code name at the end.

"Thanks," he said. "Let me have anything else."

"Of course. Go back to sleep, Tom."

"I was having a fine dream."

"Don't tell it to me," Ara said. "And maybe it will come true."

He went to sleep again and when he went to sleep he smiled because he thought that he was carrying out orders and continuing the search westward. I have her pretty far west, he thought. I don't think they meant this far west.

He slept and he dreamed that the cabin was burned and someone had killed his fawn that had grown into a young buck. Someone had killed his dog and he found him by a tree and he woke sweating.

I guess dreams aren't the solution, he said to himself. I might as well take it the same as always without any hope of anaesthetics. Go on and think it out.

All you have now is a basic problem and your intermediate problems. That is all you have so you better like it. You will never have good dreams any more so you might as well not sleep. Just rest and use your head until it won't work any more, and when you go to sleep, expect to have the horrors. The horrors were what you won in that big crap game that they run. You put it on the line and made your point and let it ride and finally you dragged down the gift of uneasy unpleasant sleep. You damned near dragged down not sleeping at all. But you traded that in for what you have so you might as well like it. You're sleepy now. So sleep and figure to wake up sweating. And what of it? Nothing at all of it. But do you remember when you used to sleep all night with the girl and always happy and never woke unless she woke you to make love? Remember that, Thomas Hudson, and see how much good it will do you.

I wonder how many dressings they have for that other wounded character? If they had time to get dressings they had time to get other stuff, too. What stuff? What do you think they have besides what you know they have? I don't think much. Maybe pistols and a few machine pistols. Maybe some demolition charges they could make something out of. I have to figure that they have the machine gun. But I don't think so. They wouldn't want to fight. They want to get the hell away and on a Spanish ship. If they had been in shape to fight they would have come back that night and taken Confites. Maybe no. Maybe something made them suspicious and they saw our drums on the beach and thought we might be basing there nights. They wouldn't know what we were. But they would see the drums and figure there was something around that burned plenty of gas. Then too they probably didn't want to fight with their wounded. But the boat with the wounded could have laid off at night while they came in and took the wireless station if they wanted to get off with that other sub. I wonder what happened with her. There's something very strange about that.

Think about something cheerful. Think about how you start with the sun at your back. And remember they have local knowledge now, along with all that salt fish, and you are going to have to use your head. He went to sleep and slept quite well until two hours before daylight when the sand flies awakened him. Thinking about the problems had made him feel better and he slept without dreaming.

12

THEY left before the sun was up and Thomas Hudson steered down the channel that was like a canal with the gray banks showing on either side. By the time the sun was up he was out through the cut between the shoals and he steered due north to get into blue water and past the dangerous rocky heads of the outer reef. It was a little longer than running on the inside but it was much safer.

When the sun rose, there was no wind and not enough swell for the sea to break on any of the rocks. The day would be hot and muggy, he knew, and there would be squalls in the afternoon.

His mate came up and looked around. Then he looked carefully at the land and along it to where the high, ugly tower of the light showed.

"We could have run down easily on the inside."

"I know it," Thomas Hudson said. "But I thought this was better."

"Another day like yesterday. But hotter."

"They can't make much time."

"They can't make any time. They're becalmed somewhere. You're going to check with the light whether they went into the cut between Paredón and Coco, aren't you?"

"Sure."

"I'll go in. I know the keeper. You can lay just inside the little key at the tip. I won't be gone long," Antonio said.

"I don't even need to anchor."

"You've got plenty of strong-backed people to get anchors up."

"Send up Ara and Willie if they've eaten. Nothing should show here this close to the light and you can't see a damned thing looking into the sun. But send up George and Henry, too. We might as well do it right."

"Remember the rocks make right up to your blue water here, Tom."

"I remember and I can see them."

"Do you want your tea cold?"

"Please. And a sandwich. Send the men up first."

"They'll be right up. I'll send the tea up and have everything ready to go ashore."

"Be careful how you talk to them."

"That's why I am going in."

"Put out a couple of lines, too. It will look better coming in on the light."

"Yes," his mate said. "We might get something we could give them at the light."

The four came up and took their usual posts and Henry said, "Did you see anything, Tom?"

"One turtle with a sea gull flying around him. I thought he was going to perch on his back. But he didn't."

"*Mi capitán*," said George, who was a taller Basque than Ara and a good athlete and fine seaman, but not nearly as strong as Ara in many ways.

"*Mi señor obispo*," said Thomas Hudson.

"OK, Tom," George said. "If I see any really big submarines do you want me to tell you?"

"If you see one as big as you saw that one time keep it to yourself."

"I dream about her nights," George said.

"Don't talk about her," Willie said. "I just ate breakfast."

"When we closed I could feel my *cojones* going up like an elevator," Ara said. "How did you really feel, Tom?"

"Scared."

"I saw her come up," Ara said. "And the next thing I heard Henry say, 'She's an aircraft carrier, Tom.' "

"That's what she looked like," Henry said. "I can't help it. I'd say the same thing again."

"She spoiled my life," Willie said. "I've never been the same since. For a nickel I'd have never gone to sea again."

"Here," said Henry. "Take twenty cents and get off at Paredón Grande. Maybe they'll give you change."

"I don't want change. I'll take a transfer."

"Would you really?" Henry asked. There had been a certain amount of bad blood between them since the last two times they had been in Havana.

"Listen, expensive," Willie said. "We're not fighting submarines or you wouldn't have come up without sneaking a quick one. We're only chasing Krauts to kill them in a decked-over half-open boat. Even you ought to be able to do that."

"Take the twenty cents anyway," Henry said. "You'll need it some day."

"To stick up—"

"Cut it out the two of you. *Cut it out,*" Thomas Hudson said. He looked at both of them.

"I'm sorry, Tom," Henry said.

"I'm not sorry," Willie said. "But I apologize."

"Look, Tom," said Ara. "Almost abeam inshore."

"That's the rock that's just awash," Thomas Hudson said. "It shows further to the eastward on the chart."

"No. I mean further in about a half a mile."

"That's a man crawfishing or hauling fish traps."

"Do you think we ought to speak to him?"

"He's from the light and Antonio's going in to talk with them at the light."

"Feesh! Feesh!" his mate called and Henry asked, "May I take him, Tom?"

"Sure. Send Gil up."

Henry went down and in a little while the fish jumped and showed he was a barracuda. Then, a little later, he heard Antonio grunt as he hit him with the gaff and then he heard the thunking knocks of the club on its head. He waited for the splash of the fish being thrown back and looked at the wake to see his size. There was no splash and he remembered that barracuda were good to eat on this stretch of the coast and Antonio was saving him to take in to the light. Just then he heard the double shout of "Feesh!" and this time there was no jumping and the line was singing out. He turned out further into the blue water and slowed down both engines. Then as the line kept going out he threw out one motor and made a half-turn toward the fish.

"Wahoo," his mate called up. "Big one."

Henry brought the fish in and they looked down over the stern and saw him long and oddly pointed, his stripes showing clearly in the blueness of the deep water. When he was nearly within reach of the gaff he turned his head and made another fast deep run that took him out of sight in the clear water in less time than a man could snap his fingers.

"They always have that one run," Ara said. "It goes like a bullet."

Henry brought him in fast and they watched over the stern as he was gaffed and brought aboard rigid and trembling. His stripes showed a bright blue and his jaws, that could cut like razors, opened and closed with spasmodic uselessness. Antonio laid him in the stern and his tail beat against the deck.

"¡Qué peto más hermoso!" Ara said.

"He's a beautiful wahoo," Thomas Hudson agreed. "But we'll be out here all morning if this keeps up. Leave out the lines but take the leaders off," he said to his mate. He steered for just outside the light on its high point of rock and tried to make up the time they had lost and still act as though they were fishing. The friction of the lines in the water bent the rods.

Henry came up and said, "He was a beautiful fish, wasn't he? I'd love to have had him on light tackle. Don't they have an extraordinarily shaped head?"

"What will he weigh?" Willie asked.

"Antonio said he'd weigh about sixty, Willie. I was sorry I didn't have time to call you. He really should have been yours."

"That's all right," Willie said. "You caught him faster than I could and we have to get the hell along. I bet we could catch plenty good fish all along here."

"We'll come sometime after the war."

"I'll bet," said Willie. "After the war I'm going to be in Hollywood and be a technical adviser on how to be a horse's ass at sea."

"You'll be good at it."

"I ought to be. I've been studying it now for over a year to train me for my career."

"What the hell have you got so much black ass about today, Willie?" Thomas Hudson asked.

"I don't know. I woke up with it."

"Well, go down to the galley and see if that bottle of tea is cold and bring it up. Antonio's butchering the fish. So make a sandwich will you, please?"

"Sure. What kind of sandwich?"

"Peanut butter and onion if there's plenty of onion."

"Peanut butter and onion it is, sir."

"And try to get rid of your black ass."

"Yes sir. Black ass gone, sir."

When he was gone Thomas Hudson said, "You take it easy with him, Henry. I need the son of a bitch and he's good at his stuff. He's just got black ass."

"I try to be good with him. But he's difficult."

"Well try a little harder. You were needling him about the twenty cents."

Thomas Hudson looked ahead at the smooth sea and the innocent-looking deadliness of the reef off his port bow. He loved to run just off a bad reef with the light behind him. It made up for the times when he had to steer into the sun and it made up for several other things.

"I'm sorry, Tom," Henry said. "I'll watch what I say and what I think."

Willie was back up with the empty rum bottle full of tea wrapped in a paper towel and with two rubber bands around it to keep the towel in place.

"She's cold, skipper," he said. "And I have insulated her."

He handed a sandwich, wrapped in a paper towel segment, to Thomas Hudson and said, "One of the highest points in the sandwich-maker's art. We call it the Mount Everest Special. For Commanders only."

In the calm, even on the bridge, Thomas Hudson smelled his breath.

"Don't you think it's a little early in the day, Willie?"

"No sir."

Thomas Hudson looked at him speculatively.

"What did you say, Willie?"

"No sir. Didn't you hear me, sir?"

"OK," Thomas Hudson said. "I heard you twice. You hear this once. Go below. Clean up the galley properly and then go up in the bow where I can see you and stand by to anchor."

"Yes sir," said Willie. "I don't feel well, sir."

"Fuck how you feel, you sea lawyer. If you don't feel well you are going to feel a damned sight worse."

"Yes sir," Willie said. "I don't feel well, sir. I should see the ship's surgeon."

"You'll find him in the bow. Knock on the door of the head and see if he's there as you go by."

"That's what I mean, sir."

"What do you mean?"

"Nothing, sir."

"He's skunk-drunk," Henry said.

"No, he's not," Thomas Hudson said. "He's drinking. But he's closer to crazy."

"He's been strange for quite a while," Ara said. "But he was always strange. None of us has ever suffered as he has. I have never even suffered at all."

"Tom's suffered," Henry said. "And he's drinking cold tea."

"Let's not talk morbid and let's not talk wet," Thomas Hudson said. "I never suffered and I like cold tea."

"You never did before."

"We learn something new all the time, Henry."

He was coming up well on the light and he saw the rock he should keep outside of now, and he thought this was a worthless conversation.

"Go up forward with him, Ara, and see how he's doing. Stick around with him. You get the lines in, Henry. George, get down and help Antonio with the dinghy. Go in with him if he wants you to."

When he was alone on the bridge he smelled the bird guano from the rock and he rounded the point and anchored in two fathoms of water. The bottom was clean and there was a big tide running. He looked up at the white-painted house and the tall old-fashioned light and then past the high rock to the green mangrove keys and beyond them the low, rocky, barren tip af Cayo Romano. They had lived, off and on, for such a long time within sight of that long, strange, and pest-ridden key and knew a part of it so well and had come in on its landmarks so many times and under such good and bad circumstances that it always made him an emotion to sight it or to leave it out of sight. Now it was there at its barest and most barren, jutting out like a scrubby desert.

There were wild horses and wild cattle and wild hogs on that great key and he wondered how many people had held the illusion that they might colonize it. It had hills rich in grass with beautiful valleys and fine stands of timber and once there had been a settlement called Versailles where Frenchmen had made their attempt at living on Romano.

Now all the frame buildings were abandoned but the one big house and one time when Thomas Hudson had gone in there to fill water, the dogs from the shacks were huddled with the pigs that had burrowed in the mud and dogs and pigs both were gray from the solid blanket of mosquitoes that covered them. It was a wonderful key when the east wind blew day and night and you could walk two days with a gun and be in good country. It was country as unspoiled as when Columbus came to this coast. Then, when the wind dropped, the mosquitoes came in clouds from the marshes. To say they came in clouds, he thought, is not a metaphor. They truly came in clouds and they could bleed a man to death. The people we are searching for would not have stopped in Romano. Not with this calm. They must have gone further up the coast.

"Ara," he called.

"What is it, Tom?" Ara asked. He always swung up onto the bridge and landed as lightly as an acrobat but with the weight of steel.

"What's the score?"

"Willie's not himself, Tom. I took him out of the sun and I made him a drink and made him lie down. He's quiet now but he looks at things too fixedly."

"Maybe he had too much sun on his bad head."

"Maybe. Maybe it is something else."

"What else?"

"Gil and Peters are sleeping. Gil had the duty to keep Peters awake last night. Henry is sleeping and George went in with Antonio."

"They should be back soon."

"They will be."

"We must keep Willie out of the sun. I was stupid to send him forward. But I did it for discipline, without thinking."

"I am disassembling and cleaning the big ones and I checked all the fuses from the dampness and rain of last night on the other stuff. Last night after the poker game we disassembled and cleaned and oiled everything."

"Now, with the dampness, we have to make a daily check, whether anything is fired or not."

"I know," Ara said. "We ought to disembark Willie. But we can't do it here."

"Cayo Francés?"

"We could. But Havana would be better and have them ship him from there. He's going to talk, Tom."

Thomas Hudson thought of something and regretted it.

"We never should have taken him after he had a medical discharge and with the bad head," Ara said.

"I know. But we did. How many damn mistakes have we made?"

"Not too many," Ara said. "Now may I go down and finish the work?"

"Yes," Thomas Hudson said. "Thank you very much."

"*A sus órdenes,*" Ara said.

"I wish to hell they were better orders," Thomas Hudson said.

Antonio and George were coming out with the dinghy and Antonio came up on the bridge immediately and let George and Henry hoist the motor and the dinghy aboard.

"Well?" Thomas Hudson said.

"They must have gone by in the night on the last of the breeze," Antonio said. "They would have seen them at the light if they came into the cut. The old man who has the skiff and the fish traps hadn't seen any turtle boat. He talks about everything and he would have mentioned it, the lightkeeper said. Do you think we ought to go back and check with him?"

"No. I think they're down at Puerto Coco or else at Guillermo."

"That's about where they would have reached with what wind they had."

"You're sure they couldn't have gone through the cut at night?"

"Not with the best pilot that ever lived."

"Then we have to find them in the lee of Coco or down by Guillermo. Let's get the anchor up and go."

It was a very dirty coast and he kept outside of everything and ran the edge of the hundred-fathom curve. Inshore there was a low rocky coast and reefs and big patches of banks that came out dry with the low tide. There was a four-man watch and Gil was on Thomas Hudson's left. Thomas Hudson looked toward the shore and saw the beginning of the green of the mangroves and thought, what a hell of a place to be now in this calm. The clouds were piled high already and he thought the squalls would come out earlier. There are about three places past Puerto Coco that I must search, he thought. I had better hook her up a little more and get in there.

"Henry," he said. "Steer 285 will you? I want to go below and see Willie. Sing out if you sight anything. You don't need to watch inshore, Gil. Take the starboard watch forward. That's all too shallow inshore for them to be in there."

"I'd like to watch inshore," Gil said. "If you don't mind, Tom. There's that crazy channel that makes in almost against the beach and the guide could have taken them there and put them in the mangroves."

"Good," said Thomas Hudson. "I'll send up Antonio."

"I could see her mast in the mangroves with these big glasses."

"I doubt it like hell. But you might."

"Please, Tom. If you don't mind."

"I agreed already."

"I'm sorry, Tom. But I thought a guide might take her in there. We went in there once."

"And we had to come out the same way we went in."

"I know. But if the wind failed them and they had to hide in a hurry. We don't want to overrun them."

"Right. But we are a long way out for you to see a mast. Besides they would probably cut mangroves to hide the mast from the air."

"I know," Gil said with Spanish stubbornness. "But I have very good eyes and these are twelve-power glasses and it is calm so I see well and—"

"I said it was OK before."

"I know. But I had to explain."

"You've explained," Thomas Hudson said. "And if you find a mast you can stick it up my ass with peanuts on it."

Gil felt a little hurt at this but he thought it was funny, especially about the peanuts, and he searched the mangroves until the big glasses almost pulled the eyes out of his head.

Below, Thomas Hudson was talking with Willie and watching the sea and the land. It was always strange how much less you saw when you were down from the bridge, and, as long as things went well below, he felt a fool to be anywhere but at his post. He tried always to keep the necessary contact and avoid the idiocy of the un-inspecting inspection. But he had delegated more and more author-ity to Antonio, who was a much better sailor than he was, and to Ara who was a much better man. They are both better men than I am, he thought, and yet I still should be in command, using their knowl-edge and talent and their characters.

"Willie," he said. "How are you really?"

"I'm sorry about acting like a fool. But I'm sort of bad, Tom."

"You know the rules about drinking," Thomas Hudson said. "There aren't any. I don't want to use chickenshit words like the honor system."

"I know," Willie said. "You know I'm not a rummy."

"We don't ship rummies."

"Except Peters."

"We didn't ship him. They gave him to us. He has his problems, too."

"Old Angus is his problem," Willie said. "And his goddam problems get to be our problems too damn fast."

"We'll skip him," Thomas Hudson said. "You have anything else eating you?"

"Just in general."

"How?"

"Well I'm half crazy and you're half crazy and then we've got this crew of half saints and desperate men."

"It isn't bad to be half saint and half desperate man."

"I know it. It's wonderful. But I was used to things being more regular."

"Willie, there's nothing eating you really. The sun bothers your head and I'm sure drinking isn't good for it."

"I'm sure, too," Willie said. "I'm not trying to be a fuck-up, Tom. But did you ever go really crazy?"

"No. I always missed it."

"It's a lot of bother," Willie said. "And however long it lasts, it lasts too long. But I'll stop drinking."

"No. Just drink easy like you always did."

"I was using the drinking to stave it off."

"We're always using drinking for something."

"Sure. But this wasn't any gag. Do you think I'd lie to you, Tom?"

"We all lie. But I don't think you'd lie on purpose."

"Go on up on your bridge," Willie said. "I see you watching the water all the time like it was some girl that was going to get away from you. I won't drink anything except sea water maybe and I'll help Ara break them to pieces and put them together again."

"Don't drink, Willie."

"If I said I won't, I won't."

"I know."

"Listen, Tom. Can I ask you something?"

"Anything."

"How bad is it with you?"

"I guess pretty bad."

"Can you sleep?"

"Not much."

"Last night?"

"Yes."

"That was from walking the beach," Willie said. "Go on up and forget about me. I'll be working with Ara at our trade."

13

THEY had searched the beach for tracks at Puerto Coco and they searched the mangroves beyond with the dinghy. There were some really good places for a turtle boat to hide. But they found nothing and the squalls came out earlier with heavy rain that made the sea look as though it were leaping into the air in white, spurting jets.

Thomas Hudson had walked the beach and gone back inland

behind the lagoon. He had found the place where the flamingoes came at high tide and he had seen many wood ibis, the *cocos* that gave the key its name, and a pair of roseate spoon-bills working in the marl of the edge of the lagoon. They were beautiful with the sharp rose of their color against the gray marl and their delicate, quick, forward-running movements, and they had the dreadful, hunger-ridden impersonality of certain wading birds. He could not watch them long because he wanted to check in case the people they were looking for had left the boat in the mangroves and camped in the high ground to be clear of the mosquitoes.

He found nothing but the site of an old charcoal-burning and he came out onto the beach after the first squall hit and Ara had picked him up in the dinghy.

Ara loved running the outboard in the rain and a bad squall and he had told Thomas Hudson none of the searchers had found anything. Everybody was on board but Willie who had taken the furthest stretch of beach beyond the mangroves.

"And you?" Ara asked.

"Me, nothing."

"This rain will cool off Willie. I'm going to get him when I put you on board. Where do you think they are, Tom?"

"At Guillermo. That's where I'd be."

"Me too. That's what Willie thinks, too."

"How was he?"

"He's trying hard, Tom. You know Willie."

"Yes," said Thomas Hudson. They came alongside and he climbed aboard.

Thomas Hudson watched Ara pivot the dinghy on her stern and go off into the white squall. Then he called down for a towel and dried himself off on the stern.

Henry said, "Don't you want a drink, Tom? You were really wet."

"I'd like one."

"Do you want straight rum?"

"That's nice," Thomas Hudson answered. He went below to get a sweatshirt and shorts and he saw that they were all cheerful.

"We all had a straight rum," Henry said and brought him a glass half-full. "I don't think that way if you dry off quickly anyone can catch cold. Do you?"

"Hi, Tom," said Peters. "Have you joined our little group of health drinkers?"

"When did you wake up?" Thomas Hudson asked him.

"When I heard a gurgling noise."

"I'll make a gurgling noise some night and see if that wakes you up."

"Don't worry, Tom. Willie does that for me every night."

Thomas Hudson decided not to drink the rum. Then, seeing them all having had a drink and being cheerful and happy on an uncheerful errand, he thought it would be pompous and priggish not to take it. He wanted it, too.

"Split this with me," he said to Peters. "You are the only son of a bitch I ever knew that could sleep better with earphones on than without them."

"That split's nothing," Peters said, entrenching himself in the retreat from formal discipline. "That split doesn't give either of us anything."

"Get one of your own, then," Thomas Hudson said. "I like the goddam stuff as well as you do."

The others were watching and Thomas Hudson could see Henry's jaw muscles twitching.

"Drink it up," Thomas Hudson said. "And run all your mysterious machines tonight as well as you can. For yourself and for the rest of us."

"For all of us," Peters said. "Who is the hardest-working man on this ship?"

"Ara," Thomas Hudson said and sipped the rum for the first time as he looked around. "And every fucking body else on board."

"Here's to you, Tom," Peters said.

"Here's to you," Thomas Hudson said and felt the words die cold and stale in his mouth. "To the earphone king," he said, in order to recover something he had lost. "To all gurgling noises," he added, being now a long way ahead as he should have been at the start.

"To my commander," Peters said, running his string out too far.

"Any way you want to take it," Thomas Hudson said. "There are no articles that cover that with us. But I'll settle for that. Say it again."

"To you, Tom."

"Thanks," Thomas Hudson said. "But I will be a sad son of a

bitch before I drink to you until all your radios and you are functioning."

Peters looked at him and into his face there came the discipline and into his body, which was in bad shape, the carriage of a man who had served three hitches in something that he had believed in and left for something else, as Willie had, and he said, automatically and without reservations, "Yes sir."

"Drink to you," Thomas Hudson said. "And crank up all your fucking miracles."

"Yes, Tom," Peters said, without any cheating and without reservations.

Well, I guess that is enough of that, Thomas Hudson thought. I better leave it as it lays and go back to the stern and watch my other problem child come aboard. I can never feel about Peters the way the rest of them all feel. I hope I know as well as they do what his defects are. But he has something. He is like the false carried so far that it is made true. It is certain that he is not up to handling what we have. But maybe he is up to much better things.

Willie's the same, he thought. One is as bad one way as the other. They ought to be in now.

He saw the dinghy coming through the rain and the white drifted water that curled and blew under the lash of the wind. They were both thoroughly wet when they came aboard. They had not used their raincoats but had kept them wrapped around their *niños*.

"Hi, Tom," Willie said. "Nothing but a wet ass and a hungry gut."

"Take these children," Ara said and handed the wrapped submachine guns aboard.

"Nothing?"

"Nothing multiplied by ten," Willie said. He was standing on the stern dripping and Thomas Hudson called to Gil to bring two towels.

Ara pulled the dinghy in by her painter and climbed aboard.

"Nothing of nothing of nothing," he said. "Tom, do we get overtime for rain?"

"We ought to clean those weapons right away," Willie said.

"We'll get dry first," Ara said. "I'm wet enough. First I could never get wet and now I have gooseflesh even on my ass."

"Tom," Willie said. "You know those sons of bitches can sail in these squalls if they reef down and have the balls to."

"I thought of that too."

"I think they lay up in the daytime with the calm and then run with these afternoon squalls."

"Where do you put them?"

"I don't put them past Guillermo. But they could be."

"We'll start at daylight and catch them at Guillermo tomorrow."

"Maybe we'll find them and maybe they'll be gone."

"Sure."

"Why the hell haven't we got radar?"

"What good would it do us right now? What do you see in the screen, Willie?"

"I'll pipe the hell down," Willie said. "Excuse me, Tom. But chasing something with UHF that hasn't got a radio . . . ?"

"I know," said Thomas Hudson. "But do you want to chase any better than we've been chasing?"

"Yes. Is that OK?"

"OK."

"I want to catch the sons of bitches and kill every one of them."

"What good would that do?"

"You don't remember the massacre?"

"Don't give me any of that massacre shit, Willie. You've been around too long for that."

"OK. I just want to kill them. Is that all right?"

"It's better than the massacre thing. But I want prisoners from a U-boat operating in these waters who can talk."

"That last one you had didn't talk much."

"No. Neither would you if you were up the creek like he was."

"OK," Willie said. "Can I draw a slug of the legal?"

"Sure. Get on dry shorts and a shirt and don't make trouble."

"With nobody?"

"Grow up," Thomas Hudson said.

"Drop dead," Willie said and grinned.

"That's the way I like you," Thomas Hudson told him. "Keep it that way."

14

THAT night there was heavy lightning and thunder and it rained until about three o'clock in the morning. Peters could get nothing on the radio and they all slept hot and muggy until the sand flies came out after the rain stopped and wakened them, one after the other. Thomas Hudson pumped Flit down below and there was coughing and then less restless moving and slapping.

He waked Peters by Flitting him thoroughly and Peters shook his head with the earphones on and said softly, "I've been trying hard, Tom, all the time. But there's nothing."

Thomas Hudson looked at the glass with a torch and it was rising. That will give them a breeze, he thought. Well, they can't say they haven't had luck again. Now I must figure that.

He went back to the stern and sprayed all the Flit he could into the cabin without waking the people.

He sat in the stern and watched the night clear and flitted himself occasionally. They were short of repellent but had plenty of Flit. It burned where a man had been sweating but it was better than sand flies. Their effect differed from mosquitoes in that you could not hear them before they hit and there was an instant itching from the bite. The bites made a swelling about the size of a very small pea. In some places on the coast and on the keys, they were more virulent than in others. At least their bites seemed to be much more annoying. But, he thought, that could be the condition that our hides are in and how much they are burned and toughened. I do not know how the natives stand them. They have to be hardy people to live on this coast in the Bahamas when the trades aren't blowing.

He sat in the stern watching and listening. There were two planes, high in the sky, and he listened to the throbbing of the motors until they no longer could be heard.

Big bombers going to Camagüey on the way to Africa or going straight through to somewhere and nothing to do with us. Well, he thought, they are not bothered by sand flies. Neither am I. The hell with them. The hell with them and the hell I'm not. But I'd like to get some daylight and get out of here. We've checked all the way up to the end of the point, thanks to Willie, and I'll run the little channel right along the edge of the bank. There's only one bad place and with the morning light I can see it OK even in a calm. Then we'll be at Guillermo.

They were underway at daylight and Gil, who had the best eyes, was watching the green shore line with the twelve-power glasses. They were close enough to shore for him to see a cut mangrove branch. Thomas Hudson was steering. Henry was watching out to sea. Willie was backing up Gil.

"They're past this part, anyway," Willie said.

"But we have to check," Ara said. He was backing up Henry.

"Sure," Willie said. "I was just commenting."

"Where's that Dawn Patrol from that damned Molasses ship at Cayo Francés?"

"They don't patrol on Sundays, do they?" Willie asked. "This must be a Sunday."

"There's going to be a breeze," Ara said. "Look at the cirrus."

"I'm afraid of one thing," Thomas Hudson said. "That they're gone in through the pass at Guillermo."

"We'll have to see."

"Let's hook the hell up and get there," Willie said. "This is getting on my nerves."

"That's the impression I get sometimes," Henry said.

Willie looked at him and spat over the side. "Thank you, Henry," he said. "That's the impression I wished to give."

"Break it up," Thomas Hudson said. "See that big coral head to starboard that's just awash? That's what we have to not hit. On the inside, gentlemen, is Guillermo. See how green she is and full of promise?"

"One more goddam key," Willie said.

"Can you make out any smoke from charcoal burning?" Thomas Hudson asked.

Gil swept it very carefully and said, "No, Tom."

"The way it rained last night there wouldn't be any smoke," Willie said.

"You're wrong for once, boy," Thomas Hudson said.

"Maybe."

"No. It could rain like hell all night and not put one of those big burnings out. I've seen it rain three days and hardly bother one."

"You know more about them than me," Willie said. "OK, there could be smoke. I hope there is."

"That's a bad shoal," Henry said. "I don't believe they could run in those squalls along here."

In the morning light they could see four terns and two gulls working around the shoal. They had found something and were diving. The terns were crying and the gulls were screaming.

"What are they into, Tom?" Henry asked.

"I don't know. It looks like a school of bait fish that is too deep for them to work."

"Those poor bastard birds have to get up earlier in the morning than we do to make a living," Willie said. "People don't appreciate the work they put in."

"How are you going to run, Tom?" Ara asked.

"Just as close in to the bank as I can and right up to the head of the key."

"Are you going to check that half-moon key with the wreck?"

"I'll make a turn around it close in and everybody glass it. Then I'll anchor in the bight inside the tip of Guillermo."

"We'll anchor," Willie said.

"That's implied. Why do you get so ornery this early in the morning?"

"I'm not ornery. I'm just admiring the ocean and this beautiful coast Columbus first cast his eyes on. I'm lucky I didn't serve under that Columbus."

"I always thought you did," Thomas Hudson said.

"I read a book about him in the hospital at San Diego," Willie said. "I'm an authority on him and he had a worse fucked-up outfit than this one."

"This isn't a fucked-up outfit."

"No," said Willie. "Not yet."

"OK, Columbus boy. Do you see that wreck that bears about twenty degrees to starboard?"

"That's for your starboard watch to see," Willie said. "But I can see it OK with my one eye that works and there is a booby bird from the Bahamas perched on it. He's probably come to reinforce us."

"Good," said Thomas Hudson. "He's what we need."

"I probably could have been a great ornithologist," Willie said. "Grandma used to raise chickens."

"Tom," Ara said. "Do you think we can work a little closer in? The tide is high now."

"Sure," Thomas Hudson answered. "Ask Antonio to get up in the bow and let me know how much water I have."

"You've got plenty of water, Tom," Antonio called. "Right in to shore. You know this channel."

"I know. I just wanted to be sure."

"Do you want me to take her?"

"Thanks," said Thomas Hudson. "I do not."

"Now we can see the high ground beautifully," Ara said. "You take all of her, Gil. I'll just back you up. Glass her really well."

"Who takes the first quarter of the sea?" Willie asked. "How come you switched on me, anyway?"

"When Tom asked you to look at the wreck. We switch automatically. When you went to starboard I went to port."

"That's too nautical for me," Willie said. "When you want to be nautical, be right or not at all. Why don't you say right or left the same as in steering?"

"It was you who said the starboard watch," Henry said.

"That's right. And from now on I'm going to say downstairs and upstairs and the front and the back of the boat."

"Willie, get over with Gil and Ara and glass the beach, will you please?" Thomas Hudson said. "The beach and carry it up to the first third of the key."

"Yes, Tom," Willie said.

It was easy to see if there was anyone living on Cayo Guillermo on this which was the windward side for nearly all of the year. But there was nothing showing as they moved close in along the coast. They came abeam of the point and Thomas Hudson said, "I'll circle the half-moon key as close as I can and you all glass it. If you notice anything we can stand by and put the dinghy in."

The breeze was starting to rise and the sea was beginning to move but it did not break yet on the shoals because of the high tide. Thomas Hudson looked ahead at the small rocky key. He knew there was a sunken wreck at the western end of it but it showed only as a red brown bulge with this high tide. There was a shallow bank and a sandy beach on the inside of this key but he would not see the beach until he had rounded the wreck.

"There's somebody living on the key," Ara said. "I see smoke."

"Right," said Willie. "It's on the leeward side and the wind is carrying it to the west."

"The smoke is about at the center of where the beach should be," Gil said.

"Can you see a mast?"

"No mast," Gil said.

"They could step the goddam mast daytimes," Willie said.

"Go to your stations," Thomas Hudson said. "Ara, you stay here with me. Willie, tell Peters to get hooked up to talk whether anybody can hear him or not."

"What do you think?" Ara asked when the others were gone.

"I think if I were fishing and drying fish that I would have come off here from Guillermo when the calms came and brought the mosquitoes."

"Me, too."

"They aren't burning any charcoal on this key and the smoke is small. So it must be a fresh fire."

"Unless it is the end of a bigger one."

"I thought of that."

"Then we'll see in five minutes."

They rounded the wreck, which had another booby bird sitting on it, and Thomas Hudson thought, our allies are checking in fast. Then they were coming up into the lee of the key and Thomas Hudson saw the sand beach, the green behind it, and a shack with smoke coming from it.

"Thank God," he said.

"Equally," Ara said. "I was afraid of the other thing, too."

There was no sign of any boats.

"We're really close to them, I think. Get in fast with Antonio and tell me what you find. I'll lay her in right along the bank. Tell them to stay at their stations and act natural."

The dinghy spun and moved in to the beach. Thomas Hudson watched Antonio and Ara walking toward the thatched shack. They were moving as fast as they could without running. They called to the shack and a woman came out. She was dark as a sea Indian and was barefooted and her long hair hung down almost to her waist. While she talked, another woman came out. She was dark, too, and long-haired and she carried a baby. As soon as she finished speaking, Ara and Antonio shook hands with the two women and came back to the dinghy. They shoved off and started the motor and came out.

Antonio and Ara came up onto the flying bridge while the dinghy was being hoisted aboard.

"There were two women," Antonio said. "The men are outside fishing. The woman with the baby saw a turtle boat go into the channel that goes inside. It went in when this breeze came up."

"That would be about an hour and a half ago," Thomas Hudson said. "With the tide falling now."

"Very strong," Antonio said. "It is dropping very fast, Tom."

"When she is down, there is not enough water to carry us through there."

"No."

"What do you think?"

"It's your ship."

Thomas Hudson swung the helm hard over and put in both motors up to twenty-seven hundred revolutions and headed for the point of the key.

"They may run aground themselves," he said. "The hell with it."

"We can anchor if it gets too bad," Antonio said. "It's a marl bottom if we run aground. Marl and mud."

"And rocky spots," Thomas Hudson said. "Get Gil up here for me to watch for the stakes. Ara, you and Willie check all the weapons. Stay up here, please, Antonio."

"The channel is a bastard," Antonio said. "But it is not impossible."

"She is impossible in low water. But maybe the other son of a bitch will ground, too, or maybe the wind will fail."

"The wind won't fail, Tom," Antonio said. "It's firm and solid now for the trade wind."

Thomas Hudson looked at the sky and saw the long white hackles of clouds of the east wind. Then he looked ahead at the point of the main key, at the spot of key and the flats that were beginning to show. There he knew his trouble would start. Then he looked at the mess of keys ahead that showed like green spots on the water.

"Can you pick up the stake yet, Gil?" he asked.

"No, Tom."

"It's probably only the branch of a tree or maybe a stick."

"I can't see anything yet."

"It ought to be dead ahead as we go."

"I see it, Tom. It's a tall stick. Dead ahead as we go."

"Thank you," Thomas Hudson said.

The flats on either side were white yellow in the sun and the tidal stream that came pouring out of the channel was the green water of the inner lagoon. It was not fouled nor cloudy from the marl of the banks because the wind had not had time to raise a sea that would disturb them. This made his piloting easier.

Then he saw how narrow the cut was beyond the stake end and he felt his scalp prickle.

"You can make it, Tom," Antonio said. "Hang close to the starboard bank. I'll see the cut when it opens up."

He hung close to the starboard bank and crawled along. Once he looked to the port bank and saw it was closer than the starboard and he inched over to the right.

"Is she throwing any mud?" he asked.

"Clouds."

They came to the wicked turn and it was not as bad as he thought it would be. The narrow part they had come through was worse. The wind had risen now and Thomas Hudson felt it blowing strongly on his bare shoulder as they ran broadside to it through this cut.

"The stake is dead ahead," Gil said. "It's only a branch of tree."

"I've got it."

"Hold her hard against the starboard bank, Tom," Antonio said. "We have this one beat."

Thomas Hudson hugged the starboard bank as though he were parking a car against a curb. It did not look like a curb, though, but like the indented muddy terrain of an old battlefield, when they fought with great concentrations of artillery, that had suddenly been revealed from the bottom of the ocean and spread out, like a relief map, on his right.

"How much mud are we throwing?"

"Plenty, Tom. We can anchor when we get through this cut. This side of Contrabando. Or in the lee of Contrabando," Antonio suggested.

Thomas Hudson turned his head and saw Cayo Contrabando looking small and green and cheerful and he said, "The hell with that. Sweep that key and the channel that shows for a turtle boat, please, Gil. I see the next two stakes."

This channel was easy. But ahead he could see the sandbar on the right that was beginning to uncover. The closer they came to Cayo Contrabando, the narrower the channel became.

"Hold her to port of that stake," Antonio said.

"That's what I'm doing."

They passed the stake which was only a dead branch. It was brown and blowing in the wind and Thomas Hudson thought that with this wind blowing up they would have much less than the Mean Low Water depths.

"How's our mud?" he asked Antonio.

"Plenty, Tom."

"Do you see anything, Gil?"

"Only the stakes."

The water was beginning to be milky now from the sea that had risen with the wind and it was impossible to see the bottom nor the banks except when the ship sucked them dry.

This is no good, Thomas Hudson thought. But it is no good for them either. And they have to tack in it. They must really be sailors. Now I have to decide whether they would take the old channel or the new one. That depends on their pilot. If he is young, he would probably take the new one. That is the one the hurricane blew out. If he is old, he will probably take the old channel from habit and because it is safer.

"Antonio," he said. "Do you want to take the old canal or the new one?"

"They're both bad. It doesn't make much difference."

"What would you do?"

"I'd anchor in the lee of Contrabando and wait for the tide."

"We won't get enough tide to make it in daylight."

"That's the problem. You only asked me what I would do."

"I'm going to try to run the son of a bitch."

"It's your ship, Tom. But if we don't catch them, somebody else will."

"But why isn't Cayo Francés flying patrols over all this all the time?"

"They made their patrol this morning. Didn't you see it?"

"No. And why didn't you tell me?"

"I thought you saw it. One of those baby seaplanes."

"Shit," Thomas Hudson said. "It must have been when I was in the head and the generator was running."

"Well, it doesn't make any difference now," Antonio said. "But, Tom, the next two stakes are out."

"Can you see the next two stakes, Gil?"

"I can't see any stakes."

"The hell with it," Thomas Hudson said. "All I have to do is hug that next chickenshit little key and keep off the sand-spit that runs north and south of it. Then we'll case that bigger key with the mangroves and then we'll try for the old or the new channel."

"The east wind is blowing all the water out."

"The hell with the east wind," Thomas Hudson said. As he said the words, they sounded like a basic and older blasphemy than any that could have to do with the Christian religion. He knew that he was speaking against one of the great friends of all people who go to sea. Since he had made the blasphemy he did not apologize. He repeated it.

"You don't mean that, Tom," Antonio said.

"I know it," Thomas Hudson said. Then he said to himself, making an act of contrition and remembering the verse unexactly, "Blow, blow, thou western wind. That the small rain down may rain. Christ, that my love were in my arms and I in my bed again." It's the same goddam wind only with the difference in latitude, he thought. They come from different continents. But they are both loyal and friendly and good. Then he repeated to himself again, Christ, that my love were in my arms and I in my bed again.

The water was so muddy now that there was nothing to steer by except the ranges and the suction the ship made of water from the banks. George was in the bow with the lead and Ara had a long pole. They measured their depths and called back to the bridge.

Thomas Hudson had the feeling that this had happened before in a bad dream. They had run many difficult channels. But this was another thing that had happened sometime in his life. Perhaps it had happened all his life. But now it was happening with such an intensification that he felt both in command and at the same time the prisoner of it.

"Can you make out anything, Gil?" he asked.

"Nothing."

"Do you want Willie up here?"

"No. I see whatever Willie would see."

"I think he ought to be up anyway."

"As you wish, Tom."

Ten minutes later they were aground.

15

THEY were aground on a patch of mud and sandy bottom that should have been marked with a stake, and the tide was still falling. The wind was blowing hard and the water was muddy. Ahead was a medium-sized green key that looked set low in the water and there was a scattering of very small keys to the left. To the left and the right there were patches of bare bank that were beginning to show as the water receded. Thomas Hudson watched flocks of shore birds wheeling and settling on the banks to feed.

Antonio had the dinghy over and he and Ara ran out a bow anchor and two light stern anchors.

"Do you think we need another bow anchor?" Thomas Hudson asked Antonio.

"No, Tom. I don't think so."

"If the wind rises it can push us against the flood when it comes."

"I don't think it will, Tom. But it could."

"Let's get a small one out to windward and shift the big one further to leeward. Then we don't have anything to worry about."

"All right," Antonio said. "I'd rather do that than run aground again in a bad place."

"Yeah," Thomas Hudson said. "We went into all that before."

"It's still the right thing to anchor."

"I know it. I just asked you to put out another small one and shift the big one."

"Yes, Tom," Antonio said.

"Ara likes to lift anchors."

"Nobody likes to lift anchors."

"Ara."

Antonio smiled and said, "Maybe. Anyway I agree with you."

"We always agree sooner or later."

"But we mustn't let it be when it is too late."

Thomas Hudson watched the maneuver and looked ahead at the green key that was showing dark now at the roots of the mangroves as the tide fell. They could be in the bight on the south side of that key, he thought. This wind is going to blow until two or three o'clock in the morning and they could try to break out and run either of the channels in daylight when the flood starts. Then they could run that big lake of a bay where there is nothing to worry about all night. They have lights and a good channel to get out with at the far end. It all depends on the wind.

Ever since they had grounded he had felt, in a way, reprieved. When they had grounded he had felt the heavy bump of the ship as though he were hit himself. He knew it was not rocky as she hit. He could feel that in his hands and through the soles of his feet. But the grounding had come to him as a personal wound. Then, later, had come the feeling of reprieve that a wound brings. He still had the feeling of the bad dream and that it all had happened before. But it had not happened in this way and now, grounded, he had the temporary reprieve. He knew that it was only a reprieve but he relaxed in it.

Ara came up on the bridge and said, "It's good holding-ground, Tom. We have them in there good with a trip line to the big one. When we raise the big one we can get out fast. We buoyed both the stern anchors with trip lines."

"I saw. Thank you."

"Don't feel bad, Tom. The sons of bitches may be just behind that other key."

"I don't feel bad. I just feel delayed."

"It's not like smashing up a car or losing a ship. We're just aground waiting for a tide."

"I know."

"Both wheels are sound. She's just in mud up to her ass."

"I know. I put her there."

"She'll come off as easy as she went in."

"Sure she will."

"Tom. Are you worried about anything?"

"What would I be worried about?"

"Nothing. I only worried if you were worried."

"The hell with worry," Thomas Hudson said. "You and Gil go down. See everybody eats well and is cheerful. Afterwards we'll go in and check that key. That's all there is to do."

"Willie and I can go now. We don't have to eat."

"No. I'm going in later with Willie and Peters."

"Not me?"

"No. Peters speaks German. Don't tell him he's going in. Just wake him up and see he drinks plenty of coffee."

"Why can't I go, too?"

"The dinghy is too damn small."

Gil left him the big glasses and went down with Ara. Thomas Hudson studied the key carefully with the big glasses and saw that the mangroves were too high for him to learn anything about what was inside. There were other trees mixed with the mangroves on the solid part of the key and they brought the height up even more so that he could not possibly see if there was any mast showing in the horseshoe-shaped shelter on the far side. The big glasses hurt his eyes and he put them in their case and hung the strap of the case on a hook and laid the glasses flat on the frag rack.

He was happy to be alone again on the flying bridge and he re-laxed for the short time of his reprieve. He watched the shore birds working on the flats and he remembered what they had meant to him when he was a boy. He could not feel the same about them now and he had no wish to kill them ever. But he remembered the early days with his father in a blind on some sand-spit with tin decoys out and how they would come in as the tide lowered and bared the flats and how he would whistle the flock in as they were circling. It was a sad whistle and he made it now and turned one flock. But they veered off from the stranded ship and went far out to feed.

He swept the horizon with the big glasses once and there was no sign of any boat. Maybe they have made it out through the new channel and into the inside passage, he thought. It would be nice if someone else caught them. We can't catch them now without a fight. They will not surrender to a dinghy.

He had been thinking so long in their heads that he was tired of it. I am really tired finally, he thought. Well, I know what I have to do, so it is simple. Duty is a wonderful thing. I do not know what I would have done without duty since young Tom died. You could have painted, he told himself. Or you could have done something use-ful. Maybe, he thought. Duty is simpler.

This is useful, he thought. Do not think against it. It helps to get it over with. That's all we are working for. Christ knows what there is beyond that. We've chased these characters quite well and now take a ten-minute break and then proceed with your duty. The hell with quite well, he thought. We've chased them very well.

"Don't you want to eat, Tom?" Ara called up.

"I don't feel hungry, kid," Thomas Hudson said. "I'll take the bottle of cold tea that's on the ice."

Ara handed it up and Thomas Hudson took it and relaxed against the corner of the flying bridge. He drank from the bottle of cold tea and watched the biggest key that was ahead. The mangrove roots were showing plainly now and the key looked as though it were on stilts. Then he saw a flight of flamingoes coming from the left. They were flying low over the water, lovely to see in the sunlight. Their long necks were slanted down and their incongruous legs were straight out; immobile while their pink and black wings beat, carrying them toward the mud bank that was ahead and to the right. Thomas Hudson watched them and marvelled at their downswept black and white bills and the rose color they made in the sky, which made their strange individual structures unimportant and still each one was an excitement to him. Then as they came up on the green key he saw them all swing sharply to the right instead of crossing the key.

"Ara," he called down.

Ara came up and said, "Yes, Tom."

"Check out three *niños* with six clips apiece and put them in the boat with a dozen frags and the middle size aid kit. Send Willie up here, please."

The flamingoes had settled on the bank to the far right and were feeding busily. Thomas Hudson was watching them when Willie said, "Look at those goddam fillamingoes."

"They spooked flying over the key. I'm pretty sure that boat or another boat is inside there. Do you want to go in with me, Willie?"

"Of course."

"Did you finish chow?"

"The condemned man ate a hearty lunch."

"Help Ara, then."

"Is Ara going with us?"

"I'm taking Peters because he speaks German."

"Can't we take Ara instead? I don't want to be with Peters in a fight."

"Peters may be able to talk us out of a fight. Listen, Willie. I want prisoners and I don't want their pilot to get killed."

"You're making a lot of conditions, Tom, with them eight or nine maybe and we three. Who the hell knows we know they have the pilot anyway?"

"We know."

"Let's not be so fucking noble."

"I asked you if you wanted to come."

"I'm coming," Willie said. "Only that Peters."

"Peters will fight. Send Antonio and Henry up, will you, please."

"Do you think they are in there, Tom?" Antonio asked.

"I'm pretty sure."

"Can't I go in with you, Tom?" Henry asked.

"No. She will only take three. If anything happens to us, try and nail her with the .50's if she tries to come out on the first of the tide. Afterwards you'll find her in the long bay. She'll be damaged. She probably won't even be able to make it out. Get a prisoner if you can and get into Cayo Francés and check in."

"Couldn't I go in instead of Peters?" Henry asked.

"No, Henry. I'm sorry. But he speaks German. You have a good crew," Thomas Hudson said to Antonio. "If everything goes well with us I'll leave Willie and Peters on board with whatever there is and bring a prisoner back in the dinghy."

"Our last prisoner didn't last very long."

"I'll try and bring a good, strong, healthy one. Go on down and see everything is secured. I want to watch the flamingoes for a little while."

He stood on the flying bridge and watched the flamingoes. It is not just their color, he thought. It's not just the black on that rose pink. It is their size and that they are ugly in detail and yet perversely beautiful. They must be a very old bird from the earliest times.

He did not watch them through the glasses because he did not want details now. He wanted the roseate mass on the gray brown flat. Two other flocks had come in now and the banks were colored in a way that he would not have dared to paint. Or I would have dared to paint and would have painted, he thought. It is nice to see flamingoes before you make this trip. I better not give them time to worry or to think too much.

He climbed down from the bridge and said, "Gil, get up there and keep your glasses on the key. Henry, if you hear a lot of noise and then the turtle boat should come out from behind the key, shoot her fucking bow off. Everybody get up and glass where the survivors are and you can hunt them tomorrow. Plug the dinghy where she is shot up and use her. The turtle boat has a skiff and you can plug her up and use her too if we don't damage her too badly."

Antonio said, "Do you have any other orders?"

"Just keep your bowels open and try to lead clean lives. We'll be back in a little while. Come on, you two gentlemen bastards. Let's go."

"Grandmother always claimed I wasn't a bastard," Peters said. "She said I was the nicest-looking, most legitimate little baby in the county."

"Mother claimed I wasn't a bastard, too," Willie said. "Where do you want us, Tom?"

"She trims best with you in the bow. But I'll take the bow if you like."

"Get in and steer her," Willie said. "You got a really good ship now."

"I got my finger on my number," Thomas Hudson said. "I'm working up. Come aboard, Mr. Peters."

"Happy to be on board, admiral," Peters said.

"Good hunting," Henry said.

"Drop dead," Willie called. The motor caught and they were off toward the silhouette of the key that was lower in the water now because of their lack of altitude.

"I'm going alongside and we'll board her without hailing."

The two men nodded, one amidships and one in the bow.

"Get your junk hung. I don't give a shit if it shows," Thomas Hudson said.

"I don't know where I'd hide it," Peters said. "I feel like one of grandma's mules now."

"Then be a mule. It's a fucking good animal."

"Tom, do I have to remember all that shit about the pilot?"

"Remember it but use your head."

"Well," said Peters. "We haven't any fucking troubles anymore."

"We better all pipe down," Thomas Hudson said. "We'll all three board at the same time and if they are below, you ask them in Kraut to come out with their hands up. We have to stop talking because they can hear voices a long way above the noise of an outboard."

"What do we do if they don't come out?"

"Willie throws in a grenade."

"What do we do if they're on deck?"

"Sweep the deck according to our sectors. Me the stern. Peters amidships. You the bow."

"Then do I throw in a grenade?"

"Sure. We ought to get woundeds that we can save. That's why I brought the kit."

"I thought that was for us."

"Us too. Now let's pipe down. Do you have it clear?"

"Clearer than shit," Willie said.

"Has there been an issue of asshole corks?" Peters asked.

"They dropped it from the plane this morning. Didn't you get yours?"

"No. But grandma always said I had the slowest digestion of any baby in the whole of the South. They got one of my diapers in the Smithsonian Institute of the Confederacy."

"Cut out the shit," Willie said, leaning back in order not to talk loudly. "Are we doing all this in daylight, Tom?"

"Now."

"I'll be a sad son of a bitch," said Willie. "I have fallen among thieves and bastards."

"Shut up, Willie, and let's see you fight."

Willie nodded his head and looked ahead with his good eye toward the green mangrove key which lay tiptoed on its brown red roots.

He only said one more thing before they rounded the point, "They've got good oysters on those roots."

Thomas Hudson nodded.

16

THEY saw the turtle boat when they rounded the point of the key and passed through the channel which separated it from another small key. She was lying with her bow close in to shore and there were vines hanging from her mast and her deck was covered with new-cut mangrove branches.

Willie leaned back and with his voice almost against Peters' ear, said in a low voice, "Her skiff's missing. Pass the word."

Peters leaned his blotched, freckled face back and said, "Her skiff's missing, Tom. There must be some ashore."

"We'll board her and sink her," Thomas Hudson said. "Same plan. Pass the word."

Peters bent forward and spoke into Willie's ear and Willie's head started to shake. Then he held up his hand with the familiar zero. Zero as in asshole, Thomas Hudson thought. They came up on her as fast as the little coffee mill of an engine would take them and Thomas Hudson put her smartly alongside without bumping. Willie lifted the grapple over the gunwale of the turtle boat and pulled it fast and the three of them were on the deck almost at the same time. Underneath their feet there were mangrove branches with their dead fresh smell and Thomas Hudson saw the vine draped mast as though now it were a dream again. He saw the hatch open and a forward hatch open and covered with branches. There was no one on deck.

Thomas Hudson waved Willie forward past this hatch and covered the other one with his submachine gun. He checked that the safety lever was on full automatic. Under his bare feet he could feel the hard roundness of the branches, the slipperiness of the leaves, and the heat of the wooden deck.

"Tell them to come out with their hands up," he said quietly to Peters.

Peters spoke in rough, throaty German. Nobody answered and nothing happened.

Thomas Hudson thought, grandma's boy has a good delivery, and he said, "Tell them again we give them ten seconds to come out. We will treat them as prisoners of war. Then count ten."

Peters spoke so it sounded like the voice of all German doom. His voice holds up magnificently, Thomas Hudson thought, and turned his head fast to see if the skiff were in sight. He could only see the brown roots and the green of the mangroves.

"Count ten and put one in," he said. "Watch that fucking forward hatch, Willie."

"It's got those fucking branches covering it."

"Push one in with your hands when Peters goes. Don't throw it."

Peters reached ten and standing there, tall, loose-jointed like a pitcher on the mound, holding his submachine gun under his left arm, he pulled the pin of the grenade with his teeth, held it spurting smoke a moment as though he were warming it, and tossed it with the underhand motion of a Carl Mays into the darkness of the hatch.

As Thomas Hudson watched him, he thought, he's a great actor and he doesn't think there is anything down there.

Thomas Hudson hit the deck, covering the mouth of the hatch with his Thompson. Peters' grenade exploded with a flashing crack and a roar and Thomas Hudson saw Willie opening the brush to drop a grenade in the forward hatch. Then to the right of the mast, where the vines hung, he saw the muzzle of a gun come up from between the branches on the same hatch where Willie was working. He fired at it but it fired five quick flashes, clattering like a child's rattle. Then Willie's grenade went with a big flash and Thomas Hudson looked and saw Willie, in the scuppers, pull the pin on another grenade to throw in. Peters was on his side with his head on the gunwale. Blood was running from his head into the scuppers.

Willie threw and the grenade had a different sound because it rolled further into the boat before it burst.

"Do you think there are any more of the cocksuckers?" Willie called.

"I'll put one more in from here," Thomas Hudson said. He ducked and ran to get out of any fire from the big hatch and pulled the pin on another grenade, gray, heavy, solid, and notched in the grip of his hand, and crossing forward of the hatch he rolled it down into the stern. There was the crack, boom, and smoke where pieces of the deck came up.

Willie was looking at Peters and Tom came over and looked at him too. He did not look very different than usual.

"Well, we've lost our interpreter," Willie said. His good eye was twitching but his voice was the same.

"She's settling fast," Thomas Hudson said.

"She was aground already. But she's going over on her beam ends now."

"We've got a lot of uncompleted business, Willie."

"And we traded even. One for one. But we sunk the damned boat."

"You better get the hell back to the ship and get back here with Ara and Henry. Tell Antonio to bring her abreast of the point as soon as he gets the tide."

"I have to check below first."

"I'll check."

"No," Willie said. "That's my trade."

"How do you feel, kid?"

"Fine. Only sorry to hear of the loss of Mr. Peters. I'll get a rag or something to put over his face. We ought to straighten him out with his head uphill now she's careening like this."

"How is the Kraut in the bow?"

"He's a mess."

17

WILLIE was gone now to bring Ara and Henry. Thomas Hudson lay behind the parapet the high gunwale of the turtle boat made. His feet were against the hatch and he was watching for the skiff. Peters lay feet downward on the other side of the hatch and his face was covered by a German navy fatigue shirt. I never realized he was so tall, Thomas Hudson thought.

He and Willie had both searched the turtle boat and it was a mess. There had only been one German on board. He was the one who had shot Peters and he had evidently taken him for the officer. There was one other Schmeisser machine pistol aboard and close to two thousand rounds of ammunition in a metal case which had been opened with pliers or a can opener. Presumably, the men who had gone ashore had been armed because there were no weapons on board. The skiff was at least a sixteen-foot, heavy turtler from the chocks and the marks that she had left on the deck. They still had a quantity of food. It was mostly dried fish and hard roasted pork. It was the wounded man who had been left on board who had shot Peters. He had a bad thigh wound that was nearly healed and another nearly healed wound in the fleshy part of his left shoulder. They had good charts of the coast and of the West Indies and there was one carton of Camels without stamps and marked Ships Supplies. They had no coffee, nor tea, nor any liquors of any sort.

The problem now was what they would do. Where were they? They must have seen or heard the small fight on the turtle boat and they might return to pick up their stores. They would have seen one man leave by himself in the dinghy with the outboard and from the shots and the explosion of the frags there could easily be three men dead or incapacitated aboard. They would come back for stores or anything else that might be hidden and then break for the mainland in the dark. They could shove the skiff off anything that she might ground on.

The skiff must be a sturdy craft. Thomas Hudson had no radio operator and it was therefore impossible to give a description of the skiff and nobody would be looking for her. Then, if they wanted to, and had the will to try it they could try to assault the ship at night. That seemed extremely unlikely.

Thomas Hudson thought it out as carefully as he could. Finally, he decided, I believe that they will go inside the mangroves and haul the skiff in and hide it. If we go in after them, they can ambush us easily. Then they will run for the open inside bay and push on and try and pass Cayo Francés at night. That is easy. They may pick up supplies, or raid for them, and they will keep on pushing to the westward and try to make one of the German outfits around Havana where they will hide them and pick them up. They can easily get a better boat.

They can jump one. Or steal one. I have to report at Cayo Francés and deliver Peters and get my orders. The trouble won't come until Havana. There's a lieutenant commanding at Cayo Francés and we won't have any trouble there and they can keep Peters.

I have enough ice to handle him to there and I gas there and get ice at Caibarién.

We are going to get these characters for better or for worse. But I am not going to put Willie and Ara and Henry into one of those burp-gun massacres in the mangroves for fuck-all nothing. There are eight of them, anyway, from the looks of everything on board. I had a chance to catch them today with their pants down and I blew it because they were too smart or too lucky and they are always efficient.

We've lost one man and he is our radio operator. But we have cut them down to a skiff now. If I see the skiff we will destroy it and blockade the island and hunt them down on it. But I'm not going to stick our necks into any of those eight against three traps. If it is my ass afterwards, it is my ass. It is going to be my ass, anyway. Now that I've lost Peters. If I lost any irregulars, nobody would give a damn. Except me and the ship.

I wish they would get back, he thought. I don't want those bastards coming out to see what gives aboard this vessel and have the battle of no-name key by myself. I wonder what they are doing in there, anyway? Maybe they went for oysters. Willie mentioned the oysters. Maybe they just didn't want to be on this turtle boat in daylight if a plane came over and spotted her. But they must know the hours those planes work on by now. Hell, I wish they would come out and get it over with. I've got good cover and they'd have to get in range before they try to come aboard. Why do you suppose that wounded man didn't open up on us when we came over the side? He must have heard the outboard. Maybe he was asleep. The outboard makes very little noise anyway.

There are too many whys in this business, he thought, and I am not at all sure I have it figured properly. Maybe I should not have jumped the boat. But I think I had to do that. We sunk the boat and lost Peters and killed one man. That is not very brilliant but it still adds up.

He heard the hum of the outboard and turned his head. He saw her coming around the point but he could only see one man in her. It was Ara in the stern. But he noticed she was loaded deep and he realized that Willie and Henry must be lying flat. Willie's really smart, he thought. Now the people on the key don't know but that there may be only one man in the dinghy and they will see it is a different man from the one that took her away. I don't know whether that is smart or not. But Willie must have figured it.

The dinghy came up in the lee of the turtle boat and Thomas Hudson saw Ara's great chest, his long arms, and his brown face that was serious now, and he could see the nervous twitching of his legs. Henry and Willie lay flat with their heads on their arms.

When the dinghy came into the lee of the turtle boat that was careened away from the key and Ara held the rail, Willie turned on his side and said, "Get aboard, Henry, and crawl up there with Tom. Ara will hand you your junk. You've got Peters' junk too."

Henry climbed cautiously up the steep deck on his belly. He took one look at Peters as he crawled by him.

"Hi, Tom," he said.

Thomas Hudson put his hand on Henry's arm and said softly, "Get up in the bow and keep absolutely flat. Don't let anything show over the gunwale."

"Yes, Tom," the big man said, and began inching down to crawl up to the bow. He had to crawl over Peters' legs and he picked up his submachine gun and clips and stuck the clips in his belt. He felt in Peters' pockets for frags and hung them on his belt. He patted Peters on the legs and holding the two submachine guns by the muzzles he crawled up to his post in the bow.

Thomas Hudson saw him look down into the blasted forward hatch as he crawled up the steep deck over the broken mangroves. His face gave no sign of what he saw there. When he was under the lee of the gunwale, he put the two submachine guns by his right hand and then tested the functioning of Peters' gun and put in a fresh clip. He laid the other clips along the gunwale and unhooked the grenades from his belt and laid them out within reach. When he saw him in position and looking out at the greenness of the key, Thomas Hudson turned his head and spoke to Willie who was lying in the bottom of the dinghy with his good and his bad eye shut against the sun. He was wearing a faded khaki shirt with sleeves and ragged shorts and he had a pair of sneakers on. Ara was sitting in the stern and Thomas Hudson noticed his thatch of black hair and the way his big hands gripped the gunwale. His legs were still jumping but Thomas Hudson had known for a long time how nervous he always was before action and how beautiful he was once things started.

"Willie," Thomas Hudson said. "You have anything figured?"

Willie opened his good eye and kept his bad eye closed against the sun.

"I ask permission to go in on the far side of the key and see what the hell gives. We can't let them get out of here."

"I'll go in with you."

"No, Tommy. I know this shit and it's my trade."

"I don't want you to go in alone."

"That's the only way on this. You trust me, Tommy. Ara will come back here and back up your play if I flush them. He can come in and pick me up on the beach if there isn't any trouble."

He had both eyes open and he was looking hard at Thomas Hudson the way a man looks who is trying to sell an appliance to someone who should really have it if they can afford it.

"I'd rather go in with you."

"Too fucking much noise, Tom. I tell you truly I know this shit good. I'm a fucking expert. You'll never find anybody like me."

"OK. Go in," Thomas Hudson said. "But bust up their skiff."

"What the hell you think I'm going to do? Go in there and jerk off?"

"If you're going in, you better get in."

"Tom. Now you've got two traps set. The ship and here. Ara makes you mobile. You have one expendable, medically discharged Marine to lose. What's holding you up?"

"You talking so much," Thomas Hudson said. "Get the hell in and shit bless you."

"Drop dead," Willie told him.

"You sound in good shape," Thomas Hudson said and explained rapidly in Spanish to Ara what they were going to do.

"Don't bother," Willie said. "I can talk to him lying down."

Ara said, "I'll be right back, Tom."

Thomas Hudson watched him yank the motor alive and watched the dinghy move out with Ara's broad back and black head in the stern and Willie lying in the bottom. He had turned around so that his head was close to Ara's feet and he could talk to him.

The good, brave, worthless son of a bitch, Thomas Hudson thought. Old Willie. He made up my mind for me when I was starting to put things off. I would rather have a good Marine, even a ruined Marine, than anything in the world when there are chips down. And we have chips down now. Good luck, Mr. Willie, he thought. And don't drop dead.

"How are you, Henry?" he asked softly.

"Fine, Tom. It was very gallant of Willie to go in, don't you think?"

"He never even heard of the word," Thomas Hudson said. "He just conceived it to be his duty."

"I'm sorry we haven't been friends."

"Everybody is friends when things are bad enough."

"I'm going to be friends from now on."

"We're all going to do a lot of things from now on," Thomas Hudson said. "I wish from now on would start."

18

THEY were lying on the hot deck watching the line of the key. The sun was strong on their backs but the wind cooled them. Their backs were nearly as brown as the sea Indian women they had seen this morning on the outer key. That seemed as long ago as all his life, Thomas Hudson thought. That and the open sea and the long breaking reefs and the dark depthless tropic sea beyond were as far away as all of his life was now. We could have just gone up the open sea with this breeze and made Cayo Francés and Peters would have answered their blinker and we all would have had cold beer tonight. Don't think about it, boy, he thought. This is what you had to do.

"Henry," he said. "How are you doing?"

"Splendidly, Tom," Henry said very softly. "A frag couldn't blow up from getting too hot in the sun could it?"

"I've never seen it. But it can increase their potency."

"I hope Ara's got some water," Henry said.

"Don't you remember them putting it in?"

"No, Tom. I was looking after my own equipment and I didn't notice."

Then against the wind they heard the noise of the outboard on the dinghy. Thomas Hudson turned his head carefully and saw her round the point. The dinghy was riding high and Ara was in the stern. He could see the width of his shoulders and his black head at this distance. Thomas Hudson turned his head again to watch the key and he saw a night heron rise from the trees in the center and fly away. Then he saw two wood ibis rise and wheel and fly off with quick-flapping, then coasting, then quick-flapping wing-beats downwind toward the little key.

Henry had watched them, too, and he said, "Willie must be getting pretty well in."

"Yes," Thomas Hudson said. "They came off the high ridge in the center of the key."

"Then nobody else was there."

"Not if it was Willie who scared them."

"That's about where Willie would be by now if he didn't have too bad going."

"Keep down low now when Ara comes."

Ara brought the dinghy along the careened lee of the turtle boat and put the grapnel aboard against the gunwale. He climbed carefully aboard with the ease of a bear. He had a water bottle and a bottle of tea in an old gin bottle each tied to a piece of heavy fishing line that suspended them over his neck. He crawled up to lie beside Thomas Hudson.

"What about some of the damn water?" Henry asked.

Ara laid his stuff down beside Thomas Hudson's, untied the water bottle from the fish line and crawled carefully along the slanted deck above the two hatches to where Henry was stationed.

"Drink it," he said. "Don't try to bathe with it."

He slapped Henry on the back and crawled back to lie beside Thomas Hudson.

"Tom," he said, speaking very low. "We saw nothing. I landed Willie on the far side almost directly opposite us and went out to the ship. There I went aboard on the lee side away from the key. I explained everything to Antonio and he understood well. Then I filled the outboard with gas and filled the reserve can and brought out the iced tea and the water."

"Good," said Thomas Hudson. He dropped down the deck a little way and took a long pull at the bottle of iced tea.

"Thank you very much for the tea."

"It was Antonio thought of it. We forgot certain things in our hurry at the start."

"Move down toward the stern so you can cover it."

"Yes, Tom," Ara said.

They lay there in the sun and the wind and each one watched the key. Occasionally a bird, or a pair of birds would fly up, and they knew these birds had been frightened either by Willie or by the others.

"The birds must make Willie angry," Ara said. "He didn't think about that when he went in."

"He might just as well be sending up balloons," Thomas Hudson answered.

He was thinking and he turned to look over his shoulder.

He did not like any of it now. There were too many birds getting up from the key. And what reason now had they to believe that the others were in there now? Why would they have gone in there in the first place? Lying on the deck he had a hollow feeling in his chest that both he and Willie had been deceived. Maybe they haven't sucked us in. But it does not look good with so many birds getting up, he thought. Another pair of wood ibis rose not far from the shore and Thomas Hudson turned to Henry and said, "Get down in the forward hatch, Henry, please, and keep watch inland."

"It's awfully messy in there."

"I know."

"All right, Tom."

"Leave your frags and clips. Just take a frag in your pocket and the *niño*."

Henry eased himself down into the hatch and looked out toward the inside keys that masked the channel. His expression had not changed. But he was tight-lipped keeping it in order.

"I'm sorry about it, Henry," Thomas Hudson said to him. "It's just the way it has to be for a while."

"I don't mind it," Henry said. Then the studied severity of his face cracked and he smiled his wonderful good smile. "It's that it isn't exactly the way I would plan to spend a summer."

"Me either. But things don't look so open and shut right now."

A bittern came out from the mangroves and Thomas Hudson heard it squawk and watched its nervous swooping flight downwind. Then he settled down to trace Willie's progress along the mangroves by the rising and the flight of the birds. When the birds stopped rising he was sure he was headed back. Then after a time they were being put up again and he knew Willie was working out the windward curve of the key. After three-quarters of an hour he saw a great white heron rise in panic and start its slow heavy wing-beats to windward and he said to Ara, "He'll be out now. Better go down to the point and pick him up."

"I see him," Ara said in a moment. "He just waved. He's lying down just in from the beach."

"Go get him and bring him back lying down."

Ara slid back down to the dinghy with his weapon and with a couple of frags in his pockets. He got into the stern of the dinghy and cast her off.

"Toss me the tea bottle, will you, Tom?"

Ara caught it using both hands for surety instead of the one-hand catch he would usually have made. He enjoyed catching frags one-handed and the hardest way possible just as he enjoyed crimping detonator caps with his teeth. But this tea was for Willie and he appreciated what Willie had been through, even though there were no results and he placed the bottle carefully under the stern and hoped it was still cool.

"What do you think, Tom?" Henry asked.

"We're fucked. For the moment."

In a little while the dinghy was alongside and Willie was lying in the bottom with the bottle of tea in both hands. His hands and face were scratched and bloody, although he had washed them with sea water, and one sleeve was torn off his shirt. His face was bulging with mosquito bites and there were lumps from mosquito bites wherever his flesh was bare.

"There's not a goddam thing, Tom," he said. "They never were on that key. You and I weren't too damned smart."

"No."

"What do you think?"

"They went inside after they grounded. Whether for keeps or to make a recon of the channels I don't know."

"Do you think they saw us board?"

"They could have seen everything or nothing. They're pretty low in the water to see."

"They ought to have heard it downwind."

"They should have."

"So now?"

"You get out to the ship and send Ara back for Henry and me. They might still be back."

"What about Peters? We can take him."

"Take him now."

"Tommy, you're parapeted up on the wrong side," Willie said. "We've both been wrong and I'm not offering any advice."

"I know it. I'm going down in the afterhatch as soon as Ara loads Peters."

"He better load him by himself," Willie said. "They could see silhouettes. But they couldn't make out an object flat on the deck without glasses."

Thomas Hudson explained to Ara and Ara climbed up and handled Peters quite easily and impersonally but he knotted the cloth behind his head. He was neither tender nor rough and all he said as he lifted him and slid him head first into the dinghy was, "He is very rigid."

"That's why they call them stiffs," Willie said. "Didn't you ever hear?"

"Yes," Ara said. "We call them *fiambres* which means cold meats as in a restaurant when you can have fish or cold meats. But I was thinking of Peters. He was always so limber."

"I'll get him right back, Tom. Do you need anything?"

"Luck," Thomas Hudson said. "Thank you for the recon, Willie."

"Just the usual shit," Willie said.

"Have Gil put Merthiolate on the scratches."

"Fuck the scratches," Willie said. "I'm going to run as a jungle man."

Thomas Hudson and Henry were looking out from the two hatches toward the broken and indented line of keys that lay between them and the long bay that formed the inland channel. They spoke in a normal tone of voice since they knew the others could not be closer than those small green islands.

"You watch," Thomas Hudson said. "I'm going to throw that ammunition of theirs overboard and have another look around below."

Below he found several things he had not noticed before and he lifted the case of ammunition out onto the deck and pushed it over the side. I suppose I should have scattered all the cartons, he thought. But the hell with it. He brought up the Schmeisser pistol and found it was not functioning. He laid it down with his own stuff.

I'll let Ara break it down, he thought. At least we know why they did not take it with them. Do you suppose they left that wounded man behind just as a reception committee and pulled out? Or do you suppose they made him comfortable and went off for a recon? How much do you think they saw and how much do you think they know?

"Don't you think we might have kept that ammo for evidence?" Henry asked.

"We're way past the evidence stage now."

"But it's always good to have it. You know how stuffy they are and they'll probably just evaluate the whole thing as doubtful. Maybe ONI won't even give it a doubtful. Do you remember the last one, Tom?"

"Yes, I remember."

"She went all the way up the mouth of the Mississippi and she's still doubtful."

"That's correct."

"I think we might have kept the ammo."

"Henry," Thomas Hudson said. "Please take it easy. The deads from the massacre are on the key. We have Schmeisser bullets from them and from the dead Kraut. We have another dead Kraut buried with the location in the log. We have this turtle boat sunk and a dead Kraut in her bows. We have two Schmeisser pistols. One is non-functioning and the other is smashed by the frag."

"A hurricane will come along and blow everything away and they will say the whole thing is doubtful."

"All right," said Thomas Hudson. "Let's concede the whole thing is doubtful. And Peters?"

"One of us probably shot him."

"Sure. We'll have to go through all that."

They heard the outboard and then saw Ara round the point. That dinghy rides as high in the bow as a canoe, Thomas Hudson thought.

"Get your junk together, Henry," he said. "We're going back to the ship."

"I'm glad to stay aboard this thing if you want me to."

"No. I want you on the ship."

After Ara came alongside Thomas Hudson changed his mind.

"Stay here, Henry, a little while and I'll send Ara for you. If they come out, get a frag into the skiff if they come alongside. Take this back hatch where you have lots of room. Use your head."

"Yes, Tom. Thank you for letting me stay."

"I'd stay and send you in. But I have to talk things over with Antonio."

"I understand. Shouldn't I fire on them when they are alongside before I throw the frag?"

"If you want. But keep your head down and then throw the frag in from the other hatch. And hold it all you can."

He was lying in the lee scuppers passing his things to Ara. Then he lowered himself over the side.

"Is there too much water for you down there?" he asked Henry.

"No, Tom. It's quite all right."

"Don't get claustrophobia and keep a good lookout. If they come in, let them get right alongside before you make your play."

"Of course, Tom."

"Think of it as a duck blind."

"I don't have to, Tom."

Thomas Hudson was lying flat on the planking of the dinghy now.

"Ara will be back as soon as you ought to come in."

"Don't worry, Tom. I can stay here all night if you like but I'd like Ara to bring out something to eat and a little rum perhaps and some more water."

"He'll be back and pick you up and we'll have a little rum on board."

Ara pulled the cord on the motor and they headed for the ship. Thomas Hudson felt the frags along his legs and the weight of the *niño* across his chest. He put his arms around it and cuddled it and Ara laughed and leaned down and said, "This is a bad life for good children."

19

THEY were all on board the ship now and it was cool in late afternoon wind. The flamingoes were gone from the flat although it was still uncovered. The flat was gray in the afternoon light and there was a flock of willets working over it. Beyond was the shallow water, the channels that could not be seen for the mud, and in the background were the keys.

Thomas Hudson was standing now on the flying bridge, leaning against a corner of it, and Antonio was talking to him.

"We don't get a high tide until after eleven tonight," Antonio said. "This wind is emptying the water right out of the bay and the flats and I don't know what sort of depths we will have."

"Will it float her or will we have to kedge off?"

"It will float her. But we haven't any moon."

"That's right. That's why we have these big springs."

"She only made last night," Antonio said. "She's new. We didn't see her last night because of the squall."

"That's right."

"I sent George and Gil in to cut some brush to stake the channel so we can get out. We can always sound it with the dinghy and get stakes on the points."

"Look. What I'd like to do when she floats is get in to where I can bring the searchlight and the .50's to bear on the turtle boat and put somebody on board to blink to us if they come out in the skiff."

"That would be ideal, Tom. But you can't get in there in the dark. You could get in there with the searchlight and the dinghy sounding ahead of you and calling the soundings and staking. But nobody would come out then. They'd never come out."

"I guess so. I've been wrong twice today."

"You were wrong," Antonio said. "But it was just chances. Like drawing a card."

"What's important is that I was wrong. Now tell me what you think."

"I think that if they haven't gone and if we make no move to act as though we were not aground they will come out to board the ship tonight. We do not look like anything except a pleasure craft. I'm sure they were inside the keys when it happened. They will feel contempt for us and they will be sure we are weak because they have seen only one man all day in the dinghy if they have watched."

"We tried to play it that way."

"Then if they find how things are on the turtle boat what then?"

"Ask Willie to come up here," he said to Antonio.

Willie came up, still lumpy-looking from the mosquito bites. His scratches looked better, though, and he was wearing only a pair of khaki shorts.

"How are you, jungle man?"

"I'm fine, Tom. Ara put some chloroform on the bites and they've stopped itching. Those damn mosquitoes are about a quarter of an inch long and black as ink."

"We've got ourselves pretty well fucked-up, Willie."

"Hell. We've been fucked-up from the start."

"Peters?"

"We've got him sewed up in canvas and some ice on him. He won't bring anything in the market. But he'll hold a couple of days."

"Listen, Willie. I was telling Antonio what I'd like to do was get in to where the .50's and the searchlight would bear on that hulk.

But he says we can't get in without spooking the whole ocean and that it's no good."

"Sure," Willie said. "He's right. That's three times you've been wrong today. I'm leading you by one less."

"Do you think they will come out and try and board the ship?"

"I doubt it like hell," Willie said.

"But they could."

"They aren't crazy. But they could be desperate enough to try it."

The two of them were sitting on the deck of the flying bridge leaning back against the stays and the canvas. Willie rubbed the part of his right shoulder that had begun to itch again on the canvas.

"They could come out," he said. "They did a crazy thing when they made that massacre."

"Not from their point of view then. You have to remember it was when they had just lost their ship and they were desperate."

"Well, they lost another ship today as well as a comrade. Maybe they were fond of the son of a bitch."

"Probably. Or they wouldn't have let him take up space."

"He was a pretty good guy," Willie said. "He took all that surrender talk and a grenade before he even made his play. He must have thought Peters was the captain because of his commanding manner and the way he spreched Kraut."

"I guess so."

"You know the frags went off below decks. They might never have heard them. How many rounds did you fire, Tom?"

"Not more than five."

"The character fired one burp."

"How loud did it all sound to you, Antonio?"

"It didn't sound loud," Antonio said. "We are downwind and to the north of it with the key between. It didn't sound loud at all. But I could hear it clearly."

"They might never have heard it," Thomas Hudson said. "But they must have seen the dinghy running around and their ship careened. They're sure to think she's a trap. I don't think they will go near her."

"I think that's right," Willie agreed.

"But do you think they'll come out here?"

"You and God know just as much about that as I do. Aren't you the one who's always thinking in the Germans' minds?"

"Sure," Thomas Hudson said. "Sometimes I'm pretty good at it. But I'm not so hot today."

"You're thinking all right," Willie said. "You just ran into a bad streak."

"We could set a trap over there."

"You're just as trapped as you're trapping on her," Willie said.

"You go over and booby-trap her while it's still light."

"Now you're talking," Willie said. "That's the old Tom. I'll booby-trap both hatches and that dead Kraut and the lee rail. You're thinking your way out of it now."

"Use plenty of stuff. We've got lots of stuff."

"She'll be booby-trapped till Christ won't have her."

"They're coming in with the dinghy," Antonio said.

"I'll get Ara and the necessary and get over there," Willie said.

"Don't blow yourself up."

"Don't think too much," Willie said. "Get some rest, Tom. You're going to be up all night."

"So are you."

"The hell I am. When you want me they can wake me."

"I'll take the watch," Thomas Hudson said to Antonio. "When does our tide turn?"

"It's turned already but it is fighting with the current that the strong east wind blows out from the bay."

"Put Gil on the .50's and give George a break. Tell everybody to get a rest for the night."

"Why don't you take a drink, Tom?"

"I don't want one. What are you giving them to eat tonight?"

"A big piece of that wahoo boiled with Spanish sauce and black beans and rice. There aren't any more canned fruits."

"There were some on the list at Confites."

"Yes. But they were crossed off."

"Do you have any dried fruits?"

"Apricots."

"Soak some tonight and give them to them for breakfast."

"Henry won't eat them for breakfast."

"Well, give them to him the first meal he eats well. Have you plenty of soup?"

"Plenty."

"How is ice?"

"We have plenty for a week if we don't use too much on Peters. Why don't you bury him at sea, Tom?"

"Maybe I will," Thomas Hudson said. "He always said he'd like it."

"He said so many things."

"Yeah."

"Tom, why don't you take a drink?"

"All right," said Thomas Hudson. "Do you have any gin left?"

"Your bottle is in the locker."

"Do you have any water coconuts?"

"Yes."

"Make me a gin and coconut water with some lime in it. If we have limes."

"We have plenty of limes. Peters has some Scotch of his hidden if I can find it. Would you rather have that?"

"No. Find it and lock it up. We might need it."

"I'll make yours and hand it up."

"Thank you. Maybe we'll have good luck and they will come out tonight."

"I can't believe they will. I am of the school of Willie. But they might."

"We look awfully tempting. And they need some sort of craft."

"Yes, Tom. But they are not fools. You would not have been able to think in their heads if they were fools."

"OK. Get the drink." Thomas Hudson was glassing the keys with the big binoculars. "I'll try to think in their heads some more."

But he did not have any luck thinking in their heads. He was not thinking very well at all. He watched the dinghy, Ara in the stern and Willie out of sight, round the point of the key. He watched the flock of willet fly up finally and turn and head for one of the outer keys. Then he was alone and he sipped the drink that Antonio had made.

He thought how he had promised himself that he would not drink this trip, not even the cool one in the evening, so that he would not think of anything but work. He thought how he had planned to drive himself so he would sleep completely exhausted. But he made no excuses for this drink nor for the broken promise.

I drove myself, he thought. I did that all right. Now I might as well have this drink and think about something besides those other people. If they come out tonight we'll have everything set for them. If they do not come out, I will go in after them tomorrow morning on the high tide.

So he sipped the drink, which was cold and clean-tasting, and he watched the broken line of the keys straight ahead and to the westward. A drink always unlocked his memory that he kept locked so carefully now and the keys reminded him of the days when they used to troll for tarpon when young Tom was a small boy. Those were different keys and the channels were wider.

There were no flamingoes but the other birds had been nearly all the same except for the flocks of big golden plover. He remembered the seasons when the plover were gray and the others when the black feathers had the golden tinge and he remembered young Tom's pride at the first one he had ever brought home when he had his first single barrel twenty-gauge. He remembered how Tom had stroked the plump white breast and touched the lovely black under-markings and how he had found the boy asleep that night in his bed with his arms around the bird. He had taken the bird away very softly hoping he would not wake the boy. The boy did not wake. His arms just closed up tightly and he rolled onto his back.

As he had taken the golden plover into the back room where the icebox was, he felt he had robbed the boy of it. But he had smoothed its plumage carefully and laid it on one of the grilled shelves of the icebox. The next day he had painted young Tom a picture of the golden plover and the boy had taken it with him when he went off to school that year. In the picture he had tried to get the fast, running quality of the bird and the background was a long beach with coconut palms.

Then he remembered one time when they were in a tourist camp. He had wakened early and Tom was still asleep. He lay on his back with his arms crossed and he looked like the sculpture of a young knight lying on his tomb. Thomas Hudson had sketched him that way using a tomb that he remembered from Salisbury Cathedral. He was going to paint a canvas of it later but he did not do it because he thought it could be bad luck. A lot of good that did, he thought.

He looked into the sun that was low now and he could see Tom high up in the sun in a Spitfire. The aircraft was very high and very tiny and it shone like a fragment of broken mirror. He liked it up there, he said to himself. And it was a good rule you made about not drinking.

But over half of the drink was still in the paper-wrapped glass and there was still ice in it.

Courtesy of Peters, he thought. Then he remembered when they lived on the island in the old days and how Tom had read about the ice age at school and he was afraid it would come again.

"Papa," he had said. "That is my only worry."

"It can't hit here," Thomas Hudson had said.

"I know. But I can't stand to think what it will do to all those people in Minnesota and Wisconsin and Michigan. Even Illinois and Indiana."

"I don't think we really have to worry about it," Thomas Hudson had said. "It's a dreadfully slow process if it comes."

"I know," young Tom had said. "But that's the only thing I ever really worry about. That and the extinction of the passenger pigeon."

That Tom, he thought, and put the drink into one of the empty frag holes and glassed the keys carefully. He saw nothing that might be a sailing skiff and he put the glasses down.

The best times they had, he thought, were on the island and out West. Except Europe, of course, and if I think about that I'll think about the girl and it will be worse. I wonder where she is now. Sleeping with some general, I suppose. Well, I hope she gets a good one.

She looked awfully well and very beautiful when I saw her in Havana. I could think about her all night. But I won't. It is indulgence enough to think about Tom. I wouldn't do that without the drink. I'm glad I took it, though. There is a time to break all your rules. Maybe not all. I will think about him for a while and then I will work out our small problem for tonight when Willie and Ara get back. They're a wonderful team. Willie learned that awful Spanish of his in the Philippines but they understand each other perfectly. Some of that is because Ara is a Basque and speaks bad Spanish, too. Christ, I'd hate to go aboard that hulk after Willie and Ara rig her.

Go ahead and drink the rest of your drink and think about something good. Tom's dead and it's all right to think about him.

You'll never get over it. But you are solid on it now. Remember some good happy times. You had plenty.

What were the happiest times? he thought. They were all happy, really, in the time of innocence and the lack of useless money and still being able to work and eat. A bicycle was more fun than a motorcar. You saw things better and it kept you in good shape and coming home after you had ridden in the Bois you could coast down the Champs Élysées well past the Rond-Point and when you looked back to see what was behind you there, with the traffic moving in two streams, there rose the high gray of the great arch against the dusk. The horse chestnuts would be in bloom now. The trees would be black in the dusk as he pedalled now toward the Place de la Concorde and the upstanding blooms would be white and waxen. He would get off the racing bicycle to push it along the gravel path and see the horse chestnut trees slowly, and feel them overhead as he pushed the bicycle and felt the gravel under the thin soles of his shoes. He had bought this pair of racing shoes second-hand from a waiter he knew at the Select who had been an Olympic champion and he had paid for them by painting a canvas of the proprietor the way the proprietor had wished to be painted.

"A little in the style of Manet, Monsieur Hudson. If you can do it."

It was not a Manet that Manet would have signed but it looked more like Manet than it did like Hudson and it looked exactly like the proprietor. Thomas Hudson got the money for the bicycle shoes from it and for a long time they could have drinks on the house as well. Finally one night when he offered to pay for a drink, the offer was accepted and Thomas Hudson knew that payment on the portrait had been finished.

There was a waiter at the Closerie des Lilas who liked them and always gave them double-sized drinks so that by adding water they needed only one for the evening. So they moved down there. They would put Tom to bed and sit there together in the evenings at the old café, completely happy to be with each other. Then they would take a walk through the dark streets of the Montagne Sainte-Geneviève where the old houses had not yet been torn down and try to come home some different way each night. They would go to bed and hear Tom breathing in his cot and the purring of the big cat that slept with him.

Thomas Hudson remembered how people were horrified that they let the cat sleep with the small boy and that they left him alone when they went out. But Tom always slept well and if he woke up, there was the cat, who was his best friend. The cat would let no one near the bed and he and Tom loved each other very much.

Now Tom was—the hell with that, he said to himself. It is something that happens to everybody. I should know about that by now. It is the only thing that is really final, though.

How do you know that? he asked himself. Going away can be final. Walking out the door can be final. Any form of real betrayal can be final. Dishonesty can be final. Selling out is final. But you are just talking now. Death is what is really final. I wish Ara and Willie would get back. They must be rigging that hulk up like a chamber of horrors. I've never liked to kill, ever. But Willie loves it. He is a strange boy and very good, too. He is just never satisfied that a thing cannot be done better.

He saw the dinghy coming. Then he heard her purring hum and then he watched her get clearer and bigger and then she was alongside.

Willie came up. He looked worse than ever and his bad eye was showing too much white. He drew himself up, saluted smartly, and said, "Permission to speak to the captain, sir?"

"Are you drunk?"

"No, Tommy. Enthusiastic."

"You've been drinking."

"Sure, Tom. We took a little rum with us for working around that cadaver. And then when we got through Ara urinated in the bottle and then booby-trapped the bottle. It's double booby-trapped."

"Did you rig her good?"

"Tommy, a little tiny gnome no bigger than a man's hand couldn't get on her without being blown clean back to gnome land. A cockroach couldn't crawl on her. Ara was afraid the flies on the cadaver would set her off. We trapped her beautifully and delicately."

"What's Ara doing?"

"He's disassembling and cleaning everything in a frenzy of enthusiasm."

"How much rum did you guys take?"

"Less than half a bottle. It was my idea. It wasn't Ara's."

"OK. Get the hell down with him and clean the weapons and check the .50's."

"You can't check them really without firing them."

"I know. But you check them completely without firing them. Throw away the ammo that's been in the breeches."

"That's smart."

"Tell Henry to come up here and bring me a small glass of this and tell him to bring a drink for himself. Antonio knows what this drink is."

"I'm glad you're drinking a little again, Tom."

"For Christ's sake, don't be glad or sad about whether I'm drinking or not drinking."

"OK, Tom. But I don't like to see you ride yourself like a horse riding on a horse's back. Why don't you be like a centaur?"

"Where did you learn about centaurs?"

"I read it in a book, Tommy. I'm educated. I'm educated far beyond my years."

"You're a good old son of a bitch," Thomas Hudson told him. "Now get the hell down and do what I told you."

"Yes sir. Tommy, when we finish this cruise will you let me buy one of the sea paintings out at the joint?"

"Don't shit me."

"I'm not doing that. Maybe the hell you don't understand all the time."

"That could be. Maybe all my life."

"Tommy, I kid a lot. But you chased pretty."

"We'll see tomorrow. Tell Henry to bring a drink up. But I don't want any."

"No, Tommy. All we have tonight is a simple fight and I don't think we'll have it."

"All right," said Thomas Hudson. "Send it up. And get down off this fucking bridge and get to work."

20

HENRY passed the two drinks up and swung up himself after them. He stood beside Thomas Hudson and leaned forward to look at the shadow of the far keys. There was a thin moon in the first quarter of the sky to the westward.

"Here's to your good health, Tom," Henry said. "I didn't look at the moon over my left shoulder."

"She's not new. She was new last night."

"Of course. And we didn't see her for the squall."

"That's right. How's everything below?"

"Excellent, Tom. Everybody's working and cheerful."

"How are Willie and Ara?"

"They drank a little rum, Tom, and it made them very cheerful. But they're not drinking now."

"No. They wouldn't."

"I look forward to this very much," Henry said. "So does Willie."

"I don't. But it's what we are here to do. You see, we want prisoners, Henry."

"I know."

"Because they made that mistake on the massacre key they don't want to be taken prisoner."

"I think that's putting it mildly," Henry said. "Do you think they will try to jump us tonight?"

"No. But we have to be alerted in case they do."

"We will be. But what do you really think they are going to do, Tom?"

"I can't figure it, Henry. If they are really desperate they will try for the ship. If they have a radio operator left, he could fix our radio up and they could go across to Anguilas and just call a taxi and wait for it to take them home. They have every reason to try for the ship. Somebody could always have talked around Havana and they might know what we are."

"Who would talk?"

"Never speak ill of the deads," Thomas Hudson said. "But I'm afraid he might have when he was drinking."

"Willie is sure he did."

"Does he know anything?"

"No. He's just sure."

"It's a possibility. But they could also just try to make the mainland and make their way overland to Havana and get a Spanish ship out. Or an Argentine ship. But they don't want to be picked up on account of the massacre business. So I think they'll try something desperate."

"I hope so."

"If we can set it up," Thomas Hudson said.

But nothing happened all night long except the movement of the stars and the steady blowing of the east wind and the sucking of the currents past the ship. There was much phosphorescence in the water from the weed that the big tides and the sea made by the wind had torn up from the bottom, and it floated in and out and in again like cold strips and patches of white, unhealthy fire in the water.

The wind dropped a little before dawn and when it was light Thomas Hudson lay down and slept on the deck, lying on his belly with his face against a corner of the canvas. Antonio covered him and his weapon with a piece of canvas but Thomas Hudson was asleep and did not feel it.

Antonio took over the watch and when the tide was high so they swung free, he woke Thomas Hudson. They got the anchors in and started in with the dinghy going ahead and sounding and staking any dubious points. The water on this flood tide was clean and clear by now and the piloting was difficult but not as it had been the day before. They had staked a branch of a tree in the channel where they had grounded the day before and Thomas Hudson looked back and saw its green leaves moving in the current.

Thomas Hudson looked ahead and followed the dinghy closely as she worked out the channel. They passed a long green key that had looked like a small round key when they had been head on to it. Then ahead in what looked like an unbroken but indented line of mangrove keys Gil, who had the glasses, said, "Stake, Tom. Dead ahead of the dinghy against the mangroves."

"Check," Thomas Hudson said. "Is it the canal?"

"It looks to be but I can't see the opening."

"It is very narrow on the chart. We will just about brush the mangroves on each side."

Then he remembered something. How could I be so stupid? he thought. But we had better go on now, anyway, and out through the channel. Then I can send them back. He had forgotten to tell Willie and Ara to detrap the hulk of the turtle boat. That is a hell of a thing to leave around if some poor fisherman comes onto it. Well, they can go back and detrap it.

The dinghy was signalling him now to keep hard over to the right of the three tiny spots of key and close against the mangroves. Then, as if to make sure he understood, they wheeled and came up. "The channel's right in along the mangroves," Willy shouted. "Leave the stake on your left. We're going ahead through. As long as you don't hear from us keep on steaming. It's just a deep creek."

"We forgot to detrap that turtle boat."

"I know," Willie shouted. "We'll go back after."

Ara grinned and spun the dinghy around and they went on ahead, Willie signalling that it was OK. They turned left and right and went out of sight into the green.

Thomas Hudson steered in their wake. There was plenty of water although no such water showed on the chart. This old channel must have been scoured out by a hurricane, he thought. Many things have happened since the U.S.S. *Nokomis* had boats sounding in here.

Then he saw there were no birds rising from the mangroves as the dinghy went into the narrow brush river of the channel.

While he steered he spoke into the tubes to Henry in the forward cockpit, "We may get jumped in this channel. Have your .50's ready to fire from either bow and abeam. Keep behind the shield and watch for the flashes and pour it onto them."

"Yes, Tom."

To Antonio he said, "We may get jumped here. Keep well down and if we are fired on, aim below the flashes and pour it on. Keep way down."

"Gil," he said. "Put your glasses away. Take two frags and straighten the pins and put them there in the rack by my right hand. Straighten two pins on those extinguishers and then put your glasses away. They'll probably hit us from both sides. That's how they ought to."

"Tell me when to throw, Tom."

"Throw when you see the flashes. But loft it plenty because it has to fall through brush."

There were no birds at all and since the tide was high he knew that the birds had to be in the mangroves. The ship was entering the narrow river now and Thomas Hudson, bareheaded and barefooted and only wearing a pair of khaki shorts, felt as naked as a man can feel.

"You lie down, Gil," he said. "I'll tell you when to get up and throw."

Gil lay on the floor with the two fire extinguishers that were loaded with dynamite and a booster charge and were fired by the detonating assembly of a regulation frag, with its charger hacksawed off at the juncture of the fuse and a dynamite cap fitted and crimped on.

Thomas Hudson looked at him once and saw how he was sweating. Then he looked at the mangroves on either side.

I could still try to back her out, he thought. But I don't believe I could, the way the tide is flowing.

He looked ahead at the green banks. The water was brown again now and the mangrove leaves were as shiny as though they were varnished. He looked to see where any had been cut or disturbed. But he saw nothing but the green leaves, the dark branches, and the roots that were exposed with the suction of the ship. There were a few crabs that showed when their holes under the mangrove roots were exposed.

They went on and the channel narrowed but he could see it opening wider ahead. Maybe I just had the jitters, he thought. Then he saw a crab come sliding out fast from the high mangrove roots and plop into the water. He looked hard into the mangroves but he could see nothing beyond the trunks and branches. Another crab came out very fast and went into the water.

Just then they opened on him. He did not see the blinking flash and he was hit before he heard the stutter of the gun and Gil was on his feet beside him. Antonio was firing tracers where he had seen the gun flash.

"Where the tracers are going," Thomas Hudson said to Gil. Thomas Hudson felt as though someone had clubbed him three times with a baseball bat and his left leg was wet.

Gil lobbed the bomb with a high overhand motion and Thomas Hudson saw its long brass cylinder and conic nose shining in the sun. It was spinning, not going end over end.

"Down, Gil," he said and thought he ought to drop himself. Then he knew he shouldn't but should hold the ship as she was. The twin .50's had opened up and he could hear them pounding and he felt the jolt of them through his bare feet. Very noisy, he thought. That will keep the bastards down.

He saw the blinding burst of the bomb before the roar came and the smoke started to rise. He smelled the smoke and the smell of broken branches and burned green leaves.

"Get up, Gil, and throw two frags. One on each side of the smoke."

Gil did not lob the frags. He threw them like the long throw from third base to first and in the air they looked like gray iron artichokes with a thin trickle of smoke coming from them.

Before they burst cracking white in the mangroves Thomas Hudson said into the tube, "Shoot the shit out of it, Henry. They can't run in there."

The smoke from the frags smelled differently from the bomb and Thomas Hudson said to Gil, "Throw two more frags. One beyond the bomb and one in this side close."

He watched the frags go and then hit the deck. He did not know whether he hit the deck or the deck hit him because the deck was very slippery from the blood that had been running down his leg and he fell hard. At the second burst he heard two fragments tear through the canvas. Others hit the hull.

"Help me up," he said to Gil. "You threw that last one close enough."

"Where are you hit, Tom?"

"A couple of places."

Ahead he saw Willie and Ara coming up the channel in the dinghy.

He spoke in the tube to Antonio and asked him to hand up a first aid kit to Gil.

Just then he saw Willie drop flat in the bow of the dinghy and start firing into the mangroves on the right. He could hear the dat-dat-dat of his Thompson gun. Then there was a longer burst. He put in both his motors and headed for them with all the speed the channel would allow. His idea of this speed was not completely accurate because he felt very sick. He felt sick into his bones and through his chest and his bowels and the ache went into his testicles. He did not feel weak yet but he could feel the first onslaught of weakness.

"Get your guns to bear on the right bank," he said to Henry. "Willie's found more of them."

"Yes, Tom. Are you all right?"

"I'm hit but I'm all right. What about you and George?"

"We're fine."

"Open up any time you see anything."

"Yes, Tom."

Thomas Hudson stopped his engines and commenced to go astern again slowly to hold the ship outside the angle where Willie was firing. Willie had a clip in now with tracers in it and he was trying to spot the target for the ship.

"You got it, Henry?" he asked through the tube.

"Yes, Tom."

"Work on it and around it with short bursts."

He heard the .50's start slamming and he waved Ara and Willie in. They came in as fast as the little motor would bring them. Willie was firing all the time until they were under the lee of the ship.

Willie jumped aboard and came up on the flying bridge while Ara made the dinghy fast.

He looked at Tom and at Gil who was putting a tourniquet on his left leg as close to the crotch as he could tighten it.

"Jesus Christ," he said. "What you got, Tommy?"

"I don't know," Thomas Hudson said. He did not know, either. He could not see any of the wounds. All he saw was the color of the blood and it was dark so he did not worry. But there was too much of it and he felt very sick.

"What's in there, Willie?"

"I don't know. There was a guy with a burp gun fired on us and I got him. Or I'm pretty sure I did."

"I didn't hear it with the noise you made."

"You guys sounded like an ammunition dump going up. Do you think there's anything still back there?"

"Still, maybe. We gave it the treatment."

"We'll have to work it out," Willie said.

"We can let these sons of bitches hang and rattle," Thomas Hudson said. "Or we can go in now and finish it."

"I'd rather take care of you."

Henry was probing with the .50's. He was as delicate as he was rough with a machine gun and with a pair of them all his qualities were doubled.

"Do you know where they are, Willie?"

"There's only one place they can be."

"Then let's go in blasting and blow the shit out of them."

"Spoken like an officer and a gentleman," Willie said. "We sunk their skiff."

"Oh. We didn't hear that either," Thomas Hudson said.

"It didn't make much noise," Willie said. "Ara chopped her open with a machete and cut the sail up. Christ couldn't repair her in a month the best day he was in that carpenter shop."

"You get up forward with Henry and George and have Ara and Antonio on the starboard side and let's go in," Thomas Hudson said. He felt very sick and strange, although there was no dizziness yet. The dressings Gil had put on contained the bleeding too easily and he knew it was internal. "Put lots of fire on and you signal me how to go. How close are they?"

"Right up against the shore behind the little rise of ground."

"Can Gil reach it all right with the big ones?"

"I'll shoot tracers to show him the target."

"They'll still be there?"

"They got no place to go. They saw us break up the skiff. They're fighting Custer's Last Stand in the mangroves. Christ, I wish I had some Anheuser Busch."

"Ice cold in cans," Thomas Hudson said. "Let's get in."

"You're awfully white, Tommy," Willie said. "And you've lost a lot of blood."

"Let's take her in fast then," Thomas Hudson said. "I'm still all right."

They closed fast with Willie with his head up over the starboard bow sometimes waving a correction.

Henry was traversing before and behind the rise that showed by the higher trees and George was working on what should be the lip of the rise.

"How is it, Willie?" Thomas Hudson said into the tube.

"You got enough hulls up here to start a brass foundry," Willie answered. "Lay her goddam bow up against the bank and swing her broadside so Ara and Antonio can bear."

Gil thought he saw something and fired. But it was the low branch of a tree that Henry had cut loose.

Thomas Hudson watched the bank come closer and closer until he could see individual leaves again. Then he swung her broadside until he heard Antonio firing and saw his tracers going in a little to the right of Willie's. Ara was firing now, too. Then he came a little astern on his motors and swung her close to the bank but not so close that Gil could not throw.

"Throw an extinguisher," he said. "Where Willie's been shooting."

Gil threw and again Thomas Hudson marvelled at the throw and at the shine of the brass cylinder whirling high through the air to drop almost exactly where it should. There was the flash and the roar and then the rising smoke and then Thomas Hudson saw a man walking toward them out of the smoke with his hands clasped over his head.

"Hold up the fire," he said as rapidly as he could into two tubes.

But Ara had already fired and he saw the man slump forward into the mangroves on his knees with his head forward.

He spoke again and said, "Resume fire." Then he said to Gil, very tiredly, "Put in another one about the same place if you can. Then put in a couple of frags."

He had had a prisoner. But he had lost him.

After a while he said, "Willie, you and Ara want to have a look?"

"Sure," Willie said. "But keep some fire on while we go in. I want to go in from the back."

"Tell Henry what you want. When do you want it off?"

"As soon as we clear the entrance."

"All right, jungle man," Thomas Hudson said and for the first time he had time to realize that he was probably going to die.

21

HE heard the noise of a grenade bursting behind the small ridge. Then there was no more noise and no firing. He leaned heavily on the wheel and he watched the smoke of the grenade thin out in the wind.

"I'm going to take her on through as soon as I see the dinghy," he said to Gil.

He felt Antonio's arm around him and heard him say, "You lie down, Tom. I'm taking her."

"All right," he said and he took a last look down the narrow, green-banked river. The water was brown but clear and the tide was flowing strong.

Gil and Antonio helped him to lie down on the planking of the bridge. Then Antonio took the wheel. He went astern a little more to hold her against the tide and Thomas Hudson could feel the sweet rhythm of the big motors.

"Loosen the tourniquet a little," he said to Gil.

"We'll get the air mattress," Gil said.

"I like it on the deck," Thomas Hudson said. "I think it is better if I don't move much."

"Get a cushion under his head," Antonio said. He was looking down the channel.

In a little while he said, "They're waving us in, Tom," and Thomas Hudson felt the motors go ahead and the ship slide forward.

"Anchor her as soon as we're out of the channel."

"Yes, Tom. Don't talk."

Henry came up and took the wheel and the controls when they anchored. Now that they were in the open again, Thomas Hudson felt her swing into the wind.

"There's lots of water in here, Tom," Henry said.

"I know. All the way to Caibarién and the two channels are clear and well marked."

"Please don't talk, Tom. Just lie quiet."

"Have Gil get a light blanket."

"I'll get it. I hope it doesn't hurt too much, Tommy."

"It hurts," Thomas Hudson said. "But not too bad. It doesn't hurt any worse than things hurt that you and I have shot together."

"Here's Willie," Henry said.

"You old son of a bitch," said Willie. "Don't talk. There were four in there with the guide. It was the main party. Then there was the one Ara got by mistake. He feels awful about it when you wanted a prisoner so much. He's crying and I told him to stay below. He just loosed off like anybody would."

"What did you throw the grenade at?"

"Just a place I didn't like the look of. Don't you talk, Tom."

"You have to go back and detrap that hulk."

"We're going right away and we'll check the other place. I wish the Christ we had a speed boat. Tommy, those goddam fire extinguishers are better than an .81mm mortar."